Date Due

THE
HOUSE
OF
FICTION

★

THE
HOUSE OF FICTION

An

Anthology of the Short Story
with Commentary

BY

Caroline Gordon

and

Allen Tate

"The House of Fiction has in short not one window, but a million—a number of possible windows not to be reckoned, rather; every one of which has been pierced or is still pierceable, in its vast front, by the need of the individual vision and by the pressure of the individual will."

From the Preface to *The Portrait of a Lady,* by Henry James

NEW YORK

CHARLES SCRIBNER'S SONS

1954

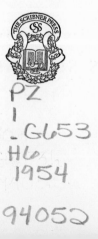

TO THE MEMORY OF

MAXWELL EVARTS PERKINS

PREFACE

O F THE thirty stories in this collection a dozen perhaps would
have to be included in any anthology of short fiction covering
the last hundred years in Europe and the United States. Only
a few have not appeared in anthologies before. We have not
sought the unfamiliar for its own sake but have tried rather
to put into one book an ample selection from the great writers who have
been called (after James's phrase) the Impressionist school. James exacted
of the work of fiction "a direct impression of life"; and very nearly his whole
demand is in the adjective. The direct impression is the opposite of the
blurred and easy impression; it creates the immediate sense of life, not the
removed report. Of this school, Flaubert, Chekhov, Crane, Joyce, and James
himself were the great masters. Since Flaubert, fiction has extended or
changed its subjects, but where it transcends its social or other documentary
origins it is still in the Impressionist tradition; or it is sometimes called the
tradition of naturalism or realism, descriptive terms with a philosophical ring,
but often standing only for a sentiment about the values of life. Neither the
sentiment of naturalism nor any other could have, unaided, produced the art
of *Madame Bovary*. A single, plainly discernible principle of imaginative
reality distinguishes this art, by means of which it has achieved something
of the self-contained objectivity of certain forms of poetry. Once you get
inside one of the great works of naturalism you find this principle informing
with a specific actuality whatever values the author may have. This actuality
reaches us as the *intense dramatic activity* of everything in the story: a snow-
storm, Emma's blue eyes, the crest of a wave, an after-dinner speech. Nothing
is left inert.

With this principle (neither a rule nor a formula) in mind, we selected
the stories and wrote the fifteen Commentaries which appear at intervals
throughout the book. Appendices A and B set forth some of the techniques
which the fictionist of the past hundred years used to develop the art of the
dramatically active detail. (It should be said here that he did not *discover*
this art; he revived and elaborated it in a *genre* in which its greatest ex-
ploitation was possible, as it was not in formal poetry. Homer knew it;
Thackeray did not.) We wanted to keep the critical discussion brief and
practical; we have therefore scanted some of the larger terms, like symbolism
and naturalism, a full treatment of which is in the provinces of philosophy;
we stopped short at the simplest possible indications of their uses in critical
reading. For this practical purpose we assumed that people cannot be taught

to write either masterpieces or family letters, but that as young persons (of whatever age) they can be taught moderately well how to read.

A glance at the Appendices and the Commentaries will reveal our failure to deal with two standard features of general discussion about fiction. We do not refer to *the* short story because it seems nowhere to exist. Mr. Robert Penn Warren has remarked that a short story is a story which is short— shorter than some other story. We have also avoided abstract discourses upon form and structure, aspects of prose fiction which will probably never yield to systematic analysis such as we constantly bring to bear upon a formalistic art like classical drama. What we have to say about form is implicit in the discussions of Point of View and of Complication and Resolution in Appendix A. We would stress again the primary aim of the book as practicability, for both reader and writer. The Commentaries and Appendices are condensed versions of methods that we have used in the past ten years in trying to get persons of all ages, and degrees of intelligence and talent, to see what is *in* the story: not what may remain in the inattentive mind— though perhaps romantically attentive to its own "desire to write"—when it lays the story down.

We are indebted to Professor Joe Lee Davis of the University of Michigan for a critical reading of the manuscript, and to Mr. Thomas J. B. Walsh and Mr. John Hall Wheelock of Charles Scribner's Sons for patient and useful advice in the preparation of this book.

C. G.
A. T.

Table of Contents

THE
HOUSE
OF
FICTION

★

Gustave Flaubert

A SIMPLE HEART

MADAME AUBAIN'S servant Félicité was the envy of the ladies of Pont-l'Évêque for half a century.

She received four pounds a year. For that she was cook and general servant, and did the sewing, washing, and ironing; she could bridle a horse, fatten poultry, and churn butter—and she remained faithful to her mistress, unamiable as the latter was.

Madame Aubain had married a gay bachelor without money who died at the beginning of 1809, leaving her with two small children and a quantity of debts. She then sold all her property except the farms of Toucques and Geffosses, which brought in two hundred pounds a year at most, and left her house in Saint-Melaine for a less expensive one that had belonged to her family and was situated behind the market.

This house had a slate roof and stood between an alley and a lane that went down to the river. There was an unevenness in the levels of the rooms which made you stumble. A narrow hall divided the kitchen from the "parlour" where Mme. Aubain spent her day, sitting in a wicker easy chair by the window. Against the panels, which were painted white, was a row of eight mahogany chairs. On an old piano under the barometer a heap of wooden and cardboard boxes rose like a pyramid. A stuffed armchair stood on either side of the Louis-Quinze chimney-piece, which was in yellow marble with a clock in the middle of it modelled like a temple of Vesta. The whole room was a little musty, as the floor was lower than the garden.

The first floor began with "Madame's" room: very large, with a pale-flowered wallpaper and a portrait of "Monsieur" as a dandy of the period. It led to a smaller room, where there were two children's cots without mattresses. Next came the drawing-room, which was always shut up and full of furniture covered with sheets. Then there was a corridor leading to a study. The shelves of a large bookcase were respectably lined with books and papers, and its three wings surrounded a broad writing-table in darkwood. The two panels at the end of the room were covered with pen-drawings, water-colour landscapes, and engravings by Audran, all relics of better days and vanished splendour. Félicité's room on the top floor got its light from a dormer-window, which looked over the meadows.

She rose at daybreak to be in time for Mass, and worked till evening without stopping. Then, when dinner was over, the plates and dishes in order, and the door shut fast, she thrust the log under the ashes and went to sleep in front of the hearth with her rosary in her hand. Félicité was the stubbornest of all bargainers; and as for cleanness, the polish on her saucepans

Translated by Arthur McDowall. Reprinted from *Three Tales* by Gustave Flaubert, by the kind permission of Alfred A. Knopf, Inc., copyright 1924 by Alfred A. Knopf, Inc.

was the despair of other servants. Thrifty in all things, she ate slowly, gathering off the table in her fingers the crumbs of her loaf—a twelve-pound loaf expressly baked for her, which lasted for three weeks.

At all times of year she wore a print handkerchief fastened with a pin behind, a bonnet that covered her hair, grey stockings, a red skirt, and a bibbed apron—such as hospital nurses wear—over her jacket.

Her face was thin and her voice sharp. At twenty-five she looked like forty. From fifty onwards she seemed of no particular age; and with her silence, straight figure, and precise movements she was like a woman made of wood, and going by clockwork.

ii

She had had her love-story like another.

Her father, a mason, had been killed by falling off some scaffolding. Then her mother died, her sisters scattered, and a farmer took her in and employed her, while she was still quite little, to herd the cows at pasture. She shivered in rags and would lie flat on the ground to drink water from the ponds; she was beaten for nothing, and finally turned out for the theft of a shilling which she did not steal. She went to another farm, where she became dairy-maid; and as she was liked by her employers her companions were jealous of her.

One evening in August (she was then eighteen) they took her to the assembly at Colleville. She was dazed and stupefied in an instant by the noise of the fiddlers, the lights in the trees, the gay medley of dresses, the lace, the gold crosses, and the throng of people jigging all together. While she kept shyly apart a young man with a well-to-do air, who was leaning on the shaft of a cart and smoking his pipe, came up to ask her to dance. He treated her to cider, coffee, and cake, and bought her a silk handkerchief; and then, imagining she had guessed his meaning, offered to see her home. At the edge of a field of oats he pushed her roughly down. She was frightened and began to cry out; and he went off.

One evening later she was on the Beaumont road. A big hay-wagon was moving slowly along; she wanted to get in front of it, and as she brushed past the wheels she recognized Theodore. He greeted her quite calmly, saying she must excuse it all because it was "the fault of the drink." She could not think of any answer and wanted to run away.

He began at once to talk about the harvest and the worthies of the commune, for his father had left Colleville for the farm at Les Écots, so that now he and she were neighbours. "Ah!" she said. He added that they thought of settling him in life. Well, he was in no hurry; he was waiting for a wife to his fancy. She dropped her head; and then he asked her if she thought of marrying. She answered with a smile that it was mean to make fun of her.

"But I am not, I swear!"—and he passed his left hand round her waist. She walked in the support of his embrace; their steps grew slower. The wind was soft, the stars glittered, the huge wagon-load of hay swayed in front of them, and dust rose from the dragging steps of the four horses. Then, without a word of command, they turned to the right. He clasped her once more in his arms, and she disappeared into the shadow.

The week after Theodore secured some assignations with her.

They met at the end of farmyards, behind a wall, or under a solitary tree. She was not innocent as young ladies are—she had learned knowledge from the animals—but her reason and the instinct of her honour would not let her fall. Her resistance exasperated Theodore's passion; so much so that to satisfy it—or perhaps quite artlessly—he made her an offer of marriage. She was in doubt whether to trust him, but he swore great oaths of fidelity.

Soon he confessed to something troublesome; the year before his parents had bought him a substitute for the army, but any day he might be taken again, and the idea of serving was a terror to him. Félicité took this cowardice of his as a sign of affection, and it redoubled hers. She stole away at night to see him, and when she reached their meeting-place Theodore racked her with his anxieties and urgings.

At last he declared that he would go himself to the prefecture for information, and would tell her the result on the following Sunday, between eleven and midnight.

When the moment came she sped towards her lover. Instead of him she found one of his friends.

He told her that she would not see Theodore any more. To ensure himself against conscription he had married an old woman, Madame Lehoussais, of Toucques, who was very rich.

There was an uncontrollable burst of grief. She threw herself on the ground, screamed, called to the God of mercy, and moaned by herself in the fields till daylight came. Then she came back to the farm and announced that she was going to leave; and at the end of the month she received her wages, tied all her small belongings with a handkerchief, and went to Pont-l'Évêque.

In front of the inn there she made inquiries of a woman in a widow's cap, who, as it happened, was just looking for a cook. The girl did not know much, but her willingness seemed so great and her demands so small that Mme. Aubain ended by saying:

"Very well, then, I will take you."

A quarter of an hour afterwards Félicité was installed in her house.

She lived there at first in a tremble, as it were, at "the style of the house" and the memory of "Monsieur" floating over it all. Paul and Virginie, the first aged seven and the other hardly four, seemed to her beings of a precious substance; she carried them on her back like a horse; it was a sorrow to her that Mme. Aubain would not let her kiss them every minute. And yet she was happy there. Her grief had melted in the pleasantness of things all round.

Every Thursday regular visitors came in for a game of boston, and Félicité got the cards and foot-warmers ready beforehand. They arrived punctually at eight and left before the stroke of eleven.

On Monday mornings the dealer who lodged in the covered passage spread out all his old iron on the ground. Then a hum of voices began to fill the town, mingled with the neighing of horses, bleating of lambs, grunting of pigs, and the sharp rattle of carts along the street. About noon, when the market was at its height, you might see a tall, hook-nosed old countryman with his cap pushed back making his appearance at the door. It was Robelin, the farmer of Geffosses. A little later came Liébard, the farmer from Toucques —short, red, and corpulent—in a grey jacket and gaiters shod with spurs.

Both had poultry or cheese to offer their landlord. Félicité was invariably a match for their cunning, and they went away filled with respect for her.

At vague intervals Mme. Aubain had a visit from the Marquis de Gremanville, one of her uncles, who had ruined himself by debauchery and now lived at Falaise on his last remaining morsel of land. He invariably came at the luncheon hour, with a dreadful poodle whose paws left all the furniture in a mess. In spite of efforts to show his breeding, which he carried to the point of raising his hat every time he mentioned "my late father," habit was too strong for him; he poured himself out glass after glass and fired off improper remarks. Félicité edged him politely out of the house—"You have had enough, Monsieur de Gremanville! Another time!"—and she shut the door on him.

She opened it with pleasure to M. Bourais, who had been a lawyer. His baldness, his white stock, frilled shirt, and roomy brown coat, his way of rounding the arm as he took snuff—his whole person, in fact, created that disturbance of mind which overtakes us at the sight of extraordinary men.

As he looked after the property of "Madame" he remained shut up with her for hours in "Monsieur's" study, though all the time he was afraid of compromising himself. He respected the magistracy immensely, and had some pretensions to Latin.

To combine instruction and amusement he gave the children a geography book made up of a series of prints. They represented scenes in different parts of the world: cannibals with feathers on their heads, a monkey carrying off a young lady, Bedouins in the desert, the harpooning of a whale, and so on. Paul explained these engravings to Félicité; and that, in fact, was the whole of her literary education. The children's education was undertaken by Guyot, a poor creature employed at the town hall, who was famous for his beautiful hand and sharpened his penknife on his boots.

When the weather was bright the household set off early for a day at Geffosses Farm.

Its courtyard is on a slope, with the farmhouse in the middle, and the sea looks like a grey streak in the distance.

Félicité brought slices of cold meat out of her basket, and they break-- fasted in a room adjoining the dairy. It was the only surviving fragment of a country house which was now no more. The wall-paper hung in tatters, and quivered in the draughts. Mme. Aubain sat with bowed head, overcome by her memories; the children became afraid to speak. "Why don't you play, then?" she would say, and off they went.

Paul climbed into the barn, caught birds, played at ducks and drakes over the pond, or hammered with his stick on the big casks which boomed like drums. Virginie fed the rabbits or dashed off to pick cornflowers, her quick legs showing their embroidered little drawers.

One autumn evening they went home by the fields. The moon was in its first quarter, lighting part of the sky; and mist floated like a scarf over the windings of the Toucques. Cattle, lying out in the middle of the grass, looked quietly at the four people as they passed. In the third meadow some of them got up and made a half-circle in front of the walkers. "There's nothing to be afraid of," said Félicité, as she stroked the nearest on the back with a kind of crooning song; he wheeled round and the others did the same. But when they crossed the next pasture there was a formidable bellow. It was a bull, hidden by the mist. Mme. Aubain was about to run. "No! no! don't go so fast!" They mended their pace, however, and heard a loud breathing behind them which came nearer. His hoofs thudded on the meadow grass like hammers; why, he was galloping now! Félicité turned round, and tore up clods of earth with both hands and threw them in his eyes. He lowered his muzzle, waved his horns, and quivered with fury, bellowing terribly. Mme. Aubain, now at the end of the pasture with her two little ones, was looking wildly for a place to get over the high bank. Félicité was retreating, still with her face to the bull, keeping up a shower of clods which blinded him, and crying all the time, "Be quick! be quick!"

Mme. Aubain went down into the ditch, pushed Virginie first and then Paul, fell several times as she tried to climb the bank, and managed it at last by dint of courage.

The bull had driven Félicité to bay against a rail-fence; his slaver was streaming into her face; another second, and he would have gored her. She had just time to slip between two of the rails, and the big animal stopped short in amazement.

This adventure was talked of at Pont-l'Évêque for many a year. Félicité did not pride herself on it in the least, not having the barest suspicion that she had done anything heroic.

Virginie was the sole object of her thoughts, for the child developed a nervous complaint as a result of her fright, and M. Poupart, the doctor, advised sea-bathing at Trouville. It was not a frequented place then. Mme. Aubain collected information, consulted Bourais, and made preparations as though for a long journey.

Her luggage started a day in advance, in Liébard's cart. The next day he brought round two horses, one of which had a lady's saddle with a velvet back to it, while a cloak was rolled up to make a kind of seat on the crupper of the other. Mme. Aubain rode on that, behind the farmer. Félicité took charge of Virginie, and Paul mounted M. Lechaptois' donkey, lent on condition that great care was taken of it.

The road was so bad that its five miles took two hours. The horses sank in the mud up to their pasterns, and their haunches jerked abruptly in the effort to get out; or else they stumbled in the ruts, and at other moments had to jump. In some places Liébard's mare came suddenly to a halt. He waited patiently until she went on again, talking about the people who had properties along the road, and adding moral reflections to their history. So it was that as they were in the middle of Toucques, and passed under some windows bowered with nasturtiums, he shrugged his shoulders and said: "There's a Mme. Lehoussais lives there; instead of taking a young man she . . ." Félicité did not hear the rest; the horses were trotting and the donkey galloping. They all turned down a bypath; a gate swung open and two boys appeared; and the party dismounted in front of a manure-heap at the very threshold of the farmhouse door.

When Mme. Liébard saw her mistress she gave lavish signs of joy. She served her a luncheon with a sirloin of beef, tripe, black-pudding, a fricassee of chicken, sparkling cider, a fruit tart, and brandied plums; seasoning it all with compliments to Madame, who seemed in better health; Mademoiselle, who was "splendid" now; and Monsieur Paul, who had "filled out" wonderfully. Nor did she forget their deceased grandparents, whom the Liébards had known, as they had been in the service of the family for several generations. The farm, like them, had the stamp of antiquity. The beams on the ceiling were worm-eaten, the walls blackened with smoke, and the window-panes grey with dust. There was an oak dresser laden with every sort of useful article—jugs, plates, pewter bowls, wolf-traps, and sheep-shears; and a huge syringe made the children laugh. There was not a tree in the three courtyards without mushrooms growing at the bottom of it or a tuft of mistletoe on its boughs. Several of them had been thrown down by the wind. They had taken root again at the middle; and all were bending under their wealth of apples. The thatched roofs, like brown velvet and of varying thickness, withstood the heaviest squalls. The cart-shed, however, was falling into ruin. Mme. Aubain said she would see about it, and ordered the animals to be saddled again.

It was another half-hour before they reached Trouville. The little caravan dismounted to pass Écores—it was an overhanging cliff with boats below it—and three minutes later they were at the end of the quay and entered the courtyard of the Golden Lamb, kept by good Mme. David.

From the first days of their stay Virginie began to feel less weak, thanks to the change of air and the effect of the sea-baths. These, for want of a bathing-dress, she took in her chemise; and her nurse dressed her afterwards in a coastguard's cabin which was used by the bathers.

In the afternoons they took the donkey and went off beyond the Black Rocks, in the direction of Hennequeville. The path climbed at first through ground with dells in it like the green sward of a park, and then reached a plateau where grass fields and arable lay side by side. Hollies rose stiffly out of the briary tangle at the edge of the road; and here and there a great withered tree made zigzags in the blue air with its branches.

They nearly always rested in a meadow, with Deauville on their left, Havre on their right, and the open sea in front. It glittered in the sunshine, smooth as a mirror and so quiet that its murmur was scarcely to be heard; sparrows chirped in hiding and the immense sky arched over it all. Mme. Aubain sat doing her needlework; Virginie plaited rushes by her side; Félicité pulled up lavender, and Paul was bored and anxious to start home.

Other days they crossed the Toucques in a boat and looked for shells. When the tide went out sea-urchins, starfish, and jelly-fish were left exposed; and the children ran in pursuit of the foam-flakes which scudded in the wind. The sleepy waves broke on the sand and unrolled all along the beach; it stretched away out of sight, bounded on the land-side by the dunes which parted it from the Marsh, a wide meadow shaped like an arena. As they came home that way, Trouville, on the hill-slope in the background, grew bigger at every step, and its miscellaneous throng of houses seemed to break into a gay disorder.

On days when it was too hot they did not leave their room. From the dazzling brilliance outside light fell in streaks between the laths of the blinds. There were no sounds in the village; and on the pavement below not a soul. This silence round them deepened the quietness of things. In the distance, where men were caulking, there was a tap of hammers as they plugged the hulls, and a sluggish breeze wafted up the smell of tar.

The chief amusement was the return of the fishing-boats. They began to tack as soon as they had passed the buoys. The sails came down on two of the three masts; and they drew on with the foresail swelling like a balloon, glided through the splash of the waves, and when they had reached the middle of the harbour suddenly dropped anchor. Then the boats drew up against the quay. The sailors threw quivering fish over the side; a row of carts was waiting, and women in cotton bonnets darted out to take the baskets and give their men a kiss.

One of them came up to Félicité one day, and she entered the lodgings a little later in a state of delight. She had found a sister again—and then Nastasie Barette, "wife of Leroux," appeared, holding an infant at her breast and another child with her right hand, while on her left was a little cabin boy with his hands on his hips and a cap over his ear.

After a quarter of an hour Mme. Aubain sent them off; but they were always to be found hanging about the kitchen, or encountered in the course of a walk. The husband never appeared.

Félicité was seized with affection for them. She bought them a blanket, some shirts, and a stove; it was clear that they were making a good thing out of her. Mme. Aubain was annoyed by this weakness of hers, and she did not like the liberties taken by the nephew, who said "thee" and "thou" to Paul. So as

Virginie was coughing and the fine weather gone, she returned to Pont-l'Évêque.

There M. Bourais enlightened her on the choice of a boys' school. The one at Caen was reputed to be the best, and Paul was sent to it. He said his good-byes bravely, content enough at going to live in a house where he would have companions. Mme. Aubain resigned herself to her son's absence as a thing that had to be. Virginie thought about it less and less. Félicité missed the noise he made. But she found an occupation to distract her; from Christmas onward she took the little girl to catechism every day.

iii

After making a genuflexion at the door she walked up between the double row of chairs under the lofty nave, opened Mme. Aubain's pew, sat down, and began to look about her. The choir stalls were filled with the boys on the right and the girls on the left, and the curé stood by the lectern. On a painted window in the apse the Holy Ghost looked down upon the Virgin. Another window showed her on her knees before the child Jesus, and a group carved in wood behind the altar-shrine represented St. Michael overthrowing the dragon.

The priest began with a sketch of sacred history. The Garden, the Flood, the Tower of Babel, cities in flames, dying nations, and overturned idols passed like a dream before her eyes; and the dizzying vision left her with reverence for the Most High and fear of His wrath. Then she wept at the story of the Passion. Why had they crucified Him, when He loved the children, fed the multitudes, healed the blind, and had willed, in His meekness, to be born among the poor, on the dung-heap of a stable? The sowings, harvests, wine-presses, all the familiar things the Gospel speaks of, were a part of her life. They had been made holy by God's passing; and she loved the lambs more tenderly for her love of the Lamb, and the doves because of the Holy Ghost.

She found it hard to imagine Him in person, for He was not merely a bird, but a flame as well, and a breath at other times. It may be His light, she thought, which flits at night about the edge of the marshes, His breathing which drives on the clouds, His voice which gives harmony to the bells; and she would sit rapt in adoration, enjoying the cool walls and the quiet of the church.

Of doctrines, she understood nothing—did not even try to understand. The curé discoursed, the children repeated their lesson, and finally she went to sleep, waking up with a start when their wooden shoes clattered on the flagstones as they went away.

It was thus that Félicité, whose religious education had been neglected in her youth, learned the catechism by dint of hearing it; and from that time she copied all Virginie's observances, fasting as she did and confessing with her. On Corpus Christi Day they made a festal altar together.

The first communion loomed distractingly ahead. She fussed over the shoes, the rosary, the book and gloves; and how she trembled as she helped Virginie's mother to dress her!

All through the mass she was racked with anxiety. She could not see one side of the choir because of M. Bourais; but straight in front of her was the flock of maidens, with white crowns above their hanging veils, making the impression of a field of snow; and she knew her dear child at a distance by her dainty neck and thoughtful air. The bell tinkled. The heads bowed, and there was silence. As the organ pealed, singers and congregation took up the "Agnus Dei"; then the procession of the boys began, and after them the girls rose. Step by step, with their hands joined in prayer, they went towards the lighted altar, knelt on the first step, received the sacrament in turn, and came back in the same order to their places. When Virginie's turn came Félicité leaned forward to see her; and with the imaginativeness of deep and tender feeling it seemed to her that she actually was the child; Virginie's face became hers, she was dressed in her clothes, it was her heart beating in her breast. As the moment came to open her mouth she closed her eyes and nearly fainted.

She appeared early in the sacristy next morning for Monsieur the curé to give her the communion. She took it with devotion, but it did not give her the same exquisite delight.

Mme. Aubain wanted to make her daughter into an accomplished person; and as Guyot could not teach her music or English she decided to place her in the Ursuline Convent at Honfleur as a boarder. The child made no objection. Félicité sighed and thought that Madame lacked feeling. Then she reflected that her mistress might be right; matters of this kind were beyond her.

So one day an old spring-van drew up at the door, and out of it stepped a nun to fetch the young lady. Félicité hoisted the luggage on to the top, admonished the driver, and put six pots of preserves, a dozen pears, and a bunch of violets under the seat.

At the last moment Virginie broke into a fit of sobbing; she threw her arms round her mother, who kissed her on the forehead, saying over and over "Come, be brave! be brave!" The step was raised, and the carriage drove off.

Then Mme. Aubain's strength gave way; and in the evening all her friends—the Lormeau family, Mme. Lechaptois, the Rochefeuille ladies, M. de Houppeville, and Bourais—came in to console her.

To be without her daughter was very painful for her at first. But she heard from Virginie three times a week, wrote to her on the other days, walked in the garden, and so filled up the empty hours.

From sheer habit Félicité went into Virginie's room in the mornings and gazed at the walls. It was boredom to her not to have to comb the child's hair now, lace up her boots, tuck her into bed—and not to see her charming face perpetually and hold her hand when they went out together. In this idle condition she tried making lace. But her fingers were too heavy and broke the threads; she could not attend to anything, she had lost her sleep, and was, in her own words, "destroyed."

To "divert herself" she asked leave to have visits from her nephew Victor.

He arrived on Sundays after mass, rosy-cheeked, bare-chested, with the scent of the country he had walked through still about him. She laid her table promptly and they had lunch, sitting opposite each other. She ate as little as possible herself to save expense, but stuffed him with food so generously that at last he went to sleep. At the first stroke of vespers she woke him up, brushed his trousers, fastened his tie, and went to church, leaning on his arm with maternal pride.

Victor was always instructed by his parents to get something out of her— a packet of moist sugar, it might be, a cake of soap, spirits, or even money at times. He brought his things for her to mend and she took over the task, only too glad to have a reason for making him come back.

In August his father took him off on a coasting voyage. It was holiday time, and she was consoled by the arrival of the children. Paul, however, was getting selfish, and Virginie was too old to be called "thou" any longer; this put a constraint and barrier between them.

Victor went to Morlaix, Dunkirk, and Brighton in succession and made Félicité a present on his return from each voyage. It was a box made of shells the first time, a coffee cup the next, and on the third occasion a large gingerbread man. Victor was growing handsome. He was well made, had a hint of a moustache, good honest eyes, and a small leather hat pushed backwards like a pilot's. He entertained her by telling stories embroidered with nautical terms.

On a Monday, July 14, 1819 (she never forgot the date), he told her that he had signed on for the big voyage and next night but one he would take the Honfleur boat and join his schooner, which was to weigh anchor from Havre before long. Perhaps he would be gone two years.

The prospect of this long absence threw Félicité into deep distress; one more good-bye she must have, and on the Wednesday evening, when Madame's dinner was finished, she put on her clogs and made short work of the twelve miles between Pont-l'Évêque and Honfleur.

When she arrived in front of the Calvary she took the turn to the right instead of the left, got lost in the timber-yards, and retraced her steps; some people to whom she spoke advised her to be quick. She went all round the harbour basin, full of ships, and knocked against hawsers; then the ground fell away, lights flashed across each other, and she thought her wits had left her, for she saw horses up in the sky.

Others were neighing by the quay-side, frightened at the sea. They were lifted by a tackle and deposited in a boat, where passengers jostled each other among cider casks, cheese baskets, and sacks of grain; fowls could be heard clucking, the captain swore; and a cabin-boy stood leaning over the bows, indifferent to it all. Félicité, who had not recognized him, called "Victor!" and he raised his head; all at once, as she was darting forwards, the gangway was drawn back.

The Honfleur packet, women singing as they hauled it, passed out of harbour. Its framework creaked and the heavy waves whipped its bows. The canvas had swung round, no one could be seen on board now; and on the moon-silvered sea the boat made a black speck which paled gradually, dipped, and vanished.

As Félicité passed by the Calvary she had a wish to commend to God what she cherished most, and she stood there praying a long time with her face bathed in tears and her eyes towards the clouds. The town was asleep, coastguards were walking to and fro; and water poured without cessation through the holes in the sluice, with the noise of a torrent. The clocks struck two.

The convent parlour would not be open before day. If Félicité were late Madame would most certainly be annoyed; and in spite of her desire to kiss the other child she turned home. The maids at the inn were waking up as she came in to Pont-l'Évêque.

So the poor slip of a boy was going to toss for months and months at sea! She had not been frightened by his previous voyages. From England or Brittany you came back safe enough; but America, the colonies, the islands— these were lost in a dim region at the other end of the world.

Félicité's thoughts from that moment ran entirely on her nephew. On sunny days she was harassed by the idea of thirst; when there was a storm she was afraid of the lightning on his account. As she listened to the wind growling in the chimney or carrying off the slates she pictured him lashed by that same tempest, at the top of a shattered mast, with his body thrown backwards under a sheet of foam; or else (with a reminiscence of the illustrated geography) he was being eaten by savages, captured in a wood by monkeys, or dying on a desert shore. And never did she mention her anxieties.

Mme. Aubain had anxieties of her own, about her daughter. The good sisters found her an affectionate but delicate child. The slightest emotion unnerved her. She had to give up the piano.

Her mother stipulated for regular letters from the convent. She lost patience one morning when the postman did not come, and walked to and fro in the parlour from her armchair to the window. It was really amazing; not a word for four days!

To console Mme. Aubain by her own example Félicité remarked:

"As for me, Madame, it's six months since I heard . . ."

"From whom, pray?"

"Why . . . from my nephew," the servant answered gently.

"Oh! your nephew!" And Mme. Aubain resumed her walk with a shrug of the shoulders, as much as to say: "I was not thinking of him! And what is more, it's absurd! A scamp of a cabin-boy—what does he matter? . . . whereas my daughter . . . why, just think!"

Félicité, though she had been brought up on harshness, felt indignant with Madame—and then forgot. It seemed the simplest thing in the world to her to lose one's head over the little girl. For her the two children were equally important; a bond in her heart made them one, and their destinies must be the same.

She heard from the chemist that Victor's ship had arrived at Havana. He had read this piece of news in a gazette.

Cigars—they made her imagine Havana as a place where no one does anything but smoke, and there was Victor moving among the negroes in a cloud of tobacco. Could you, she wondered, "in case you needed," return by land? What was the distance from Pont-l'Évêque? She questioned M. Bourais to find out.

He reached for his atlas and began explaining the longitudes; Félicité's consternation provoked a fine pedantic smile. Finally he marked with his pencil a black, imperceptible point in the indentations of an oval spot, and said as he did so, "Here it is." She bent over the map; the maze of coloured lines wearied her eyes without conveying anything; and on an invitation from Bourais to tell him her difficulty, she begged him to show her the house where Victor was living. Bourais threw up his arms, sneezed, and laughed immensely: a simplicity like hers was a positive joy. And Félicité did not understand the reason; how could she when she expected, very likely, to see the actual image of her nephew—so stunted was her mind!

A fortnight afterwards Liébard came into the kitchen at market-time as usual and handed her a letter from her brother-in-law. As neither of them could read she took it to her mistress.

Mme. Aubain, who was counting the stitches in her knitting, put the work down by her side, broke the seal of the letter, started, and said in a low voice, with a look of meaning:

"It is bad news . . . that they have to tell you. Your nephew . . ."

He was dead. The letter said no more

Félicité fell on to a chair, leaning her head against the wainscot; and she closed her eyelids, which suddenly flushed pink. Then with bent forehead, hands hanging, and fixed eyes, she said at intervals:

"Poor little lad! poor little lad!"

Liébard watched her and heaved sighs. Mme. Aubain trembled a little.

She suggested that Félicité should go to see her sister at Trouville. Félicité answered by a gesture that she had no need.

There was a silence. The worthy Liébard thought it was time for them to withdraw.

Then Félicité said:

"They don't care, not they!"

Her head dropped again; and she took up mechanically, from time to time, the long needles on her work-table.

Women passed in the yard with a barrow of dripping linen.

As she saw them through the window-panes she remembered her washing; she had put it to soak the day before, to-day she must wring it out; and she left the room.

Her plank and tub were at the edge of the Toucques. She threw a pile of linen on the bank, rolled up her sleeves, and taking her wooden beater dealt lusty blows whose sound carried to the neighbouring gardens. The meadows were empty, the river stirred in the wind; and down below long grasses wavered, like the hair of corpses floating in the water. She kept her grief down and was very brave until the evening; but once in her room she surrendered to it utterly, lying stretched on the mattress with her face in the pillow and her hands clenched against her temples.

Much later she heard, from the captain himself, the circumstances of Victor's end. They had bled him too much at the hospital for yellow fever. Four doctors held him at once. He had died instantly, and the chief had said:

"Bah! there goes another!"

His parents had always been brutal to him. She preferred not to see them again; and they made no advances, either because they forgot her or from the callousness of the wretchedly poor.

Virginie began to grow weaker.

Tightness in her chest, coughing, continual fever, and veinings on her cheek-bones betrayed some deep-seated complaint. M. Poupart had advised a stay in Provence. Mme. Aubain determined on it, and would have brought her daughter home at once but for the climate of Pont-l'Évêque.

She made an arrangement with a job-master, and he drove her to the convent every Tuesday. There is a terrace in the garden, with a view over the Seine. Virginie took walks there over the fallen vine-leaves, on her mother's arm. A shaft of sunlight through the clouds made her blink some-times, as she gazed at the sails in the distance and the whole horizon from the castle of Tancarville to the lighthouses at Havre. Afterwards they rested in the arbour. Her mother had secured a little cask of excellent Malaga; and Virginie, laughing at the idea of getting tipsy, drank a thimble-full of it, no more.

Her strength came back visibly. The autumn glided gently away. Félicité reassured Mme. Aubain. But one evening, when she had been out on a commission in the neighbourhood, she found M. Poupart's gig at the door. He was in the hall, and Mme. Aubain was tying her bonnet.

"Give me my foot-warmer, purse, gloves! Quicker, come!"

Virginie had inflammation of the lungs; perhaps it was hopeless.

"Not yet!" said the doctor, and they both got into the carriage under whirling flakes of snow. Night was coming on and it was very cold.

Félicité rushed into the church to light a taper. Then she ran after the gig, came up with it in an hour, and jumped lightly in behind. As she hung on by the fringes a thought came into her mind: "The courtyard has not been shut up; supposing burglars got in!" And she jumped down.

At dawn next day she presented herself at the doctor's. He had come in and started for the country again. Then she waited in the inn, thinking that a letter would come by some hand or other. Finally, when it was twilight, she took the Lisieux coach.

The convent was at the end of a steep lane. When she was about half-way up it she heard strange sounds—a death-bell tolling. "It is for someone else," thought Félicité, and she pulled the knocker violently.

After some minutes there was a sound of trailing slippers, the door opened ajar, and a nun appeared.

The good sister, with an air of compunction, said that "she had just passed away." On the instant the bell of St. Leonard's tolled twice as fast.

Félicité went up to the second floor.

From the doorway she saw Virginie stretched on her back, with her hands joined, her mouth open, and head thrown back under a black crucifix that leaned towards her, between curtains that hung stiffly, less pale than was her face. Mme. Aubain, at the foot of the bed which she clasped with her arms, was choking with sobs of agony. The mother superior stood on the right. Three candlesticks on the chest of drawers made spots of red, and the mist came whitely through the windows. Nuns came and took Mme. Aubain away.

For two nights Félicité never left the dead child. She repeated the same prayers, sprinkled holy water over the sheets, came and sat down again, and watched her. At the end of the first vigil she noticed that the face had grown yellow, the lips turned blue, the nose was sharper, and the eyes sunk in. She kissed them several times, and would not have been immensely surprised if Virginie had opened them again; to minds like hers the supernatural is quite simple. She made the girl's toilette, wrapped her in her shroud, lifted her down into her bier, put a garland on her head, and spread out her hair. It was fair, and extraordinarily long for her age. Félicité cut off a big lock and slipped half of it into her bosom, determined that she should never part with it.

The body was brought back to Pont-l'Évêque, as Mme. Aubain intended; she followed the hearse in a closed carriage.

It took another three-quarters of an hour after the mass to reach the cemetery. Paul walked in front, sobbing. M. Bourais was behind, and then came the chief residents, the women shrouded in black mantles, and Félicité. She thought of her nephew; and because she had not been able to pay these honours to him her grief was doubled, as though the one were being buried with the other.

Mme. Aubain's despair was boundless. It was against God that she first rebelled, thinking it unjust of Him to have taken her daughter from her—she had never done evil and her conscience was so clear! Ah, no!—she ought to have taken Virginie off to the south. Other doctors would have saved her. She accused herself now, wanted to join her child, and broke into cries of distress in the middle of her dreams. One dream haunted her above all. Her husband, dressed as a sailor, was returning from a long voyage, and shedding tears he told her that he had been ordered to take Virginie away. Then they consulted how to hide her somewhere.

She came in once from the garden quite upset. A moment ago—and she pointed out the place—the father and daughter had appeared to her, standing side by side, and they did nothing, but they looked at her.

For several months after this she stayed inertly in her room. Félicité lectured her gently; she must live for her son's sake, and for the other, in remembrance of "her."

"Her?" answered Mme. Aubain, as though she were just waking up. "Ah, yes! . . . yes! . . . You do not forget her!" This was an allusion to the cemetery, where she was strictly forbidden to go.

Félicité went there every day.

Precisely at four she skirted the houses, climbed the hill, opened the gate, and came to Virginie's grave. It was a little column of pink marble with a stone underneath and a garden plot enclosed by chains. The beds were hidden under a coverlet of flowers. She watered their leaves, freshened the gravel, and knelt down to break up the earth better. When Mme. Aubain was able to come there she felt a relief and a sort of consolation.

Then years slipped away, one like another, and their only episodes were the great festivals as they recurred—Easter, the Assumption, All Saints' Day. Household occurrences marked dates that were referred to afterwards. In 1825, for instance, two glaziers whitewashed the hall; in 1827 a piece of the roof fell into the courtyard and nearly killed a man. In the summer of 1828 it was Madame's turn to offer the consecrated bread; Bourais, about this time, mysteriously absented himself; and one by one the old acquaintances passed away: Guyot, Liébard, Mme. Lechaptois, Robelin, and Uncle Gremanville, who had been paralysed for a long time.

One night the driver of the mail-coach announced the Revolution of July in Pont-l'Évêque. A new sub-prefect was appointed a few days later—Baron de Larsonnière, who had been consul in America, and brought with him, besides his wife, a sister-in-law and three young ladies, already growing up. They were to be seen about on their lawn, in loose blouses, and they had a negro and a parrot. They paid a call on Mme. Aubain which she did not fail to return. The moment they were seen in the distance Félicité ran to let her mistress know. But only one thing could really move her feelings—the letters from her son.

He was swallowed up in a tavern life and could follow no career. She paid his debts, he made new ones; and the sighs that Mme. Aubain uttered as she sat knitting by the window reached Félicité at her spinning-wheel in the kitchen.

They took walks together along the espaliered wall, always talking of Virginie and wondering if such and such a thing would have pleased her and what, on some occasion, she would have been likely to say.

All her small belongings filled a cupboard in the two-bedded room. Mme. Aubain inspected them as seldom as she could. One summer day she made up her mind to it—and some moths flew out of the wardrobe.

Virginie's dresses were in a row underneath a shelf, on which there were three dolls, some hoops, a set of toy pots and pans, and the basin that she used. They took out her petticoats as well, and the stockings and handkerchiefs, and laid them out on the two beds before folding them up again. The sunshine lit up these poor things, bringing out their stains and the creases made by the body's movements. The air was warm and blue, a blackbird warbled, life seemed bathed in a deep sweetness. They found a little plush hat with thick, chestnut-coloured pile; but it was eaten all over by moths. Félicité begged it for her own. Their eyes met fixedly and filled with tears; at last the mistress opened her arms, the servant threw herself into them, and they embraced each other, satisfying their grief in a kiss that made them equal.

It was the first time in their lives, Mme. Aubain's nature not being expansive. Félicité was as grateful as though she had received a favour, and cherished her mistress from that moment with the devotion of an animal and a religious worship.

The kindness of her heart unfolded.

When she heard the drums of a marching regiment in the street she posted herself at the door with a pitcher of cider and asked the soldiers to drink. She nursed cholera patients and protected the Polish refugees; one of these even declared that he wished to marry her. They quarrelled, however; for when she came back from the Angelus one morning she found that he had got into her kitchen and made himself a vinegar salad which he was quietly eating.

After the Poles came Father Colmiche, an old man who was supposed to have committed atrocities in '93. He lived by the side of the river in the ruins of a pigsty. The little boys watched him through the cracks in the wall, and threw pebbles at him which fell on the pallet where he lay constantly shaken by a catarrh; his hair was very long, his eyes inflamed, and there was a tumour on his arm bigger than his head. She got him some linen and tried to clean up his miserable hole; her dream was to establish him in the bakehouse, without letting him annoy Madame. When the tumour burst she dressed it every day; sometimes she brought him cake, and would put him in the sunshine on a truss of straw. The poor old man, slobbering and trembling, thanked her in his worn-out voice, was terrified that he might lose her, and stretched out his hands when he saw her go away. He died; and she had a mass said for the repose of his soul.

That very day a great happiness befell her; just at dinner-time appeared Mme. de Larsonnière's negro, carrying the parrot in its cage, with perch, chain, and padlock. A note from the baroness informed Mme. Aubain that her husband had been raised to a prefecture and they were starting that evening; she begged her to accept the bird as a memento and mark of her regard.

For a long time he had absorbed Félicité's imagination, because he came from America; and that name reminded her of Victor, so much so that she made inquiries of the negro. She had once gone so far as to say, "How Madame would enjoy having him!"

The negro repeated the remark to his mistress; and as she could not take the bird away with her she chose this way of getting rid of him.

iv

His name was Loulou. His body was green and the tips of his wings rose-pink; his forehead was blue and his throat golden.

But he had the tiresome habits of biting his perch, tearing out his feathers, sprinkling his dirt about, and spattering the water of his tub. He annoyed Mme. Aubain, and she gave him to Félicité for good.

She endeavoured to train him; soon he could repeat "Nice boy! Your servant, sir! Good morning, Marie!" He was placed by the side of the door, and astonished several people by not answering to the name Jacquot, for all parrots are called Jacquot. People compared him to a turkey and a log of wood, and stabbed Félicité to the heart each time. Strange obstinacy on Loulou's part!—directly you looked at him he refused to speak.

None the less he was eager for society; for on Sundays, while the Rochefeuille ladies, M. de Houppeville, and new familiars—Onfroy the apothecary, Monsieur Varin, and Captain Mathieu—were playing their game of cards, he beat the windows with his wings and threw himself about so frantically that they could not hear each other speak.

Bourais' face, undoubtedly, struck him as extremely droll. Directly he saw it he began to laugh—and laugh with all his might. His peals rang through the courtyard and were repeated by the echo; the neighbours came to their windows and laughed too; while M. Bourais, gliding along under the wall to escape the parrot's eye, and hiding his profile with his hat, got to the river and then entered by the garden gate. There was a lack of tenderness in the looks which he darted at the bird.

Loulou had been slapped by the butcher-boy for making so free as to plunge his head into his basket; and since then he was always trying to nip him through his shirt. Fabu threatened to wring his neck, although he was not cruel, for all his tattooed arms and large whiskers. Far from it; he really rather liked the parrot, and in a jovial humour even wanted to teach him to swear. Félicité, who was alarmed by such proceedings, put the bird in the kitchen. His little chain was taken off and he roamed about the house.

His way of going downstairs was to lean on each step with the curve of his beak, raise the right foot, and then the left; and Félicité was afraid that these gymnastics brought on fits of giddiness. He fell ill and could not talk or eat any longer. There was a growth under his tongue, such as fowls have sometimes. She cured him by tearing the pellicle off with her fingernails. Mr. Paul was thoughtless enough one day to blow some cigar smoke into his nostrils, and another time when Mme. Lormeau was teasing him with the end of her umbrella he snapped at the ferrule. Finally he got lost.

Félicité had put him on the grass to refresh him, and gone away for a minute, and when she came back—no sign of the parrot! She began by looking for him in the shrubs, by the waterside, and over the roofs, without listening to her mistress's cries of "Take care, do! You are out of your wits!" Then she investigated all the gardens in Pont-l'Évêque, and stopped the passers-by. "You don't ever happen to have seen my parrot, by any chance, do you?" And she gave a description of the parrot to those who did not know him. Suddenly, behind the mills at the foot of the hill she thought she could make out something green that fluttered. But on the top of the hill there was nothing. A hawker assured her that he had come across the parrot just before, at Saint-Melaine, in Mère Simon's shop. She rushed there; they had no idea of what she meant. At last she came home exhausted, with her slippers in shreds and despair in her soul; and as she was sitting in the middle of the garden-seat at Madame's side, telling the whole story of her efforts, a light weight dropped on to her shoulder—it was Loulou! What on earth had he been doing? Taking a walk in the neighbourhood, perhaps!

She had some trouble in recovering from this, or rather never did recover. As the result of a chill she had an attack of quinsy, and soon afterwards an earache. Three years later she was deaf; and she spoke very loud, even in church. Though Félicité's sins might have been published in every corner of the diocese without dishonour to her or scandal to anybody, his Reverence the priest thought it right now to hear her confession in the sacristy only.

Imaginary noises in the head completed her upset. Her mistress often said to her, "Heavens! how stupid you are!" "Yes, Madame," she replied, and looked about for something.

Her little circle of ideas grew still narrower; the peal of church-bells and the lowing of cattle ceased to exist for her. All living beings moved as silently as ghosts. One sound only reached her ears now—the parrot's voice.

Loulou, as though to amuse her, reproduced the click-clack of the turn-spit, the shrill call of a man selling fish, and the noise of the saw in the joiner's house opposite; when the bell rang he imitated Mme. Aubain's "Félicité! the door! the door!"

They carried on conversations, he endlessly reciting the three phrases in his repertory, to which she replied with words that were just as disconnected but uttered what was in her heart. Loulou was almost a son and a lover to her in her isolated state. He climbed up her fingers, nibbled at her lips, and clung to her kerchief; and when she bent her forehead and shook her head gently to and fro, as nurses do, the great wings of her bonnet and the bird's wings quivered together.

When the clouds massed and the thunder rumbled Loulou broke into cries, perhaps remembering the downpours in his native forests. The streaming rain made him absolutely mad; he fluttered wildly about, dashed up to the ceiling, upset everything, and went out through the window to dabble in the garden; but he was back quickly to perch on one of the fire-dogs and hopped about to dry himself, exhibiting his tail and his beak in turn.

One morning in the terrible winter of 1837 she had put him in front of the fireplace because of the cold. She found him dead, in the middle of his cage: head downwards, with his claws in the wires. He had died from congestion, no doubt. But Félicité thought he had been poisoned with parsley, and though there was no proof of any kind her suspicions inclined to Fabu.

She wept so piteously that her mistress said to her, "Well, then, have him stuffed!"

She asked advice from the chemist, who had always been kind to the parrot. He wrote to Havre, and a person called Fellacher undertook the business. But as parcels sometimes got lost in the coach she decided to take the parrot as far as Honfleur herself.

Along the sides of the road were leafless apple-trees, one after the other. Ice covered the ditches. Dogs barked about the farms; and Félicité, with her hands under her cloak, her little black sabots and her basket, walked briskly in the middle of the road.

She crossed the forest, passed High Oak, and reached St. Gatien.

A cloud of dust rose behind her, and in it a mail-coach, carried away by the steep hill, rushed down at full gallop like a hurricane. Seeing this woman who would not get out of the way, the driver stood up in front and the postilion shouted too. He could not hold in his four horses, which increased their pace, and the two leaders were grazing her when he threw them to one side with a jerk of the reins. But he was wild with rage, and lifting his arm as he passed at full speed, gave her such a lash from waist to neck with his big whip that she fell on her back.

Her first act, when she recovered consciousness, was to open her basket. Loulou was happily none the worse. She felt a burn in her right cheek, and when she put her hands against it they were red; the blood was flowing.

She sat down on a heap of stones and bound up her face with her handkerchief. Then she ate a crust of bread which she had put in the basket as a precaution, and found a consolation for her wound in gazing at the bird.

When she reached the crest of Ecquemauville she saw the Honfleur lights sparkling in the night sky like a company of stars; beyond, the sea stretched dimly. Then a faintness overtook her and she stopped; her wretched childhood, the disillusion of her first love, her nephew's going away, and Virginie's death all came back to her at once like the waves of an oncoming tide, rose to her throat, and choked her.

Afterwards, at the boat, she made a point of speaking to the captain, begging him to take care of the parcel, though she did not tell him what was in it.

Fellacher kept the parrot a long time. He was always promising it for the following week. After six months he announced that a packing-case had started, and then nothing more was heard of it. It really seemed as though Loulou was never coming back. "Ah, they have stolen him!" she thought.

He arrived at last, and looked superb. There he was, erect upon a branch which screwed into a mahogany socket, with a foot in the air and his head on one side, biting a nut which the bird-stuffer—with a taste for impressiveness—had gilded.

Félicité shut him up in her room. It was a place to which few people were admitted, and held so many religious objects and miscellaneous things that it looked like a chapel and bazaar in one.

A big cupboard impeded you as you opened the door. Opposite the window commanding the garden a little round one looked into the court; there was a table by the folding-bed with a water-jug, two combs, and a cube of blue soap in a chipped plate. On the walls hung rosaries, medals, several benign Virgins, and a holy water vessel made out of coconut; on the chest of drawers, which was covered with a cloth like an altar, was the shell box that Victor had given her, and after that a watering-can, a toy-balloon, exercise-books, the illustrated geography, and a pair of young lady's boots; and, fastened by its ribbons to the nail of the looking-glass, hung the little plush hat! Félicité carried observances of this kind so far as to keep one of Monsieur's frock-coats. All the old rubbish which Mme. Aubain did not want any longer she laid hands on for her room. That was why there were artificial flowers along the edge of the chest of drawers and a portrait of the Comte d'Artois in the little window recess.

With the aid of a bracket Loulou was established over the chimney, which jutted into the room. Every morning when she woke up she saw him there in the dawning light, and recalled old days and the smallest details of insignificant acts in a deep quietness which knew no pain.

Holding, as she did, no communication with anyone, Félicité lived as insensibly as if she were walking in her sleep. The Corpus Christi processions roused her to life again. Then she went round begging mats and candlesticks from the neighbours to decorate the altar they put up in the street.

In church she was always gazing at the Holy Ghost in the window, and observed that there was something of the parrot in him. The likeness was still clearer, she thought, on a crude colour-print representing the baptism of Our Lord. With his purple wings and emerald body he was the very image of Loulou.

She bought him, and hung him up instead of the Comte d'Artois, so that she could see them both together in one glance. They were linked in her thoughts; and the parrot was consecrated by his association with the Holy Ghost, which became more vivid to her eye and more intelligible. The Father could not have chosen to express Himself through a dove, for such creatures cannot speak; it must have been one of Loulou's ancestors, surely. And though Félicité looked at the picture while she said her prayers she swerved a little from time to time towards the parrot.

She wanted to join the Ladies of the Virgin but Mme. Aubain dissuaded her.

And then a great event loomed up before them—Paul's marriage.

He had been a solicitor's clerk to begin with, and then tried business, the Customs, the Inland Revenue, and made efforts, even, to get into the Rivers and Forests. By an inspiration from heaven he had suddenly, at thirty-six, discovered his real line—the Registrar's Office. And there he showed such marked capacity that an inspector had offered him his daughter's hand and promised him his influence.

So Paul, grown serious, brought the lady to see his mother.

She sniffed at the ways of Pont-l'Évêque, gave herself great airs, and wounded Félicité's feelings. Mme. Aubain was relieved at her departure.

The week after came news of M. Bourais' death in an inn in Lower Brittany. The rumour of suicide was confirmed, and doubts arose as to his honesty. Mme. Aubain studied his accounts, and soon found out the whole tale of his misdoings—embezzled arrears, secret sales of wood, forged receipts, etc. Besides that he had an illegitimate child, and "relations with a person at Dozulé."

These shameful facts distressed her greatly. In March 1853 she was seized with a pain in the chest; her tongue seemed to be covered with film, and leeches did not ease the difficult breathing. On the ninth evening of her illness she died, just at seventy-two.

She passed as being younger, owing to the bands of brown hair which framed her pale, pock-marked face. There were few friends to regret her, for she had a stiffness of manner which kept people at a distance.

But Félicité mourned for her as one seldom mourns for a master. It upset her ideas and seemed contrary to the order of things, impossible and monstrous, that Madame should die before her.

Ten days afterwards, which was the time it took to hurry there from Besançon, the heirs arrived. The daughter-in-law ransacked the drawers, chose some furniture, and sold the rest; and then they went back to their registering.

Madame's armchair, her small round table, her foot-warmer, and the eight chairs were gone! Yellow patches in the middle of the panels showed where the engravings had hung. They had carried off the two little beds and the mattresses, and all Virginie's belongings had disappeared from the cupboard. Félicité went from floor to floor dazed with sorrow.

The next day there was a notice on the door, and the apothecary shouted in her ear that the house was for sale.

She tottered, and was obliged to sit down. What distressed her most of all was to give up her room, so suitable as it was for poor Loulou. She enveloped him with a look of anguish when she was imploring the Holy Ghost, and formed the idolatrous habit of kneeling in front of the parrot to say her prayers. Sometimes the sun shone in at the attic window and caught his glass eye, and a great luminous ray shot out of it and put her in an ecstasy.

She had a pension of fifteen pounds a year which her mistress had left her. The garden gave her a supply of vegetables. As for clothes, she had enough to last her to the end of her days, and she economized in candles by going to bed at dusk.

She hardly ever went out, as she did not like passing the dealer's shop, where some of the old furniture was exposed for sale. Since her fit of giddiness she dragged one leg; and as her strength was failing Mère Simon, whose grocery business had collapsed, came every morning to split the wood and pump water for her.

Her eyes grew feeble. The shutters ceased to be thrown open. Years and years passed, and the house was neither let nor sold.

Félicité never asked for repairs because she was afraid of being sent away. The boards on the roof rotted; her bolster was wet for a whole winter. After Easter she spat blood.

Then Mère Simon called in a doctor. Félicité wanted to know what was the matter with her. But she was too deaf to hear, and the only word which reached her was "pneumonia." It was a word she knew, and she answered softly "Ah! like Madame," thinking it natural that she should follow her mistress.

The time for the festal shrines was coming near. The first one was always at the bottom of the hill, the second in front of the post-office, and the third towards the middle of the street. There was some rivalry in the matter of this one, and the women of the parish ended by choosing Mme. Aubain's court-yard.

The hard breathing and fever increased. Félicité was vexed at doing nothing for the altar. If only she could at least have put something there! Then she thought of the parrot. The neighbours objected that it would not be decent. But the priest gave her permission, which so intensely delighted her that she begged him to accept Loulou, her sole possession, when she died.

From Tuesday to Saturday, the eve of the festival, she coughed more often. By the evening her face had shrivelled, her lips stuck to her gums, and she had vomitings; and at twilight next morning, feeling herself very low, she sent for a priest.

Three kindly women were round her during the extreme unction. Then she announced that she must speak to Fabu. He arrived in his Sunday clothes, by no means at his ease in the funereal atmosphere.

"Forgive me," she said, with an effort to stretch out her arm; "I thought it was you who had killed him."

What did she mean by such stories? She suspected him of murder—a man like him! He waxed indignant, and was on the point of making a row.

"There," said the women, "she is no longer in her senses, you can see it well enough!"

Félicité spoke to shadows of her own from time to time. The women went away, and Mère Simon had breakfast. A little later she took Loulou and brought him close to Félicité with the words:

"Come, now, say good-bye to him!"

Loulou was not a corpse, but the worms devoured him; one of his wings was broken, and the tow was coming out of his stomach. But she was blind now; she kissed him on the forehead and kept him close against her cheek. Mère Simon took him back from her to put him on the altar.

V

Summer scents came up from the meadows; flies buzzed; the sun made the river glitter and heated the slates. Mère Simon came back into the room and fell softly asleep.

She woke at the noise of bells; the people were coming out from vespers. Félicité's delirium subsided. She thought of the procession and saw it as if she had been there.

All the school children, the church-singers, and the firemen walked on the pavement, while in the middle of the road the verger armed with his hallebard and the beadle with a large cross advanced in front. Then came the schoolmaster, with an eye on the boys, and the sister, anxious about her little girls; three of the daintiest, with angelic curls, scattered rose-petals in the air; the deacon controlled the band with outstretched arms; and two censer-bearers turned back at every step towards the Holy Sacrament, which was borne by Monsieur the curé, wearing his beautiful chasuble, under a canopy of dark-red velvet held up by four churchwardens. A crowd of people pressed behind, between the white cloths covering the house walls, and they reached the bottom of the hill.

A cold sweat moistened Félicité's temples. Mère Simon sponged her with a piece of linen, saying to herself that one day she would have to go that way.

The hum of the crowd increased, was very loud for an instant, and then went further away.

A fusillade shook the window-panes. It was the postilions saluting the monstrance. Félicité rolled her eyes and said as audibly as she could: "Does he look well?" The parrot was weighing on her mind.

Her agony began. A death-rattle that grew more and more convulsed made her sides heave. Bubbles of froth came at the corners of her mouth and her whole body trembled.

Soon the booming of the ophicleides, the high voices of the children, and the deep voices of the men were distinguishable. At intervals all was silent, and the tread of feet, deadened by the flowers they walked on, sounded like a flock pattering on grass.

The clergy appeared in the courtyard. Mère Simon clambered on to a chair to reach the attic window, and so looked down straight upon the shrine. Green garlands hung over the altar, which was decked with a flounce of English lace. In the middle was a small frame with relics in it; there were two orange-trees at the corners, and all along stood silver candlesticks and china vases, with sunflowers, lilies, peonies, foxgloves, and tufts of hortensia. This heap of blazing colour slanted from the level of the altar to the carpet which went on over the pavement; and some rare objects caught the eye. There was a silver-gilt sugar-basin with a crown of violets; pendants of Alençon stone glittered on the moss, and two Chinese screens displayed their landscapes. Loulou was hidden under roses, and showed nothing but his blue forehead, like a plaque of lapis lazuli.

The churchwardens, singers, and children took their places round the three sides of the court. The priest went slowly up the steps, and placed his great, radiant golden sun upon the lace. Everyone knelt down. There was a deep silence; and the censers glided to and fro on the full swing of their chains.

An azure vapour rose up into Félicité's room. Her nostrils met it; she inhaled it sensuously, mystically; and then closed her eyes. Her lips smiled. The beats of her heart lessened one by one, vaguer each time and softer, as a fountain sinks, an echo disappears; and when she sighed her last breath she thought she saw an opening in the heavens, and a gigantic parrot hovering above her head.

COMMENTARY

Flaubert sent "A Simple Heart" (*Un Cœur Simple*) to Georges Sand, with the remark that it was *his* idea of what a story should be like. The story is, indeed, a rebuke to his volatile friend and to all writers of her kind, but it is more than that. It is a brilliant illustration of Flaubert's great discovery that in fiction no object exists *until it has acted upon or been acted upon by some other object*. This discovery (which was to be carried further by Henry James) is the fundamental principle which activates all of Flaubert's mature work. For him the five senses are the palette from which he contrives his illusion of life. He rarely attempted to render a phenomenon by portraying only one of its aspects. If the sense of sight is the only sense appealed to it will be appealed to more than once. In "A Simple Heart" Félicité recognizes Virginie among the communicants by her slender neck *and* devout bearing. But more often more than one sense is appealed to:

> On days when it was too hot they did not leave their room. From the dazzling brilliance outside light fell in streaks between the laths of the blinds. There were no sounds in the village; and on the pavement below not a soul. This silence round them deepened the quietness of things. In the distance, where men were caulking, there was a tap of hammers as they plugged the hulls, and a sluggish breeze wafted up the smell of tar.

Over and over Flaubert gets his effects by a scrupulous rendering of the complex of sensations in which we have our being. In such a passage one detail rests upon and sustains another. *The sound of the caulkers' hammers comes more clearly to our ears because of the smell of tar in the air.*

"A Simple Heart" shows Flaubert at his best. Its theme, like almost all of Flaubert's themes, is religious, a fact which has gone almost unremarked by his critics, past or present. One finds the prototype of its heroine in Catherine Leroux, the old peasant woman in *Madame Bovary* whose face has "a monastic rigidity." After fifty-four years of service on the same farm Catherine is rewarded by a silver medal, of the value of twenty-five francs.

But Félicité, in the end, obtains a higher reward. For her the heavens open and the Holy Ghost descends.

The viewpoint is omniscient (see Appendix A, p. 623), with alternations of panoramic and scenic views. The panoramic views are not general statements but are made up of details as vivid and brilliant as those in the scenic views, muted only by distance. The student will do well to study Flaubert's method of handling panoramic views. It is as if he directed our attention to a bed of flowers. The colors, scarlet and gold and pink and blue, all run together. We would have to go closer to ascertain whether the flowers are asters and dahlias, or marigolds and asters and Canterbury Bells; but even from where we stand the colors show themselves as scarlet and gold and pink and blue. "A Simple Heart" opens with a masterly panoramic view:

> Madame Aubain's servant Félicité was the envy of the ladies of Pont-l'Évêque for half a century.
> She received four pounds a year. For that she was cook and general servant, and did the sewing, washing, and ironing; she could bridle a horse, fatten poultry, and churn butter—and she remained faithful to her mistress, unamiable as the latter was.

Flaubert's principle, that no object exists in fiction until it has acted upon or been acted upon by some other object, is here extended to include persons. Félicité's faithfulness and goodness are thrown into relief by her mistress' lack of amiability. And so it will be throughout the story. Félicité, as we come to know her, could not exist without the background of the self-centered, indifferent Aubain family.

The story's Enveloping Action (see Appendix A, p. 631) is, indeed, the lives of the members of this family. Except for an unhappy love affair Félicité's own life is barren of outward incident. In the Complication (see Appendix A, p. 630) of this story Flaubert seems to have posed himself the same problem that confronts his heroine: how to find interest in such a life. He solves it by making it a drama of Christian renunciation.

He prepares thoroughly for his Resolution. Félicité's love of the beautiful and strange is roused when Paul Aubain explains to her a series of geographical prints, showing "cannibals with feathers on their heads, a monkey carrying off a young lady, Bedouins in the desert," and the like—scenes which enormously appealed to Flaubert himself. He tells us that this was Félicité's sole literary education: the simple or knowing heart can survive on scanty fare. The habit of renunciation grows so strong with Félicité that even spiritual and aesthetic joys have more savor when tasted vicariously. She feels more rapture at Virginie's first communion than at her own, and when she first sees the parrot she says, "How Madame would enjoy having him!"

All the scenes, whether panoramic or scenic (see Appendix A, p. 627) are rendered through masses of carefully chosen, superbly rendered details.

Flaubert never indulges in what Henry James calls "weak specification." He knew that in order for us to believe in Félicité's adoration of the parrot it was necessary for us to *see* the parrot as he appeared to her, and so he presents the parrot to us as a thing of beauty, with "solid" specifications:

> Green garlands hung over the altar, which was decked with a flounce of English lace. In the middle was a small frame with relics in it; there were two orange-trees at the corners, and all along stood silver candlesticks and china vases, with sunflowers, lilies, peonies, foxgloves, and tufts of hortensia. This heap of blazing colour slanted from the level of the altar to the carpet which went on over the pavement; and some rare objects caught the eye. There was a silver-gilt sugar-basin with a crown of violets; pendants of Alençon stone glittered on the moss, and two Chinese screens displayed their landscapes. Loulou was hidden under roses, and showed nothing but his blue forehead, like a plaque of lapis lazuli.

The exotic is deliberately stressed throughout this passage. Loulou appears not only beautiful but strange. This is an excellent preparation for the Resolution, in which he will appear to Félicité in an even stranger guise, as the Holy Ghost, coming down from Heaven. The breathtaking beauty and strangeness of the altar also prepares us for the vision which is the climax of her life.

The Tonal Unity (see Appendix A, p. 632) of this story is remarkable— some of it even comes through in translation. For Flaubert the story was evidently a series of carefully wrought tonal effects, one depending upon the other. When a friend suggested that he leave out one of the sentences about the parrot he replied that if he did the whole structure would collapse.

His Symbolism (see Appendix A, p. 633) is not apparent throughout the action, as in William Faulkner's work, for instance, but is more cryptic, moving underground, so to speak, to emerge in a great flood at the end. It is only when we look back that we see that Félicité's life follows the same pattern as that of the early Christians. She renounces earthly joys and under- goes many of the same trials that they underwent; she confronts wild beasts— when she saves Madame Aubain and the children from an enraged bull; comforts the sick and the dying—Père Colmiche, with his cancerous sores, bears a marked resemblance to the lepers to whom the early Christians min- istered; is scourged—when, as she is on her way to St. Gatien, carrying the basket which contains the dead Loulou, a passing carter "gave her such a lash from waist to neck with his big whip that she fell on her back." "Then she ate a crust of bread which she had put in the basket as a precaution, and found a consolation for her wound in gazing at the bird," the most beauti- ful object that has come into her life. As a result of her lifelong self-denial and innocence she is rewarded by the kind of vision which comes to saints. For her the heavens open and the Holy Ghost appears in the form of the parrot she has so loved in life.

Nathaniel Hawthorne

YOUNG GOODMAN BROWN

YOUNG GOODMAN BROWN came forth at sunset into the street at Salem village; but put his head back, after crossing the threshold, to exchange a parting kiss with his young wife. And Faith, as the wife was aptly named, thrust her own pretty head into the street, letting the wind play with the pink ribbons of her cap while she called to Goodman Brown.

"Dearest heart," whispered she, softly and rather sadly, when her lips were close to his ear, "prithee put off your journey until sunrise and sleep in your own bed to-night. A lone woman is troubled with such dreams and such thoughts that she's afeard of herself sometimes. Pray tarry with me this night, dear husband, of all nights in the year."

"My love and my Faith," replied young Goodman Brown, "of all nights in the year, this one night must I tarry away from thee. My journey, as thou callest it, forth and back again, must needs be done 'twixt now and sunrise. What, my sweet, pretty wife, dost thou doubt me already, and we but three months married?"

"Then God bless you!" said Faith, with the pink ribbons; "and may you find all well when you come back."

"Amen!" cried Goodman Brown. "Say thy prayers, dear Faith, and go to bed at dusk, and no harm will come to thee."

So they parted; and the young man pursued his way until, being about to turn the corner by the meeting-house, he looked back and saw the head of Faith still peeping after him with a melancholy air, in spite of her pink ribbons.

"Poor little Faith!" thought he, for his heart smote him. "What a wretch am I to leave her on such an errand! She talks of dreams, too. Methought as she spoke there was trouble in her face, as if a dream had warned her what work is to be done to-night. But no, no; 't would kill her to think it. Well, she's a blessed angel on earth; and after this one night I'll cling to her skirts and follow her to heaven."

With this excellent resolve for the future, Goodman Brown felt himself justified in making more haste on his present evil purpose. He had taken a dreary road, darkened by all the gloomiest trees of the forest, which barely stood aside to let the narrow path creep through, and closed immediately behind. It was all as lonely as could be; and there is this peculiarity in such a solitude, that the traveller knows not who may be concealed by the innumerable trunks and the thick boughs overhead; so that with lonely footsteps he may yet be passing through an unseen multitude.

"There may be a devilish Indian behind every tree," said Goodman Brown to himself; and he glanced fearfully behind him as he added, "What if the devil himself should be at my very elbow!"

His head being turned back, he passed a crook of the road, and, looking forward again, beheld the figure of a man, in grave and decent attire, seated at the foot of an old tree. He arose at Goodman Brown's approach and walked onward side by side with him.

"You are late, Goodman Brown," said he. "The clock of the Old South was striking as I came through Boston, and that is full fifteen minutes agone."

"Faith kept me back a while," replied the young man, with a tremor in his voice, caused by the sudden appearance of his companion, though not wholly unexpected.

It was now deep dusk in the forest, and deepest in that part of it where these two were journeying. As nearly as could be discerned, the second traveller was about fifty years old, apparently in the same rank of life as Goodman Brown, and bearing a considerable resemblance to him, though perhaps more in expression than features. Still they might have been taken for father and son. And yet, though the elder person was as simply clad as the younger, and as simple in manner too, he had an indescribable air of one who knew the world, and who would not have felt abashed at the governor's dinner table or in King William's court, were it possible that his affairs should call him thither. But the only thing about him that could be fixed upon as remarkable was his staff, which bore the likeness of a great black snake, so curiously wrought that it might almost be seen to twist and wriggle itself like a living serpent. This, of course, must have been an ocular deception, assisted by the uncertain light.

"Come, Goodman Brown," cried his fellow-traveller, "this is a dull pace for the beginning of a journey. Take my staff, if you are so soon weary."

"Friend," said the other, exchanging his slow pace for a full stop, "having kept covenant by meeting thee here, it is my purpose now to return whence I came. I have scruples touching the matter thou wot'st of."

"Sayest thou so?" replied he of the serpent, smiling apart. "Let us walk on, nevertheless, reasoning as we go; and if I convince thee not thou shalt turn back. We are but a little way in the forest yet."

"Too far! too far!" exclaimed the goodman, unconsciously resuming his walk. "My father never went into the woods on such an errand, nor his father before him. We have been a race of honest men and good Christians since the days of the martyrs; and shall I be the first of the name of Brown that ever took this path and kept—"

"Such company, thou wouldst say," observed the elder person, interpreting his pause. "Well said, Goodman Brown! I have been as well acquainted with your family as with ever a one among the Puritans; and that's no trifle to say. I helped your grandfather, the constable, when he lashed the Quaker woman so smartly through the streets of Salem; and it was I that brought your father a pitch-pine knot, kindled at my own hearth, to set fire to an Indian village, in King Philip's war. They were my good friends, both; and many a pleasant walk have we had along this path, and returned merrily after midnight. I would fain be friends with you for their sake."

"If it be as thou sayest," replied Goodman Brown, "I marvel they never spoke of these matters; or, verily, I marvel not, seeing that the least rumor of the sort would have driven them from New England. We are a people of prayer, and good works to boot, and abide no such wickedness."

"Wickedness or not," said the traveller with the twisted staff, "I have a very general acquaintance here in New England. The deacons of many a church have drunk the communion wine with me; the selectmen of divers towns make me their chairman; and a majority of the Great and General Court are firm supporters of my interest. The governor and I, too—But these are state secrets."

"Can this be so?" cried Goodman Brown, with a stare of amazement at his undisturbed companion. "Howbeit, I have nothing to do with the governor and council; they have their own ways, and are no rule for a simple husbandman like me. But, were I to go on with thee, how should I meet the eye of that good old man, our minister, at Salem village? Oh, his voice would make me tremble both Sabbath day and lecture day."

Thus far the elder traveller had listened with due gravity; but now burst into a fit of irrepressible mirth, shaking himself so violently that his snake-like staff actually seemed to wriggle in sympathy.

"Ha! ha! ha!" shouted he again and again; then composing himself, "Well, go on, Goodman Brown, go on; but, prithee, don't kill me with laughing."

"Well, then, to end the matter at once," said Goodman Brown, considerably nettled, "there is my wife, Faith. It would break her dear little heart; and I'd rather break my own."

"Nay, if that be the case," answered the other, "e'en go thy ways, Goodman Brown. I would not for twenty old women like the one hobbling before us that Faith should come to any harm."

As he spoke he pointed his staff at a female figure on the path, in whom Goodman Brown recognized a very pious and exemplary dame, who had taught him his catechism in youth, and was still his moral and spiritual adviser, jointly with the minister and Deacon Gookin.

"A marvel, truly, that Goody Cloyse should be so far in the wilderness at nightfall," said he. "But with your leave, friend, I shall take a cut through the woods until we have left this Christian woman behind. Being a stranger to you, she might ask whom I was consorting with and whither I was going."

"Be it so," said his fellow-traveller. "Betake you to the woods, and let me keep the path."

Accordingly the young man turned aside, but took care to watch his companion, who advanced softly along the road until he had come within a staff's length of the old dame. She, meanwhile, was making the best of her way, with singular speed for so aged a woman, and mumbling some indistinct words—a prayer, doubtless—as she went. The traveller put forth his staff and touched her withered neck with what seemed the serpent's tail.

"The devil!" screamed the pious old lady.

"Then Goody Cloyse knows her old friend?" observed the traveller, confronting her and leaning on his writhing stick.

"Ah, forsooth, and is it your worship indeed?" cried the good dame. "Yea, truly is it, and in the very image of my old gossip, Goodman Brown, the grandfather of the silly fellow that now is. But—would your worship believe it?—my broomstick hath strangely disappeared, stolen, as I suspect, by that unhanged witch, Goody Cory, and that, too, when I was all anointed with the juice of smallage, and cinquefoil, and wolf's bane—"

"Mingled with fine wheat and the fat of a new-born babe," said the shape of old Goodman Brown.

"Ah, your worship knows the recipe," cried the old lady, cackling aloud. "So, as I was saying, being all ready for the meeting, and no horse to ride on, I made up my mind to foot it; for they tell me there is a nice young man to be taken into communion to-night. But now your good worship will lend me your arm, and we shall be there in a twinkling.

"That can hardly be," answered her friend. "I may not spare you my arm, Goody Cloyse; but here is my staff, if you will."

So saying, he threw it down at her feet, where, perhaps, it assumed life, being one of the rods which its owner had formerly lent to the Egyptian magi. Of this fact, however, Goodman Brown could not take cognizance. He had cast up his eyes in astonishment, and, looking down again, beheld neither Goody Cloyse nor the serpentine staff, but this fellow-traveller alone, who waited for him as calmly as if nothing had happened.

"That old woman taught me my catechism," said the young man; and there was a world of meaning in this simple comment.

They continued to walk onward, while the elder traveller exhorted his companion to make good speed and persevere in the path, discoursing so aptly that his arguments seemed rather to spring up in the bosom of his auditor than to be suggested by himself. As they went, he plucked a branch of maple to serve for a walking stick, and began to strip it of the twigs and little boughs, which were wet with evening dew. The moment his fingers touched them they became strangely withered and dried up as with a week's sunshine. Thus the pair proceeded, at a good free pace, until suddenly, in a gloomy hollow of the road, Goodman Brown sat himself down on the stump of a tree and refused to go any farther.

"Friend," said he, stubbornly, "my mind is made up. Not another step will I budge on this errand. What if a wretched old woman do choose to go to the devil when I thought she was going to heaven: is that any reason why I should quit my dear Faith and go after her?"

"You will think better of this by and by," said his acquaintance, composedly. "Sit here and rest yourself a while; and when you feel like moving again, there is my staff to help you along."

Without more words, he threw his companion the maple stick, and was as speedily out of sight as if he had vanished into the deepening gloom. The young man sat a few moments by the roadside, applauding himself greatly, and thinking with how clear a conscience he should meet the minister in his morning walk, nor shrink from the eye of good old Deacon Gookin. And what calm sleep would be his that very night, which was to have been spent so wickedly, but so purely and sweetly now, in the arms of Faith! Amidst these pleasant and praiseworthy meditations, Goodman Brown heard the tramp of horses along the road, and deemed it advisable to conceal himself within the verge of the forest, conscious of the guilty purpose that had brought him thither, though now so happily turned from it.

On came the hoof tramps and the voices of the riders, two grave old voices, conversing soberly as they drew near. These mingled sounds appeared to pass along the road, within a few yards of the young man's hiding-place; but, owing doubtless to the depth of the gloom at that particular spot, neither the travellers nor their steeds were visible. Though their figures brushed the small boughs by the wayside, it could not be seen that they intercepted, even for a moment, the faint gleam from the strip of bright sky athwart which they must have passed. Goodman Brown alternately crouched and stood on tiptoe, pulling aside the branches and thrusting forth his head as far as he durst without discerning so much as a shadow. It vexed him the more, because he could have sworn, were such a thing possible, that he recognized the voices of the minister and Deacon Gookin, jogging along quietly, as they were wont to do, when bound to some ordination or ecclesiastical council. While yet within hearing, one of the riders stopped to pluck a switch.

"Of the two, reverend sir," said the voice like the deacon's, "I had rather miss an ordination dinner than to-night's meeting. They tell me that some of our community are to be here from Falmouth and beyond, and others from Connecticut and Rhode Island, besides several of the Indian powwows, who, after their fashion, know almost as much deviltry as the best of us. Moreover, there is a goodly young woman to be taken into communion."

"Mighty well, Deacon Gookin!" replied the solemn old tones of the minister. "Spur up, or we shall be late. Nothing can be done, you know, until I get on the ground."

The hoofs clattered again; and the voices, talking so strangely in the empty air, passed on through the forest, where no church had ever been gathered or solitary Christian prayed. Whither, then, could these holy men be journeying so deep into the heathen wilderness? Young Goodman Brown caught hold of a tree for support, being ready to sink down on the ground, faint and overburdened with the heavy sickness of his heart. He looked up to the sky, doubting whether there really was a heaven above him. Yet there was the blue arch, and the stars brightening in it.

"With heaven above and Faith below, I will yet stand firm against the devil!" cried Goodman Brown.

While he still gazed upward into the deep arch of the firmament and had lifted his hands to pray, a cloud, though no wind was stirring, hurried across the zenith and hid the brightening stars. The blue sky was still visible, except directly overhead, where this black mass of cloud was sweeping swiftly northward. Aloft in the air, as if from the depths of the cloud, came a confused and doubtful sound of voices. Once the listener fancied that he could distinguish the accents of towns-people of his own, men and women, both pious and ungodly, many of whom he had met at the communion table, and had seen others rioting at the tavern. The next moment, so indistinct were the sounds, he doubted whether he had heard aught but the murmur of the old forest, whispering without a wind. Then came a stronger swell of those familiar tones, heard daily in the sunshine at Salem village, but never until now from a cloud of night. There was one voice, of a young woman, uttering lamentations, yet with an uncertain sorrow, and entreating for some favor, which, perhaps, it would grieve her to obtain; and all the unseen multitude, both saints and sinners, seemed to encourage her onward.

"Faith!" shouted Goodman Brown, in a voice of agony and desperation; and the echoes of the forest mocked him, crying, "Faith! Faith!" as if bewildered wretches were seeking her all through the wilderness.

The cry of grief, rage, and terror was yet piercing the night, when the unhappy husband held his breath for a response. There was a scream, drowned immediately in a louder murmur of voices, fading into far-off laughter, as the dark cloud swept away, leaving the clear and silent sky above Goodman Brown. But something fluttered lightly down through the air and caught on the branch of a tree. The young man seized it, and beheld a pink ribbon.

"My Faith is gone!" cried he, after one stupefied moment. "There is no good on earth; and sin is but a name. Come, devil; for to thee is this world given."

And, maddened with despair, so that he laughed loud and long, did Goodman Brown grasp his staff and set forth again, at such a rate that he seemed to fly along the forest path rather than to walk or run. The road grew wilder and drearier and more faintly traced, and vanished at length, leaving him in the heart of the dark wilderness, still rushing onward with the instinct that guides mortal man to evil. The whole forest was peopled with frightful sounds—the creaking of the trees, the howling of wild beasts, and the yell of Indians; while sometimes the wind tolled like a distant church bell, and sometimes gave a broad roar around the traveller, as if all Nature were laughing him to scorn. But he was himself the chief horror of the scene, and shrank not from its other horrors.

"Ha! ha! ha!" roared Goodman Brown when the wind laughed at him. "Let us hear which will laugh loudest. Think not to frighten me with your deviltry. Come witch, come wizard, come Indian powwow, come devil himself, and here comes Goodman Brown. You may as well fear him as he fear you."

In truth, all through the haunted forest there could be nothing more frightful than the figure of Goodman Brown. On he flew among the black pines, brandishing his staff with frenzied gestures, now giving vent to an inspiration of horrid blasphemy, and now shouting forth such laughter as set all the echoes of the forest laughing like demons around him. The fiend in his own shape is less hideous than when he rages in the breast of man. Thus sped the demoniac on his course, until, quivering among the trees, he saw a red light before him, as when the felled trunks and branches of a clearing have been set on fire, and throw up their lurid blaze against the sky, at the hour of midnight. He paused, in a lull of the tempest that had driven him onward, and heard the swell of what seemed a hymn, rolling solemnly from a distance with the weight of many voices. He knew the tune; it was a familiar one in the choir of the village meeting-house. The verse died heavily away, and was lengthened by a chorus, not of human voices, but of all the sounds of the benighted wilderness pealing in awful harmony together. Goodman Brown cried out, and his cry was lost to his own ear by its unison with the cry of the desert.

In the interval of silence he stole forward until the light glared full upon his eyes. At one extremity of an open space, hemmed in by the dark wall of the forest, arose a rock, bearing some rude, natural resemblance either to an altar or a pulpit, and surrounded by four blazing pines, their tops aflame, their stems untouched, like candles at an evening meeting. The mass of foliage that had overgrown the summit of the rock was all on fire, blazing high into the night and fitfully illuminating the whole field. Each pendent twig and leafy festoon was in a blaze. As the red light arose and fell, a numerous congregation alternately shone forth, then disappeared in shadow, and again grew, as it were, out of the darkness, peopling the heart of the solitary woods at once.

"A grave and dark-clad company," quoth Goodman Brown.

In truth they were such. Among them, quivering to and fro between gloom and splendor, appeared faces that would be seen next day at the council board of the province, and others which, Sabbath after Sabbath, looked devoutly heavenward, and benignantly over the crowded pews, from the holiest pulpits in the land. Some affirm that the lady of the governor was there. At least there were high dames well known to her, and wives of honored husbands, and widows, a great multitude, and ancient maidens, all of excellent repute, and fair young girls, who trembled lest their mothers should espy them. Either the sudden gleams of light flashing over the obscure field bedazzled Goodman Brown, or he recognized a score of the church members of Salem village famous for their especial sanctity. Good old Deacon Gookin had arrived, and waited at the skirts of that venerable saint, his revered pastor. But, irreverently consorting with these grave, reputable, and pious people, these elders of the church, these chaste dames and dewy virgins, there were men of dissolute lives and women of spotted fame, wretches given over to all mean and filthy vice, and suspected even of horrid crimes. It was strange to see that the good shrank not from the wicked, nor were the sinners abashed by the saints. Scattered also among their pale-faced enemies were the Indian priests, or powwows, who had often scared their native forest with more hideous incantations than any known to English witchcraft.

"But where is Faith?" thought Goodman Brown; and, as hope came into his heart, he trembled.

Another verse of the hymn arose, a slow and mournful strain, such as the pious love, but joined to words which expressed all that our nature can conceive of sin, and darkly hinted at far more. Unfathomable to mere mortals is the lore of fiends. Verse after verse was sung; and still the chorus of the desert swelled between like the deepest tone of a mighty organ; and with the final peal of that dreadful anthem there came a sound, as if the roaring wind, the rushing streams, the howling beasts, and every other voice of the unconcerted wilderness were mingling and according with the voice of guilty man in homage to the prince of all. The four blazing pines threw up a loftier flame, and obscurely discovered shapes and visages of horror on the smoke wreaths above the impious assembly. At the same moment the fire on the rock shot redly forth and formed a glowing arch above its base, where now appeared a figure. With reverence be it spoken, the figure bore no slight similitude, both in garb and manner, to some grave divine of the New England churches.

"Bring forth the converts!" cried a voice that echoed through the field and rolled into the forest.

At the word, Goodman Brown stepped forth from the shadow of the trees and approached the congregation, with whom he felt a loathful brotherhood by the sympathy of all that was wicked in his heart. He could have well-nigh sworn that the shape of his own dead father beckoned him to advance, looking downward from a smoke wreath, while a woman, with dim features of despair, threw out her hand to warn him back. Was it his mother? But he had no power to retreat one step, nor to resist, even in thought, when the minister and good old Deacon Gookin seized his arms and led him to the blazing rock. Thither came also the slender form of a veiled female, led between Goody Cloyse, that pious teacher of the catechism, and Martha Carrier, who had received the devil's promise to be queen of hell. A rampant hag was she. And there stood the proselytes beneath the canopy of fire.

"Welcome, my children," said the dark figure, "to the communion of your race. Ye have found thus young your nature and your destiny. My children, look behind you!"

They turned; and flashing forth, as it were, in a sheet of flame, the fiend worshippers were seen; the smile of welcome gleamed darkly on every visage.

"There," resumed the sable form, "are all whom ye have reverenced from youth. Ye deemed them holier than yourselves, and shrank from your own sin, contrasting it with their lives of righteousness and prayerful aspirations heavenward. Yet here are they all in my worshipping assembly. This night it shall be granted you to know their secret deeds: how hoary-bearded elders of the church have whispered wanton words to the young maids of their households; how many a woman, eager for widows' weeds, has given her husband a drink at bedtime and let him sleep his last sleep in her bosom; how beardless youths have made haste to inherit their fathers' wealth; and how fair damsels—blush not, sweet ones—have dug little graves in the garden, and bidden me, the sole guest, to an infant's funeral. By the sympathy of your human hearts for sin ye shall scent out all the places—whether in church, bed-chamber, street, field, or forest—where crime has been committed, and shall exult to behold the whole earth one stain of guilt, one mighty blood spot. Far more than this. It shall be yours to penetrate, in every bosom, the deep mystery of sin, the fountain of all wicked arts, and which inexhaustibly supplies more evil impulses than human power—than my power at its utmost —can make manifest in deeds. And now, my children, look upon each other."

They did so; and, by the blaze of the hell-kindled torches, the wretched man beheld his Faith, and the wife her husband, trembling before that unhallowed altar.

"Lo, there ye stand, my children," said the figure, in a deep and solemn tone, almost sad with its despairing awfulness, as if his once angelic nature could yet mourn for our miserable race. "Depending upon one another's hearts, ye had still hoped that virtue were not all a dream. Now are ye unde-ceived. Evil is the nature of mankind. Evil must be your only happiness. Welcome again, my children, to the communion of your race."

"Welcome," repeated the fiend worshippers, in one cry of despair and triumph.

And there they stood, the only pair, as it seemed, who were yet hesitating on the verge of wickedness in this dark world. A basin was hollowed, naturally, in the rock. Did it contain water, reddened by the lurid light? or was it blood? or, perchance, a liquid flame? Herein did the shape of evil dip his hand and prepare to lay the mark of baptism upon their foreheads, that they might be partakers of the mystery of sin, more conscious of the secret guilt of others, both in deed and thought, than they could now be of their own. The husband cast one look at his pale wife, and Faith at him. What polluted wretches would the next glance show them to each other, shudder-ing alike at what they disclosed and what they saw!

"Faith! Faith!" cried the husband, "look up to heaven, and resist the wicked one."

Whether Faith obeyed he knew not. Hardly had he spoken when he found himself amid calm night and solitude, listening to a roar of the wind which died heavily away through the forest. He staggered against the rock, and felt it chill and damp; while a hanging twig, that had been all on fire, besprinkled his cheek with the coldest dew.

The next morning young Goodman Brown came slowly into the street of Salem village, staring around him like a bewildered man. The good old

minister was taking a walk along the graveyard to get an appetite for breakfast and meditate his sermon, and bestowed a blessing, as he passed, on
Goodman Brown. He shrank from the venerable saint as if to avoid an
anathema. Old Deacon Gookin was at domestic worship, and the holy words
of his prayer were heard through the open window. "What God doth the
wizard pray to?" quoth Goodman Brown. Goody Cloyse, that excellent old
Christian, stood in the early sunshine at her own lattice, catechizing a little
girl who had brought her a pint of morning's milk. Goodman Brown
snatched away the child as from the grasp of the fiend himself. Turning the
corner by the meeting-house, he spied the head of Faith, with the pink
ribbons, gazing anxiously forth, and bursting into such joy at sight of him
that she skipped along the street and almost kissed her husband before the
whole village. But Goodman Brown looked sternly and sadly into her face,
and passed on without a greeting.

Had Goodman Brown fallen asleep in the forest and only dreamed a
wild dream of a witch-meeting?

Be it so if you will; but, alas! it was a dream of evil omen for young
Goodman Brown. A stern, a sad, a darkly meditative, a distrustful, if not a
desperate man did he become from the night of that fearful dream. On the
Sabbath day, when the congregation were singing a holy psalm, he could not
listen because an anthem of sin rushed loudly upon his ear and drowned all
the blessed strain. When the minister spoke from the pulpit with power and
fervid eloquence, and, with his hand on the open Bible, of the sacred truths
of our religion, and of saint-like lives and triumphant deaths, and of future
bliss or misery unutterable, then did Goodman Brown turn pale, dreading
lest the roof should thunder down upon the gray blasphemer and his hearers.
Often, awaking suddenly at midnight, he shrank from the bosom of Faith;
and at morning or eventide, when the family knelt down at prayer, he
scowled and muttered to himself, and gazed sternly at his wife, and turned
away. And when he had lived long, and was borne to his grave a hoary
corpse, followed by Faith, an aged woman, and children and grandchildren, a
goodly procession, besides neighbors not a few, they carved no hopeful verse
upon his tombstone, for his dying hour was gloom.

COMMENTARY

Hawthorne was the first writer of fiction in America to deal profoundly
with the most serious problem that confronts man: the problem of good and
evil. In Hawthorne's stories man is almost always shown in relation to
supernatural forces. For many years he kept a note-book in which he set
down ideas that struck him as suitable material for fictions. Here are some
of the entries:

> A snake taken into a man's stomach and nourished there from
> fifteen years to thirty-five, tormenting him most horribly. A type of envy
> or some other evil passion.

A man to swallow a small snake—and it to be a symbol of cherished sin.

A young man and girl meet together, each in search of a person to be known by some peculiar sign. They watch and wait a great while for that person to pass. At last special circumstance discloses that each is the one that the other is waiting for. Moral—that what we need for our happiness is often close at hand, if we knew but how to seek it.

Distrust to be thus exemplified: Various good and desirable things to be presented to a young man, and offered to his acceptance, as a friend, a wife, a fortune; but he to refuse them all, suspecting that it is merly a delusion. Yet all to be real, and he to be told so, when too late.

Hawthorne was haunted by a vision of original sin. Malcolm Cowley says that some of his stories "so testify to his sense of guilt that they might have been cries from a convocation of damned souls. Like Goodman Brown, he had wandered alone into the forest of his mind, and had suddenly found himself alone in the midst of a witches' sabbath."

"The loss of Heaven and the pains of Hell" are the consequences of original sin. Hawthorne several times set down in his note-books the theme of the young man or young woman who is proffered happiness but refuses it, waiting for some peculiar sign, and finds out only too late that it has been close at hand all along. That is, in essence, the theme of James's "The Beast in the Jungle" and Joyce's "The Dead."

James felt a kinship with Hawthorne and pointed out his preëminence as a master of what he called "the deeper psychology." T. S. Eliot says that both Hawthorne and James "have a kind of sense, a receptive medium which is not of sight. Not that they fail to make you see, so far as is necessary, but sight is not the essential sense. They perceive by antennae: and the 'deeper psychology' is here." Eliot also points out that "the deeper psychology" led Hawthorne to "some of his absurdest and most characteristic excesses; it was forever tailing off into the fanciful, even the allegorical, which is a lazy substitute for profundity."

The student can profitably compare Hawthorne with a contemporary writer, Franz Kafka (for Kafka may be considered our contemporary, since his work was not published until after his death). Kafka also deals with the supernatural, with good and evil, but the surface pattern of his stories is strictly naturalistic. In Hawthorne, the allegory is often a part of the action and he frequently weakens his dramatic sequences by an unadroit mingling of the supernatural and the natural, the allegorical and the real.

Hawthorne, important as he is, was never able to bring his craft to the pitch of perfection which Kafka attained in his short lifetime. He never solved the central technical problem (which occupied so much of James's working life), the question: On whose authority is the story told? (See Appendix A, p. 621)

Austin Warren, in his *Rage for Order*, has made some interesting comments in this connection. He says that "the technique available to Hawthorne as a narrative writer concerning the states of the soul was, primarily, the technique of the Gothic romance . . . Hawthorne has himself indicated his lineage within prose fiction by calling his work 'romance' and by expressly distinguishing this from the realistic novel: 'When a writer calls his work "Romance" it need hardly be observed that he wishes to claim a certain latitude both as to its fashion and its material.' " Hawthorne, Mr. Warren holds, "does not wish to explain all at the end. He has two chief ways of giving a sense of the mysterious while offering a concurrent rationale. One is to offer alternative natural and supernatural explanations—as, for instance, with the incision of the letter A upon the breast of Dimmesdale—generally attaching the latter to the credulous speculations of the community, the fanciful gossip of the uneducated, yet meanwhile intimating that the gossip may be wiser than the science."

This clumsy solution of the problem sometimes leaves the climax of Hawthorne's stories "up in the air." The natural and the supernatural are competing for the last word, and the reader, hearing two voices, sometimes grows confused as to what really happened. Kafka manages his Resolution (see Appendix A, p. 630) more cleanly. The naturalistic surface pattern persists to the end. We apprehend with our five senses what has happened. It is only after we have laid the book down that the subterranean, supernatural voice roars in our ears.

In "Young Goodman Brown," one of his best stories, Hawthorne is dealing with his favorite theme: the unhappiness which the human heart suffers as the result of its innate depravity.

The viewpoint is that of the roving narrator (see Appendix A, p. 626). The scenes are pictorial, but auctorial comment is scattered throughout the action.

The Complication (see Appendix A, p. 630) arises out of young Brown's desire to taste the joys of a Witch's Sabbath, in spite of the protestations of his wife, Faith, who is aptly named. It is furthered when he discovers that the fellow townsmen whom he has particularly revered, the minister, the old dame who taught him his catechism, and even his wife, Faith, are among the revellers. The Complication is resolved in the effect that this discovery has on him. The dramatic impact would have been stronger if Hawthorne had let the incidents tell their own story: Goodman Brown's behavior to his neighbors and finally to his wife *show* us that he is a changed man. Since fiction is a kind of shorthand of human behavior and one moment may represent years in a man's life, we would have concluded that the change was to last his entire life. But Hawthorne's weakness for moralizing and his insufficient technical equipment betray him into the anticlimax of the last paragraph.

The Enveloping Action (see Appendix A, p. 631) comprises the relations which Brown's neighbors and wife have with the Devil; it is woven into the Complication of the story and shows itself boldly in the climax. Brown was willing to lend his own soul to the Devil for a night, but he cannot face the discovery that every other soul has a similar desire and, having lost his faith to the Devil, comes to hate his fellow man.

Hawthorne has an acute ear. The speech of his characters is consistently authentic and dramatic. His eloquence, at times Miltonic, in phrases such as "the smile of welcome gleamed darkly on every visage," contributes to the action as well as to the tonal effect of the whole. The Symbolism (see Appendix A, p. 633) is on the grand scale, and that, in the end, is the distinguishing feature of Hawthorne's work. Even when we deplore flaws in the execution of his stories we stand amazed at the loftiness of his conceptions. In him we see the play of a first-rate imagination whose workings remain, in the end, unaccountable.

Herman Melville

BENITO CERENO

IN THE YEAR 1799, Captain Amasa Delano, of Duxbury, in Massachusetts, commanding a large sealer and general trader, lay at anchor, with a valuable cargo, in the harbour of St. Maria—a small, desert, uninhabited island towards the southern extremity of the long coast of Chili. There he had touched for water.

On the second day, not long after dawn, while lying in his berth, his mate came below, informing him that a strange sail was coming into the bay. Ships were then not so plenty in those waters as now. He rose, dressed, and went on deck.

The morning was one peculiar to that coast. Everything was mute and calm; everything grey. The sea, though undulated into long roods of swells, seemed fixed, and was sleeked at the surface like waved lead that has cooled and set in the smelter's mould. The sky seemed a grey mantle. Flights of troubled grey fowl, kith and kin with flights of troubled grey vapours among which they were mixed, skimmed low and fitfully over the waters, as swallows over meadows before storms. Shadows present, foreshadowing deeper shadows to come.

To Captain Delano's surprise, the stranger, viewed through the glass, showed no colours; though to do so upon entering a haven, however uninhabited in its shores, where but a single other ship might be lying, was the custom among peaceful seamen of all nations. Considering the lawlessness and loneliness of the spot, and the sort of stories, at that day, associated with those seas, Captain Delano's surprise might have deepened into some uneasiness had he not been a person of a singularly undistrustful good nature, not liable, except on extraordinary and repeated excitement, and hardly then, to indulge in personal alarms, any way involving the imputation of malign evil in man. Whether, in view of what humanity is capable, such a trait implies, along with a benevolent heart, more than ordinary quickness and accuracy of intellectual perception, may be left to the wise to determine.

But whatever misgivings might have obtruded on first seeing the stranger, would almost, in any seaman's mind, have been dissipated by observing that the ship, in navigating into the harbour, was drawing too near the land, for her own safety's sake, owing to a sunken reef making out off her bow. This seemed to prove her a stranger, indeed, not only to the sealer, but the island; consequently, she could be no wonted freebooter on that ocean. With no small interest, Captain Delano continued to watch her—a proceeding not much facilitated by the vapours partly mantling the hull, through which the far matin light from her cabin streamed equivocally enough; much like the sun—by this time crescented on the rim of the horizon, and apparently, in company with the strange ship, entering the harbour—which, wimpled by the same low, creeping clouds, showed not unlike a Lima intriguante's one sinister eye peering across the Plaza from the Indian loop-hole of her dusk *saya-y-manta*.

It might have been but a deception of the vapours, but, the longer the stranger was watched, the more singular appeared her manœuvres. Ere long it seemed hard to decide whether she meant to come in or no—what she wanted, or what she was about. The wind, which had breezed up a little during the night, was now extremely light and baffling, which the more increased the apparent uncertainty of her movements.

Surmising, at last, that it might be a ship in distress, Captain Delano ordered his whale-boat to be dropped, and, much to the wary opposition of his mate, prepared to board her, and, at the least, pilot her in. On the night previous, a fishing-party of the seamen had gone a long distance to some detached rocks out of sight from the sealer, and, an hour or two before day-break, had returned, having met with no small success. Presuming that the stranger might have been long off soundings, the good captain put several baskets of the fish, for presents, into his boat, and so pulled away. From her continuing too near the sunken reef, deeming her in danger, calling to his men, he made all haste to apprise those on board of their situation. But, some time ere the boat came up, the wind, light though it was, having shifted, had headed the vessel off, as well as partly broken the vapours from about her.

Upon gaining a less remote view, the ship, when made signally visible on the verge of the leaden-hued swells, with the shreds of fog here and there raggedly furring her, appeared like a white-washed monastery after a thunder-storm, seen perched upon some dun cliff among the Pyrenees. But it was no purely fanciful resemblance which now, for a moment, almost led Captain Delano to think that nothing less than a ship-load of monks was before him. Peering over the bulwarks were what really seemed, in the hazy distance, throngs of dark cowls; while, fitfully revealed through the open port-holes, other dark moving figures were dimly descried, as of Black Friars pacing the cloisters.

Upon a still nigher approach, this appearance was modified, and the true character of the vessel was plain—a Spanish merchantman of the first class; carrying negro slaves, amongst other valuable freight, from one colonial port to another. A very large, and, in its time, a very fine vessel, such as in those days were at intervals encountered along that main; sometimes superseded Acapulco treasure-ships, or retired frigates of the Spanish king's navy, which, like superannuated Italian palaces, still, under a decline of masters, preserved signs of former state.

As the whale-boat drew more and more nigh, the cause of the peculiar pipe-clayed aspect of the stranger was seen in the slovenly neglect pervading her. The spars, ropes, and great part of the bulwarks, looked woolly, from long unacquaintance with the scraper, tar, and the brush. Her keel seemed laid, her ribs put together, and she launched, from Ezekiel's Valley of Dry Bones.

In the present business in which she was engaged, the ship's general model and rig appeared to have undergone no material change from their original warlike and Froissart pattern. However, no guns were seen.

The tops were large, and were railed about with what had once been octagonal net-work, all now in sad disrepair. These tops hung overhead like three ruinous aviaries, in one of which was seen perched, on a ratlin, a white noddy, a strange fowl, so called from its lethargic somnambulistic character, being frequently caught by hand at sea. Battered and mouldy, the castellated forecastle seemed some ancient turret, long ago taken by assault, and then left to decay. Towards the stern, two high-raised quarter galleries—the balustrades here and there covered with dry, tindery sea-moss—opening out from the unoccupied state-cabin, whose dead lights, for all the mild weather, were hermetically closed and caulked—these tenantless balconies hung over the sea as if it were the grand Venetian canal. But the principal relic of faded grandeur was the ample oval of the shield-like stern-piece, intricately carved with the arms of Castile and Leon, medallioned about by groups of mythological or symbolical devices; uppermost and central of which was a dark satyr in a mask, holding his foot on the prostrate neck of a writhing figure, likewise masked.

Whether the ship had a figure-head, or only a plain beak, was not quite certain, owing to canvas wrapped about that part, either to protect it while undergoing a refurbishing, or else decently to hide its decay. Rudely painted or chalked, as in a sailor freak, along the forward side of a sort of pedestal below the canvas, was the sentence, *"Seguid vuestro jefe,"* (follow your leader); while upon the tarnished head-boards, near by, appeared, in stately capitals, once gilt, the ship's name, "San Dominick," each letter streakingly corroded with tricklings of copper-spike rust; while, like mourning weeds, dark festoons of sea-grass slimily swept to and fro over the name, with every hearse-like roll of the hull.

As at last the boat was hooked from the bow along toward the gangway amidship, its keel, while yet some inches separated from the hull, harshly grated as on a sunken coral reef. It proved a huge bunch of conglobated barnacles adhering below the water to the side like a wen; a token of baffling airs and long calms passed somewhere in those seas.

Climbing the side, the visitor was at once surrounded by a clamorous throng of whites and blacks, but the latter outnumbering the former more than could have been expected, negro transportation-ship as the stranger in port was. But, in one language, and as with one voice, all poured out a common tale of suffering; in which the negresses, of whom there were not a few, exceeded the others in their dolorous vehemence. The scurvy, together with a fever, had swept off a great part of their number, more especially the Spaniards. Off Cape Horn, they had narrowly escaped shipwreck;

then, for days together, they had lain tranced without wind; their provisions were low; their water next to none; their lips that moment were baked.

While Captain Delano was thus made the mark of all eager tongues, his one eager glance took in all the faces, with every other object about him.

Always upon first boarding a large and populous ship at sea, especially a foreign one, with a nondescript crew such as Lascars or Manilla men, the impression varies in a peculiar way from that produced by first entering a strange house with strange inmates in a strange land. Both house and ship, the one by its walls and blinds, the other by its high bulwarks like ramparts, hoard from view their interiors till the last moment; but in the case of the ship there is this addition: that the living spectacle it contains, upon its sudden and complete disclosure, has, in contrast with the blank ocean which zones it, something of the effect of enchantment. The ship seems unreal; these strange costumes, gestures, and faces, but a shadowy tableau just emerged from the deep, which directly must receive back what it gave.

Perhaps it was some such influence as above is attempted to be described which, in Captain Delano's mind, heightened whatever, upon a staid scrutiny, might have seemed unusual; especially the conspicuous figures of four elderly grizzled negroes, their heads like black, doddered willow tops, who, in venerable contrast to the tumult below them, were couched sphynxlike, one on the starboard cat-head, another on the larboard, and the remaining pair face to face on the opposite bulwarks above the main-chains. They each had bits of unstranded old junk in their hands, and, with a sort of stoical self-content, were picking the junk into oakum, a small heap of which lay by their sides. They accompanied the task with a continuous, low, monotonous chant; droning and drooling away like so many grey-headed bag-pipers playing a funeral march.

The quarter-deck rose into an ample elevated poop, upon the forward verge of which, lifted, like the oakum-pickers, some eight feet above the general throng, sat along in a row, separated by regular spaces, the cross-legged figures of six other blacks; each with a rusty hatchet in his hand, which, with a bit of brick and a rag, he was engaged like a scullion in scouring; while between each two was a small stack of hatchets, their rusted edges turned forward awaiting a like operation. Though occasionally the four oakum-pickers would briefly address some person or persons in the crowd below, yet the six hatchet-polishers neither spoke to others, nor breathed a whisper among themselves, but sat intent upon their task, except at intervals, when, with the peculiar love in negroes of uniting industry with pastime, two-and-two they sideways clashed their hatchets together, like cymbals, with a barbarous din. All six, unlike the generality, had the raw aspect of unsophisticated Africans.

But that first comprehensive glance which took in those ten figures, with scores less conspicuous, rested but an instant upon them, as, impatient of the hubbub of voices, the visitor turned in quest of whomsoever it might be that commanded the ship.

But as if not unwilling to let nature make known her own case among his suffering charge, or else in despair of restraining it for the time, the Spanish captain, a gentlemanly, reserved-looking, and rather young man to a stranger's eye, dressed with singular richness, but bearing plain traces of recent sleepless cares and disquietudes, stood passively by, leaning against the main-mast, at one moment casting a dreary, spiritless look upon his excited people, at the next an unhappy glance toward his visitor. By his side stood a black of small stature, in whose rude face, as occasionally, like a shepherd's dog, he mutely turned it up into the Spaniard's, sorrow and affection were equally blended.

Struggling through the throng, the American advanced to the Spaniard, assuring him of his sympathies, and offering to render whatever assistance might be in his power. To which the Spaniard returned, for the present, but grave and ceremonious acknowledgments, his national formality dusked by the saturnine mood of ill health.

But losing no time in mere compliments, Captain Delano, returning to the gangway, had his baskets of fish brought up, and as the wind still continued light, so that some hours at least must elapse ere the ship could be brought to the anchorage, he bade his men return to the sealer, and fetch back as much water as the whale-boat could carry, with whatever soft bread the steward might have, all the remaining pumpkins on board, with a box of sugar, and a dozen of his private bottles of cider.

Not many minutes after the boat's pushing off, to the vexation of all, the wind entirely died away, and the tide turning, began drifting back the ship helplessly seaward. But trusting this would not long last, Captain Delano sought with good hopes to cheer up the strangers, feeling no small satisfaction that with persons in their condition he could—thanks to his frequent voyages along the Spanish main—converse with some freedom in their native tongue.

While left alone with them, he was not long in observing some things tending to heighten his first impressions; but surprise was lost in pity, both for the Spaniards and blacks, alike evidently reduced from scarcity of water and provisions; while long-continued suffering seemed to have brought out the less good-natured qualities of the negroes, besides, at the same time, impairing the Spaniard's authority over them. But, under the circumstances, precisely this condition of things was to have been anticipated. In armies, navies, cities, or families—in nature herself—nothing more relaxes good order than misery. Still, Captain Delano was not without the idea, that had Benito Cereno been a man of greater energy, misrule would hardly have come to the present pass. But the debility, constitutional or induced by the hardships, bodily and mental, of the Spanish captain, was too obvious to be overlooked. A prey to settled dejection, as if long mocked with hope he would not now indulge it, even when it had ceased to be a mock, the prospect of that day or evening at furthest, lying at anchor, with plenty of water for his people, and a brother captain to counsel and befriend, seemed in no perceptible degree to encourage him. His mind appeared unstrung, if not still more seriously affected. Shut up in these oaken walls, chained to one dull round of command, whose unconditionality cloyed him, like some hypochondriac abbot he moved slowly about, at times suddenly pausing, starting, or staring, biting his lip, biting his fingernail, flushing, paling, twitching his beard, with other symptoms of an absent or moody mind. This distempered spirit was lodged, as before hinted, in as distempered a frame. He was rather tall, but seemed never to have been robust, and now with nervous suffering was almost worn to a skeleton. A tendency to some pulmonary complaint appeared to have been lately confirmed. His voice was like that of one with lungs half gone, hoarsely suppressed, a husky whisper. No wonder that, as in this state he tottered about, his private servant apprehensively followed him. Sometimes the negro gave his master his arm, or took his handkerchief out of his pocket for him; performing these and similar offices with that affectionate zeal which transmutes into something filial or fraternal acts in themselves but menial; and which has gained for the negro the repute of making the most pleasing body-servant in the world; one, too, whom a master need be on no stiffly superior terms with, but may treat with familiar trust; less a servant than a devoted companion.

Marking the noisy indocility of the blacks in general, as well as what seemed the sullen inefficiency of the whites, it was not without humane satisfaction that Captain Delano witnessed the steady good conduct of Babo.

But the good conduct of Babo, hardly more than the ill-behaviour of others, seemed to withdraw the half-lunatic Don Benito from his cloudy languor. Not that such precisely was the impression made by the Spaniard on the mind of his visitor. The Spaniard's individual unrest was, for the present, but noted as a conspicuous feature in the ship's general affliction. Still, Captain Delano was not a little concerned at what he could not help taking for the time to be Don Benito's unfriendly indifference toward himself. The Spaniard's manner, too, conveyed a sort of sour and gloomy disdain, which he seemed at no pains to disguise. But this the American in charity ascribed to the harassing effects of sickness, since, in former instances, he had noted that there are peculiar natures on whom prolonged physical suffering seems to cancel every social instinct of kindness; as if forced to black bread themselves, they deemed it but equity that each person coming nigh them should, indirectly, by some slight or affront, be made to partake of their fare.

But ere long Captain Delano bethought him that, indulgent as he was at the first, in judging the Spaniard, he might not, after all, have exercised charity enough. At bottom it was Don Benito's reserve which displeased him; but the same reserve was shown toward all but his personal attendant. Even the formal reports which, according to sea-usage, were at stated times made to him by some petty underling (either a white, mulatto or black), he hardly had patience enough to listen to, without betraying contemptuous aversion. His manner upon such occasions was, in its degree, not unlike that which might be supposed to have been his imperial countryman's, Charles V., just previous to the anchoritish retirement of that monarch from the throne.

This splenetic disrelish of his place was evinced in almost every function pertaining to it. Proud as he was moody, he condescended to no personal mandate. Whatever special orders were necessary, their delivery was delegated to his body-servant, who in turn transferred them to their ultimate destination, through runners, alert Spanish boys or slave boys, like pages or pilot-fish within easy call continually hovering round Don Benito. So that to have beheld this undemonstrative invalid gliding about, apathetic and mute, no landsman could have dreamed that in him was lodged a dictatorship beyond which, while at sea, there was no earthly appeal.

Thus, the Spaniard, regarded in his reserve, seemed as the involuntary victim of mental disorder. But, in fact, his reserve might, in some degree, have proceeded from design. If so, then in Don Benito was evinced the unhealthy climax of that icy though conscientious policy, more or less adopted by all commanders of large ships, which, except in signal emergencies, obliterates alike the manifestation of sway with every trace of sociality; transforming the man into a block, or rather into a loaded cannon, which, until there is call for thunder, has nothing to say.

Viewing him in this light, it seemed but a natural token of the perverse habit induced by a long course of such hard self-restraint, that, notwithstanding the present condition of his ship, the Spaniard should still persist in a demeanour, which, however harmless—or it may be, appropriate—in a well-appointed vessel, such as the *San Dominick* might have been at the outset of the voyage, was anything but judicious now. But the Spaniard perhaps thought that it was with captains as with gods: reserve, under all events, must still be their cue. But more probably this appearance of slumbering dominion might have been but an attempted disguise to conscious imbecility—not deep policy, but shallow device. But be all this as it might, whether Don Benito's manner was designed or not, the more Captain Delano noted its pervading reserve, the less he felt uneasiness at any particular manifestation of that reserve toward himself.

Neither were his thoughts taken up by the captain alone. Wonted to the quiet orderliness of the sealer's comfortable family of a crew, the noisy confusion of the *San Dominick's* suffering host repeatedly challenged his eye. Some prominent breaches not only of discipline but of decency were observed. These Captain Delano could not but ascribe, in the main, to the absence of those subordinate deck-officers to whom, along with higher duties, is entrusted what may be styled the police department of a populous ship. True, the old oakum-pickers appeared at times to act the part of monitorial constables to their countrymen, the blacks; but though occasionally succeeding in allaying trifling outbreaks now and then between man and man, they could do little or nothing toward establishing general quiet. The *San Dominick* was in the condition of a transatlantic emigrant ship, among whose multitude of living freight are some individuals, doubtless, as little troublesome as crates and bales; but the friendly remonstrances of such with their ruder companions are of not so much avail as the unfriendly arm of the mate. What the *San Dominick* wanted was, what the emigrant ship has, stern superior officers. But on these decks not so much as a fourth mate was to be seen.

The visitor's curiosity was roused to learn the particulars of those mishaps which had brought about such absenteeism, with its consequences; because, though deriving some inkling of the voyage from the wails which at the first moment had greeted him, yet of the details no clear understanding had been had. The best account would, doubtless, be given by the captain. Yet at first the visitor was loth to ask it, unwilling to provoke some distant rebuff. But plucking up courage, he at last accosted Don Benito, renewing the expression of his benevolent interest, adding, that did he (Captain Delano) but know the particulars of the ship's misfortunes, he would, perhaps, be better able in the end to relieve them. Would Don Benito favour him with the whole story?

Don Benito faltered; then, like some somnambulist suddenly interfered with, vacantly stared at his visitor, and ended by looking down on the deck. He maintained this posture so long, that Captain Delano, almost equally disconcerted, and involuntarily almost as rude, turned suddenly from him, walking forward to accost one of the Spanish seamen for the desired information. But he had hardly gone five paces, when with a sort of eagerness Don Benito invited him back, regretting his momentary absence of mind, and professing readiness to gratify him.

While most part of the story was being given, the two captains stood on the after part of the main-deck, a privileged spot, no one being near but the servant.

"It is now a hundred and ninety days," began the Spaniard, in his husky whisper, "that this ship, well officered and well manned, with several cabin passengers—some fifty Spaniards in all—sailed from Buenos Ayres bound to Lima, with a general cargo, Paraguay tea and the like—and," pointing forward, "that parcel of negroes, now not more than a hundred and fifty, as you see, but then numbering over three hundred souls. Off Cape Horn we had heavy gales. In one moment, by night, three of my best officers, with fifteen sailors, were lost, with the main-yard; the spar snapping under them in the slings, as they sought, with heavers, to beat down the icy sail. To lighten the hull, the heavier sacks of mata were thrown into the sea, with most of the water-pipes lashed on deck at the time. And this last necessity it was, combined with the prolonged detentions afterwards experienced, which eventually brought about our chief causes of suffering. When—"

Here there was a sudden fainting attack of his cough, brought on, no doubt, by his mental distress. His servant sustained him, and drawing a cordial from his pocket placed it to his lips. He a little revived. But unwilling to leave him unsupported while yet imperfectly restored, the black with one arm still encircled his master, at the same time keeping his eye fixed on his face, as if to watch for the first sign of complete restoration, or relapse, as the event might prove.

The Spaniard proceeded, but brokenly and obscurely, as one in a dream.

—"Oh, my God! rather than pass through what I have, with joy I would have hailed the most terrible gales; but—"

His cough returned and with increased violence; this subsiding, with reddened lips and closed eyes he fell heavily against his supporter.

"His mind wanders. He was thinking of the plague that followed the gales," plaintively sighed the servant; "my poor, poor master!" wringing one hand, and with the other wiping the mouth. "But be patient, Señor," again turning to Captain Delano, "these fits do not last long; master will soon be himself."

Don Benito reviving, went on; but as this portion of the story was very brokenly delivered, the substance only will here be set down.

It appeared that after the ship had been many days tossed in storms off the Cape, the scurvy broke out, carrying off numbers of the whites and blacks. When at last they had worked round into the Pacific, their spars and sails were so damaged, and so inadequately handled by the surviving mariners, most of whom were become invalids, that, unable to lay her northerly course by the wind, which was powerful, the unmanageable ship for successive days and nights was blown northwestward, where the breeze suddenly deserted her, in unknown waters, to sultry calms. The absence of the water-pipes now proved as fatal to life as before their presence had menaced it. Induced, or at least aggravated, by the more than scanty allowance of water, a malignant fever followed the scurvy; with the excessive heat of the lengthened calm, making such short work of it as to sweep away, as by billows, whole families of the Africans, and a yet larger number, proportionably, of the Spanish, including, by a luckless fatality, every officer on board. Consequently, in the smart west winds eventually following the calm, the already rent sails having to be simply dropped, not furled, at need, had been gradually reduced to the beggar's rags they were now. To procure substitutes for his lost sailors, as well as supplies of water and sails, the captain at the earliest opportunity had made for Baldivia, the southernmost civilized port of Chili and South America; but upon nearing the coast the thick weather had prevented him from so much as sighting that harbour. Since which period, almost without a crew, and almost without canvas and almost without water, and at intervals giving its added dead to the sea, the *San Dominick* had been battledored about by contrary winds, inveigled by currents, or grown weedy in calms. Like a man lost in woods, more than once she had doubled upon her own track.

"But throughout these calamities," huskily continued Don Benito, painfully turning in the half embrace of his servant, "I have to thank those negroes you see, who, though to your inexperienced eyes appearing unruly, have, indeed, conducted themselves with less of restlessness than even their owner could have thought possible under such circumstances."

Here he again fell faintly back. Again his mind wandered: but he rallied, and less obscurely proceeded.

"Yes, their owner was quite right in assuring me that no fetters would be needed with his blacks; so that while, as is wont in this transportation, those negroes have always remained upon deck—not thrust below, as in the Guineamen—they have, also, from the beginning, been freely permitted to range within given bounds at their pleasure."

Once more the faintness returned—his mind roved—but, recovering, he resumed:

"But it is Babo here to whom, under God, I owe not only my own preservation, but likewise to him, chiefly, the merit is due, of pacifying his more ignorant brethren, when at intervals tempted to murmurings."

"Ah, master," sighed the black, bowing his face, "don't speak of me; Babo is nothing; what Babo has done was but duty."

"Faithful fellow!" cried Captain Delano. "Don Benito, I envy you such a friend; slave I cannot call him."

As master and man stood before him, the black upholding the white, Captain Delano could not but bethink him of the beauty of that relationship which could present such a spectacle of fidelity on the one hand and confidence on the other. The scene was heightened by the contrast in dress, denoting their relative positions. The Spaniard wore a loose Chili jacket of dark velvet; white small clothes and stockings, with silver buckles at the knee and instep; a high-crowned sombrero, of fine grass; a slender sword, silver mounted, hung from a knot in his sash; the last being an almost invariable adjunct, more for utility than ornament, of a South American gentleman's dress to this hour. Excepting when his occasional nervous contortions brought about disarray, there was a certain precision in his attire, curiously at variance with the unsightly disorder around; especially in the belittered Ghetto, forward of the main-mast, wholly occupied by the blacks.

The servant wore nothing but wide trousers, apparently, from their coarseness and patches, made out of some old topsail; they were clean, and confined at the waist by a bit of unstranded rope, which, with his composed, deprecatory air at times, made him look something like a begging friar of St. Francis.

However unsuitable for the time and place, at least in the blunt-thinking American's eyes, and however strangely surviving in the midst of all his afflictions, the toilette of Don Benito might not, in fashion at least, have gone beyond the style of the day among South Americans of his class. Though on the present voyage sailing from Buenos Ayres, he had avowed himself a native and resident of Chili, whose inhabitants had not so generally adopted the plain coat and once plebeian pantaloons; but, with a becoming modification, adhered to their provincial costume, picturesque as any in the world. Still, relatively to the pale history of the voyage, and his own pale face, there seemed something so incongruous in the Spaniard's apparel, as almost to suggest the image of an invalid courtier tottering about London streets in the time of the plague.

The portion of the narrative which, perhaps, most excited interest, as well as some surprise, considering the latitudes in question, was the long calms spoken of, and more particularly the ship's so long drifting about. Without communicating the opinion, of course, the American could not but impute at least part of the detentions both to clumsy seamanship and faulty navigation. Eyeing Don Benito's small, yellow hands, he easily inferred that the young captain had not got into command at the hawse-hole but the cabin-window, and if so, why wonder at incompetence in youth, sickness, and aristocracy united? Such was his democratic conclusion.

But drowning criticism in compassion, after a fresh repetition of his sympathies, Captain Delano having heard out his story, not only engaged, as in the first place, to see Don Benito and his people supplied in their immediate bodily needs, but, also, now further promised to assist him in procuring a large permanent supply of water, as well as some sails and rigging; and, though it would involve no small embarrassment to himself, yet he would spare three of his best seamen for temporary deck officers; so that without delay the ship might proceed to Concepción, there fully to refit for Lima, her destined port.

Such generosity was not without its effect, even upon the invalid. His face lighted up; eager and hectic, he met the honest glance of his visitor. With gratitude he seemed overcome.

"This excitement is bad for master," whispered the servant, taking his arm, and with soothing words gently drawing him aside.

When Don Benito returned, the American was pained to observe that his hopefulness, like the sudden kindling in his cheek, was but febrile and transient.

Ere long, with a joyless mien, looking up toward the poop, the host invited his guest to accompany him there, for the benefit of what little breath of wind might be stirring.

As during the telling of the story, Captain Delano had once or twice started at the occasional cymballing of the hatchet-polishers, wondering why such an interruption should be allowed, especially in that part of the ship, and in the ears of an invalid; and, moreover, as the hatchets had anything but an attractive look, and the handlers of them still less so, it was, therefore, to tell the truth, not without some lurking reluctance, or even shrinking, it may be, that Captain Delano, with apparent complaisance, acquiesced in his host's invitation. The more so, since with an untimely caprice of punctilio, rendered distressing by his cadaverous aspect, Don Benito, with Castilian bows, solemnly insisted upon his guest's preceding him up the ladder leading to the elevation; where, one on each side of the last step, sat four armorial supporters and sentries, two of the ominous file. Gingerly enough stepped good Captain Delano between them, and in the instant of leaving them behind, like one running the gauntlet, he felt an apprehensive twitch in the calves of his legs.

But when, facing about, he saw the whole file, like so many organ-grinders, still stupidly intent on their work, unmindful of everything beside, he could not but smile at his late fidgeting panic.

Presently, while standing with Don Benito, looking forward upon the decks below, he was struck by one of those instances of insubordination previously alluded to. Three black boys, with two Spanish boys, were sitting together on the hatchets, scraping a rude wooden platter, in which some scanty mess had recently been cooked. Suddenly, one of the black boys, enraged at a word dropped by one of his white companions, seized a knife, and though called to forbear by one of the oakum-pickers, struck the lad over the head, inflicting a gash from which blood flowed.

In amazement, Captain Delano inquired what this meant. To which the pale Benito dully muttered, that it was merely the sport of the lad.

"Pretty serious sport, truly," rejoined Captain Delano. "Had such a thing happened on board the *Bachelor's Delight,* instant punishment would have followed."

At these words the Spaniard turned upon the American one of his sudden, staring, half-lunatic looks; then, relapsing into his torpor, answered, "Doubtless, doubtless, Señor."

Is it, thought Captain Delano, that this helpless man is one of those paper captains I've known, who by policy wink at what by power they cannot put down? I know no sadder sight than a commander who has little of command but the name.

"I should think, Don Benito," he now said, glancing toward the oakum-picker who had sought to interfere with the boys, "that you would find it advantageous to keep all your blacks employed, especially the younger ones, no matter at what useless task, and no matter what happens to the ship. Why, even with my little band, I find such a course indispensable. I once kept a crew on my quarter-deck thrumming mats for my cabin, when, for three days, I had given up my ship—mats, men, and all—for a speedy loss, owing to the violence of a gale in which we could do nothing but helplessly drive before it."

"Doubtless, doubtless," muttered Don Benito.

"But," continued Captain Delano, again glancing upon the oakum-pickers and then at the hatchet-polishers, near by, "I see you keep some at least of your host employed."

"Yes," was again the vacant response.

"Those old men there, shaking their pows from their pulpits," continued Captain Delano, pointing to the oakum-pickers, "seem to act the part of old dominies to the rest, little heeded as their admonitions are at times. Is this voluntary on their part, Don Benito, or have you appointed them shepherds to your flock of black sheep?"

"What posts they fill, I appointed them," rejoined the Spaniard in an acrid tone, as if resenting some supposed satiric reflection.

"And these others, these Ashantee conjurors here," continued Captain Delano, rather uneasily eyeing the brandished steel of the hatchet-polishers, where in spots it had been brought to a shine, "this seems a curious business they are at, Don Benito?"

"In the gales we met," answered the Spaniard, "what of our general cargo was not thrown overboard was much damaged by the brine. Since coming into calm weather, I have had several cases of knives and hatchets daily brought up for overhauling and cleaning."

"A prudent idea, Don Benito. You are part owner of ship and cargo, I presume; but not of the slaves, perhaps?"

"I am owner of all you see," impatiently returned Don Benito, "except the main company of blacks, who belonged to my late friend, Alexandro Aranda."

As he mentioned this name, his air was heart-broken, his knees shook; his servant supported him.

Thinking he divined the cause of such unusual emotion, to confirm his surmise, Captain Delano, after a pause, said, "And may I ask, Don Benito, whether—since awhile ago you spoke of some cabin passengers—the friend, whose loss so afflicts you, at the outset of the voyage accompanied his blacks?"

"Yes."

"But died of the fever?"

"Died of the fever.—Oh, could I but—"

Again quivering, the Spaniard paused.

"Pardon me," said Captain Delano slowly, "but I think that, by a sympathetic experience, I conjecture, Don Benito, what it is that gives the keener edge to your grief. It was once my hard fortune to lose at sea a dear friend, my own brother, then supercargo. Assured of the welfare of his spirit, its departure I could have borne like a man; but that honest eye, that honest hand—both of which had so often met mine—and that warm heart; all, all— like scraps to the dogs—to throw all to the sharks! It was then I vowed never to have for fellow-voyager a man I loved, unless, unbeknown to him, I had provided every requisite, in case of a fatality, for embalming his mortal part for interment on shore. Were your friend's remains now on board this ship, Don Benito, not thus strangely would the mention of his name affect you."

"On board this ship?" echoed the Spaniard. Then, with horrified gestures, as directed against some spectre, he unconsciously fell into the ready arms of his attendant, who, with a silent appeal toward Captain Delano, seemed beseeching him not again to broach a theme so unspeakably distressing to his master.

This poor fellow now, thought the pained American, is the victim of that sad superstition which associates goblins with the deserted body of man, as ghosts with an abandoned house. How unlike are we made! What to me, in like case, would have been a solemn satisfaction, the bare suggestion, even, terrifies the Spaniard into this trance. Poor Alexandro Aranda! what would you say could you here see your friend—who, on former voyages, when you for months were left behind, has, I dare say, often longed, and longed, for one peep at you—now transported with terror at the least thought of having you anyway nigh him.

At this moment, with a dreary graveyard toll, betokening a flaw, the ship's forecastle bell, smote by one of the grizzled oakum-pickers, proclaimed ten o'clock through the leaden calm; when Captain Delano's attention was caught by the moving figure of a gigantic black, emerging from the general crowd below, and slowly advancing toward the elevated poop. An iron collar was about his neck, from which depended a chain, thrice wound round his body; the terminating links padlocked together at a broad band of iron, his girdle.

"How like a mute Atufal moves," murmured the servant.

The black mounted the steps of the poop, and, like a brave prisoner, brought up to receive sentence, stood in unquailing muteness before Don Benito, now recovered from his attack.

At the first glimpse of his approach, Don Benito had started, a resentful shadow swept over his face; and, as with the sudden memory of bootless rage, his white lips glued together.

This is some mulish mutineeer, thought Captain Delano, surveying, not without a mixture of admiration, the colossal form of the negro.

"See, he waits your question, master," said the servant.

Thus reminded, Don Benito, nervously averting his glance, as if shunning, by anticipation, some rebellious response, in a disconcerted voice, thus spoke:

"Atufal, will you ask my pardon now?"

The black was silent.

"Again, master," murmured the servant, with bitter upbraiding eyeing his countryman; "Again, master; he will bend to master yet."

"Answer," said Don Benito, still averting his glance, "say but the one word *pardon,* and your chains shall be off."

Upon this, the black, slowly raising both arms, let them lifelessly fall, his links clanking, his head bowed; as much as to say, "No, I am content."

"Go," said Don Benito, with inkept and unknown emotion.

Deliberately as he had come, the black obeyed.

"Excuse me, Don Benito," said Captain Delano, "but this scene surprises me; what means it, pray?"

"It means that that negro alone, of all the band, has given me peculiar cause of offence. I have put him in chains; I—"

Here he paused; his hand to his head, as if there were a swimming there, or a sudden bewilderment of memory had come over him; but meeting his servant's kindly glance seemed reassured, and proceeded:

"I could not scourge such a form. But I told him he must ask my pardon.

As yet he has not. At my command, every two hours he stands before me."

"And how long has this been?"

"Some sixty days."

"And obedient in all else? And respectful?"

"Yes."

"Upon my conscience, then," exclaimed Captain Delano, impulsively, "he has a royal spirit in him, this fellow."

"He may have some right to it," bitterly returned Don Benito; "he says he was king in his own land."

"Yes," said the servant, entering a word, "those slits in Atufal's ears once held wedges of gold; but poor Babo here, in his own land, was only a poor slave; a black man's slave was Babo, who now is the white's."

Somewhat annoyed by these conversational familiarities, Captain Delano turned curiously upon the attendant, then glanced inquiringly at his master; but, as if long wonted to these little informalities, neither master nor man seemed to understand him.

"What, pray, was Atufal's offence, Don Benito?" asked Captain Delano; "if it was not something very serious, take a fool's advice, and, in view of his general docility, as well as in some natural respect for his spirit, remit his penalty."

"No, no, master never will do that," here murmured the servant to himself, "proud Atufal must first ask master's pardon. The slave there carries the padlock, but master here carries the key."

His attention thus directed, Captain Delano now noticed for the first time that, suspended by a slender silken cord, from Don Benito's neck hung a key. At once, from the servant's muttered syllables divining the key's purpose, he smiled and said: "So, Don Benito—padlock and key—significant symbols, truly."

Biting his lip, Don Benito faltered.

Though the remark of Captain Delano, a man of such native simplicity as to be incapable of satire or irony, had been dropped in playful allusion to the Spaniard's singularly evidenced lordship over the black; yet the hypochondriac seemed in some way to have taken it as a malicious reflection upon his confessed inability thus far to break down, at least, on a verbal summons, the entrenched will of the slave. Deploring this supposed misconception, yet despairing of correcting it, Captain Delano shifted the subject; but finding his companion more than ever withdrawn, as if still slowly digesting the lees of the presumed affront above-mentioned, by-and-by Captain Delano likewise became less talkative, oppressed, against his own will, by what seemed the secret vindictiveness of the morbidly sensitive Spaniard. But the good sailor himself, of a quite contrary disposition, refrained, on his part, alike from the appearance as from the feeling of resentment, and if silent, was only so from contagion.

Presently the Spaniard, assisted by his servant, somewhat discourteously crossed over from Captain Delano; a procedure which, sensibly enough, might have been allowed to pass for idle caprice of ill-humour, had not master and man, lingering round the corner of the elevated skylight, begun whispering together in low voices. This was unpleasing. And more: the moody air of the Spaniard, which at times had not been without a sort of valetudinarian stateliness, now seemed anything but dignified; while the menial familiarity of the servant lost its original charm of simple-hearted attachment.

In his embarrassment, the visitor turned his face to the other side of the ship. By so doing, his glance accidentally fell on a young Spanish sailor, a coil of rope in his hand, just stepped from the deck to the first round of the mizzen-rigging. Perhaps the man would not have been particularly noticed, were it not that, during his ascent to one of the yards, he, with a sort of covert intentness, kept his eye fixed on Captain Delano, from whom, presently, it passed, as if by a natural sequence, to the two whisperers.

His own attention thus redirected to that quarter, Captain Delano gave a slight start. From something in Don Benito's manner just then, it seemed as if the visitor had, at least partly, been the subject of the withdrawn consultation going on—a conjecture as little agreeable to the guest as it was little flattering to the host.

The singular alternations of courtesy and ill-breeding in the Spanish captain were unaccountable, except on one of two suppositions—innocent lunacy, or wicked imposture.

But the first idea, though it might naturally have occurred to an indifferent observer, and, in some respects, had not hitherto been wholly a stranger to Captain Delano's mind, yet, now that, in an incipient way, he began to regard the stranger's conduct something in the light of an intentional affront, of course the idea of lunacy was virtually vacated. But if not a lunatic, what then? Under the circumstances, would a gentleman, nay, any honest boor, act the part now acted by his host? The man was an impostor. Some lowborn adventurer, masquerading as an oceanic grandee; yet so ignorant of the first requisites of mere gentlemanhood as to be betrayed into the present remarkable indecorum. That strange ceremoniousness, too, at other times evinced, seemed not uncharacteristic of one playing a part above his real level. Benito Cereno—Don Benito Cereno—a sounding name. One, too, at that period, not unknown, in the surname, to supercargoes and sea captains trading along the Spanish Main, as belonging to one of the most enterprising and extensive mercantile families in all those provinces; several members of it having titles; a sort of Castilian Rothschild, with a noble brother, or cousin, in every great trading town of South America. The alleged Don Benito was in early manhood, about twenty-nine or thirty. To assume a sort of roving cadetship in the maritime affairs of such a house, what more likely scheme for a young knave of talent and spirit? But the Spaniard was a pale invalid. Never mind. For even to the degree of simulating mortal disease, the craft of some tricksters had been known to attain. To think that, under the aspect of infantile weakness, the most savage energies might be couched—those velvets of the Spaniard but the velvet paw to his fangs.

From no train of thought did these fancies come; not from within, but from without; suddenly, too, and in one throng, like hoar frost; yet as soon to vanish as the mild sun of Captain Delano's good-nature regained its meridian.

Glancing over once again toward Don Benito—whose side-face, revealed above the skylight, was now turned toward him—Captain Delano was struck by the profile, whose clearness of cut was refined by the thinness incident to ill-health, as well as ennobled about the chin by the beard. Away with suspicion. He was a true off-shoot of a true hidalgo Cereno.

Relieved by these and other better thoughts, the visitor, lightly humming a tune, now began indifferently pacing the poop, so as not to betray to Don Benito that he had at all mistrusted incivility, much less duplicity; for such mistrust would yet be proved illusory, and by the event; though, for the present, the circumstance which had provoked that distrust remained unexplained. But when that little mystery should have been cleared up, Captain Delano thought he might extremely regret it, did he allow Don Benito to become aware that he had indulged in ungenerous surmises. In short, to the Spaniard's black-letter text, it was best, for a while, to leave open margin.

Presently, his pale face twitching and overcast, the Spaniard, still supported by his attendant, moved over toward his guest, when, with even more than his usual embarrassment, and a strange sort of intriguing intonation in his husky whisper, the following conversation began:

"Señor, may I ask how long you have lain at this isle?"

"Oh, but a day or two, Don Benito."

"And from what port are you last?"

"Canton."

"And there, Señor, you exchanged your seal-skins for teas and silks, I think you said?"

"Yes. Silks, mostly."

"And the balance you took in specie, perhaps?"

Captain Delano, fidgeting a little, answered—

"Yes; some silver; not a very great deal, though."

"Ah—well. May I ask how many men have you on board, Señor?"

Captain Delano slightly started, but answered:

"About five-and-twenty, all told."

"And at present, Señor, all on board, I suppose?"

"All on board, Don Benito," replied the captain now with satisfaction.

"And will be to-night, Señor?"

At this last question, following so many pertinacious ones, for the soul of him Captain Delano could not but look very earnestly at the questioner, who, instead of meeting the glance, with every token of craven discomposure dropped his eyes to the deck; presenting an unworthy contrast to his servant, who, just then, was kneeling at his feet adjusting a loose shoe-buckle; his disengaged face meantime, with humble curiosity, turned openly up into his master's downcast one.

The Spaniard, still with a guilty shuffle, repeated his question:

"And—will be to-night, Señor?"

"Yes, for aught I know," returned Captain Delano,—"but nay," rallying himself into fearless truth, "some of them talked of going off on another fishing party about midnight."

"Your ships generally go—go more or less armed, I believe, Señor?"

"Oh, a six-pounder or two, in case of emergency," was the intrepidly indifferent reply, "with a small stock of muskets, sealing-spears, and cutlasses, you know."

As he thus responded, Captain Delano again glanced at Don Benito, but the latter's eyes were averted; while abruptly and awkwardly shifting the subject, he made some peevish allusion to the calm, and then, without apology, once more, with his attendant, withdrew to the opposite bulwarks, where the whispering was resumed.

At this moment, and ere Captain Delano could cast a cool thought upon what had just passed, the young Spanish sailor before mentioned was seen descending from the rigging. In act of stooping over to spring inboard to the deck, his voluminous, unconfined frock, or shirt, of coarse woollen, much spotted with tar, opened out far down the chest, revealing a soiled under-garment of what seemed the finest linen, edged, about the neck, with a narrow blue ribbon, sadly faded and worn. At this moment the young sailor's eye was again fixed on the whisperers, and Captain Delano thought he observed a lurking significance in it, as if silent signs of some freemason sort had that instant been interchanged.

This once more impelled his own glance in the direction of Don Benito, and, as before, he could not but infer that himself formed the subject of the conference. He paused. The sound of the hatchet-polishing fell on his ears. He cast another swift side-look at the two. They had the air of conspirators. In connection with the late questionings, and the incident of the young sailor, these things now begat such return of involuntary suspicion, that the singular guilelessness of the American could not endure it. Plucking up a gay and humorous expression, he crossed over to the two rapidly, saying: "Ha, Don Benito, your black here seems high in your trust; a sort of privy-counsellor, in fact."

Upon this, the servant looked up with a good-natured grin, but the master started as from a venomous bite. It was a moment or two before the Spaniard sufficiently recovered himself to reply; which he did, at last, with cold constraint: "Yes, Señor, I have trust in Babo."

Here Babo, changing his previous grin of mere animal humour into an intelligent smile, not ungratefully eyed his master.

Finding that the Spaniard now stood silent and reserved, as if invol-untarily, or purposely giving hint that his guest's proximity was inconvenient just then, Captain Delano, unwilling to appear uncivil even to incivility itself, made some trivial remark and moved off; again and again turning over in his mind the mysterious demeanour of Don Benito Cereno.

He had descended from the poop, and, wrapped in thought, was passing near a dark hatchway, leading down into the steerage, when, perceiving motion there, he looked to see what moved. The same instant there was a sparkle in the shadowy hatchway, and he saw one of the Spanish sailors, prowling there, hurriedly placing his hand in the bosom of his frock, as if hiding something. Before the man could have been certain who it was that was passing, he slunk below out of sight. But enough was seen of him to make it sure that he was the same young sailor before noticed in the rigging.

What was that which so sparkled? thought Captain Delano. It was no lamp—no match—no live coal. Could it have been a jewel? But how come sailors with jewels?—or with silk-trimmed under-shirts either? Has he been robbing the trunks of the dead cabin passengers? But if so, he would hardly wear one of the stolen articles on board ship here. Ah,—if now that was, indeed, a secret sign I saw passing between this suspicious fellow and his captain awhile since; if I could only be certain that in my uneasiness my senses did not deceive me, then—

Here, passing from one suspicious thing to another, his mind revolved the point of the strange questions put to him concerning his ship.

By a curious coincidence, as each point was recalled, the black wizards of Ashantee would strike up with their hatchets, as in ominous comment on the white stranger's thoughts. Pressed by such enigmas and portents, it would have been almost against nature, had not, even into the least distrustful heart, some ugly misgivings obtruded.

Observing the ship now helplessly fallen into a current, with enchanted sails, drifting with increased rapidity seaward; and noting that, from a lately intercepted projection of the land, the sealer was hidden, the stout mariner began to quake at thoughts which he barely durst confess to himself. Above all, he began to feel a ghostly dread of Don Benito. And yet when he roused himself, dilated his chest, felt himself strong on his legs, and coolly considered it—what did all these phantoms amount to?

Had the Spaniard any sinister scheme, it must have reference not so much to him (Captain Delano) as to his ship (the *Bachelor's Delight*). Hence the present drifting away of the one ship from the other, instead of favouring any such possible scheme, was, for the time at least, opposed to it. Clearly any suspicion, combining such contradictions, must need be delusive. Beside, was it not absurd to think of a vessel in distress—a vessel by sickness almost dismanned of her crew—a vessel whose inmates were parched for water—was it not a thousand times absurd that such a craft should, at present, be of a piratical character; or her commander, either for himself or those under him, cherish any desire but for speedy relief and refreshment? But then, might not general distress, and thirst in particular, be affected? And might not that same undiminished Spanish crew, alleged to have perished off to a remnant, be at that very moment lurking in the hold? On heart-broken pretence of entreating a cup of cold water, fiends in human form had got into lonely dwellings, nor retired until a dark deed had been done. And among the Malay pirates, it was no unusual thing to lure ships after them into their treacherous harbours, or entice boarders from a declared enemy at sea, by the spectacle of thinly manned or vacant decks, beneath which prowled a hundred spears with yellow arms ready to up-thrust them through the mats. Not that Captain Delano had entirely credited such things. He had heard of them—and now, as stories, they recurred. The present destination of the ship was the anchorage. There she would be near his own vessel. Upon gaining that vicinity, might not the *San Dominick,* like a slumbering volcano, suddenly let loose energies now hid?

He recalled the Spaniard's manner while telling his story. There was a gloomy hesitancy and subterfuge about it. It was just the manner of one making up his tale for evil purposes, as he goes. But if that story was not true, what was the truth? That the ship had unlawfully come into the Spaniard's possession? But in many of its details, especially in reference to the more calamitous parts, such as the fatalities among the seamen, the consequent prolonged beating about, the past sufferings from obstinate calms, and still continued suffering from thirst; in all these points, as well as other, Don Benito's story had corroborated not only the wailing ejaculations of the indiscriminate multitude, white and black, but likewise—what seemed impossible to be counterfeit—by the very expression and play of every human feature, which Captain Delano saw. If Don Benito's story was throughout an invention, then every soul on board, down to the youngest negress, was his carefully drilled recruit in the plot: an incredible inference. And yet, if there was ground for mistrusting the Spanish captain's veracity, that inference was a legitimate one.

In short, scarce an uneasiness entered the honest sailor's mind but, by a subsequent spontaneous act of good sense, it was ejected. At last he began to laugh at these forebodings; and laugh at the strange ship for, in its aspect, someway siding with them, as it were; and laugh, too, at the odd-looking blacks, particularly those old scissors-grinders, the Ashantees; and those bed-ridden old knitting-women, the oakum-pickers; and, in a human way, he almost began to laugh at the dark Spaniard himself, the central hobgoblin of all.

For the rest, whatever in a serious way seemed enigmatical, was now good-naturedly explained away by the thought that, for the most part, the poor invalid scarcely knew what he was about; either sulking in black vapours, or putting random questions without sense or object. Evidently, for the present, the man was not fit to be entrusted with the ship. On some benevolent plea withdrawing the command from him, Captain Delano would yet have to send her to Concepción in charge of his second mate, a worthy person and good navigator—a plan which would prove no wiser for the *San Dominick* than for Don Benito; for—relieved from all anxiety, keeping wholly to his cabin—the sick man, under the good nursing of his servant, would probably, by the end of the passage, be in a measure restored to health and with that he should also be restored to authority.

Such were the American's thoughts. They were tranquillizing. There was a difference between the idea of Don Benito's darkly pre-ordaining Captain Delano's fate, and Captain Delano's lightly arranging Don Benito's. Nevertheless, it was not without something of relief that the good seaman presently perceived his whale-boat in the distance. Its absence had been prolonged by unexpected detention at the sealer's side, as well as its returning trip lengthened by the continual recession of the goal.

The advancing speck was observed by the blacks. Their shouts attracted the attention of Don Benito, who, with a return of courtesy, approaching Captain Delano, expressed satisfaction at the coming of some supplies, slight and temporary as they must necessarily prove.

Captain Delano responded; but while doing so, his attention was drawn to something passing on the deck below: among the crowd climbing the landward bulwarks, anxiously watching the coming boat, two blacks, to all appearances accidentally incommoded by one of the sailors, flew out against him with horrible curses, which the sailor someway resenting, the two blacks dashed him to the deck and jumped upon him, despite the earnest cries of the oakum-pickers.

"Don Benito," said Captain Delano quickly, "do you see what is going one there? Look!"

But, seized by his cough, the Spaniard staggered, with both hands to his face, on the point of falling. Captain Delano would have supported him, but the servant was more alert, who, with one hand sustaining his master, with the other applied the cordial. Don Benito restored, the black withdrew his support, slipping aside a little, but dutifully remaining within call of a whisper. Such discretion was here evinced as quite wiped away, in the visitor's eyes, any blemish of impropriety which might have attached to the attendant, from the indecorous conferences before mentioned; showing, too, that if the servant were to blame, it might be more the master's fault than his own, since when left to himself he could conduct thus well.

His glance thus called away from the spectacle of disorder to the more pleasing one before him, Captain Delano could not avoid again congratulating Don Benito upon possessing such a servant, who, though perhaps a little too forward now and then, must upon the whole be invaluable to one in the invalid's situation.

"Tell me, Don Benito," he added, with a smile—"I should like to have your man here myself—what will you take for him? Would fifty doubloons be any object?"

"Master wouldn't part with Babo for a thousand doubloons," murmured the black, overhearing the offer, and taking it in earnest, and, with the strange vanity of a faithful slave appreciated by his master, scorning to hear so paltry a valuation put upon him by a stranger. But Don Benito, apparently hardly yet completely restored, and again interrupted by his cough, made but some broken reply.

Soon his physical distress became so great, affecting his mind, too, apparently, that, as if to screen the sad spectacle, the servant gently conducted his master below.

Left to himself, the American, to while away the time till his boat should arrive, would have pleasantly accosted some one of the few Spanish seamen he saw; but recalling something that Don Benito had said touching their ill conduct, he refrained, as a ship-master indisposed to countenance cowardice or unfaithfulness in seamen.

While, with these thoughts, standing with eye directed forward toward that handful of sailors—suddenly he thought that some of them returned the glance and with a sort of meaning. He rubbed his eyes, and looked again; but again seemed to see the same thing. Under a new form, but more obscure than any previous one, the old suspicions recurred, but, in the absence of Don Benito, with less of panic than before. Despite the bad account given of the sailors, Captain Delano resolved forthwith to accost one of them. Descending the poop, he made his way through the blacks, his movement drawing a queer cry from the oakum-pickers, prompted by whom the negroes, twitching each other aside, divided before him; but, as if curious to see what was the object of this deliberate visit to their Ghetto, closing in behind, in tolerable order, followed the white stranger up. His progress thus proclaimed as by mounted kings-at-arms, and escorted as by a Caffre guard of honour, Captain Delano, assuming a good-humoured, off-hand air, continued to advance; now and then saying a blithe word to the negroes, and his eye curiously surveying the white faces, here and there sparsely mixed in with the blacks, like stray white pawns venturously involved in the ranks of the chessmen opposed.

While thinking which of them to select for his purpose, he chanced to observe a sailor seated on the deck engaged in tarring the strap of a large block, with a circle of blacks squatted round him inquisitively eyeing the process.

The mean employment of the man was in contrast with something superior in his figure. His hand, black with continually thrusting it into the tar-pot held for him by a negro, seemed not naturally allied to his face, a face which would have been a very fine one but for its haggardness. Whether this haggardness had aught to do with criminality, could not be determined; since, as intense heat and cold, though unlike, produce like sensations, so innocence and guilt, when, through casual association with mental pain, stamping any visible impress, use one seal—a hacked one.

Not again that this reflection occurred to Captain Delano at the time, charitable man as he was. Rather another idea. Because observing so singular a haggardness to be combined with a dark eye, averted as in trouble and shame, and then, however illogically, uniting in his mind his own private suspicions of the crew with the confessed ill-opinion on the part of their captain, he was insensibly operated upon by certain general notions, which, while disconnecting pain and abashment from virtue, as invariably link them with vice.

If, indeed, there be any wickedness on board this ship, thought Captain Delano, be sure that man there has fouled his hand in it, even as now he fouls it in the pitch. I don't like to accost him. I will speak to this other, this old Jack here on the windlass.

He advanced to an old Barcelona tar, in ragged red breeches and dirty night-cap, cheeks trenched and bronzed, whiskers dense as thorn hedges. Seated between two sleepy-looking Africans, this mariner, like his younger shipmate, was employed upon some rigging—splicing a cable—the sleepy-looking blacks performing the inferior function of holding the outer parts of the ropes for him.

Upon Captain Delano's approach, the man at once hung his head below its previous level; the one necessary for business. It appeared as if he desired to be thought absorbed, with more than common fidelity, in his task. Being addressed, he glanced up, but with what seemed a furtive, diffident air, which sat strangely enough on his weather-beaten visage, much as if a grizzly bear, instead of growling and biting, should simper and cast sheep's eyes. He was asked several questions concerning the voyage—questions purposely referring to several particulars in Don Benito's narrative—not previously corroborated by those impulsive cries greeting the visitor on first coming on board. The questions were briefly answered, confirming all that remained to be confirmed of the story. The negroes about the windlass joined in with the old sailor, but, as they became talkative, he by degrees became mute, and at length quite glum, seemed morosely unwilling to answer more questions, and yet, all the while, this ursine air was somehow mixed with his sheepish one.

Despairing of getting into unembarrassed talk with such a centaur, Captain Delano, after glancing round for a more promising countenance, but seeing none, spoke pleasantly to the blacks to make way for him; and so, amid various grins and grimaces, returned to the poop, feeling a little strange at first, he could hardly tell why, but upon the whole with regained confidence in Benito Cereno.

How plainly, thought he, did that old whiskerando yonder betray a consciousness of ill-desert. No doubt, when he saw me coming, he dreaded lest I, apprised by his captain of the crew's general misbehaviour, came with sharp words for him, and so down with his head. And yet—and yet, now that I think of it, that very old fellow, if I err not, was one of those who seemed so earnestly eyeing me here awhile since. Ah, these currents spin one's head round almost as much as they do the ship. Ha, there now's a pleasant sort of sunny sight; quite sociable, too.

His attention had been drawn to a slumbering negress, partly disclosed through the lace-work of some rigging, lying, with youthful limbs carelessly disposed, under the lee of the bulwarks, like a doe in the shade of a woodland rock. Sprawling at her lapped breasts was her wide-awake fawn, stark naked, its black little body half lifted from the deck, crosswise with its dam's; its hands, like two paws, clambering upon her; its mouth and nose ineffectually rooting to get at the mark; and meantime giving a vexatious half-grunt, blending with the composed snore of the negress.

The uncommon vigour of the child at length roused the mother. She started up, at distance facing Captain Delano. But, as if not at all concerned at the attitude in which she had been caught, delightedly she caught the child up, with maternal transports, covering it with kisses.

There's naked nature, now; pure tenderness and love, thought Captain Delano, well pleased.

This incident prompted him to remark the other negresses more particularly than before. He was gratified with their manners; like most uncivilized women, they seemed at once tender of heart and tough of constitution; equally ready to die for their infants or fight for them. Unsophisticated as leopardesses; loving as doves. Ah! thought Captain Delano, these perhaps are some of the very women whom Mungo Park saw in Africa, and gave such a noble account of.

These natural sights somehow insensibly deepened his confidence and ease. At last he looked to see how his boat was getting on; but it was still pretty remote. He turned to see if Don Benito had returned; but he had not.

To change the scene, as well as to please himself with a leisurely observation of the coming boat, stepping over into the mizzen-chains he clambered his way into the starboard quarter-gallery; one of those abandoned Venetian-looking water-balconies previously mentioned; retreats cut off from the deck. As his foot pressed the half-damp, half-dry sea-mosses matting the place, and a chance phantom cats-paw—an islet of breeze, unheralded, unfollowed—as this ghostly cats-paw came fanning his cheek, as his glance fell upon the row of small, round dead-lights, all closed like coppered eyes of the coffined, and the state-cabin door, once connecting with the gallery, even as the dead-lights had once looked out upon it, but now caulked fast like a sarcophagus lid, to a purple-black, tarred-over panel, threshold, and post; and he bethought him of the time, when that state-cabin and this state-balcony had heard the voices of the Spanish king's officers, and the forms of the Lima viceroy's daughters had perhaps leaned where he stood—as these and other images flitted through his mind, as the cats-paw through the calm, gradually he felt rising a dreamy inquietude, like that of one who alone on the prairie feels unrest from the repose of the noon.

He leaned against the carved balustrade, again looking off toward his boat; but found his eye falling upon the ribboned grass, trailing along the ship's water-line, straight as a border of green box; and parterres of sea-weed, broad ovals and crescents, floating nigh and far, with what seemed long formal alleys between, crossing the terraces of swells, and sweeping round as if leading to the grottoes below. And overhanging all was the balustrade by his arm, which, partly stained with pitch and partly embossed with moss,

seemed the charred ruin of some summer-house in a grand garden long
running to waste.

Trying to break one charm, he was but becharmed anew. Though upon
the wide sea, he seemed in some far inland country; prisoner in some deserted
château, left to stare at empty grounds, and peer out at vague roads, where
never wagon or wayfarer passed.

But these enchantments were a little disenchanted as his eye fell on the
corroded main-chains. Of an ancient style, massy and rusty in link, shackle
and bolt, they seemed even more fit for the ship's present business than the
one for which probably she had been built.

Presently he thought something moved nigh the chains. He rubbed his
eyes, and looked hard. Groves of rigging were about the chains; and there,
peering from behind a great stay, like an Indian from behind a hemlock, a
Spanish sailor, a marlingspike in his hand, was seen, who made what seemed
an imperfect gesture toward the balcony—but immediately, as if alarmed by
some advancing step along the deck within, vanished into the recesses of the
hempen forest, like a poacher.

What meant this? Something the man had sought to communicate, unbeknown to any one, even to his captain. Did the secret involve aught un-
favourable to his captain? Were those previous misgivings of Captain
Delano's about to be verified? Or, in his haunted mood at the moment,
had some random, unintentional motion of the man, while busy with the
stay, as if repairing it, been mistaken for a significant beckoning?

Not unbewildered, again he gazed off for his boat. But it was temporarily hidden by a rocky spur of the isle. As with some eagerness he bent
forward, watching for the first shooting view of its beak, the balustrade
gave way before him like charcoal. Had he not clutched an outreaching rope
he would have fallen into the sea. The crash, though feeble, and the fall,
though hollow, of the rotten fragments, must have been overheard. He
glanced up. With sober curiosity peering down upon him was one of the
old oakum-pickers, slipped from his perch to an outside boom; while below
the old negro—and, invisible to him, reconnotring from a port-hole like a
fox from the mouth of its den—crouched the Spanish sailor again. From
something suddenly suggested by the man's air, the mad idea now darted
into Captain Delano's mind; that Don Benito's plea of indisposition, in
withdrawing below, was but a pretence: that he was engaged there maturing
some plot, of which the sailor, by some means gaining an inkling, had a
mind to warn the stranger against; incited, it may be, by gratitude for a kind
word on first boarding the ship. Was it from foreseeing some possible
interference like this, that Don Benito had, beforehand, given such a bad
character of his sailors, while praising the negroes; though, indeed, the
former seemed as docile as the latter the contrary? The whites, too, by
nature, were the shrewder race. A man with some evil design, would not he
be likely to speak well of that stupidity which was blind to his depravity,
and malign that intelligence from which it might not be hidden? Not un-

likely, perhaps. But if the whites had dark secrets concerning Don Benito, could then Don Benito be any way in complicity with the blacks? But they were too stupid. Besides, who ever heard of a white so far a renegade as to apostatize from his very species almost, by leaguing in against it with negroes? These difficulties recalled former ones. Lost in their mazes, Captain Delano, who had now regained the deck, was uneasily advancing along it, when he observed a new face: an aged sailor seated cross-legged near the main hatchway. His skin was shrunk up with wrinkles like a pelican's empty pouch, his hair frosted, his countenance grave and composed. His hands were full of ropes, which he was working into a large knot. Some blacks were about him obligingly dipping the strands for him, here and there, as the exigencies of the operation demanded.

Captain Delano crossed over to him, and stood in silence surveying the knot; his mind, by a not uncongenial transition, passing from its own entanglements to those of the hemp. For intricacy such a knot he had never seen in an American ship, or indeed any other. The old man looked like an Egyptian priest, making gordian knots for the temple of Ammon. The knot seemed a combination of double-bowline-knot, treble-crown-knot, back-handed-well-knot, knot-in-and-out-knot, and jamming-knot.

At last, puzzled to comprehend the meaning of such a knot, Captain Delano addressed the knotter:—

"What are you knotting there, my man?"

"The knot," was the brief reply, without looking up.

"So it seems; but what is it for?"

"For some one else to undo," muttered back the old man, plying his fingers harder than ever, the knot being now nearly completed.

While Captain Delano stood watching him, suddenly the old man threw the knot toward him, and said in broken English,—the first heard in the ship,—something to this effect—"Undo it, cut it, quick." It was said lowly, but with such condensation of rapidity, that the long, slow words in Spanish, which had preceded and followed, almost operated as covers to the brief English between.

For a moment, knot in hand, and knot in head, Captain Delano stood mute; while, without further heeding him, the old man was now intent upon other ropes. Presently there was a slight stir behind Captain Delano. Turning, he saw the chained negro, Atufal, standing quietly there. The next moment the old sailor rose, muttering, and, followed by his subordinate negroes, removed to the forward part of the ship, where in the crowd he disappeared.

An elderly negro, in a clout like an infant's, and with a pepper and salt head, and a kind of attorney air, now approached Captain Delano. In tolerable Spanish, and with a good-natured, knowing wink, he informed him that the old knotter was simple-witted, but harmless; often playing his old tricks. The negro concluded by begging the knot, for of course the stranger would not care to be troubled with it. Unconsciously, it was handed to him. With a sort of congé, the negro received it, and turning his back ferreted into it like a detective Custom House officer after smuggled laces. Soon, with some African word, equivalent to pshaw, he tossed the knot overboard.

All this is very queer now, thought Captain Delano, with a qualmish sort of emotion; but as one feeling incipient seasickness, he strove, by ignoring the symptoms, to get rid of the malady. Once more he looked off for his boat. To his delight, it was now again in view, leaving the rocky spur astern.

The sensation here experienced, after at first relieving his uneasiness, with unforeseen efficiency, soon began to remove it. The less distant sight of that well-known boat—showing it, not as before, half blended with the haze, but with outline defined, so that its individuality, like a man's, was manifest; that boat, *Rover* by name, which though now in strange seas, had often pressed the beach of Captain Delano's home, and, brought to its threshold for repairs, had famiilarly lain there, as a Newfoundland dog; the sight of that household boat evoked a thousand trustful associations, which, contrasted with previous suspicions, filled him not only with lightsome confidence, but somehow with half humorous self-reproaches at his former lack of it.

"What, I, Amasa Delano—Jack of the Beach, as they called me when a lad—I, Amasa; the same that, duck-satchel in hand, used to paddle along the waterside to the schoolhouse made from the old hulk;—I, little Jack of the Beach, that used to go berrying with cousin Nat and the rest; I to be murdered here at the ends of the earth, on board a haunted pirate-ship by a horrible Spaniard?—Too nonsensical to think of! Who would murder Amasa Delano? His conscience is clean. There is some one above. Fie, fie, Jack of the Beach! you are a child indeed; a child of the second childhood, old boy; you are beginning to dote and drule, I'm afraid."

Light of heart and foot, he stepped aft, and there was met by Don Benito's servant, who, with a pleasing expression, responsive to his own present feelings, informed him that his master had recovered from the effects of his coughing fit, and had just ordered him to go present his compliments to his good guest, Don Amasa, and say that he (Don Benito) would soon have the happiness to rejoin him.

There now, do you mark that? again thought Captain Delano, walking the poop. What a donkey I was. This kind gentleman who here sends me his kind compliments, he, but ten minutes ago, dark-lantern in hand, was dodging round some old grind-stone in the hold, sharpening a hatchet for me, I thought. Well, well; these long calms have a morbid effect on the mind, I've often heard, though I never believed it before. Ha! glancing toward the boat; there's *Rover*; a good dog; a white bone in her mouth. A pretty big bone though, seems to me.—What? Yes, she has fallen afoul of the bubbling tide-rip there. It sets her the other way, too, for the time. Patience.

It was now about noon, though, from the greyness of everything, it seemed to be getting toward dusk.

The calm was confirmed. In the far distance, away from the influence of land, the leaden ocean seemed laid out and leaded up, its course finished, soul gone, defunct. But the current from landward, where the ship was, increased; silently sweeping her further and further toward the tranced waters beyond.

Still, from his knowledge of those latitudes, cherishing hopes of a breeze, and a fair and fresh one, at any moment, Captain Delano, despite present prospects, buoyantly counted upon bringing the *San Dominick* safely to anchor ere night. The distance swept over was nothing; since, with a good wind, ten minutes' sailing would retrace more than sixty minutes' drifting. Meantime, one moment turning to mark *Rover* fighting the tide-rip, and the next to see Don Benito approaching, he continued walking the poop.

Gradually he felt a vexation arising from the delay of his boat; this soon merged into uneasiness; and at last, his eye falling continually, as from a stage-box into the pit, upon the strange crowd before and below him, and by-and-by recognizing there the face—now composed to indifference—of the Spanish sailor who had seemed to beckon from the main chains, something of his old trepidations returned.

Ah, thought he—gravely enough—this is like the ague: because it went off, it follows not that it won't come back.

Though ashamed of the relapse, he could not altogether subdue it; and so, exerting his good nature to the utmost, insensibly he came to a compromise.

Yes, this is a strange craft; a strange history, too, and strange folks on board. But—nothing more.

By way of keeping his mind out of mischief till the boat should arrive, he tried to occupy it with turning over and over, in a purely speculative sort of way, some lesser peculiarities of the captain and crew. Among others, four curious points recurred.

First, the affair of the Spanish lad assailed with a knife by the slave boy; an act winked at by Don Benito. Second, the tyranny in Don Benito's treatment of Atufal, the black; as if a child should lead a bull of the Nile by the ring in his nose. Third, the trampling of the sailor by the two negroes; a piece of insolence passed over without so much as a reprimand. Fourth, the cringing submission to their master of all the ship's underlings, mostly blacks; as if by the least inadvertence they feared to draw down his despotic displeasure.

Coupling these points, they seemed somewhat contradictory. But what then, thought Captain Delano, glancing toward his now nearing boat,—what then? Why, this Don Benito is a very capricious commander. But he is not the first of the sort I have seen; though it's true he rather exceeds any other. But as a nation—continued he in his reveries—these Spaniards are all an odd set; the very word Spaniard has a curious, conspirator, Guy-Fawkish twang to it. And yet, I dare say, Spaniards in the main are as good folks as any in Duxbury, Massachusetts. Ah, good! At last *Rover* has come.

As, with its welcome freight, the boat touched the side, the oakum-pickers, with venerable gestures, sought to restrain the blacks, who, at the sight of three gurried water-casks in its bottom, and a pile of wilted pumpkins in its bow, hung over the bulwarks in disorderly raptures.

Don Benito with his servant now appeared; his coming, perhaps, hastened by hearing the noise. Of him Captain Delano sought permission to serve out the water, so that all might share alike, and none injure themselves by unfair excess. But sensible, and, on Don Benito's account, kind as this offer was, it was received with what seemed impatience; as if aware that he lacked energy as a commander, Don Benito, with the true jealousy of weakness, resented as an affront any interference. So, at least, Captain Delano inferred.

In another moment the casks were being hoisted in, when some of the eager negroes accidentally jostled Captain Delano, where he stood by the gangway; so that, unmindful of Don Benito, yielding to the impulse of the moment, with good-natured authority he bade the blacks stand back; to enforce his words making use of a half-mirthful, half-menacing gesture. Instantly the blacks paused, just where they were, each negro and negress suspended in his or her posture, exactly as the word had found them—for a few seconds continuing so—while, as between the responsive posts of a telegraph, an unknown syllable ran from man to man among the perched oakum-pickers. While Captain Delano's attention was fixed by this scene, suddenly the hatchet-polishers half rose, and a rapid cry came from Don Benito.

Thinking that at the signal of the Spaniard he was about to be massacred, Captain Delano would have sprung for his boat, but paused, as the oakum-pickers, dropping down into the crowd with earnest exclamations, forced every white and every negro back, at the same moment, with gestures friendly and familiar, almost jocose, bidding him, in substance, not be a fool. Simultaneously the hatchet-polishers resumed their seats, quietly as so many tailors, and at once, as if nothing had happened, the work of hoisting in the casks was resumed, whites and blacks singing at the tackle.

Captain Delano glanced toward Don Benito. As he saw his meagre form in the act of recovering itself from reclining in the servant's arms, into which the agitated invalid had fallen, he could not but marvel at the panic by which himself had been surprised on the darting supposition that such a commander, who upon a legitimate occasion, so trivial, too, as it now appeared, could lose all self-command, was, with energetic iniquity, going to bring about his murder.

The casks being on deck, Captain Delano was handed a number of jars and cups by one of the steward's aides, who, in the name of Don Benito, entreated him to do as he had proposed: dole out the water. He complied, with republican impartiality as to this republican element, which always seeks one level, serving the oldest white no better than the youngest black;

excepting, indeed, poor Don Benito, whose condition, if not rank, demanded an extra allowance. To him, in the first place, Captain Delano presented a fair pitcher of the fluid; but, thirsting as he was for fresh water, Don Benito quaffed not a drop until after several grave bows and salutes: a reciprocation of courtesies which the sight-loving Africans hailed with clapping of hands.

Two of the less wilted pumpkins being reserved for the cabin table, the residue were minced up on the spot for the general regalement. But the soft bread, sugar, and bottled cider, Captain Delano would have given the Spaniards alone, and in chief Don Benito; but the latter objected; which disinterestedness, on his part, not a little pleased the American; and so mouthfuls all around were given alike to whites and blacks; excepting one bottle of cider, which Babo insisted upon setting aside for his master.

Here it may be observed that as, on the first visit of the boat, the American had not permitted his men to board the ship, neither did he now; being unwilling to add to the confusion of the decks.

Not uninfluenced by the peculiar good humour at present prevailing, and for the time oblivious of any but benevolent thoughts, Captain Delano, who from recent indications counted upon a breeze within an hour or two at furthest, despatched the boat back to the sealer with orders for all the hands that could be spared immediately to set about rafting casks to the watering-place and filling them. Likewise he bade word be carried to his chief officer, that if against present expectation the ship was not brought to anchor by sunset, he need be under no concern, for as there was to be a full moon that night, he (Captain Delano) would remain on board ready to play the pilot, should the wind come soon or late.

As the two captains stood together, observing the departing boat—the servant as it happened having just spied a spot on his master's velvet sleeve, and silently engaged rubbing it out—the American expressed his regrets that the *San Dominick* had no boats; none, at least, but the unseaworthy old hulk of the long-boat, which, warped as a camel's skeleton in the desert, and almost as bleached, lay pot-wise inverted amidships, one side a little tipped, furnishing a subterranean sort of den for family groups of the blacks, mostly women and small children; who, squatting on old mats below, or perched above in the dark dome, on the elevated seats, were descried, some distance within, like a social circle of bats, sheltering in some friendly cave; at intervals, ebon flights of naked boys and girls, three or four years old, darting in and out of the den's mouth.

"Had you three or four boats now, Don Benito," said Captain Delano, "I think that, by tugging at the oars, your negroes here might help along matters some.—Did you sail from port without boats, Don Benito?"

"They were stove in the gales, Señor."

"That was bad. Many men, too, you lost then. Boats and men.—Those must have been hard gales, Don Benito."

"Past all speech," cringed the Spaniard.

"Tell me, Don Benito," continued his companion with increased interest, "tell me, were these gales immediately off the pitch of Cape Horn?"

"Cape Horn?—who spoke of Cape Horn?"

"Yourself did, when giving me an account of your voyage," answered Captain Delano with almost equal astonishment at this eating of his own words, even as he ever seemed eating his own heart, on the part of the Spaniard. "You yourself, Don Benito, spoke of Cape Horn," he emphatically repeated.

The Spaniard turned, in a sort of stooping posture, pausing an instant, as one about to make a plunging exchange of elements, as from air to water.

At this moment a messenger-boy, a white, hurried by, in the regular performance of his function carrying the last expired half-hour forward to the forecastle, from the cabin time-piece, to have it struck at the ship's large bell.

"Master," said the servant, discontinuing his work on the coat sleeve, and addressing the rapt Spaniard with a sort of timid apprehensiveness, as one charged with a duty, the discharge of which, it was foreseen, would prove irksome to the very person who had imposed it, and for whose benefit it was intended, "master told me never mind where he was, or how engaged, always to remind him, to a minute, when shaving-time comes. Miguel has gone to strike the half-hour afternoon. It is *now,* master. Will master go into the cuddy?"

"Ah—yes," answered the Spaniard, starting, somewhat as from dreams into realities; then turning upon Captain Delano, he said that ere long he would resume the conversation.

"Then if master means to talk more to Don Amasa," said the servant, "why not let Don Amasa sit by master in the cuddy, and master can talk, and Don Amasa can listen, while Babo here lathers and strops."

"Yes," said Captain Delano, not unpleased with this sociable plan, "yes, Don Benito, unless you had rather not, I will go with you."

"Be it so, Señor."

As the three passed aft, the American could not but think it another strange instance of his host's capriciousness, this being shaved with such uncommon punctuality in the middle of the day. But he deemed it more than likely that the servant's anxious fidelity had something to do with the matter; inasmuch as the timely interruption served to rally his master from the mood which had evidently been coming upon him.

The place called the cuddy was a light deck-cabin formed by the poop, a sort of attic to the large cabin below. Part of it had formerly been the quarters of the officers; but since their death all the partitionings had been thrown down, and the whole interior converted into one spacious and airy marine hall; for absence of fine furniture and picturesque disarray, of odd appurtenances, somewhat answering to the wide, cluttered hall of some eccentric bachelor-squire in the country, who hangs his shooting-jacket and tobacco-pouch on deer antlers, and keeps his fishing-rod, tongs, and walking-stick in the same corner.

The similitude was heightened, if not originally suggested, by glimpses of the surrounding sea; since, in one aspect, the country and the ocean seem cousins-german.

The floor of the cuddy was matted. Overhead, four or five old muskets were stuck into horizontal holes along the beams. On one side was a claw-footed old table lashed to the deck; a thumbed missal on it, and over it a small, meagre crucifix attached to the bulkhead. Under the table lay a dented cutlass or two, with a hacked harpoon, among some melancholy old rigging, like a heap of poor friars' girdles. There were also two long, sharp-ribbed settees of malacca cane, black with age, and uncomfortable to look at as inquisitors' racks, with a large, misshapen arm-chair, which, furnished with a rude barber's crutch at the back, working with a screw, seemed some grotesque Middle Age engine of torment. A flag locker was in one corner, exposing various coloured bunting, some rolled up, others half unrolled, still others tumbled. Opposite was a cumbrous washstand, of black mahogany, all of one block, with a pedestal, like a font, and over it a railed shelf, containing combs, brushes, and other implements of the toilet. A torn hammock of stained grass swung near; the sheets tossed, and the pillow wrinkled up like a brow, as if whoever slept here slept but illy, with alternate visitations of sad thoughts and bad dreams.

The further extremity of the cuddy, overhanging the ship's stern, was pierced with three openings, windows or port holes, according as men or cannon might peer, socially or unsocially, out of them. At present neither men nor cannon were seen, though huge ring-bolts and other rusty iron fixtures of the wood-work hinted of twenty-four-pounders.

Glancing toward the hammock as he entered, Captain Delano said, "You sleep here, Don Benito?"

"Yes, Señor, since we got into mild weather."

"This seems a sort of dormitory, sitting-room, sail-loft, chapel, armoury, and private closet together, Don Benito," added Captain Delano, looking round.

"Yes, Señor; events have not been favourable to much order in my arrangements."

Here the servant, napkin on arm, made a motion as if waiting his master's good pleasure. Don Benito signified his readiness, when, seating him in the malacca arm-chair, and for the guest's convenience drawing opposite it one of the settees, the servant commenced operations by throwing back his master's collar and loosening his cravat.

There is something in the negro which, in a peculiar way, fits him for avocations about one's person. Most negroes are natural valets and hair-dressers; taking to the comb and brush congenially as to the castanets, and flourishing them apparently with almost equal satisfaction. There is, too, a smooth tact about them in this employment, with a marvellous, noiseless, gliding briskness, not ungraceful in its way, singularly pleasing to behold, and still more so to be the manipulated subject of. And above all is the great gift of good humour. Not the mere grin or laugh is here meant. Those were unsuitable. But a certain easy cheerfulness, harmonious in every glance and gesture; as though God had set the whole negro to some pleasant tune.

When to all this is added the docility arising from the unaspiring contentment of a limited mind, and that susceptibility of blind attachment sometimes inhering in indisputable inferiors, one readily perceives why those hypochondriacs, Johnson and Byron—it may be something like the hypochondriac, Benito Cereno—took to their hearts, almost to the exclusion of the entire white race, their serving men, the negroes, Barber and Fletcher. But if there be that in the negro which exempts him from the inflicted sourness of the morbid or cynical mind, how, in his most prepossessing aspects, must he appear to a benevolent one? When at ease with respect to exterior things, Captain Delano's nature was not only benign, but familiarly and humorously so. At home, he had often taken rare satisfaction in sitting in his door, watching some free man of colour at his work or play. If on a voyage he chanced to have a black sailor, invariably he was on chatty, and half-gamesome terms with him. In fact, like most men of a good, blithe heart, Captain Delano took to negroes, not philanthropically, but genially, just as other men to Newfoundland dogs.

Hitherto the circumstances in which he found the *San Dominick* had repressed the tendency. But in the cuddy, relieved from his former uneasiness, and, for various reasons, more sociably inclined than at any previous period of the day, and seeing the coloured servant, napkin on arm, so debonair about his master, in a business so familiar as that of shaving, too, all his old weakness for negroes returned.

Among other things, he was amused with an odd instance of the African love of bright colours and fine shows, in the black's informally taking from the flag-locker a great piece of bunting of all hues, and lavishly tucking it under his master's chin for an apron.

The mode of shaving among the Spaniards is a little different from what it is with other nations. They have a basin, specially called a barber's basin, which on one side is scooped out, so as accurately to receive the chin, against which it is closely held in lathering; which is done, not with a brush, but with soap dipped in the water of the basin and rubbed on the face.

In the present instance salt-water was used for lack of better; and the parts lathered were only the upper lip, and low down under the throat, all the rest being cultivated beard.

These preliminaries being somewhat novel to Captain Delano he sat curiously eyeing them, so that no conversation took place, nor for the present did Don Benito appear disposed to renew any.

Setting down his basin, the negro searched among the razors, as for the sharpest, and having found it, gave it an additional edge by expertly stropping it on the firm, smooth, oily skin of his open palm; he then made a gesture as if to begin, but midway stood suspended for an instant, one hand elevating the razor, the other professionally dabbling among the bubbling suds on the Spaniard's lank neck. Not unaffected by the close sight of the gleaming steel, Don Benito nervously shuddered; his usual ghastliness was heightened by the lather, which lather, again, was intensified in its hue by the contrasting sootiness of the negro's body. Altogether the scene was somewhat peculiar, at least to Captain Delano, nor, as he saw the two thus postured, could he resist the vagary, that in the black he saw a headsman, and in the white, a man at the block. But this was one of those antic conceits, appearing and vanishing in a breath, from which, perhaps, the best regulated mind is not free.

Meantime the agitation of the Spaniard had a little loosened the bunting from around him, so that one broad fold swept curtain-like over the chair-arm to the floor, revealing, amid a profusion of armorial bars and ground-colours—black, blue and yellow—a closed castle in a blood-red field diagonal with a lion rampant in a white.

"The castle and the lion," exclaimed Captain Delano—"why, Don Benito, this is the flag of Spain you use here. It's well it's only I, and not the King, that sees this," he added with a smile, "but"—turning toward the black, —"it's all one, I suppose, so the colours be gay," which playful remark did not fail somewhat to tickle the negro.

"Now, master," he said, readjusting the flag, and pressing the head gently further back into the crotch of the chair; "now master," and the steel glanced nigh the throat.

Again Don Benito faintly shuddered.

"You must not shake so, master.—See, Don Amasa, master always shakes when I shave him. And yet master knows I never yet have drawn blood, though it's true, if master will shake so, I may some of these times. Now, master," he continued. "And now, Don Amasa, please go on with your talk about the gale, and all that, master can hear, and between times master can answer."

"Ah yes, these gales," said Captain Delano; "but the more I think of your voyage, Don Benito, the more I wonder, not at the gales, terrible as they must have been, but at the disastrous interval following them. For here, by your account, have you been these two months and more getting from Cape Horn to St. Maria, a distance which I myself, with a good wind, have sailed in a few days. True, you had calms, and long ones, but to be becalmed for two months, that is, at least, unusual. Why, Don Benito, had almost any other gentleman told me such a story, I should have been half disposed to a little incredulity."

Here an involuntary expression came over the Spaniard, similar to that just before on the deck, and whether it was the start he gave, or a sudden gawky roll of the hull in the calm, or a momentary unsteadiness of the servant's hand; however it was, just then the razor drew blood, spots of which stained the creamy lather under the throat; immediately the black barber drew back his steel, and remaining in his professional attitude, back to Captain Delano, and face to Don Benito, held up the trickling razor, saying, with a sort of half humorous sorrow, "See, master,—you shook so—here's Babo's first blood."

No sword drawn before James the First of England, no assassination in that timid King's presence, could have produced a more terrified aspect than was now presented by Don Benito.

Poor fellow, thought Captain Delano, so nervous he can't even bear the sight of barber's blood; and this unstrung, sick man, is it credible that I should have imagined he meant to spill all my blood, who can't endure the sight of one little drop of his own? Surely, Amasa Delano, you have been beside yourself this day. Tell it not when you get home, sappy Amasa. Well, well, he looks like a murderer, doesn't he? More like as if himself were to be done for. Well, well, this day's experience shall be a good lesson.

Meantime, while these things were running through the honest seaman's mind, the servant had taken the napkin from his arm, and to Don Benito had said: "But answer Don Amasa, please, master, while I wipe this ugly stuff off the razor, and strop it again."

As he said the words, his face was turned half round, so as to be alike visible to the Spaniard and the American, and seemed by its expression to hint, that he was desirous, by getting his master to go on with the conversation, considerably to withdraw his attention from the recent annoying accident. As if glad to snatch the offered relief, Don Benito resumed, rehearsing to Captain Delano, that not only were the calms of unusual duration, but the ship had fallen in with obstinate currents; and other things he added, some of which were but repetitions of former statements, to explain how it came to pass that the passage from Cape Horn to St. Maria had been so exceedingly long, now and then mingling with his words, incidental praises, less qualified than before, to the blacks, for their general good conduct.

These particulars were not given consecutively, the servant now and then using his razor, and so between the intervals of shaving, the story and panegyric went on with more than usual huskiness.

To Captain Delano's imagination, now again not wholly at rest, there was something so hollow in the Spaniard's manner, with apparently some reciprocal hollowness in the servant's dusky comment of silence, that the idea flashed across him, that possibly master and man, for some unknown purpose, were acting out, both in word and deed, nay, to the very tremor of Don Benito's limbs, some juggling play before him. Neither did the suspicion of collusion lack apparent support, from the fact of those whispered conferences before mentioned. But then, what could be the object of enacting this play of the barber before him? At last, regarding the notion as a whimsy, insensibly suggested, perhaps, by the theatrical aspect of Don Benito in his harlequin ensign, Captain Delano speedily banished it.

The shaving over, the servant bestirred himself with a small bottle of scented waters, pouring a few drops on the head, and then diligently rubbing; the vehemence of the exercise causing the muscles of his face to twitch rather strangely.

His next operation was with comb, scissors and brush; going round and round, smoothing a curl here, clipping an unruly whisker-hair there, giving a graceful sweep to the temple-lock, with other impromptu touches evincing the hand of a master; while, like any resigned gentleman in barber's hands, Don Benito bore all, much less uneasily, at least, than he had done the razoring; indeed, he sat so pale and rigid now, that the negro seemed a Nubian sculptor finishing off a white statue-head.

All being over at last, the standard of Spain removed, tumbled up, and tossed back into the flag-locker, the negro's warm breath blowing away any stray hair which might have lodged down his master's neck; collar and cravat readjusted; a speck of lint whisked off the velvet lapel; all this being done; backing off a little space, and pausing with an expression of subdued self-complacency, the servant for a moment surveyed his master, as, in toilet at least, the creature of his own tasteful hands.

Captain Delano playfully complimented him upon his achievement; at the same time congratulating Don Benito.

But neither sweet waters, nor shampooing, nor fidelity, nor sociality, delighted the Spaniard. Seeing him relapsing into forbidding gloom, and still remaining seated, Captain Delano, thinking that his presence was undesired just then, withdrew, on pretence of seeing whether, as he had prophesied, any signs of a breeze were visible.

Walking forward to the mainmast, he stood awhile thinking over the scene, and not without some undefined misgivings, when he heard a noise near the cuddy, and turning, saw the negro, his hand to his cheek. Advancing, Captain Delano perceived that the cheek was bleeding. He was about to ask the cause, when the negro's wailing soliloquy enlightened him.

"Ah, when will master get better from his sickness; only the sour heart that sour sickness breeds made him serve Babo so; cutting Babo with the razor, because, only by accident, Babo had given master one little scratch; and for the first time in so many a day, too. Ah, ah, ah," holding his hand to his face.

Is it possible, thought Captain Delano; was it to wreak in private his Spanish spite against this poor friend of his, that Don Benito, by his sullen manner, impelled me to withdraw? Ah, this slavery breeds ugly passions in man! Poor fellow!

He was about to speak in sympathy to the negro, but with a timid reluctance he now re-entered the cuddy.

Presently master and man came forth; Don Benito leaning on his servant as if nothing had happened.

But a sort of love-quarrel, after all, thought Captain Delano.

He accosted Don Benito, and they slowly walked together. They had gone but a few paces, when the steward—a tall, rajah-looking mulatto, orientally set off with a pagoda turban formed by three or four Madras handkerchiefs wound about his head, tier on tier—approaching with a salaam, announced lunch in the cabin.

On their way thither, the two captains were preceded by the mulatto, who, turning round as he advanced, with continual smiles and bows, ushered them in, a display of elegance which quite completed the insignificance of the small bare-headed Babo, who, as if not unconscious of inferiority, eyed askance the graceful steward. But in part, Captain Delano imputed his jealous watchfulness to that peculiar feeling which the full-blooded African entertains for the adulterated one. As for the steward, his manner, if not bespeaking much dignity of self-respect, yet evidenced his extreme desire to please; which is doubly meritorious, as at once Christian and Chesterfieldian.

Captain Delano observed with interest that while the complexion of the mulatto was hybrid, his physiognomy was European; classically so.

"Don Benito," whispered he, "I am glad to see this usher-of-the-golden-rod of yours; the sight refutes an ugly remark once made to me by a Barbados planter that when a mulatto has a regular European face, look out for him; he is a devil. But see, your steward here has features more regular than King George's of England; and yet there he nods, and bows, and smiles; a king, indeed—the king of kind hearts and polite fellows. What a pleasant voice he has, too?"

"He has, Señor."

"But, tell me, has he not, so far as you have known him, always proved a good, worthy fellow?" said Captain Delano, pausing, while with a final genuflexion the steward disappeared into the cabin; "come, for the reason just mentioned, I am curious to know."

"Francesco is a good man," rather sluggishly responded Don Benito, like a phlegmatic appreciator, who would neither find fault nor flatter.

"Ah, I thought so. For it were strange indeed, and not very creditable to us white-skins, if a little of our blood mixed with the African's, should, far from improving the latter's quality, have the sad effect of pouring vitriolic acid into black broth; improving the hue, perhaps, but not the wholesomeness."

"Doubtless, doubtless, Señor, but"—glancing at Babo—"not to speak of negroes, your planter's remark I have heard applied to the Spanish and Indian intermixtures in our provinces. But I know nothing about the matter," he listlessly added.

And here they entered the cabin.

The lunch was a frugal one. Some of Captain Delano's fresh fish and pumpkins, biscuit and salt beef, the reserved bottle of cider, and the *San Dominick's* last bottle of Canary.

As they entered, Francesco, with two or three coloured aids, was hovering over the table giving the last adjustments. Upon perceiving their master they withdrew, Francesco making a smiling congé, and the Spaniard, without condescending to notice it, fastidiously remarking to his companion that he relished not superfluous attendance.

Without companions, host and guest sat down, like a childless married couple, at opposite ends of the table, Don Benito waving Captain Delano to his place, and, weak as he was, insisting upon that gentleman being seated before himself.

The negro placed a rug under Don Benito's feet, and a cushion behind his back, and then stood behind, not his master's chair, but Captain Delano's. At first, this a little surprised the latter. But it was soon evident that, in taking his position, the black was still true to his master; since by facing him he could the more readily anticipate his slightest want.

"This is an uncommonly intelligent fellow of yours, Don Benito," whispered Captain Delano across the table.

"You say true, Señor."

During the repast, the guest again reverted to parts of Don Benito's story, begging further particulars here and there. He inquired how it was that the scurvy and fever should have committed such wholesale havoc upon the whites, while destroying less than half of the blacks. As if this question reproduced the whole scene of plague before the Spaniard's eyes, miserably reminding him of his solitude in a cabin where before he had had so many friends and officers round him, his hand shook, his face became hueless, broken words escaped; but directly the same memory of the past seemed replaced by insane terrors of the present. With starting eyes he stared before him at vacancy. For nothing was to be seen but the hand of his servant pushing the Canary over towards him. At length a few sips served partially to restore him. He made random reference to the different constitutions of races, enabling one to offer more resistance to certain maladies than another. The thought was new to his companion.

Presently Captain Delano, intending to say something to his host concerning the pecuniary part of the business he had undertaken for him, especially—since he was strictly accountable to his owners—with reference to the new suit of sails, and other things of that sort; and naturally preferring to conduct such affairs in private, was desirous that the servant should withdraw; imagining that Don Benito for a few minutes could dispense with his attendance. He, however, waited awhile; thinking that, as the conversation proceeded, Don Benito, without being prompted, would perceive the propriety of the step.

But it was otherwise. At last catching his host's eye, Captain Delano, with a slight backward gesture of his thumb, whispered, "Don Benito, pardon me, but there is an interference with the full expression of what I have to say to you."

Upon this the Spaniard changed countenance; which was imputed to his resenting the hint, as in some way a reflection upon his servant. After a moment's pause, he assured his guest that the black's remaining with them could be of no disservice; because since losing his officers he had made Babo (whose original office, it now appeared, had been captain of the slaves) not only his constant attendant and companion, but in all things his confidant.

After this, nothing more could be said; though, indeed, Captain Delano could hardly avoid some little tinge of irritation upon being left ungratified in so inconsiderable a wish, by one, too, for whom he intended such solid services. But it is only his querulousness, thought he; and so filling his glass he proceeded to business.

The price of the sails and other matters was fixed upon. But while this was being done, the American observed that, though his original offer of assistance had been hailed with hectic animation, yet now when it was reduced to a business transaction, indifference and apathy were betrayed. Don Benito, in fact, appeared to submit to hearing the details more out of regard to common propriety, than from any impression that weighty benefit to himself and his voyage was involved.

Soon, this manner became still more reserved. The effort was vain to seek to draw him into social talk. Gnawed by his splenetic mood, he sat twitching his beard, while to little purpose the hand of his servant, mute as that on the wall, slowly pushed over the Canary.

Lunch being over, they sat down on the cushioned transom; the servant placing a pillow behind his master. The long continuance of the calm had now affected the atmosphere. Don Benito sighed heavily, as if for breath.

"Why not adjourn to the cuddy," said Captain Delano; "there is more air there." But the host sat silent and motionless.

Meantime his servant knelt before him, with a large fan of feathers. And Francesco, coming in on tiptoes, handed the negro a little cup of aromatic waters, with which at intervals he chafted his master's brow, smoothing the hair along the temples as a nurse does a child's. He spoke no word. He only rested his eye on his master's, as if, amid all Don Benito's distress, a little to refresh his spirit by the silent sight of fidelity.

Presently the ship's bell sounded two o'clock; and through the cabin-windows a slight rippling of the sea was discerned; and from the desired direction.

"There," exclaimed Captain Delano, "I told you so, Don Benito, look!"

He had risen to his feet, speaking in a very animated tone, with a view the more to rouse his companion. But though the crimson curtain of the stern-window near him that moment fluttered against his pale cheek, Don Benito seemed to have even less welcome for the breeze than the calm.

Poor fellow, thought Captain Delano, bitter experience has taught him that one ripple does not make a wind, any more than one swallow a summer. But he is mistaken for once. I will get his ship in for him, and prove it.

Briefly alluding to his weak condition, he urged his host to remain quietly where he was, since he (Captain Delano) would with pleasure take upon himself the responsibility of making the best use of the wind.

Upon gaining the deck, Captain Delano started at the unexpected figure of Atufal, monumentally fixed at the threshold, like one of those sculptured porters of black marble guarding the porches of Egyptian tombs.

But this time the start was, perhaps, purely physical. Atufal's presence, singularly attesting docility even in sullenness, was contrasted with that of the hatchet-polishers, who in patience evinced their industry; while both spectacles showed, that lax as Don Benito's general authority might be, still, whenever he chose to exert it, no man so savage or colossal but must, more or less, bow.

Snatching a trumpet which hung from the bulwarks, with a free step Captain Delano advanced to the forward edge of the poop, issuing his orders in his best Spanish. The few sailors and many negroes, all equally pleased, obediently set about heading the ship toward the harbour.

While giving some directions about setting a lower stu'n'-sail, suddenly Captain Delano heard a voice faithfully repeating his orders. Turning, he saw Babo, now for the time acting, under the pilot, his original part of captain of the slaves. This assistance proved valuable. Tattered sails and warped yards were soon brought into some trim. And no brace or halyard was pulled but to the blithe songs of the inspirited negroes.

Good fellows, thought Captain Delano, a little training would make fine sailors of them. Why see, the very women pull and sing, too. These must be some of those Ashantee negresses that make such capital soldiers, I've heard. But who's at the helm? I must have a good hand there.

He went to see.

The *San Dominick* steered with a cumbrous tiller, with large horizontal pullies attached. At each pulley-end stood a subordinate black, and between them, at the tiller-head, the responsible post, a Spanish seaman, whose countenance evinced his due share in the general hopefulness and confidence at the coming of the breeze.

He proved the same man who had behaved with so shamefaced an air on the windlass.

"Ah,—it is you, my man," exclaimed Captain Delano—"well, no more sheep's-eyes now;—look straightforward and keep the ship so. Good hand, I trust? And want to get into the harbour, don't you?"

"Sí, Señor," assented the man with an inward chuckle, grasping the tiller-head firmly. Upon this, unperceived by the American, the two blacks eyed the sailor askance.

Finding all right at the helm, the pilot went forward to the forecastle, to see how matters stood there.

The ship now had way enough to breast the current. With the approach of evening, the breeze would be sure to freshen.

Having done all that was needed for the present, Captain Delano, giving his last orders to the sailors, turned aft to report affairs to Don Benito in the cabin; perhaps additionally incited to rejoin him by the hope of snatching a moment's private chat while his servant was engaged upon deck.

From opposite sides, there were, beneath the poop, two approaches to the cabin; one further forward than the other, and consequently communicating with a longer passage. Marking the servant still above, Captain Delano, taking the nighest entrance—the one last named, and at whose porch Atufal still stood—hurried on his way, till, arrived at the cabin threshold, he paused an instant, a little to recover from his eagerness. Then, with the words of his intended business upon his lips, he entered. As he advanced toward the Spaniard, on the transom, he heard another footstep, keeping time with his. From the opposite door, a salver in hand, the servant was likewise advancing.

"Confound the faithful fellow," thought Captain Delano; "what a vexatious coincidence."

Possibly, the vexation might have been something different, were it not for the buoyant confidence inspired by the breeze. But even as it was, he felt a slight twinge, from a sudden involuntary association in his mind of Babo with Atufal.

"Don Benito," said he, "I give you joy; the breeze will hold, and will increase. By the way, your tall man and time-piece, Atufal, stands without. By your order, of course?"

Don Benito recoiled, as if at some bland satirical touch, delivered with such adroit garnish of apparent good-breeding as to present no handle for retort.

He is like one flayed alive, thought Captain Delano; where may one touch him without causing a shrink?

The servant moved before his master, adjusting a cushion; recalled to civility, the Spaniard stiffly replied: "You are right. The slave appears where you saw him, according to my command; which is, that if at the given hour I am below, he must take his stand and abide my coming."

"Ah now, pardon me, but that is treating the poor fellow like an ex-king denied. Ah, Don Benito," smiling, "for all the license you permit in some things, I fear lest, at bottom, you are a bitter hard master."

Again Don Benito shrank; and this time, as the good sailor thought, from a genuine twinge of his conscience.

Conversation now became constrained. In vain Captain Delano called attention to the now perceptible motion of the keel gently cleaving the sea; with lack-lustre eye, Don Benito returned words few and reserved.

By-and-by, the wind having steadily risen, and still blowing right into the harbour, bore the *San Dominick* swiftly on. Rounding a point of land, the sealer at distance came into open view.

Meantime Captain Delano had again repaired to the deck, remaining there some time. Having at last altered the ship's course, so as to give the reef a wide berth, he returned for a few moments below.

I will cheer up my poor friend, this time, thought he.

"Better and better, Don Benito," he cried as he blithely re-entered; "there will soon be an end to your cares, at least for awhile. For when, after a long, sad voyage, you know, the anchor drops into the haven, all its vast weight seems lifted from the captain's heart. We are getting on famously, Don Benito. My ship is in sight. Look through this side-light here; there she is; all a-taunt-o! The *Bachelor's Delight,* my good friend. Ah, how this wind braces one up. Come, you must take a cup of coffee with me this evening. My old steward will give you as fine a cup as ever any sultan tasted. What say you, Don Benito, will you?"

At first, the Spaniard glanced feverishly up, casting a longing look toward the sealer, while with mute concern his servant gazed into his face. Suddenly the old ague of coldness returned, and dropping back to his cushions he was silent.

"You do not answer. Come, all day you have been my host; would you have hospitality all on one side?"

"I cannot go," was the response.

"What? It will not fatigue you. The ships will lie together as near as they can, without swinging foul. It will be little more than stepping from deck to deck; which is but as from room to room. Come, come, you must not refuse me."

"I cannot go," decisively and repulsively repeated Don Benito.

Renouncing all but the last appearance of courtesy, with a sort of cadaverous sullenness, and biting his thin nails to the quick, he glanced, almost glared, at his guest; as if impatient that a stranger's presence should interfere with the full indulgence of his morbid hour. Meantime the sound of the parted waters came more and more gurglingly and merrily in at the windows; as reproaching him for his dark spleen; as telling him that, sulk as he might, and go mad with it, nature cared not a jot; since, whose fault was it, pray?

But the foul mood was now at its depth as the fair wind at its height.

There was something in the man so far beyond any mere unsociality or sourness previously evinced, that even the forbearing good-nature of his guest could no longer endure it. Wholly at a loss to account for such demeanour, and deeming sickness with eccentricity, however extreme, no adequate excuse, well satisfied, too, that nothing in his own conduct could justify it, Captain Delano's pride began to be roused. Himself became reserved. But all seemed one to the Spaniard. Quitting him, therefore, Captain Delano once more went to the deck.

The ship was now within less than two miles of the sealer. The whaleboat was seen darting over the interval.

To be brief, the two vessels, thanks to the pilot's skill, ere long in neighbourly style lay anchored together.

Before returning to his own vessel, Captain Delano had intended communicating to Don Benito the practical details of the proposed services to be rendered. But, as it was, unwilling anew to subject himself to rebuffs, he resolved, now that he had seen the *San Dominick* safely moored, immediately to quit her, without further allusion to hospitality or business. Indefinitely postponing his ulterior plans, he would regulate his future actions according to future circumstances. His boat was ready to receive him; but his host still tarried below. Well, thought Captain Delano, if he has little breeding, the more need to show mine. He descended to the cabin to bid a ceremonious, and, it may be, tacitly rebukeful adieu. But to his great satisfaction, Don Benito, as if he began to feel the weight of that treatment with which his slighted guest had, not indecorously, retaliated upon him, now supported by his servant, rose to his feet, and grasping Captain Delano's hand, stood tremulous; too much agitated to speak. But the good augury hence drawn was suddenly dashed, by his resuming all his previous reserve, with augmented gloom, as, with half-averted eyes, he silently reseated himself on his cushions. With a corresponding return of his own chilled feelings, Captain Delano bowed and withdrew.

He was hardly midway in the narrow corridor, dim as a tunnel, leading from the cabin to the stairs, when a sound, as of the tolling for execution in some jail-yard, fell on his ears. It was the echo of the ships' flawed bell, striking the hour, drearily reverberated in this subterranean vault. Instantly, by a fatality not to be withstood, his mind, responsive to the portent, swarmed with superstitious suspicions. He paused. In images far swifter than these sentences, the minutest details of all his former distrusts swept through him.

Hitherto, credulous good-nature had been too ready to furnish excuses for reasonable fears. Why was the Spaniard, so superfluously punctilious at times, now heedless of common propriety in not accompanying to the side his departing guest? Did indisposition forbid? Indisposition had not forbidden more irksome exertion that day. His last equivocal demeanour recurred. He had risen to his feet, grasped his guest's hand, motioned toward his hat; then, in an instant, all was eclipsed in sinister muteness and gloom. Did this imply one brief, repentant relenting at the final moment, from some iniquitous plot, followed by remorseless return to it? His last glance seemed to express a calamitous, yet acquiescent farewell to Captain Delano for ever. Why decline the invitation to visit the sealer that evening? Or was the Spaniard less hardened than the Jew, who refrained not from supping at the board of him whom the same night he meant to betray? What imported all those day-long enigmas and contradictions, except they were intended to mystify, preliminary to some stealthy blow? Atufal, the pretended rebel, but punctual shadow, that moment lurked by the threshold without. He seemed a sentry and more. Who by his own confession had stationed him there? Was the negro now lying in wait?

The Spaniard behind—his creature before: to rush from darkness to light was the involuntary choice.

The next moment with clenched jaw and hand, he passed Atufal, and stood unharmed in the light. As he saw his trim ship lying peacefully at her anchor, and almost within ordinary call; as he saw his household boat, with familiar faces in it, patiently rising and falling on the short waves by the *San Dominick's* side; and then, glancing about the decks where he stood, saw the oakum-pickers still gravely plying their fingers; and heard the low, buzzing whistle and industrious hum of the hatchet-polishers, still bestirring themselves over their endless occupation; and more than all, as he saw the benign aspect of Nature, taking her innocent repose in the evening; the screened sun in the quiet camp of the west shining out like the mild light from Abraham's tent; as his charmed eye and ear took in all these, with the chained figure of the black, the clenched jaw and hand relaxed. Once again he smiled at the phantoms which had mocked him, and felt something like a tinge of remorse, that, by indulging them even for a moment, he should, be implication, have betrayed an almost atheist doubt of the ever-watchful Providence above.

There was a few minutes' delay, while, in obedience to his orders, the boat was being hooked along to the gangway. During this interval, a sort of saddened satisfaction stole over Captain Delano, at thinking of the kindly offices he had that day discharged for a stranger. Ah, thought he, after good actions one's conscience is never ungrateful, however much so the benefited party may be.

Presently, his foot, in the first act of descent into the boat, pressed the first round of the side-ladder, his face presented inward upon the deck. In the same moment, he heard his name courteously sounded; and, to his pleased surprise, saw Don Benito advancing—an unwonted energy in his air, as if, at the last moment, intent upon making amends for his recent discourtesy. With instinctive good feeling, Captain Delano, revoking his foot, turned and reciprocally advanced. As he did so, the Spaniard's nervous eagerness increased, but his vital energy failed; so that, the better to support him, the servant, placing his master's hand on his naked shoulder, and gently holding it there, formed himself into a sort of crutch.

When the two captains met, the Spaniard again fervently took the hand of the American, at the same time casting an earnest glance into his eyes, but, as before, too much overcome to speak.

I have done him wrong, self-reproachfully thought Captain Delano; his apparent coldness has deceived me; in no instance has he meant to offend.

Meantime, as if fearful that the continuance of the scene might too much unstring his master, the servant seemed anxious to terminate it. And so, still presenting himself as a crutch, and walking between the two captains, he advanced with them toward the gangway; while still, as if full of kindly contrition, Don Benito would not let go the hand of Captain Delano, but retained it in his, across the black's body.

Soon they were standing by the side, looking over into the boat, whose crew turned up their curious eyes. Waiting a moment for the Spaniard to relinquish his hold, the now embarrassed Captain Delano lifted his foot, to overstep the threshold of the open gangway; but still Don Benito would not let go his hand. And yet, with an agitated tone, he said, "I can go no further; here I must bid you adieu. Adieu, my dear, dear Don Amasa. Go—go!" suddenly tearing his hand loose, "go, and God guard you better than me, my best friend."

Not unaffected, Captain Delano would now have lingered; but catching the meekly admonitory eye of the servant, with a hasty farewell he descended into his boat, followed by the continual adieus of Don Benito, standing rooted in the gangway.

Seating himself in the stern, Captain Delano, making a last salute, ordered the boat shoved off. The crew had their oars on end. The bowsman pushed the boat a sufficient distance for the oars to be lengthwise dropped. The instant that was done, Don Benito sprang over the bulwarks, falling at the feet of Captain Delano; at the same time, calling towards his ship, but in tones so frenzied, that none in the boat could understand him. But, as if not equally obtuse, three Spanish sailors, from three different and distant parts of the ship, splashed into the sea, swimming after their captain, as if intent upon rescue.

The dismayed officer of the boat eagerly asked what this meant. To which, Captain Delano, turning a disdainful smile upon the unaccountable Benito Cereno, answered that, for his part, he neither knew nor cared; but it seemed as if the Spaniard had taken it into his head to produce the impression among his people that the boat wanted to kidnap him. "Or else—give way for your lives," he wildly added, starting at a clattering hubbub in the ship, above which rang the tocsin of the hatchet-polishers; and seizing Don Benito by the throat he added, "this plotting pirate means murder!" Here, in apparent verification of the words, the servant, a dagger in his hand, was seen on the rail overhead, poised, in the act of leaping, as if with desperate fidelity to befriend his master to the last; while, seemingly to aid the black, the three Spanish sailors were trying to clamber into the hampered bow. Meantime, the whole host of negroes, as if inflamed at the sight of their jeopardized captain, impended in one sooty avalanche over the bulwarks.

All this, with what preceded, and what followed, occurred with such involutions of rapidity, that past, present, and future seemed one.

Seeing the negro coming, Captain Delano had flung the Spaniard aside, almost in the very act of clutching him, and, by the unconscious recoil, shifting his place, with arms thrown up, so promptly grappled the servant in his descent, that with dagger presented at Captain Delano's heart, the black seemed of purpose to have leaped there as to his mark. But the weapon was wrenched away, and the assailant dashed down into the bottom of the boat, which now, with disentangled oars, began to speed through the sea.

At this juncture, the left hand of Captain Delano, on one side, again clutched the half-reclined Don Benito, heedless that he was in a speechless faint, while his right foot, on the other side, ground the prostrate negro; and his right arm pressed for added speed on the after oar, his eye bent forward, encouraging his men to their utmost.

But here, the officer of the boat, who had at last succeeded in beating off the towing Spanish sailors, and was now, with face turned aft, assisting the bowsman at his oar, suddenly called to Captain Delano, to see what the black was about; while a Portuguese oarsman shouted to him to give heed to what the Spaniard was saying.

Glancing down at his feet Captain Delano saw the freed hand of the servant aiming with a second dagger—a small one, before concealed in his wool—with this he was snakishly writhing up from the boat's bottom, at the heart of his master, his countenance lividly vindictive, expressing the centred purpose of his soul; while the Spaniard, half-choked, was vainly shrinking away, with husky words, incoherent to all but the Portuguese.

That moment, across the long benighted mind of Captain Delano, a flash of revelation swept illuminating in unanticipated clearness Benito Cereno's whole mysterious demeanour with every enigmatic event of the day, as well as the entire past voyage of the *San Dominick*. He smote Babo's hand down, but his own heart smote him harder. With infinite pity he withdrew his hold from Don Benito. Not Captain Delano, but Don Benito, the black, in leaping into the boat, had intended to stab.

Both the black's hands were held, as, glancing up toward the *San Dominick*, Captain Delano, now with the scales dropped from his eyes, saw the negroes, not in misrule, not in tumult, not as if frantically concerned for Don Benito, but with mask torn away, flourishing hatchets and knives, in ferocious piratical revolt. Like delirious black dervishes, the six Ashantees danced on the poop. Prevented by their foes from springing into the water, the Spanish boys were hurrying up to the topmost spars, while such of the few Spanish sailors, not already in the sea, less alert, were descried, helplessly mixed in, on deck, with the blacks.

Meantime Captain Delano hailed his own vessel, ordering the ports up, and the guns run out. But by this time the cable of the *San Dominick* had been cut; and the fag-end, in lashing out, whipped away the canvas shroud about the beak, suddenly revealing, as the bleached hull swung round toward the open ocean, death for the figurehead, in a human skeleton; chalky comment on the chalked words below, *"Follow your leader."*

At the sight, Don Benito, covering his face, wailed out: " 'Tis he, Aranda! my murdered, unburied friend!"

Upon reaching the sealer, calling for ropes, Captain Delano bound the negro, who made no resistance, and had him hoisted to the deck. He would then have assisted the now almost helpless Don Benito up the side; but Don Benito, wan as he was, refused to move, or be moved, until the negro should have been first put below out of view. When, presently assured that it was done, he no more shrank from the ascent.

The boat was immediately despatched back to pick up the three swimming sailors. Meantime, the guns were in readiness, though, owing to the *San Dominick* having glided somewhat astern of the sealer, only the aftermost one could be brought to bear. With this, they fired six times; thinking to cripple the fugitive ship by bring down her spars. But only a few inconsiderable ropes were shot away. Soon the ship was beyond the guns' range, steering broad out of the bay; the blacks thickly clustering round the bowsprit, one moment with taunting cries toward the whites, the next with upthrown gestures hailing the now dusky expanse of ocean—cawing crows escaped from the hand of the fowler.

The first impulse was to slip the cables and give chase. But, upon second thought, to pursue with whale-boat and yawl seemed more promising.

Upon inquiring of Don Benito what firearms they had on board the

San Dominick, Captain Delano was answered that they had none that could
be used; because, in the earlier stages of the mutiny, a cabin-passenger, since
dead, had secretly put out of order the locks of what few muskets there were.
But with all his remaining strength, Don Benito entreated the American not
to give chase, either with ship or boat; for the negroes had already proved
themselves such desperadoes, that, in case of a present assault, nothing but
a total massacre of the whites could be looked for. But, regarding this
warning as coming from one whose spirit had been crushed by misery, the
American did not give up his design.

The boats were got ready and armed. Captain Delano ordered twenty-
five men into them. He was going himself when Don Benito grasped his arm.

"What! have you saved my life, Señor, and are you now going to throw
away your own?"

The officers also, for reasons connected with their interests and those
of the voyage, and a duty owing to the owners, strongly objected against
their commander's going. Weighing their remonstrances a moment, Captain
Delano felt bound to remain; appointing his chief mate—an athletic and
resolute man, who had been a privateer's man, and, as his enemies whispered,
a pirate—to head the party. The more to encourage the sailors, they were told
that the Spanish captain considered his ship as good as lost; that she and her
cargo, including some gold and silver, were worth upwards of ten thousand
doubloons. Take her, and no small part should be theirs. The sailors replied
with a shout.

The fugitives had now almost gained an offing. It was nearly night; but
the moon was rising. After hard, prolonged pulling, the boats came up on the
ship's quarters, at a suitable distance laying upon their oars to discharge
their muskets. Having no bullets to return, the negroes sent their yells. But,
upon the second volley, Indian-like, they hurtled their hatchets. One took
off a sailor's fingers. Another struck the whale-boat's bow, cutting off the
rope there, and remaining stuck in the gunwale, like a woodman's axe.
Snatching it, quivering from its lodgment, the mate hurled it back. The
returned gauntlet now stuck in the ship's broken quarter-gallery, and so
remained.

The negroes giving too hot a reception, the whites kept a more respectful
distance. Hovering now just out of reach of the hurtling hatchets, they, with
a view to the close encounter which must soon come, sought to decoy the
blacks into entirely disarming themselves of their most murderous weapons
in a hand-to-hand fight, by foolishly flinging them, as missiles, short of the
mark, into the sea. But ere long perceiving the stratagem, the negroes
desisted, though not before many of them had to replace their lost hatchets
with handspikes; an exchange which, as counted upon, proved in the end
favourable to the assailants.

Meantime, with strong wind, the ship still clove the water; the boats
alternately falling behind, and pulling up, to discharge fresh volleys.

The fire was mostly directed toward the stern, since there, chiefly, the negroes, at present, were clustering. But to kill or maim the negroes was not the object. To take them, with the ship, was the object. To do it, the ship must be boarded; which could not be done by boats while she was sailing so fast.

A thought now struck the mate. Observing the Spanish boys still aloft, high as they could get, he called to them to descend to the yards, and cut adrift the sails. It was done. About this time, owing to causes hereafter to be shown, two Spaniards, in the dress of sailors and conspicuously showing themselves, were killed; not by volleys, but by deliberate marksman's shots; while, as it afterwards appeared, during one of the general discharges, Atufal, the black, and the Spaniard at the helm likewise were killed. What now, with the loss of the sails, and loss of leaders, the ship became unmanageable to the negroes.

With creaking masts she came heavily round to the wind; the prow slowly swinging into view of the boats, its skeleton gleaming in the horizontal moonlight, and casting a gigantic ribbed shadow upon the water. One extended arm of the ghost seemed beckoning the whites to avenge it.

"Follow your leader!" cried the mate; and, one on each bow, the boats boarded. Scaling-spears and cutlasses crossed hatchets and handspikes. Huddled upon the long-boat amidships, the negresses raised a wailing chant, whose chorus was the clash of the steel.

For a time, the attack wavered; the negroes wedging themselves to beat it back; the half-repelled sailors, as yet unable to gain a footing, fighting as troopers in the saddle, one leg sideways flung over the bulwarks, and one without, plying their cutlasses like carters' whips. But in vain. They were almost overborne, when, rallying themselves into a squad as one man, with a huzza, they sprang inboard; where, entangled, they involuntarily separated again. For a few breaths' space there was a vague, muffled, inner sound as of submerged sword-fish rushing hither and thither through shoals of black-fish. Soon, in a reunited band, and joined by the Spanish seamen, the whites came to the surface, irresistibly driving the negroes toward the stern. But a barricade of casks and sacks, from side to side, had been thrown up by the mainmast. Here the negroes faced about, and though scorning peace or truce, yet fain would have had a respite. But, without pause, overleaping the barrier, the unflagging sailors again closed. Exhausted, the blacks now fought in despair. Their red tongues lolled, wolf-like, from their black mouths. But the pale sailors' teeth were set; not a word was spoken; and, in five minutes more, the ship was won.

Nearly a score of the negroes were killed. Exclusive of those by the balls, many were mangled; their wounds—mostly inflicted by the long-edged scaling-spears—resembling those shaven ones of the English at Preston Pans, made by the poled scythes of the Highlanders. On the other side, none were killed, though several were wounded; some severely, including the mate. The surviving negroes were temporarily secured, and the ship, towed back into the harbour at midnight, once more lay anchored.

Omitting the incidents and arrangements ensuing, suffice it that, after two days spent in refitting, the two ships sailed in company for Concepcion in Chili, and thence for Lima in Peru; where, before the vice-regal courts, the whole affair, from the beginning, underwent investigation.

Though, midway on the passage, the ill-fated Spaniard, relaxed from constraint, showed some signs of regaining health with free-will; yet, agreeably to his own foreboding, shortly before arriving at Lima, he relapsed, finally becoming so reduced as to be carried ashore in arms. Hearing of his story and plight, one of the many religious institutions of the City of Kings opened an hospitable refuge to him, where both physician and priest were his nurses, and a member of the order volunteered to be his one special guardian and consoler, by night and by day.

The following extracts, translated from one of the official Spanish documents, will, it is hoped, shed light on the preceding narrative, as well as, in the first place, reveal the true port of departure and true history of the *San Dominick's* voyage, down to the time of her touching at the island of Santa Maria.

But, ere the extracts come, it may be well to preface them with a remark.

The document selected, from among many others, for partial translation, contains the deposition of Benito Cereno; the first taken in the case. Some disclosures therein were, at the time, held dubious for both learned and natural reasons. The tribunal inclined to the opinion that the deponent, not undisturbed in his mind by recent events, raved of some things which could never have happened. But subsequent depositions of the surviving sailors, bearing out the revelations of their captain in several of the strangest particulars, gave credence to the rest. So that the tribunal, in its final decision, rested its capital sentences upon statements which, had they lacked confirmation, it would have deemed it but duty to reject.

    .   .   .   .

I, Don José de Abos and Padilla, His Majesty's Notary for the Royal Revenue, and Register of this Province, and Notary Public of the Holy Crusade of this Bishopric, etc.

Do certify and declare, as much as is requisite in law, that, in the criminal cause commenced the twenty-fourth of the month of September, in the year seventeen hundred and ninety-nine, against the Senegal negroes of the ship *San Dominick*, the following declaration before me was made.

Declaration of the first witness,
Don Benito Cereno.

The same day, and month, and year, His Honour, Doctor Juan Martinez de Dozas, Councilor of the Royal Audience of this Kingdom, and learned in the law of this Intendancy, ordered the captain of the ship *San Dominick*, Don Benito Cereno, to appear; which he did in his litter, attended by the monk Infelez; of whom he received, before Don José de Abos and Padilla, Notary Public of the Holy Crusade, the oath, which he took by God, our Lord, and a sign of the Cross; under which he promised to tell the truth of whatever he should know and should be asked;—and being interrogated agreeably to the tenor of the act commencing the process, he said, that on the twentieth of May last, he set sail with his ship from the port of Valparaiso, bound to that of Callao; loaded with the produce of the country and one hundred and sixty blacks, of both sexes, mostly belonging to Don Alexandro Aranda, gentleman, of the city of Mendoza; that the crew of the ship consisted of thirty-six men, beside the persons who went as passengers; that the negroes were in part as follows:

[*Here, in the original, follows a list of some fifty names, descriptions, and ages, compiled from certain recovered documents of Aranda's, and also from recollections of the deponent, from which portions only are extracted*]

—One, from about eighteen to nineteen years, named José, and this was the man that waited upon his master, Don Alexandro, and who speaks well the Spanish, having served him four or five years; . . . a mulatto, named Francesco, the cabin steward, of a good person and voice, having sung in the Valparaiso churches, native of the province of Buenos Ayres, aged about thirty-five years. . . . A smart negro, named Dago, who had been for many years a grave-digger among the Spaniards, aged forty-six years. . . . Four old negroes, born in Africa, from sixty to seventy, but sound, caulkers by trade, whose names are as follows:—the first was named Muri, and he was killed (as was also his son named Diamelo); the second, Nacta; the third, Yola, likewise killed; the fourth, Ghofan; and six full-grown negroes, aged from thirty to forty-five, all raw, and born among the Ashantees—Martinqui, Yan, Lecbe, Mapenda, Yambaio, Akim; four of whom were killed; . . . a powerful negro named Atufal, who, being supposed to have been a chief in Africa, his owners set great store by him. . . . And a small negro of Senegal, but some years among the Spaniards, aged about thirty, which negro's name was Babo; . . . that he does not remember the names of the others, but that still expecting the residue of Don Alexandro's papers will be found, will then take due account of them all, and remit to the court; . . . and thirty-nine women and children of all ages.

[*After the catalogue, the deposition goes on as follows:*]

. . . That all the negroes slept upon deck, as is customary in this navigation, and none wore fetters, because the owner, his friend Aranda, told him that they were all tractable; . . . that on the seventh day after leaving port, at three o'clock in the morning, all the Spaniards being asleep except the two officers on the watch, who were the boatswain, Juan Robles, and the carpenter, Juan Bautista Gayete, and the helmsman and his boy, the negroes revolted suddenly, wounded dangerously the boatswain and the carpenter, and successively killed eighteen men of those who were sleeping upon deck, some with handspikes and hatchets, and others by throwing them alive overboard, after tying them; that of the Spaniards upon deck, they left about seven, as he thinks, alive and tied, to manœuvre the ship and three or four more who hid themselves, remained also alive. Although in the act of revolt the negroes made themselves masters of the hatchway, six or seven wounded went through it to the cockpit, without any hindrance on their part; that in the act of revolt, the mate and another person, whose name he does not recollect, attempted to come up through the hatchway, but having been wounded at the onset, they were obliged to return to the cabin; that the deponent resolved at break of day to come up the companionway, where the negro Babo was, being the ringleader, and Atufal, who assisted him, and having spoken to them, exhorted them to cease committing such atrocities, asking them, at the same time, what they wanted and intended to do, offering, himself, to obey their commands; that, notwithstanding this, they threw, in his presence, three men, alive and tied, overboard; that they told the deponent to come up, and that they would not kill him; which having done, the negro Babo asked him whether there were in those seas any negro countries where they might be carried, and he answered them, No; that the negro Babo afterwards told him to carry them to Senegal, or to the neighbouring islands of St. Nicholas; and he answered, that this was impossible, on account of the great distance, the necessity involved of rounding Cape Horn, the bad condition of the vessel, the want of provisions, sails, and water; but that the negro Babo replied to him he must carry them in any way; that they would do and conform themselves to everything the deponent should require as to eating and drinking; that after a long conference, being absolutely compelled to please them, for they threatened him to kill all the whites if they were not, at all events, carried to Senegal, he told them that what was most wanting for the voyage was water; that they would go near the coast to take it, and hence they would proceed on their course; that the negro Babo agreed to it; and the deponent steered toward the intermediate ports, hoping to meet some Spanish or foreign vessel that would save them; that within ten or eleven days they saw the land, and continued their course by it in the vicinity of Nasca; that the deponent observed that the negroes were now restless and mutinous, because he did not effect the taking in of water, the negro Babo having required, with threats, that it should be done, without fail, the following day; he told him he saw plainly that the coast was steep, and the rivers designated in the maps were not to be found, with other reasons suitable to the circumstances; that the best way would be to go to the island of Santa Maria, where they might water and victual easily, it being a desert island, as the foreigners did; that the deponent did not go to Pisco, that was near, nor make any other port of the coast, because the negro Babo had intimated to him several times, that he would kill all the whites the very moment he should perceive any city, town, or settlement of any kind on the shores to which they should be carried: that having determined to go to the island of Santa Maria, as the deponent had planned, for the purpose of trying whether, in the passage or in the island itself, they could find any vessel that should favour them, or whether he could escape from it in a boat to the neighbouring coast of Arruco; to adopt the necessary means he immediately changed his course, steering for the island; that the negroes Babo and Atufal held daily conferences, in which they discussed what was necessary for their design of returning to Senegal, whether they were to kill all the Spaniards, and particularly the deponent; that eight days after parting from the coast of Nasca, the deponent being on the watch a little after day-break, and soon after the negroes had their meeting, the negro Babo came to the place where the deponent was, and told him that he had determined to kill his master, Don Alexandro Aranda, both because he and his companions could not otherwise be sure of their liberty, and that, to keep the seamen in subjection, he wanted to prepare a warning of what road they should be made to take did they or any of them oppose him; and that, by means of the death of Don Alexandro, that warning would best be given; but, that what this last meant, the deponent did not at the time comprehend, nor could not, further than the death of Don Alexandro was intended; and moreover, the negro Babo proposed to the deponent to call the mate Raneds, who was sleeping in the cabin, before the thing was done, for fear, as the deponent understood it, that the mate, who was a good navigator, should be killed with Don Alexandro and the rest; that the deponent, who was the friend from youth of Don Alexandro, prayed and conjured, but all was useless; for the negro Babo answered him that the thing could not be prevented, and that all the Spaniards risked their death if they should attempt to frustrate his will in this matter, or any other; that, in this conflict, the deponent called the mate, Raneds, who was forced to go apart, and immediately the negro Babo commanded the Ashantee Martiniqui and the Ashantee Lecbe to go and commit the murder; that those two went down with hatchets to the berth of Don Alexandro; that, yet half alive and mangled, they dragged him on deck; that they were going to throw him overboard in that state, but the negro Babo stopped them, bidding the murder be completed on the deck before him, which was done, when, by his orders, the body was carried below, forward; that nothing more was seen of it by the deponent for three days; . . . that Don Alonzo Sidonia, an old man, long resident at Valparaiso, and lately appointed to a civil office in Peru, whither he had taken passage, was at the time sleeping in the berth opposite Don Alexandro's; that, awakening at his cries, surprised by them, and at the sight of the negroes with their bloody hatchets in their hands, he threw himself into the sea through a window which was near him, and was drowned, without it being in the power of the deponent to assist or take him up; . . . that, a short time after killing Aranda, they brought upon deck his german-cousin, of middle-age, Don Francisco Masa, of Mendoza, and the young Don Joaquin, Marques de Aramboalaza, then lately from

Spain, with his Spanish servant Ponce, and the three young clerks of Aranda,
José Mozairi, Lorenzo Bargas, and Hermenegildo Gandix, all of Cadiz; that
Don Joaquin and Hermenegildo Gandix, the negro Babo for purposes hereafter to appear, preserved alive; but Don Francisco Masa, José Mozairi, and
Lorenzo Bargas, with Ponce, the servant, beside the boatswain, Juan Robles,
the boatswain's mates, Manual Viscaya and Roderigo Hurta, and four of
the sailors, the negro Baba ordered to be thrown alive into the sea, although
they made no resistance, nor begged for anything else but mercy; that the
boatswain, Juan Robles, who knew how to swim, kept the longest above
water, making acts of contrition, and, in the last words he uttered, charged
this deponent to cause mass to be said for his soul to our Lady of Suc-
cour . . . that, during the three days which followed, the deponent, uncertain
what fate had befallen the remains of Don Alexandro, frequently asked the
negro Babo where they were, and, if still on board, whether they were to be
preserved for interment ashore, entreating him so to order it; that the negro
Babo answered nothing till the fourth day, when at sunrise, the deponent
coming on deck, the negro Babo showed him a skeleton, which had been
substituted for the ship's proper figure-head, the image of Christopher Colon,
the discoverer of the New World; that the negro Babo asked him whose
skeleton that was, and whether, from its whiteness, he should not think it a
white's; that, upon his covering his face, the negro Babo, coming close, said
words to this effect: "Keep faith with the blacks from here to Senegal, or
you shall in spirit, as now in body, follow your leader," pointing to the
prow; . . . that the same morning the negro Babo took by succession each
Spaniard forward, and asked him whose skeleton that was, and whether,
from its whiteness, he should not think it a white's; that each Spaniard
covered his face; that then to each the negro Babo repeated the words in the
first place said to the deponent; . . . that they (the Spaniards), being then
assembled aft, the negro Babo harangued them, saying that he had now done
all; that the deponent (as navigator for the negroes) might pursue his course,
warning him and all of them that they should, soul and body, go the way of
Don Alexandro if he saw them (the Spaniards) speak or plot anything
against them (the negroes)—a threat which was repeated every day; that,
before the events last mentioned, they had tied the cook to throw him overboard, for it is not known what thing they heard him speak, but finally the
negro Babo spared his life, at the request of the deponent; that a few days
after, the deponent, endeavouring not to omit any means to preserve the
lives of the remaining whites, spoke to the negroes peace and tranquillity,
and agreed to draw up a paper, signed by the deponent and the sailors who
could write, as also by the negro Babo, for himself and all the blacks, in which
the deponent obliged himself to carry them to Senegal, and they not to kill any
more, and he formally to make over to them the ship, with the cargo, with
which they were for that time satisfied and quieted. . . . But the next day,
the more surely to guard against the sailors' escape, the negro Babo commanded all the boats to be destroyed but the long-boat, which was unsea-

worthy, and another, a cutter in good condition, which, knowing it would yet be wanted for lowering the water casks, he had it lowered down into the hold.

[*Various particulars of the prolonged and perplexed navigation ensuing here follow, with incidents of a calamitous calm, from which portion one passage is extracted, to wit:*]

—That on the fifth day of the calm, all on board suffering much from the heat, and want of water, and five having died in fits, and mad, the negroes became irritable, and for a chance gesture, which they deemed suspicious— though it was harmless—made by the mate, Raneds, to the deponent, in the act of handing a quadrant, they killed him; but that for this they afterwards were sorry, the mate being the only remaining navigator on board, except the deponent.

—That omitting other events, which daily happened, and which can only serve uselessly to recall past misfortunes and conflicts, after seventy-three days' navigation, reckoned from the time they sailed from Nasca, during which they navigated under a scanty allowance of water, and were afflicted with the calms before mentioned, they at last arrived at the island of Santa Maria, on the seventeenth of the month of August, at about six o'clock in the afternoon, at which hour they cast anchor very near the American ship, *Bachelor's Delight,* which lay in the same bay, commanded by the generous Captain Amasa Delano; but at six o'clock in the morning, they had already descried the port, and the negroes became uneasy, as soon as at distance they saw the ship, not having expected to see one there; that the negro Babo pacified them, assuring them that no fear need be had; that straightway he ordered the figure on the bow to be covered with canvas, as for repairs, and had the decks a little set in order; that for a time the negro Babo and the negro Atufal conferred; that the negro Atufal was for sailing away, but the negro Babo would not, and, by himself, cast about what to do; that at last he came to the deponent, proposing to him to say and do all that the deponent declares to have said and done to the American captain; . . . that the negro Babo warned him that if he varied in the least, or uttered any word, or gave any look that should give the least intimation of the past events or present state, he would instantly kill him, with all his companions, showing a dagger, which he carried hid, saying something which, as he understood it, meant that that dagger would be alert as his eye; that the negro Babo then announced the plan to all his companions, which pleased them; that he then, the better to disguise the truth, devised many expedients, in some of them uniting deceit and defence; that of this sort was the device of the six Ashantees before named, who were his bravos; that them he stationed on the break of the poop, as if to clean certain hatchets (in cases, which were part of the cargo), but in reality to use them, and distribute them at need, and at a given word he told them; that, among

other devices, was the device of presenting Atufal, his right-hand man, as
chained, though in a moment the chains could be dropped; that in every
particular he informed the deponent what part he was expected to enact in
every device, and what story he was to tell on every occasion, always threatening him with instant death if he varied in the least: that, conscious that
many of the negroes would be turbulent, the negro Babo appointed the four
aged negroes, who were caulkers, to keep what domestic order they could
on the decks; that again and again he harangued the Spaniards and his companions, informing them of his intent, and of his devices, and of the invented
story that this deponent was to tell, charging them lest any of them varied
from that story; that these arrangements were made and matured during the
interval of two or three hours, between their first sighting the ship and the
arrival on board of Captain Amasa Delano; that this happened at about half-
past seven in the morning, Captain Amasa Delano coming in his boat, and
all gladly receiving him; that the deponent, as well as he could force himself,
acting then the part of principal owner, and a free captain of the ship, told
Captain Amasa Delano, when called upon, that he came from Buenos Ayres,
bound to Lima, with three hundred negroes; that off Cape Horn, and in a
subsequent fever, many negroes had died; that also, by similar casualties,
all the sea officers and the greatest part of the crew had died.

[*And so the deposition goes on, circumstantially recounting the fictitious
story dictated to the deponent by Babo, and through the deponent imposed
upon Captain Delano; and also recounting the friendly offers of Captain
Delano, with other things, but all of which is here omitted. After the fictitious strange story, etc., the deposition proceeds:*]

—That the generous Captain Amasa Delano remained on board all the day,
till he left the ship anchored at six o'clock in the evening, deponent speaking
to him always of his pretended misfortunes, under the fore-mentioned principles, without having had it in his power to tell a single word, or give him
the least hint, that he might know the truth and state of things; because the
negro Babo, performing the office of an officious servant with all the appearance of submission of the humble slave, did not leave the deponent one
moment; that this was in order to observe the deponent's actions and words,
for the negro Babo understands well the Spanish; and besides, there were
thereabout some others who were constantly on the watch, and likewise
understood the Spanish; . . . that upon one occasion, while deponent was
standing on the deck conversing with Amasa Delano, by a secret sign the
negro Babo drew him (the deponent) aside, the act appearing as if origi-
nating with the deponent; that then, he being drawn aside, the negro Babo
proposed to him to gain from Amasa Delano full particulars about his ship,
and crew, and arms; that the deponent asked "For what?" that the negro
Babo answered he might conceive; that, grieved at the prospect of what
might overtake the generous Captain Amasa Delano, the deponent at first

refused to ask the desired questions, and used every argument to induce the negro Babo to give up this new design; that the negro Babo showed the point of his dagger; that, after the information had been obtained, the negro Babo again drew him aside, telling him that that very night he (the deponent) would be captain of two ships instead of one, for that, great part of the American's ship's crew being to be absent fishing, the six Ashantees, without any one else, would easily take it; that at this time he said other things to the same purpose; that no entreaties availed; that before Amasa Delano's coming on board, no hint had been given touching the capture of the American ship: that to prevent this project the deponent was powerless; . . . —that in some things his memory is confused, he cannot distinctly recall every event; . . . —that as soon as they had cast anchor at six of the clock in the evening, as has before been stated, the American captain took leave to return to his vessel; that upon a sudden impulse, which the deponent believes to have come from God and his angels, he, after the farewell had been said, followed the generous Captain Amasa Delano as far as the gunwale, where he stayed, under the pretence of taking leave, until Amasa Delano should have been seated in his boat; that on shoving off, the deponent sprang from the gunwale, into the boat, and fell into it, he knows not how, God guarding him; that—

[*Here, in the original, follows the account of what further happened at the escape, and how the "San Dominick" was retaken, and of the passage to the coast; including in the recital many expressions of "eternal gratitude" to the "generous Captain Amasa Delano." The deposition then proceeds with recapitulatory remarks, and a partial renumeration of the negroes, making record of their individual part in the past events, with a view to furnishing, according to command of the court, the data whereon to found the criminal sentences to be pronounced. From this portion is the following:*]

—That he believes that all the negroes, though not in the first place knowing to the design of revolt, when it was accomplished, approved it. . . . That the negro, José, eighteen years old, and in the personal service of Don Alexandro, was the one who communicated the information to the negro Babo, about the state of things in the cabin, before the revolt; that this is known, because, in the preceding midnight, he used to come from his berth, which was under his master's, in the cabin, to the deck where the ringleader and his associates were, and had secret conversations with the negro Babo, in which he was several times seen by the mate; that, one night, the mate drove him away twice; . . . that this same negro José was the one who, without being commanded to do so by the negro Babo, as Lecbe and Martinqui were, stabbed his master, Don Alexandro, after he had been dragged half-lifeless to the deck; . . . that the mulatto steward, Francesco, was of the first band of revolters, that he was, in all things, the creature and tool of the negro Babo; that, to make his court, he, just before a repast in

the cabin, proposed, to the negro Babo, poisoning a dish for the generous
Captain Amasa Delano; this is known and believed, because the negroes
have said it; but that the negro Babo, having another design, forbade Fran-
ceso; . . . that the Ashantee Lecbe was one of the worst of them; for that,
on the day the ship was retaken, he assisted in the defence of her, with a
hatchet in each hand, with one of which he wounded, in the breast, the chief
mate of Amasa Delano, in the first act of boarding; this all knew; that, in
sight of the deponent, Lecbe struck, with a hatchet, Don Francisco Masa
when, by the negro Babo's orders, he was carrying him to throw him overboard, alive; beside participating in the murder, before mentioned, of Don
Alexandro Aranda, and others of the cabin-passengers; that, owing to the
fury with which the Ashantees fought in the engagement with the boats,
but this Lecbe and Yan survived; that Yan was bad as Lecbe; that Yan was
the man who, by Babo's command, willingly prepared the skeleton of Don
Alexandro, in a way the negroes afterwards told the deponent, but which
he, so long as reason is left him, can never divulge; that Yan and Lecbe
were the two who, in a calm by night, riveted the skeleton to the bow; this
also the negroes told him; that the negro Babo was he who traced the in-
scription below it; that the negro Babo was the plotter from first to last; he
ordered every murder, and was the helm and keel of the revolt; that Atufal
was his lieutenant in all; but Atufal, with his own hand, committed no
murder; nor did the negro Babo; . . . that Atufal was shot, being killed
in the fight with the boats, ere boarding; . . . that the negresses, of age,
were knowing to the revolt, and testified themselves satisfied at the death of
their master, Don Alexandro; that, had the negroes not restrained them,
they would have tortured to death, instead of simply killing, the Spaniards
slain by command of the negro Babo; that the negresses used their utmost
influence to have the deponent made away with; that, in the various acts
of murder, they sang songs and danced—not gaily, but solemnly; and
before the engagement with the boats, as well as during the action, they
sang melancholy songs to the negroes, and that this melancholy tone was
more inflaming than a different one would have been, and was so intended;
that all this is believed, because the negroes have said it.

—That of the thirty-six men of the crew—exclusive of the passengers
(all of whom are now dead), which the deponent had knowledge of—six
only remained alive, with four cabin-boys and ship-boys, not included with
the crew; . . . —that the negroes broke an arm of one of the cabin-boys and
gave him strokes with hatchets.

[*Then follow various random disclosures referring to various periods of
time. The following are extracted:*]

—That during the presence of Captain Amasa Delano on board, some
attempts were made by the sailors, and one by Hermenegildo Gandix, to
convey hints to him of the true state of affairs; but that these attempts were

ineffectual, owing to fear of incurring death, and furthermore owing to the devices which offered contradictions to the true state of affairs; as well as owing to the generosity and piety of Amasa Delano, incapable of sounding such wickedness; . . . that Luys Galgo, a sailor about sixty years of age, and formerly of the king's navy, was one of those who sought to convey tokens to Captain Amasa Delano; but his intent, though undiscovered, being suspected, he was, on a pretence, made to retire out of sight, and at last into the hold, and there was made away with. This the negroes have since said; . . . that one of the ship-boys feeling, from Captain Amasa Delano's presence, some hopes of release, and not having enough prudence, dropped some chance-word respecting his expectations, which being overheard and understood by a slave-boy with whom he was eating at the time, the latter struck him on the head with a knife, inflicting a bad wound, but of which the boy is now healing; that likewise, not long before the ship was brought to anchor, one of the seamen, steering at the time, endangered himself by letting the blacks remark a certain unconscious hopeful expression in his countenance, arising from some cause similar to the above; but this sailor, by his heedful after conduct, escaped; . . . that these statements are made to show the court that from the beginning to the end of the revolt, it was impossible for the deponent and his men to act otherwise than they did; . . . —that the third clerk, Hermenegildo Gandix, who before had been forced to live among the seamen, wearing a seaman's habit, and in all respects appearing to be one for the time; he, Gandix, was killed by a musket-ball fired through a mistake from the American boats before boarding; having in his fright ran up the mizzen-rigging, calling to the boats— "don't board," lest upon their boarding the negroes should kill him; that this inducing the Americans to believe he some way favoured the cause of the negroes, they fired two balls at him, so that he fell wounded from the rigging, and was drowned in the sea; . . . —that the young Don Joaquin, Marques de Arambaolaza, like Hermenegildo Gandix, the third clerk, was degraded to the office and appearance of a common seaman; that upon one occasion, when Don Joaquin shrank, the negro Babo commanded the Ashantee Lecbe to take tar and heat it, and pour it upon Don Joaquin's hands; . . . —that Don Joaquin was killed owing to another mistake of the Americans, but one impossible to be avoided, as upon the approach of the boats, Don Joaquin, with a hatchet tied edge out and upright to his hand, was made by the negroes to appear on the bulwarks; whereupon, seen with arms in his hands and in a questionable attitude, he was shot for a renegade seaman; . . . —that on the person of Don Joaquin was found secreted a jewel, which, by papers that were discovered, proved to have been meant for the shrine of our Lady of Mercy in Lima; a votive offering, beforehand prepared and guarded, to attest his gratitude, when he should have landed in Peru, his last destination, for the safe conclusion of his entire voyage from Spain; . . . —that the jewel, with the other effects of the late Don Joaquin, is in the custody of the brethren of the Hospital de Sacerdotes, awaiting the decision of the honourable court; . . . —that, owing to the condition of the deponent, as well as the haste in which the boats departed for the attack, the Americans were not forewarned that there were, among the apparent crew, a passenger and one of the clerks disguised by the negro Babo; . . . —that, beside the negroes killed in the action, some were killed after the capture and re-anchoring at night, when shackled to the ring-bolts on deck; that these deaths were committed by the sailors, ere they could be prevented. That so soon as informed of it, Captain Amasa Delano used all his authority, and, in particular with his own hand, struck down Martinez Gola, who, having found a razor in the pocket of an old jacket of his, which one of the shackled negroes had on, was aiming it at the negro's throat; that the noble Captain Amasa Delano also wrenched from the hand of Bartholomew Barlo, a dagger secreted at the time of the massacre of the whites, with which he was in the act of stabbing a shackled negro, who, the same day, with another negro, had thrown him down and jumped upon him; . . . —that, for all the events, befalling through so long a time, during which the ship was in the hands of the negro Babo, he cannot here give account; but that, what he has said is the most substantial of what occurs to him at present, and is the truth under the oath which he has taken; which declaration he affirmed and ratified, after hearing it read to him.

He said that he is twenty-nine years of age, and broken in body and mind; that when finally dismissed by the court, he shall not return home to Chili, but betake himself to the monastery on Mount Agonia without; and signed with his honour, and crossed himself, and, for the time, departed as he came, in his litter, with the monk Infelez, to the Hospital de Sacerdotes.

BENITO CERENO.

DOCTOR ROZAS.

If the deposition of Benito Cereno has served as the key to fit into the lock of the complications which preceded it, then, as a vault whose door has been flung back, the *San Dominick's* hull lies open to-day.

Hitherto the nature of this narrative, besides rendering the intricacies in the beginning unavoidable, has more or less required that many things, instead of being set down in the order of occurrence, should be retrospectively, or irregularly given; this last is the case with the following passages, which will conclude the account:

During the long, mild voyage to Lima, there was, as before hinted, a period during which Don Benito a little recovered his health, or, at least in some degree, his tranquillity. Ere the decided relapse which came, the two captains had many cordial conversations—their fraternal unreserve in singular contrast with former withdrawments.

Again and again, it was repeated, how hard it had been to enact the part forced on the Spaniard by Babo.

"Ah, my dear Don Amasa," Don Benito once said, "at those very times when you thought me so morose and ungrateful—nay when, as you now admit, you half thought me plotting your murder—at those very times my heart was frozen; I could not look at you, thinking of what, both on board this ship and your own, hung, from other hands, over my kind benefactor. And as God lives, Don Amasa, I know not whether desire for my own safety alone could have nerved me to that leap into your boat, had it not been for the thought that, did you, unenlightened, return to your ship, you, my best friend, with all who might be with you, stolen upon, that night, in your hammocks, would never in this world have wakened again. Do but think how you walked this deck, how you sat in this cabin, every inch of ground mined into honey-combs under you. Had I dropped the least hint, made the least advance toward an understanding between us, death, explosive death—yours as mine—would have ended the scene."

"True, true," cried Captain Delano, starting, "you saved my life, Don Benito, more than I yours; saved it, too, against my knowledge and will."

"Nay, my friend," rejoined the Spaniard, courteous even to the point of religion, "God charmed your life, but you saved mine. To think of some things you did—those smilings and chattings, rash pointings and gesturings. For less than these, they slew my mate, Raneds; but you had the Prince of Heaven's safe conduct through all ambuscades."

"Yes, all is owing to Providence, I know; but the temper of my mind that morning was more than commonly pleasant, while the sight of so much suffering—more apparent than real—added to my good nature, compassion, and charity, happily interweaving the three. Had it been otherwise, doubtless, as you hint, some of my interferences with the blacks might have ended unhappily enough. Besides that, those feelings I spoke of enabled me to get the better of momentary distrust, at times when acuteness might have cost me my life, without saving another's. Only at the end did my suspicions get the better of me, and you know how wide of the mark they then proved."

"Wide, indeed," said Don Benito, sadly; "you were with me all day; stood with me, sat with me, talked with me, looked at me, ate with me, drank with me; and yet, your last act was to clutch for a villain, not only an innocent man, but the most pitiable of all men. To such degree may malign machinations and deceptions impose. So far may even the best men err, in judging the conduct of one with the recesses of whose condition he is not acquainted. But you were forced to it; and you were in time undeceived. Would that, in both respects, it was so ever, and with all men."

"I think I understand you; you generalize, Don Benito; and mournfully enough. But the past is passed; why moralize upon it? Forget it. See, yon bright sun has forgotten it all, and the blue sea, and the blue sky; these have turned over new leaves."

"Because they have no memory," he dejectedly replied; "because they are not human."

"But these mild trades that now fan your cheek, Don Benito, do they not come with a human-like healing to you? Warm friends, steadfast friends are the trades."

"With their steadfastness they but waft me to my tomb, Señor," was the foreboding response.

"You are saved, Don Benito," cried Captain Delano, more and more astonished and pained; "you are saved; what has cast such a shadow upon you?"

"The negro."

There was silence, while the moody man sat, slowly and unconsciously gathering his mantle about him, as if it were a pall.

There was no more conversation that day.

But if the Spaniard's melancholy sometimes ended in muteness upon topics like the above, there were others upon which he never spoke at all; on which, indeed, all his old reserves were piled. Pass over the worst and, only to elucidate, let an item or two of these be cited. The dress so precise and costly, worn by him on the day whose events have been narrated, had not willingly been put on. And that silver-mounted sword, apparent symbol of despotic command, was not, indeed, a sword, but the ghost of one. The scabbard, artificially stiffened, was empty.

As for the black—whose brain, not body, had schemed and led the revolt, with the plot—his slight frame, inadequate to that which it held, had at once yielded to the superior muscular strength of his captor, in the boat. Seeing all was over, he uttered no sound, and could not be forced to. His aspect seemed to say: since I cannot do deeds, I will not speak words. Put in irons in the hold, with the rest, he was carried to Lima. During the passage Don Benito did not visit him. Nor then, nor at any time after, would he look at him. Before the tribunal he refused. When pressed by the judges he fainted. On the testimony of the sailors alone rested the legal identity of Babo. And yet the Spaniard would, upon occasion, verbally refer to the negro, as has been shown; but look on him he would not, or could not.

Some months after, dragged to the gibbet at the tail of a mule, the black met his voiceless end. The body was burned to ashes; but for many days, the head, that hive of subtlety, fixed on a pole in the Plaza, met, unabashed, the gaze of the whites; and across the Plaza looked toward St. Bartholomew's church, in whose vaults slept then, as now, the recovered bones of Aranda; and across the Rimac bridge looked toward the monastery, on Mount Agonia without; where, three months after being dismissed by the court, Benito Cereno, borne on the bier, did, indeed, follow his leader.

Edgar Allan Poe

THE FALL OF THE HOUSE OF USHER

Son cœur est un luth suspendu;
Sitôt qu'on le touche il résonne.

—DE BÉRANGER

URING THE WHOLE of a dull, dark, and soundless day in the autumn of the year, when the clouds hung oppressively low in the heavens, I had been passing alone, on horseback, through a singularly dreary tract of country; and at length found myself, as the shades of the evening drew on, within view of the melancholy House of Usher. I know not how it was—but, with the first glimpse of the building, a sense of insufferable gloom pervaded my spirit. I say insufferable; for the feeling was unrelieved by any of that half-pleasurable, because poetic, sentiment, with which the mind usually receives even the sternest natural images of the desolate or terrible. I looked upon the scene before me—upon the mere house, and the simple landscape features of the domain, upon the bleak walls, upon the vacant eye-like windows, upon a few rank sedges, and upon a few white trunks of decayed trees—with an utter depression of soul which I can compare to no earthly sensation more properly than to the after-dream of the reveller upon opium: the bitter lapse into everyday life, the hideous dropping off of the veil. There was an iciness, a sinking, a sickening of the heart, an unredeemed dreariness of thought which no goading of the imagination could torture into aught of the sublime. What was it—I paused to think—what was it that so unnerved me in the contemplation of the House of Usher? It was a mystery all insoluble; nor could I grapple with the shadowy fancies that crowded upon me as I pondered. I was forced to fall back upon the unsatisfactory conclusion, that while, beyond doubt, there *are* combinations of very simple natural objects which have the power of thus affecting us, still the analysis of this power lies among considerations beyond our depth. It was possible, I reflected, that a mere different arrangement of the particulars of the scene, of the details of the picture, would be sufficient to modify, or perhaps to annihilate its capacity for sorrowful impression; and, acting upon this idea, I reined my horse to the precipitous brink of a black and lurid tarn that lay in unruffled lustre by the dwelling, and gazed down—but with a shudder even more thrilling than before—upon the remodelled and inverted images of the gray sedge, and the ghastly tree-stems, and the vacant and eye-like windows.

Nevertheless, in this mansion of gloom I now proposed to myself a sojourn of some weeks. Its proprietor, Roderick Usher, had been one of my boon companions in boyhood; but many years had elapsed since our last meeting. A letter, however, had lately reached me in a distant part of the country—a letter from him—which, in its wildly importunate nature, had admitted of no other than a personal reply. The MS. gave evidence of nervous agitation. The writer spoke of acute bodily illness, of a mental disorder which oppressed him, and of an earnest desire to see me, as his best, and indeed his only personal friend, with a view of attempting, by the cheerfulness of my society, some alleviation of his malady. It was the manner in which all this, and much more, was said—it was the apparent *heart* that went with his request—which allowed me no room for hesitation; and I accordingly obeyed forthwith what I still considered a very singular summons.

Although, as boys, we had been even intimate associates, yet I really knew little of my friend. His reserve had been always excessive and habitual. I was aware, however, that his very ancient family had been noted, time out of mind, for a peculiar sensibility of temperament, displaying itself, through long ages, in many works of exalted art, and manifested, of late, in repeated deeds of munificent yet unobtrusive charity, as well as in a passionate devotion to the intricacies, perhaps even more than to the orthodox and easily recognizable beauties, of musical science. I had learned, too, the very remarkable fact, that the stem of the Usher race, all time-honored as it was, had put forth, at no period, any enduring branch; in other words, that the entire family lay in the direct line of descent, and had always, with very trifling and very temporary variation, so lain. It was this deficiency, I considered, while running over in thought the perfect keeping of the character of the premises with the accredited character of the people, and while speculating upon the possible influence which the one, in the long lapse of centuries, might have exercised upon the other—it was this deficiency, perhaps, of collateral issue, and the consequent undeviating transmission, from sire to son, of the patrimony with the name, which had, at length, so identified the two as to merge the original title of the estate in the quaint and equivocal appellation of the "House of Usher"—an appellation which seemed to include, in the minds of the peasantry who used it, both the family and the family mansion.

I have said that the sole effect of my somewhat childish experiment, that of looking down within the tarn, had been to deepen the first singular impression. There can be no doubt that the consciousness of the rapid increase of my superstition—for why should I not so term it?—served mainly to accelerate the increase itself. Such, I have long known, is the paradoxical law of all sentiments having terror as a basis. And it might have been for this reason only, that, when I again uplifted my eyes to the house itself, from its image in the pool, there grew in my mind a strange fancy—a fancy so ridiculous, indeed, that I but mention it to show the vivid force of the sensations which oppressed me. I had so worked upon my imagination as really to believe that about the whole mansion and domain there hung an atmosphere peculiar to themselves and their immediate vicinity: an atmosphere which had no affinity with the air of heaven, but which had reeked up from the decayed trees, and the gray wall, and the silent tarn: a pestilent and mystic vapor, dull, sluggish, faintly discernible, and leaden-hued.

Shaking off from my spirit what *must* have been a dream, I scanned more narrowly the real aspect of the building. Its principal feature seemed to be that of an excessive antiquity. The discoloration of ages had been great. Minute fungi overspread the whole exterior, hanging in a fine tangled web-work from the eaves. Yet all this was apart from any extraordinary dilapidation. No portion of the masonry had fallen; and there appeared to be a wild inconsistency between its still perfect adaptation of parts and the crumbling condition of the individual stones. In this there was much that reminded me of the specious totality of old wood-work which has rotted for long years in some neglected vault, with no disturbance from the breath of the external air. Beyond this indication of extensive decay, however, the fabric gave little token of instability. Perhaps the eye of a scrutinizing observer might have discovered a barely perceptible fissure, which, extending from the roof of the building in front, made its way down the wall in a zigzag direction, until it became lost in the sullen waters of the tarn.

Noticing these things, I rode over a short causeway to the house. A servant in waiting took my horse, and I entered the Gothic archway of the hall. A valet, of stealthy step, thence conducted me, in silence, through many dark and intricate passages in my progress to the *studio* of his master. Much that I encountered on the way contributed, I know not how, to heighten the vague sentiments of which I have already spoken. While the objects around me—while the carvings of the ceilings, the sombre tapestries of the walls, the ebon blackness of the floors, and the phantasmagoric armorial trophies which rattled as I strode, were but matters to which, or to such as which, I had been accustomed from my infancy—while I hesitated not to acknowledge how familiar was all this—I still wondered to find how unfamiliar were the fancies which ordinary images were stirring up. On one of the staircases, I met the physician of the family. His countenance, I thought, wore a mingled expression of low cunning and perplexity. He accosted me with trepidation and passed on. The valet now threw open a door and ushered me into the presence of his master.

The room in which I found myself was very large and lofty. The windows were long, narrow, and pointed, and at so vast a distance from the black oaken floor as to be altogether inaccessible from within. Feeble gleams of encrimsoned light made their way through the trellised panes, and served to render sufficiently distinct the more prominent objects around; the eye, however, struggled in vain to reach the remoter angles of the chamber, or the recesses of the vaulted and fretted ceiling. Dark draperies hung upon the walls. The general furniture was profuse, comfortless, antique, and tattered. Many books and musical instruments lay scattered about, but failed to give any vitality to the scene. I felt that I breathed an atmosphere of sorrow. An air of stern, deep, and irredeemable gloom hung over and pervaded all.

Upon my entrance, Usher arose from a sofa on which he had been lying at full length, and greeted me with a vivacious warmth which had much in it, I at first thought, of an overdone cordiality—of the constrained effort of the *ennuyé* man of the world. A glance, however, at his countenance, convinced me of his perfect sincerity. We sat down; and for some moments, while he spoke not, I gazed upon him with a feeling half of pity, half of awe. Surely, man had never before so terribly altered, in so brief a period, as had Roderick Usher! It was with difficulty that I could bring myself to admit the identity of the wan being before me with the companion of my early boyhood. Yet the character of his face had been at all times remarkable. A cadaverousness of complexion; an eye large, liquid, and luminous beyond comparison, lips somewhat thin and very pallid, but of a surpassingly beautiful curve; a nose of a delicate Hebrew model, but with a breadth of nostril unusual in similar formations; a finely moulded chin, speaking, in its want of prominence, of a want of moral energy; hair of a more than web-like softness and tenuity; these features, with an inordinate expansion above the regions of the temple, made up altogether a countenance not easily to be forgotten. And now in the mere exaggeration of the prevailing character of these features, and of the expression they were wont to convey, lay so much of change that I doubted to whom I spoke. The now ghastly pallor of the skin, and the now miraculous lustre of the eye, above all things startled and even awed me. The silken hair, too, had been suffered to grow all unheeded, and as, in its wild gossamer texture, it floated rather than fell about the face, I could not, even with effort, connect its Arabesque expression with any idea of simple humanity.

In the manner of my friend I was at once struck with an incoherence, an inconsistency; and I soon found this to arise from a series of feeble and futile struggles to overcome an habitual trepidancy, an excessive nervous agitation. For something of this nature I had indeed been prepared, no less by his letter, than by reminiscences of certain boyish traits, and by conclusions deduced from his peculiar physical conformation and temperament. His action was alternately vivacious and sullen. His voice varied rapidly from a tremulous indecision (when the animal spirits seemed utterly in abeyance) to that species of energetic concision—that abrupt, weighty, unhurried, and hollow-sounding enunciation—that leaden, self-balanced and perfectly modulated guttural utterance, which may be observed in the lost drunkard, or the irreclaimable eater of opium, during the periods of his most intense excitement.

It was thus that he spoke of the object of my visit, of his earnest desire to see me, and of the solace he expected me to afford him. He entered, at some length, into what he conceived to be the nature of his malady. It was, he said, a constitutional and a family evil, and one for which he despaired to find a remedy—a mere nervous affection, he immediately added, which would undoubtedly soon pass off. It displayed itself in a host of unnatural sensations. Some of these, as he detailed them, interested and bewildered me; although, perhaps, the terms, and the general manner of the narration had their weight. He suffered much from a morbid acuteness of the senses; the most insipid food was alone endurable; he could wear only garments of certain texture; the odors of all flowers were oppressive; his eyes were tortured by even a faint light; and there were but peculiar sounds, and these from stringed instruments, which did not inspire him with horror.

To an anomalous species of terror I found him a bounden slave. 'I shall perish,' said he, 'I *must* perish in this deplorable folly. Thus, thus, and not otherwise, shall I be lost. I dread the events of the future, not in themselves, but in their results. I shudder at the thought of any, even the most trivial, incident, which may operate upon this intolerable agitation of soul. I have, indeed, no abhorrence of danger, except in its absolute effect—in terror. In this unnerved—in this pitiable condition, I feel that the period will sooner or later arrive when I must abandon life and reason together, in some struggle with the grim phantasm, FEAR.'

I learned, moreover, at intervals, and through broken and equivocal hints, another singular feature of his mental condition. He was enchained by certain superstitious impressions in regard to the dwelling which he tenanted, and whence, for many years, he had never ventured forth—in regard to an influence whose supposititious force was conveyed in terms too shadowy here to be re-stated—an influence which some peculiarities in the mere form and substance of his family mansion, had, by dint of long sufferance, he said, obtained over his spirit—an effect which the *physique* of the gray walls and turrets, and of the dim tarn into which they all looked down, had, at length, brought about upon the *morale* of his existence.

He admitted, however, although with hesitation, that much of the peculiar gloom which thus afflicted him could be traced to a more natural and far more palpable origin—to the severe and long-continued illness, indeed to the evidently approaching dissolution, of a tenderly beloved sister—his sole companion for long years, his last and only relative on earth. 'Her decease,' he said, with a bitterness which I can never forget, 'would leave him (him the hopeless and the frail) the last of the ancient race of the Ushers.' While he spoke, the lady Madeline (for so was she called) passed slowly through a remote portion of the apartment, and, without having noticed my presence, disappeared. I regarded her with an utter astonishment not unmingled with dread, and yet I found it impossible to account for such feelings. A sensation of stupor oppressed me, as my eyes followed her retreating steps. When a door, at length, closed upon her, my glance sought instinctively and eagerly the countenance of the brother; but he had buried his face in his hands, and I could only perceive that a far more than ordinary wanness had overspread the emaciated fingers through which trickled many passionate tears.

The disease of the lady Madeline had long baffled the skill of her physicians. A settled apathy, a gradual wasting away of the person, and frequent although transient affections of a partially cataleptical character, were the unusual diagnosis. Hitherto she had steadily borne up against the pressure of her malady, and had not betaken herself finally to bed; but, on the closing in of the evening of my arrival at the house, she succumbed (as her brother told me at night with inexpressible agitation) to the prostrating power of the destroyer; and I learned that the glimpse I had obtained of her person would thus probably be the last I should obtain—that the lady, at least while living, would be seen by me no more.

For several days ensuing, her name was unmentioned by either Usher or myself: and during this period I was busied in earnest endeavors to alleviate the melancholy of my friend. We painted and read together; or I listened, as if in a dream, to the wild improvisations of his speaking guitar. And thus, as a closer and still closer intimacy admitted me more unreservedly into the recesses of his spirit, the more bitterly did I perceive the futility of all attempt at cheering a mind from which darkness, as if an inherent positive quality, poured forth upon all objects of the moral and physical universe, in one unceasing radiation of gloom.

I shall ever bear about me a memory of the many solemn hours I thus spent alone with the master of the House of Usher. Yet I should fail in any attempt to convey an idea of the exact character of the studies, or of the occupations, in which he involved me, or led me the way. An excited and highly distempered ideality threw a sulphureous lustre over all. His long improvised dirges will ring forever in my ears. Among other things, I hold painfully in mind a certain singular perversion and amplification of the wild air of the last waltz of Von Weber. From the paintings over which his elaborate fancy brooded, and which grew, touch by touch, into vaguenesses at which I shuddered the more thrillingly, because I shuddered knowing not why;—from these paintings (vivid as their images now are before me) I would in vain endeavor to educe more than a small portion which should lie within the compass of merely written words. By the utter simplicity, by the nakedness of his designs, he arrested and overawed attention. If ever mortal painted an idea, that mortal was Roderick Usher. For me at least, in the circumstances then surrounding me, there arose out of the pure abstractions which the hypochondriac contrived to throw upon his canvas, an intensity of intolerable awe, no shadow of which felt I ever yet in the contemplation of the certainly glowing yet too concrete reveries of Fuseli.

One of the phantasmagoric conceptions of my friend, partaking not so rigidly of the spirit of abstraction, may be shadowed forth, although feebly, in words. A small picture presented the interior of an immensely long and rectangular vault or tunnel, with low walls, smooth, white, and without interruption or device. Certain accessory points of the design served well to convey the idea that this excavation lay at an exceeding depth below the surface of the earth. No outlet was observed in any portion of its vast extent, and no torch, or other artificial source of light was discernible; yet a flood of intense rays rolled throughout, and bathed the whole in a ghastly and inappropriate splendor.

I have just spoken of that morbid condition of the auditory nerve which rendered all music intolerable to the sufferer, with the exception of certain effects of stringed instruments. It was, perhaps, the narrow limits to which he thus confined himself upon the guitar, which gave birth, in great measure, to the fantastic character of his performances. But the fervid *facility* of his *impromptus* could not be so accounted for. They must have been, and were, in the notes, as well as in the words of his wild fantasias (for he not unfrequently accompanied himself with rhymed verbal improvisations), the result of that intense mental collectedness and concentration to which I have previously alluded as observable only in particular moments of the highest artificial excitement. The words of one of these rhapsodies I have easily remembered. I was, perhaps, the more forcibly impressed with it, as he gave it, because, in the under or mystic current of its meaning, I fancied that I perceived, and for the first time, a full consciousness on the part of Usher, of the tottering of his lofty reason upon her throne. The verses, which were entitled 'The Haunted Palace,' ran very nearly, if not accurately, thus:

> In the greenest of our valleys
>   By good angels tenanted,
> Once a fair and stately palace—
>   Radiant palace—reared its head.
> In the monarch Thought's dominion,
>   It stood there!
> Never seraph spread a pinion
>   Over fabric half so fair!
>
> Banners yellow, glorious, golden,
>   On its roof did float and flow
> (This—all this—was in the olden
>   Time long ago)
> And every gentle air that dallied,
>   In that sweet day,
> Along the ramparts plumed and pallid,
>   A wingèd odor went away.
>
> Wanderers in that happy valley,
>   Through two luminous windows, saw
> Spirits moving musically
>   To a lute's well-tunèd law,
> Round about a throne where, sitting,
>   Porphyrogene!
> In state his glory well befitting,
>   The ruler of the realm was seen.
>
> And all with pearl and ruby glowing
>   Was the fair palace door,

Through which came flowing, flowing, flowing
    And sparkling evermore,
A troop of Echoes, whose sweet duty
    Was but to sing,
In voices of surpassing beauty,
    The wit and wisdom of their king.

But evil things, in robes of sorrow,
    Assailed the monarch's high estate;
(Ah, let us mourn!—for never morrow
    Shall dawn upon him, desolate!)
And round about his home the glory
    That blushed and bloomed
Is but a dim-remembered story
    Of the old time entombed.

And travellers, now, within that valley,
    Through the red-litten windows see
Vast forms that move fantastically
    To a discordant melody;
While, like a ghastly rapid river,
    Through the pale door
A hideous throng rush out forever,
    And laugh—but smile no more.

I well remember that suggestions arising from this ballad, led us into a train of thought wherein there became manifest an opinion of Usher's which I mention not so much on account of its novelty, (for other men have thought thus), as on account of the pertinacity with which he maintained it. This opinion, in its general form, was that of the sentience of all vegetable things. But, in his disordered fancy, the idea had assumed a more daring character, and trespassed, under certain conditions, upon the kingdom of inorganization. I lack words to express the full extent, or the earnest *abandon* of his persuasion. The belief, however, was connected (as I have previously hinted) with the gray stones of the home of his forefathers. The conditions of the sentience had been here, he imagined, fulfilled in the method of collocation of these stones—in the order of their arrangement, as well as in that of the many *fungi* which overspread them, and of the decayed trees which stood around—above all, in the long undisturbed endurance of this arrangement, and in its reduplication in the still waters of the tarn. Its evidence—the evidence of the sentience—was to be seen, he said, (and I here started as he spoke), in the gradual yet certain condensation of an atmosphere of their own about the waters and the walls. The result was discoverable, he added, in that silent, yet importunate and terrible influence which for centuries had moulded the destinies of his family, and which made *him* what I now saw him—what he was. Such opinions need no comment, and I will make none.

Our books—the books which, for years, had formed no small portion of the mental existence of the invalid—were, as might be supposed, in strict keeping with this character of phantasm. We pored together over such works as the *Ververt et Chartreuse* of Gresset; the *Belphegor* of Machiavelli; the *Heaven and Hell* of Swedenborg; the *Subterranean Voyage of Nicholas Klimm* by Holberg; the *Chiromancy* of Robert Flud, of Jean D'Indaginé, and of De la Chambre; the *Journey into the Blue Distance* of Tieck; and the *City of the Sun* of Campanella. One favorite volume was a small octavo edition of the *Directorium Inquisitorum,* by the Dominican Eymeric de Gironne; and there were passages in Pomponius Mela, about the old African Satyrs and Ægipans, over which Usher would sit dreaming for hours. His chief delight, however, was found in the perusal of an exceedingly rare and curious book in quarto Gothic—the manual of a forgotten church—the *Vigilæ Mortuorum Secundum Chorum Ecclesiæ Maguntinæ.*

I could not help thinking of the wild ritual of this work, and of its probable influence upon the hypochondriac, when, one evening, having informed me abruptly that the lady Madeline was no more, he stated his intention of preserving her corpse for a fortnight, (previously to its final interment), in one of the numerous vaults within the main walls of the building. The worldly reason, however, assigned for this singular proceeding, was one which I did not feel at liberty to dispute. The brother had been led to his resolution (so he told me) by consideration of the unusual character of the malady of the deceased, of certain obtrusive and eager inquiries on the part of her medical men, and of the remote and exposed situation of the burial-ground of the family. I will not deny that when I called to mind the sinister countenance of the person whom I met upon the staircase, on the day of my arrival at the house, I had no desire to oppose what I regarded as at best but a harmless, and by no means an unnatural, precaution.

At the request of Usher, I personally aided him in the arrangements for the temporary emtombment. The body having been encoffined, we two alone bore it to its rest. The vault in which we placed it (and which had been so long unopened that our torches, half smothered in its oppressive atmosphere, gave us little opportunity for investigation) was small, damp, and entirely without means of admission for light; lying, at great depth, immediately beneath that portion of the building in which was my own sleeping apartment. It had been used, apparently, in remote feudal times, for the worst purposes of a donjon-keep, and, in later days, as a place of deposit for powder, or some other highly combustible substance, as a portion of its floor, and the whole interior of a long archway through which we reached it, were carefully sheathed with copper. The door, of massive iron, had been, also, similarly protected. Its immense weight caused an unusually sharp grating sound, as it moved upon its hinges.

Having deposited our mournful burden upon tressels within this region of horror, we partially turned aside the yet unscrewed lid of the coffin, and looked upon the face of the tenant. A striking similitude between the brother and sister now first arrested my attention; and Usher, divining, perhaps, my thoughts, murmured out some few words from which I learned that the deceased and himself had been twins, and that sympathies of a scarcely intelligible nature had always existed between them. Our glances, however, rested not long upon the dead—for we could not regard her unawed. The disease which had thus entombed the lady in the maturity of youth, had left, as usual in all maladies of a strictly cataleptical character, the mockery of a faint blush upon the bosom and the face, and that suspiciously lingering smile upon the lip which is so terrible in death. We replaced and screwed down the lid, and, having secured the door of iron, made our way, with toil, into the scarcely less gloomy apartments of the upper portion of the house.

And now, some days of bitter grief having elapsed, an observable change came over the features of the mental disorder of my friend. His ordinary manner had vanished. His ordinary occupations were neglected or forgotten. He roamed from chamber to chamber with hurried, unequal, and objectless step. The pallor of his countenance had assumed, if possible, a more ghastly hue—but the luminousness of his eye had utterly gone out. The once occasional huskiness of his tone was heard no more; and a tremulous quaver, as if of extreme terror, habitually characterized his utterance. There were times, indeed, when I thought his unceasingly agitated mind was laboring with some oppressive secret, to divulge which he struggled for the necessary courage. At times, again, I was obliged to resolve all into the mere inexplicable vagaries of madness, for I beheld him gazing upon vacancy for long hours, in an attitude of the profoundest attention, as if listening to some imaginary sound. It was no wonder that his condition terrified—that it infected me. I felt creeping upon me, by slow yet certain degrees, the wild influences of his own fantastic yet impressive superstitions.

It was, especially, upon retiring to bed late in the night of the seventh or eighth day after the placing of the lady Madeline within the donjon, that I experienced the full power of such feelings. Sleep came not near my couch, while the hours waned and waned away. I struggled to reason off the nervousness which had dominion over me. I endeavored to believe that much, if not all of what I felt, was due to the bewildering influence of the gloomy furniture of the room—of the dark and tattered draperies, which, tortured into motion by the breath of a rising tempest, swayed fitfully to and fro upon the walls, and rustled uneasily about the decorations of the bed. But my efforts were fruitless. An irrepressible tremor gradually pervaded my frame; and, at length, there sat upon my very heart an incubus of utterly causeless alarm. Shaking this off with a gasp and a struggle, I uplifted myself upon the pillows, and, peering earnestly within the intense darkness of the chamber, hearkened—I know not why, except that an instinctive spirit prompted me—to certain low and indefinite sounds which came, through the pauses of the storm, at long intervals I knew not whence. Overpowered by an intense sentiment of horror, unaccountable yet unendurable, I threw on my clothes with haste (for I felt that I should sleep no more during the night), and endeavored to arouse myself from the pitiable condition into which I had fallen, by pacing rapidly to and fro through the apartment.

I had taken but few turns in this manner, when a light step on an adjoining staircase arrested my attention. I presently recognized it as that of Usher. In an instant afterward he rapped, with a gentle touch, at my door, and entered, bearing a lamp. His countenance was, as usual, cadaverously wan— but, moreover, there was a species of mad hilarity in his eyes—an evidently restrained *hysteria* in his whole demeanor. His air appalled me—but anything was preferable to the solitude which I had so long endured, and I even welcomed his presence as a relief.

'And you have not seen it?' he said abruptly, after having stared about him for some moments in silence—'you have not then seen it?—but, stay! you shall.' Thus speaking, and having carefully shaded his lamp, he hurried to one of the casements and threw it freely open to the storm.

The impetuous fury of the entering gust nearly lifted us from our feet. It was, indeed, a tempestuous yet sternly beautiful night, and one wildly singular in its terror and its beauty. A whirlwind had apparently collected its force in our vicinity; for there were frequent and violent alterations in the direction of the wind; and the exceeding density of the clouds (which hung so low as to press upon the turrets of the house) did not prevent our perceiving the life-like velocity with which they flew careering from all points against each other, without passing away into the distance. I say that even their exceeding density did not prevent our perceiving this; yet we had no glimpse of the moon or stars, nor was there any flashing forth of the lightning. But the under surfaces of the huge masses of agitated vapor, as well as all terrestrial objects immediately around us, were glowing in the unnatural light of a faintly luminous and distinctly visible gaseous exhalation which hung about and enshrouded the mansion.

'You must not—you shall not behold this!' said I, shudderingly, to Usher, as I led him, with a gentle violence, from the window to a seat. 'These appearances, which bewilder you, are merely electrical phenomena not uncommon—or it may be that they have their ghastly origin in the rank miasma of the tarn. Let us close this casement; the air is chilling and dangerous to your frame. Here is one of your favorite romances. I will read, and you shall listen;—and so we will pass away this terrible night together.'

The antique volume which I had taken up was the *Mad Trist* of Sir Launcelot Canning; but I had called it a favorite of Usher's more in sad jest than in earnest; for, in truth, there is little in its uncouth and unimaginative prolixity which could have had interest for the lofty and spiritual ideality of my friend. It was, however, the only book immediately at hand; and I indulged a vague hope that the excitement which now agitated the hypochondriac might find relief (for the history of mental disorder is full of similar anomalies) even in the extremeness of the folly which I should read. Could I have judged, indeed, by the wild overstrained air of vivacity with which he hearkened, or apparently hearkened, to the words of the tale, I might well have congratulated myself upon the success of my design.

I had arrived at that well-known portion of the story where Ethelred, the hero of the *Trist,* having sought in vain for peaceable admission into the dwelling of the hermit, proceeds to make good an entrance by force. Here, it will be remembered, the words of the narrative run thus:

> 'And Ethelred, who was by nature of a doughty heart, and who was now mighty withal, on account of the powerfulness of the wine which he had drunken, waited no longer to hold parley with the hermit, who, in sooth, was of an obstinate and maliceful turn, but, feeling the rain upon his shoulders, and fearing the rising of the tempest, uplifted his mace outright, and, with blows, made quickly room in the plankings of the door for his gauntleted hand; and now pulling therewith sturdily, he so cracked, and ripped, and tore all asunder, that the noise of the dry and hollow-sounding wood alarumed and reverberated throughout the forest.'

At the termination of this sentence I started, and for a moment, paused; for it appeared to me (although I at once concluded that my excited fancy had deceived me)—it appeared to me that, from some very remote portion of the mansion, there came, indistinctly, to my ears, what might have been, in its exact similarity of character, the echo (but a stifled and dull one certainly) of the very cracking and ripping sound which Sir Launcelot had so particularly described. It was, beyond doubt, the coincidence alone which had arrested my attention; for, amid the rattling of the sashes of the casements, and the ordinary commingled noises of the still increasing storm, the sound, in itself, had nothing, surely, which should have interested or disturbed me. I continued the story:

> 'But the good champion Ethelred, now entering within the door, was sore enraged and amazed to perceive no signal of the maliceful hermit; but, in the stead thereof, a dragon of a scaly and prodigious demeanor, and of a fiery tongue, which sate in guard before a palace of gold, with a floor of silver; and upon the wall there hung a shield of shining brass with this legend enwritten—
>
> *Who entereth herein, a conqueror hath bin;*
> *Who slayeth the dragon, the shield he shall win;*
>
> And Ethelred uplifted his mace, and struck upon the head of the dragon, which fell before him, and gave up his pesty breath, with a shriek so horrid and harsh, and withal so piercing, that Ethelred had fain to close his ears with his hands against the dreadful noise of it, the like whereof was never before heard.'

Here again I paused abruptly, and now with a feeling of wild amazement—for there could be no doubt whatever that, in this instance, I did actually hear (although from what direction it proceeded I found it impossible to say) a low and apparently distant, but harsh, protracted, and most unusual screaming or grating sound—the exact counterpart of what my fancy had already conjured up for the dragon's unnatural shriek as described by the romancer.

Oppressed, as I certainly was, upon the occurrence of the second and most extraordinary coincidence, by a thousand conflicting sensations, in which wonder and extreme terror were predominant, I still retained sufficient presence of mind to avoid exciting, by any observation, the sensitive nervousness of my companion. I was by no means certain that he had noticed the sounds in question; although, assuredly, a strange alteration had, during the last few minutes, taken place in his demeanor. From a position fronting my own, he had gradually brought round his chair, so as to sit with his face to the door of the chamber; and thus I could but partially perceive his features, although I saw that his lips trembled as if he were murmuring inaudibly. His head had dropped upon his breast—yet I knew that he was not asleep, from the wide and rigid opening of the eye as I caught a glance of it in profile. The motion of his body, too, was at variance with this idea—for he rocked from side to side with a gentle yet constant and uniform sway. Having rapidly taken notice of all this, I resumed the narrative of Sir Launcelot, which thus proceeded:

'And now, the champion, having escaped from the terrible fury of the dragon, bethinking himself of the brazen shield, and of the breaking up of the enchantment which was upon it, removed the carcass from out of the way before him, and approached valorously over the silver pavement of the castle to where the shield was upon the wall; which in sooth tarried not for his full coming, but fell down at his feet upon the silver floor, with a mighty great and terrible ringing sound.'

No sooner had these syllables passed my lips, than—as if a shield of brass had indeed, at the moment, fallen heavily upon a floor of silver—I became aware of a distinct, hollow, metallic and clangorous yet apparently muffled reverberation. Completely unnerved, I leaped to my feet; but the measured rocking movement of Usher was undisturbed. I rushed to the chair in which he sat. His eyes were bent fixedly before him, and throughout his whole countenance there reigned a stony rigidity. But as I placed my hand upon his shoulder, there came a strong shudder over his whole person; a sickly smile quivered about his lips; and I saw that he spoke in a low, hurried, and gibbering murmur, as if unconscious of my presence. Bending closely over him, I at length drank in the hideous import of his words.

'Not hear it?—yes, I hear it, and *have* heard it. Long—long—long—many minutes, many hours, many days, have I heard it—yet I dared not—oh, pity me, miserable wretch that I am!—I dared not—I *dared* not speak! *We have put her living in the tomb!* Said I not that my senses were acute? I *now* tell you that I heard her first feeble movements in the hollow coffin. I heard them—many, many days ago—yet I dared not—*I dared not speak!* And now

—to-night—Ethelred—ha! ha!—the breaking of the hermit's door, and the death-cry of the dragon, and the clangor of the shield!—say, rather, the rending of her coffin, and the grating of the iron hinges of her prison, and her struggles within the coppered archway of the vault! Oh whither shall I fly? Will she not be here anon? Is she not hurrying to upbraid me for my haste? Have I not heard her footstep on the stair? Do I not distinguish that heavy and horrible beating of her heart? MADMAN!' here he sprang furiously to his feet, and shrieked out his syllables, as if in the effort he were giving up his soul—'*Madman! I tell you that she now stands without the door!*'

As if in the superhuman energy of his utterance there had been found the potency of a spell, the huge antique panels to which the speaker pointed, threw slowly back, upon the instant, their ponderous and ebony jaws. It was the work of the rushing gust—but then without those doors there DID stand the lofty and enshrouded figure of the lady Madeline of Usher. There was blood upon her white robes, and the evidence of some bitter struggle upon every portion of her emaciated frame. For a moment she remained trembling and reeling to and fro upon the threshold—then, with a low moaning cry, fell heavily inward upon the person of her brother, and in her violent and now final death-agonies, bore him to the floor a corpse, and a victim to the terrors he had anticipated.

From that chamber, and from that mansion, I fled aghast. The storm was still abroad in all its wrath as I found myself crossing the old causeway. Suddenly there shot along the path a wild light, and I turned to see whence a gleam so unusual could have issued; for the vast house and its shadows were alone behind me. The radiance was that of the full, setting, and blood-red moon which now shone vividly through that once barely-discernible fissure of which I have before spoken as extending from the roof of the building, in a zigzag direction, to the base. While I gazed, this fissure rapidly widened—there came a fierce breath of the whirlwind—the entire orb of the satellite burst at once upon my sight—my brain reeled as I saw the mighty walls rushing asunder—there was a long tumultuous shouting sound like the voice of a thousand waters—and the deep and dank tarn at my feet closed sullenly and silently over the fragments of the HOUSE OF USHER.

COMMENTARY

This famous story is perhaps not Poe's best, but for the purposes of this book it has significant features which ought to illuminate some of the later, more mature work in the naturalistic-symbolic technique of Flaubert, Joyce, and James. Poe's insistence upon the unity of effect, from first word to last, in the famous review of Hawthorne, part of which is quoted elsewhere in this book (p. 419), anticipates from one point of view the high claims of James in his essay "The Art of Fiction." James asserts that the imaginative writer must take his art at least as seriously as the historian takes his; that is to say, he must no longer apologize, he must not say "it *may* have happened this way"; he must, since he cannot rely upon the reader's acceptance of known historical incident, create the illusion of reality, so that the reader may have a "direct impression" of it. It was towards this complete achievement of "direct impression" that Poe was moving, in his tales and in his criticism; he, like Hawthorne, was a great forerunner. The reasons why he did not himself fully achieve it (perhaps less even than Hawthorne) are perceptible in "The Fall of the House of Usher."

Like Hawthorne again, Poe seems to have been very little influenced by the common-sense realism of the eighteenth-century English novel. What has been known in our time as the romantic sensibility reached him from two directions: the Gothic tale of Walpole and Monk Lewis, and the poetry of Coleridge. Roderick Usher is a "Gothic" character taken seriously; that is to say, Poe takes the Gothic setting, with all its machinery and *décor,* and the preposterous Gothic hero, and transforms them into the material of serious literary art. Usher becomes the prototype of the Joycean and Jamesian hero who cannot function in the ordinary world. He has two characteristic traits of this later fictional hero of our own time. First, he is afflicted with the split personality of the manic depressive:

> His action was alternately vivacious and sullen. His voice varied rapidly from a tremulous indecision (when the animal spirits seemed utterly in abeyance) to that species of energetic concision . . . and perfectly modulated guttural utterance, which may be observed in the lost drunkard, or the irreclaimable eater of opium, during the periods of his most intense excitement.

Secondly, certain musical sounds (for some unmusical reason Poe selects the notes of the guitar) are alone tolerable to him: "He suffered from a morbid acuteness of the senses." He cannot thus live in the real world; he is constantly exacerbated. At the same time he "has a passionate devotion to the intricacies . . . of musical science"; and his paintings are "pure abstractions" which have "an intensity of intolerable awe."

Usher is, of course, both our old and our new friend; his new name is Monsieur Teste, and much of the history of modern French literature is in that name. Usher's "want of moral energy," along with a hypertrophy of sensibility and intellect in a split personality, places him in the ancestry of Gabriel Conroy, John Marcher, J. Alfred Prufrock, Mrs. Dalloway—a forbear of whose somewhat tawdry accessories they might well be a little ashamed; or they might enjoy a degree of moral complacency in contemplating their own luck in having had greater literary artists than Poe present them to us in a more credible imaginative reality.

We have referred to the Gothic trappings and the poetry of Coleridge as the sources of Poe's romanticism. In trying to understand the kind of unity of effect that Poe demanded of the writer of fiction we must bear in mind two things. First, unity of *plot,* the emphasis upon which led him to the invention of the "tale of ratiocination"; but plot is not so necessary to the serious story of moral perversion of which "The Fall of the House of Usher," "Ligeia," and "Morella" are the supreme examples. Secondly, unity of tone (see Appendix A, p. 632), a quality that had not been consciously aimed at in fiction before Poe. It is this particular kind of unity, a poetical rather than a fictional characteristic, which Poe must have got from the Romantic poets, Coleridge especially, and from Coleridge's criticism as well as "Kubla Khan" and "Christabel." Unity of plot and tone can exist without the *created, active detail* which came into this tradition of fiction with Flaubert, to be perfected later by James, Chekhov, and Joyce.

For example, in "The Fall of the House of Usher," *there is not one instance of dramatized detail.* Although Poe's first person narrator is in direct contact with the scene, he merely reports it; he does not show us scene and character in action; it is all description. The closest approach in the entire story to active detail is the glimpse, at the beginning, that the narrator gives us of the furtive doctor as he passes him on "one of the staircases." If we contrast the remoteness of Poe's reporting in the entire range of this story with the brilliant recreation of the character of Michael Furey by Gretta Conroy in "The Dead," we shall be able to form some conception of the advance in the techniques of reality that was achieved in the seventy-odd years between Poe and Joyce. The powerful description of the façade of the House of Usher, as the narrator approaches it, sets up unity of tone, but the description is never woven into the action of the story: the "metaphysical" identity of scene and character reaches our consciousness through *lyrical assertion.* The fissure in the wall of the house remains an inert symbol of Usher's split personality. At the climax of the story Poe uses an incredibly clumsy device in the effort to make the collapse of Usher active dramatically; that is, he employs the mechanical device of coincidence. The narrator is reading to Usher the absurd tale of the "Mad Trist" of Sir Launcelot Canning. The knight has slain the dragon and now approaches the "brazen shield," which falls with tremendous clatter. Usher has been "hearing" it, but what he has been actually hearing is the rending of the lid of his sister Madeline's coffin and the grating of the iron door of the tomb; until at the end the sister (who has been in a cataleptic trance) stands outside Usher's door. The door opens; she stands before them. The narrator flees and the House of Usher, collapsing, sinks forever with its master into the waters of the "tarn."

We could dwell upon the symbolism (see Appendix A, p. 633) of the identity of house and master, of the burial alive of Madeline, of the fissure in the wall of the house and the fissure in the psyche of Usher. What we should emphasize here is the dominance of symbolism over its visible base: symbolism external and "lyrical," not intrinsic and dramatic. The active structure of the story is mechanical and thus negligible; but its lyrical structure is impressive. Poe's plots seem most successful when the reality of scene and character is of secondary importance in the total effect; that is, in the tale of "ratiocination." He seemed unable to combine incident with his gift for "insight symbolism"; as a result his symbolic tales are insecurely based upon scenic reality. But the insight was great. In Roderick Usher, as we have said, we get for the first time the archetypal hero of modern fiction. In the history of literature the discoverer of the subject is almost never the perfecter of the techniques for making the subject real.

Leo Tolstoy

THREE DEATHS

i

IT WAS AUTUMN. Two carriages were driving at a rapid trot along the highroad. In the foremost sat two women. One was a lady, thin and pale; the other, her maid, was plump, with shining, red cheeks. Her short, coarse hair stood out under her faded hat; her red hand, in a torn glove, kept hurriedly putting it tidy; her high bosom, covered with a tapestry kerchief, was eloquent of health; her quick, black eyes watched out of the window the fields flying past, then glanced timidly at her mistress, then shifted uneasily about the corners of carriage. Just before the maid's nose swung the lady's hat, hanging from the rack above; on her lap lay a puppy. Her feet were kept from the floor by the boxes that stood on the carriage floor, and could be faintly heard knocking on them through the shaking of the springs and the rattling of the windows.

With her hands clasped on her knees and her eyes closed, the lady swayed feebly to and fro on the cushions that had been put at her back, and with a slight frown she coughed inwardly. On her head she wore a white nightcap, and a light blue kerchief was tied on her soft, white neck. A straight parting, retreating under her cap, divided her fair, pomaded, exceedingly flat hair, and there was a dry, deathlike look about the whiteness of the skin of this wide parting. The faded, yellowish skin hung loose on her delicate and beautiful features, and was flushed on her cheeks. Her lips were dry and restless, her eyelashes were thin and straight, and her cloth travelling cloak fell in straight folds over her sunken bosom. Though her eyes were closed, the lady's face expressed fatigue, irritation, and habitual suffering. A footman was dozing on the box, one elbow on the rail of the seat. The driver, hired from the posting-station, shouted briskly to the four sturdy, sweating horses, and looked round now and then at the other driver, who called to him from behind on the coach. Smoothly and rapidly the wheels made their broad, parallel tracks along the chalky mud of the road. The sky was gray and cold; a damp mist was falling over the fields and the road. The carriage was close, and smelt of eau de Cologne and dust. The sick woman stretched her head back and slowly opened the eyes. Her large, handsome, dark eyes were very bright.

"Again," she said, her beautiful, thin hand nervously thrusting away a corner of the maid's cloak which was just brushing against her knees, and

Translated by Constance Garnett, reprinted from *A Treasury of Great Russian Short Stories*, copyright 1944 by The Macmillan Company and used with their kind permission.

her mouth twitched painfully. Matryosha gathered up her cloak in both hands, lifted it up on her lap, and edged further away. Her blooming face flushed bright red. The sick woman's fine dark eyes kept eager watch on the servant's actions. She leaned with both hands on the seat and tried to raise herself, so as to be sitting higher up; but her strength failed her. Her mouth twitched and her whole face worked with an expression of helpless, wrathful irony. "You might at least help me! . . . Ah, you needn't! I can do it myself, only be so good as not to lay your bundles, bags, or whatever they are behind me, please! You had better not touch me if you're so awkward!"

The lady shut her eyes, and rapidly raising her eyelids again glanced at the maid. Matryosha was staring at her and biting her red underlip. A heavy sigh rose from the sick woman's chest, but changed to a cough before it was uttered. She turned away, frowning, and clutched at her chest with both hands. When the cough was over, she closed her eyes again and sat without stirring. The carriage and the coach drove into a village. Matryosha put her stout arm out from under her kerchief and crossed herself.

"What is it?" asked the lady.

"A station, madam."

"What do you cross yourself for, I ask?"

"A church, madam."

The sick woman turned towards the window, and began slowly crossing herself, her great eyes fastened on the big village church as the carriage drove by it.

The two carriages stopped together at the station. The sick woman's husband and the doctor got out of the other carriage and came up to her.

"How do you feel?" asked the doctor, taking her pulse.

"Well, how are you, my dear—not tired?" asked her husband, in French. "Wouldn't you like to get out?"

Matryosha, gathering up her bundles, squeezed into a corner so as not to be in their way as they talked.

"Just the same," answered the lady. "I won't get out."

Her husband stayed a little while beside the carriage, then went into the station-house. Matryosha got out of the carriage and ran on tiptoe through the mud to the gates.

"If I am ill, it's no reason you shouldn't have your lunch," the invalid said with a faint smile to the doctor, who was standing at the carriage window.

"None of them care anything about me," she added to herself, as soon as the doctor had moved with sedate step away from her and run at a trot up the steps of the station-house. "They are all right, so they don't care. O my God!"

"Well, Eduard Ivanovich," said her husband, meeting the doctor and rubbing his hands, with a cheery smile. "I've ordered the case of wine to be brought in. What do you say to a bottle?"

"I shouldn't say no," answered the doctor.

"Well, how is she?" the husband asked with a sigh, lifting his eyebrows and dropping his voice.

"I have told you she can't possibly get as far as Italy; if she reaches Moscow it will be a wonder, especially in this weather."

"What are we to do! O my God! my God!" The husband put his hand over his eyes. "Put it here," he added to the servant who brought in the case of wine.

"You should have kept her at home," the doctor answered, shrugging his shoulders.

"But tell me, what could I do?" protested the husband. "I did everything I could, you know, to keep her. I talked to her of our means, and of the children whom we should have to leave behind, and of my business—she won't hear a word of anything. She makes plans for her life abroad as though she were strong and well. And to tell her of her position would be the death of her."

"But death has hold of her already, you ought to know it, Vasily Dmitrich. A person can't live without lungs, and the lungs can't grow again. It's distressing and terrible, but what's one to do? My duty and yours is simply to see that her end should be as easy as possible. It's the priest who is needed now."

"O my God! But conceive my position, having to speak to her of the last sacrament. Come what will, I can't tell her. You know how good she is."

"You must try, all the same, to persuade her to wait till the roads are frozen," said the doctor, shaking his head significantly, "or we may have a disaster on the road."

"Aksyusha, hey, Aksyusha!" shrieked the stationmaster's daughter, flinging a jacket over her head, and stamping on the dirty back steps of the station; "let's go and have a look at the lady from Shirkin; they say she's being taken abroad for her lungs. I've never seen what people look like in consumption."

Aksyusha darted out at the doorway, and arm in arm they ran by the gate. Slackening their pace, they walked by the carriage, and peeped in at the lowered window. The sick woman turned her head towards them, but noticing their curiosity, she frowned and turned away.

"My gra-a-cious!" said the stationmaster's daughter, turning her head away quickly. "Such a wonderful beauty as she was, and what does she look like now. Enough to frighten one, really. Did you see, did you see, Aksyusha?"

"Yes, she is thin!" Aksyusha assented. "Let's go by and get another look at her, as though we were going to the well. She turned away before I'd seen her properly. I am sorry for her, Masha!"

"And the mud's awful!" answered Masha, and both ran back to the gate.

"I've grown frightful, it seems," thought the invalid. "Ah, to make haste, to make haste to get abroad, then I shall soon be better!"

"Well, how are you, my dear?" said her husband, still munching as he came up to the carriage.

"Always that invariable question," thought the sick woman, "and he goes on eating too!"

"Just the same," she muttered through her teeth.

"Do you know, my dear, I'm afraid the journey will be bad for you in this weather, and Eduard Ivanovich says so too. Hadn't we better turn back?"

She kept wrathfully silent.

"The weather will change, and the roads perhaps will be hard, and that would make it better for you; and then we would all go together."

"Excuse me. If I hadn't listened to you long ago, I should be in Berlin by now and should be quite well."

"That couldn't be helped, my angel; it was out of the question, as you know! But now, if you would wait for a month, you would be ever so much better. I should have settled my business, and we could take the children."

"The children are quite well, and I am not."

"But consider, my dear, with this weather if you get worse on the road . . . there, at any rate, you're at home."

"And if I am at home? . . . To die at home?" the sick woman answered hotly. But the word "die" evidently terrified her; she bent an imploring, questioning look upon her husband. He dropped his eyes and did not speak. The sick woman's mouth puckered all at once like a child's, and tears dropped from her eyes. Her husband buried his face in his handkerchief, and walked away from the carriage without speaking.

"No, I am going," said the sick woman, lifting her eyes towards heaven, and she fell to whispering disconnected words. "My God, what for?" she said, and the tears flowed more freely. For a long while she prayed fervently, but there was still the same pain and tightness on her chest. The sky, the fields, and the road were just as gray and cheerless; and the same autumn mist, neither thicker nor clearer, hung over the mud of the road, the roofs of the huts, the carriage and the sheepskin coats of the drivers, who were greasing and harnessing a carriage, chatting together in their vigorous, merry voices.

ii

The horses were put in the shafts; but the driver lingered. He went into the drivers' hut. It was hot and stifling, dark and oppressive in the hut; there was a smell of human beings, baking bread, and cabbage, and sheepskins. There were several drivers in the room; the cook was busy at the stove; on the top of the stove lay a sick man wrapped in sheepskins.

"Uncle Fyodor! hey, Uncle Fyodor!" said the driver as he came into the room. He was a young fellow, in a sheepskin coat with a whip stuck in his belt, and he was addressing the sick man.

"What do you want Fedya for, you windbag?" one of the drivers interposed. "They are waiting for you in the carriage."

"I want to ask him for his boots; I've worn mine out," answered the young fellow, tossing back his hair and straightening the gloves in his belt. "Is he asleep? Hey, Uncle Fyodor?" he repeated, going up to the stove.

"What?" a weak voice was heard in reply, and a thin face with a red beard bent over from the stove. A big, wasted, white hand, covered with hair, pulled up a coat on the bony shoulder in the dirty shirt. "Give me a drink, brother; what do you want?"

The young man handed him a dipper of water.

"Well, Fedya," he said, hesitating, "you won't be wanting your new boots now; give them to me; you won't be going out, you know."

Pressing his weary head to the shining dipper, and wetting his scanty, hanging mustaches in the turbid water, the sick man drank feebly and eagerly. His tangled beard was not clean, his sunken, lusterless eyes were lifted with an effort to the young man's face. When he had finished drinking he tried to lift his hand to wipe his wet lips, but he could not, and he wiped them on the sleeve of the coat. Without uttering a sound, but breathing heavily through his nose, he looked straight into the young man's eyes, trying to rally his strength.

"Maybe you've promised them to someone already?" said the young man; "if so, never mind. The thing is, it's soaking wet outside, and I've to go out on a job; and I said to myself, why, I'll ask Fedya for his boots, he'll not need them, for sure. If you are likely to need them yourself, say so."

There was a gurgle and a rattle in the sick man's throat; he bent over and was choked by a deep, stifling cough.

"He need them!" the cook cried out in sudden anger, filling the whole hut with her voice. "He's not got off the stove these two months! Why, he coughs fit to split himself; it makes me ache inside simply to hear him. How could he want boots? He won't wear new boots to be buried! And time he was, too, long ago—God forgive me the sin! Why, he coughs fit to split himself. He ought to be moved into another hut, or somewhere! There are hospitals, I've heard say, for such in the town; he takes up the whole place, and what's one to do? One hasn't room to turn round. And then they expect me to keep the place clean!"

"Hi, Seryoga! go and take your seat; the gentry are waiting," the stationmaster shouted at the door.

Seryoga would have gone away without waiting for an answer, but the sick man's eyes, while he was coughing, had told him he wanted to answer.

"You take the boots, Seryoga," said he, stifling the cough and taking breath a minute. "Only buy me a stone when I die, do you hear?" he added huskily.

"Thanks, uncle, so I'll take them; and as to the stone, ay, ay, I'll buy it."

"There, lads, you hear?" the sick man managed to articulate, and again he bent over and began choking.

"All right, we heard," said one of the drivers. "Go along, Seryoga, or the overseer will be running after you again. The lady from Shirkin is ill."

Seryoga quickly pulled off his torn boots, which were much too large for him, and thrust them under a bench. Uncle Fyodor's new boots fitted his feet perfectly, and Seryoga went out to the carriage looking at them.

"What grand boots! let me grease them for you," said a driver with the greasepot in his hand, as Seryoga got on the box and picked up the reins. "Did he give them you for nothing?"

"Why, are you jealous?" answered Seryoga, getting up and shaking down the skirts of his coat about his legs. "Hi, get up, my darlings!" he shouted to the horses, brandishing the whip, and the two carriages, with their occupants, boxes, and baggage, rolled swiftly along the wet road, and vanished into the gray autumn mist.

The sick driver remained lying on the stove in the stifling hut. Unrelieved by coughing, he turned over on the other side with an effort, and was quiet. All day till evening, men were coming and going and dining in the hut; there was no sound from the sick man. At nightfall, the cook clambered up onto the stove and reached across his legs to get a sheepskin. "Don't you be angry with me, Nastasya," said the sick man; "I shall soon clear out of your place."

"That's all right, that's all right; why, I didn't mean it," muttered Nastasya. "But what is it that's wrong with you, uncle? Tell me about it."

"All my inside's wasted away. God knows what it is."

"My word! and does your throat hurt when you cough!"

"It hurts me all over. My death is at hand—that's what it is. Oh, oh, oh!" moaned the sick man.

"Cover your legs up like this," said Nastasya, pulling a coat over him as she crept off the stove.

A night-light glimmered dimly all night in the hut. Nastasya and some ten drivers lay on the floor and the benches asleep, and snoring loudly. The sick man alone moaned faintly, coughed, and turned over on the stove. Towards morning he became quite still.

"A queer dream I had in the night," said the cook, stretching next morning in the half-light. "I dreamed that Uncle Fyodor got down from the stove and went out to chop wood. 'Nastasya,' says he, 'I'll split you some'; and I says to him, 'How can you chop wood?' and he snatches up the axe and starts chopping so fast, so fast that the chips were flying. 'Why,' says I, 'you were ill, weren't you?' 'No,' says he, 'I'm all right,' and he swings the axe, so that it gave me quite a fright. I screamed out and waked up. Isn't he dead, perhaps? Uncle Fyodor! Hey, uncle!"

Fyodor made no sound in reply.

"May be he is dead. I'll get up and see," said one of the drivers who was awake.

A thin hand, covered with reddish hairs, hung down from the stove; it was cold and pale.

"I'll go and tell the overseer. He's dead, seemingly," said the driver.

Fyodor had no relations—he had come from distant parts. The next day he was buried in the new graveyard beyond the copse, and for several days after Nastasya told every one of the dream she had had, and how she had been the first to discover that Uncle Fyodor was dead.

iii

Spring had come. Streams of water hurried gurgling between the frozen dung-heaps in the wet streets of the town. The people moving to and fro were gayly dressed and gayly chattering. Behind the fences of the little gardens the buds on the trees were swelling, and their branches rustled faintly in the fresh breeze. Everywhere there was a running and a dripping of clear drops. . . . The sparrows chattered incoherently, and fluttered to and fro on their little wings. On the sunny side, on fences, trees, and houses, all was movement. There was youth and gladness in the sky and on the earth and in the heart of man. In one of the principal streets there was straw lying in front of a large house; in the house lay the dying woman who had been hastening abroad.

At the closed door of her room stood the patient's husband and her cousin, an elderly woman; on a sofa sat a priest with downcast eyes, holding something wrapped up in his stole. In a corner an old lady, the patient's mother, lay in an armchair, weeping bitterly. Near her stood a maid holding a clean pocket-handkerchief in readiness for the old lady when she should ask for it. Another maid was rubbing the old lady's temples with something and blowing on her gray head under her cap.

"Well, Christ be with you, my dear," said the husband to the elderly woman who was standing with him at the door; "she has such confidence in you, you know so well how to talk to her; go in, and have a good talk with her." He would have opened the door; but the cousin restrained him, put her handkerchief several times to her eyes, and shook her head.

"Come, now, I don't look as if I had been crying, I think," she said, and opening the door herself, she went into the sickroom.

The husband was in great excitement, and seemed utterly distraught. He walked towards the old lady, but stopped short a few paces from her, turned, walked about the room, and went up to the priest. The priest looked at him, raised his eyebrows heavenwards, and sighed. His thick, grizzled beard turned upwards too, and then sank again.

"My God! my God!" said the husband.

"There is nothing one can do," said the priest, and again his brows and his beard were elevated and drooped again.

"And her mother here!" the husband said, almost in despair. "She will never be able to bear this! She loves her, she loves her so that she . . . I don't know. If you, father, would attempt to soothe her and to persuade her to go out of this room."

The priest rose and went to the old lady.

"True it is, that none can sound the depths of a mother's heart," said he; "but God is merciful."

The old lady's face began suddenly twitching, and she sobbed hysterically.

"God is merciful," the priest went on, when she was a little calmer. "In my parish, I must tell you, there was a man ill, much worse than Marya Dmitryevna, and a simple artisan cured him with herbs in a very short time. And this same artisan is in Moscow now, indeed. I told Vasily Dmitryevich —he might try him. Any way, it would be a comfort to the sick woman. To God all things are possible."

"No, she can't live," said the old lady; "if it could have been me, but God takes her." And her hysterics grew so violent that she fainted.

The sick woman's husband hid his face in his hands, and ran out of the room.

The first person that met him in the corridor was a boy of six, who was running at full speed after a little girl younger than himself.

"Shouldn't I take the children to see their mamma?" asked the nurse.

"No, she doesn't want to see them. It upsets her."

The boy stood still for a moment, staring intently into his father's face, then suddenly kicking up his foot, with a merry shriek he ran on.

"I'm pretending she's my black horse, papa!" shouted the boy, pointing to his sister.

Meanwhile in the next room the cousin was sitting by the sick woman's bedside, and trying by skillfully leading up to the subject to prepare her for the idea of death. The doctor was at the other window mixing a draught.

The sick woman, in a white dressing-gown, sat propped up with pillows in bed, and gazed at the cousin without speaking.

"Ah, my dear," she said, suddenly interrupting her, "don't try to prepare me. Don't treat me as a child. I am a Christian. I know all about it. I know I haven't long to live; I know that if my husband would have listened to me sooner, I should have been in Italy, and perhaps, most likely indeed, should have been quite well. Everyone told him so. But it can't be helped, it seems that it was God's will. We are all great sinners, I know that; but I put my trust in God's mercy: He will forgive all, surely, all. I try to understand myself. I, too, have sinned greatly, my dear. But, to make up, how I have suffered. I have tried to bear my sufferings with patience. . . ."

"Then may I send for the priest, my dear? You will feel all the easier after the sacrament," said the cousin. The sick woman bowed her head in token of assent. "God forgive me, a sinner!" she murmured.

The cousin went out and beckoned to the priest.

"She is an angel!" she said to the husband with tears in her eyes. The husband began to weep; the priest went in at the door; the old lady was still unconscious, and in the outer room there was a complete stillness. Five minutes later the priest came out, and taking off his stole smoothed back his hair.

"Thank God, the lady is calmer now," he said; "she wants to see you."

The cousin and the husband went in. The sick woman was weeping quietly, gazing at the holy picture.

"I congratulate you, my dear," said her husband.

"Thank you! How happy I am now, what unspeakable joy I am feeling!" said the sick woman, and a faint smile played about her thin lips. "How merciful is God! Is it not true? Is He not merciful and almighty?" And again with eyes full of tears she gazed at the holy picture in eager prayer.

Then suddenly something seemed to recur to her mind. She beckoned her husband to her.

"You never will do what I ask," she said in a weak, irritable voice.

Her husband, craning his neck forward, listened submissively.

"What is it, my dear?"

"How often I've told you those doctors don't know anything; there are plain women healers, who work cures. . . . The priest told me . . . an artisan . . . send for him."

"For whom, my dear?"

"My God, he won't understand anything!" . . .

And the sick woman frowned and covered her eyes. The doctor went up and took her hand. The pulse was growing perceptibly weaker and weaker. He made a sign to the husband. The sick woman noticed this gesture and looking round in alarm. The cousin turned away, and burst into tears.

"Don't cry, don't torture yourself and me," said the sick woman. "That destroys all the calm left me."

"You are an angel!" said the cousin, kissing her hand.

"No, kiss me here, it's only the dead who are kissed on the hand. My God! my God!"

The same evening the sick woman was a corpse, and the corpse lay in a coffin in the drawing-room of the great house. The doors of the big room were closed, and in it a deacon sat alone, reading the Psalms of David aloud in a rhythmic, nasal tone. The bright light of the wax candles in the tall silver candlesticks fell on the pale brow of the dead woman, on the heavy, waxen hands and the stonelike folds of the shroud, that jutted up horribly at the knees and toes. The deacon read on rhythmically without taking in the meaning of his own words, and the words echoed and died away strangely in the still room. From time to time the sounds of children's voices and the tramp of their feet came from a far-away room.

" 'Hidest thou thy face, they are troubled,' " the psalm-reader boomed; " 'thou takest away their breath, they die and return to their dust. Thou sendest forth thy spirit, they are created; and thou renewest the face of the earth. The glory of the Lord shall endure for ever.' "

The face of the dead woman was stern and solemn. Nothing stirred the pure, cold brow and the firmly set lips. She was all attention. But did she even now understand those grand words?

iv

A month later a stone chapel was raised over the dead woman's grave. But there was still no stone over the driver's grave, and there was nothing but the bright green grass over the mound, which was the only sign of a man's past existence.

"You will be sinning, Seryoga," the cook at the station said one day, "if you don't buy a stone for Fyodor. You were always saying it was winter, but now why don't you keep your word? I was by at the time. He's come back once already to ask you for it; if you don't buy it, he'll come again and stifle you."

"Why, did I say I wasn't going to?" answered Seryoga; "I'll buy a stone as I said I would; I'll buy one for a silver rouble and a half. I've not forgotten, but it must be fetched, you know. As soon as I've a chance to go to the town I'll buy it."

"You might put a cross up anyway," put in an old driver, "or else it's a downright shame. You're wearing the boots."

"Where's one to get a cross? You wouldn't cut one out of a log of firewood?"

"What are you talking about? You can't hew it out of a log. You take an axe and go early in the morning into the copse; you can cut a cross there. An aspen or something you can fell. And it'll make a fine wooden monument too. Or else you'll have to go and stand the forester a drink of vodka. One doesn't want to have to give him a drink for every trifle. The other day I broke a splinter-bar; I cut myself a first-rate new one, and no one said a word to me."

In the early morning, when it was hardly light, Seryoga took his axe and went into the wood. Over all lay a chill, even-colored veil of still-falling dew, not lighted up by the sun. The east was imperceptibly growing clearer, reflecting its faint light on the arch of sky covered with fine clouds. Not a blade of grass below, not a leaf on the topmost twig stirred. The stillness of the forest was only broken at intervals by the sound of wings in a tree or a rustle on the ground. Suddenly a strange sound, not one of nature's own, rang out and died away on the edge of the forest. But again the sound was heard, and began to be repeated at regular intervals near the trunk of one of the motionless trees. One of the treetops began shaking in a strange way; its sappy leaves whispered something; and a warbler that had been perched on one of its branches fluttered round it twice, and uttering a whistle and wagging its tail, settled on another tree.

The sound of the axe was more and more muffled, the sappy, white chips flew out on the dewy grass, and a faint crackling sound followed each blow. The tree shuddered all over, bowed, and quickly stood up straight again, trembling in dismay on its roots. For a moment all was still, but again the tree bent; a crack was heard in its trunk, and with a snapping of twigs its branches dropped, and it crashed down with its top on the damp earth. The sounds of the axe and of steps died away. The warbler whistled and flew up higher. The branch in which it had caught its wings shook for a little while in all its leaves, then became still like the rest. The trees displayed their motionless branches more gladly than ever in the newly opened space.

The first beams of the sun, piercing the delicate cloud, shone out in the sky and darted over the earth. The mist began rolling in waves in the hollows; the dew glittered sparkling on the green grass; the translucent clouds turned white, and floated in haste across the blue sky. The birds flitted to and fro in the thickets and twittered some happy song, like mad things. The sappy leaves whispered joyously and calmly on the treetops, and the branches of the living trees, slowly, majestically, swayed above the fallen dead tree.

Ivan Turgenev

BYÉZHIN MEADOW

I T WAS a magnificent July day, one of those days which come only when the weather has been fair for a long time. From the very earliest dawn the sky is clear; the morning glow does not flame like a conflagration: it pours itself forth in a gentle flush. The sun, not fiery, not red-hot, as in the season of sultry drought, not of a dull crimson, as before a tempest, but bright, and agreeably radiant, glides up peacefully under a long, narrow cloudlet, beams freshly, and plunges into its lilac mist. The thin upper edges of the outstretched cloudlet begin to flash like darting serpents; their gleam resembles the gleam of hammered silver. . . . But now the sportive rays have burst forth once more,—and the mighty luminary rises merrily and majestically, as though flying. In the neighbourhood of midday, a multitude of round, high-hanging clouds make their appearance, of a golden-grey hue, with tender white rims. Like islands, scattered upon a river which has overflowed to an endless extent, and streams around them in profoundly-transparent branches of level azure, they hardly stir from their places. Further away, toward the horizon, they move to meet each other, press close upon one another, and there is no azure to be seen between them, but they themselves are as blue as the sky: they are all permeated, through and through, with light and warmth. The colour of the horizon, a light, pale lilac, does not undergo any change all day long, and is the same all the way round; nowhere does it grow darker, nowhere is a thunder-storm brewing; here and there, perhaps, bluish streaks run downward from above, or a barely perceptible shower sprinkles down. Toward evening, these clouds vanish; the last of them, blackish and undefined in form, like smoke, lie in rosy, curling wreaths over against the setting sun; at the place where it has gone down as tranquilly as it rose in the sky, a scarlet aureole stands, for a little while, above the darkening earth, and, flickering softly, like a carefully carried taper, the evening star kindles in it. On such days, the colours are all softened, bright but not gaudy; over everything rests the imprint of a certain touching gentleness. On such days the heat is sometimes very great; sometimes, even, it is "stewing hot" on the slopes of the fields; but the breeze chases away, disperses the accumulated sultriness, circling wind-gusts—an unfailing sign of settled weather—wander in tall white columns of dust along the roads across the tilled land. The dry, pure air is redolent of wormwood, crushed rye, buckwheat; even an hour before nightfall, you will feel no dampness. This is the sort of weather which the farmer craves for harvesting his grain.

On precisely such a day, I was once hunting partridges in the Tchyórnoye district of the Túla government. I had found and shot quite a lot of game; my well-filled game-bag was cutting pitlessly into my shoulder; but the evening glow had already died out, and in the air, which was still light, although no longer illuminated by the rays of the setting sun, the chilly shadows were beginning to thicken and spread abroad when, at last, I decided to return home. With swift strides I traversed a long "square" of second-growth bushes, climbed a hill, and, instead of the familiar level stretch with its oak copse, which I had expected to see on my right, and the low-browed white church in the distance, I beheld an entirely different set of places, with which I was not acquainted. At my feet stretched a narrow vale; directly opposite, a dense grove of aspen trees rose in a steep wall. I halted in bewilderment, and glanced about me. . . . "Oho!" I thought: "why, I have lost my way completely: I have kept too much to the right," and, amazed at my mistake, I briskly descended the hill. I was immediately beset by a disagreeable, motionless dampness, as though I had entered a cellar: the thick, tall grass on the floor of the vale, all wet through, gleamed like a smooth, white tablecloth; somehow, one felt uneasy about stepping on it. I scrambled up the opposite slope as alertly as possible, keeping to the left, along the aspen grove. Bats were already flitting above its slumbering crests, mysteriously circling and quivering against the confusedly-clear sky; a belated hawk flew past smartly and directly upward, hurrying to its nest. "Now, as soon as I turn yonder corner," I thought to myself, "I shall immediately strike the road;—but I have made a loop of a verst!"

At last, I reached the corner of the forest, but there was no road: some low-growing, unfelled bushes spread out broadly in front of me, and beyond them, far, far away, a stretch of waste land was visible. Again I came to a standstill. "What's the meaning of this? . . . Why, where am I?"—I began to recall how and where I had roamed during the course of the day. . . . "Eh! why, these are the Parákhinsko bushes!" I exclaimed at last: "that's it exactly! that must be the Sindyéevo copse yonder. . . . But how in the world did I get here? So far? . . . 'Tis strange! Now I must keep to the right again."

I went to the right, through the bushes. In the meantime night was drawing on, and growing like a thunder-cloud; it seemed as though, along with the nocturnal exhalations, the darkness rose from all directions, and even streamed down from on high. I hit upon an unbeaten, overgrown path; I advanced along it, attentively gazing ahead. Everything around was swiftly growing black and silent,—only the quails uttered a call from time to time. A small night bird, darting inaudibly and low on its soft wings, almost came into collision with me, and dived aside in affright. I emerged upon the edge of the bush-growth, and wended my way along the boundary strip of sward between two fields. Already I could make out distant objects only with difficulty: the field gleamed dimly white around me; beyond it, moving nearer with every passing moment in huge masses, surged up the grim gloom. My footsteps resounded dully in the chilly air. The sky, which had paled, began to turn blue again,—but it was the nocturnal blue now. Tiny stars began to twinkle, to stir in it.

That which I had been on the point of taking for a grove, turned out to be a dark, round hillock. "But where am I, then?" I repeated, once more, aloud, halted for the third time, and stared inquiringly at my English, yellow-spotted hound, Dianka, positively the cleverest of all four-footed creatures. But the cleverest of quadrupeds only wagged her tail, blinked her weary eyes dolefully, and gave me no practical advice. I felt ashamed in her presence, and rushed desperately onward, as though I had suddenly divined whither I ought to go, skirted the hillock, and found myself in a shallow depression, tilled all around. A strange feeling immediately took possession of me. This hollow had almost the form of a regular kettle, with sloping sides; on its bottom several large, white boulders reared themselves on end,— they seemed to have crawled down there to hold a secret conference, and the place was so deaf and dumb, the sky hung over it so flatly, so dejectedly, that my heart contracted within me. Some sort of a small, wild animal was whining weakly and pitifully among the boulders. I made haste to retreat behind the hillock. Up to this moment, I had not yet lost hope of finding my way home; but now I became definitively convinced that I was completely lost, and without making the slightest further effort to recognise my surroundings, which were almost entirely drowned in the mist, I walked straight ahead, guided by the stars, at random. . . . I continued to walk thus for about half an hour, with difficulty putting one foot before the other. It seemed to me that, never since I was born, had I been in such desert places: not a single light twinkled anywhere, not a sound was audible. One sloping hill succeeded another, fields stretched out after fields in endless succession, bushes seemed fairly to spring out of the earth in front of my very nose. I kept walking on and on, and was already making ready to lie down somewhere until the morning, when, suddenly, I found myself on the brink of a frightful abyss.

I hastily drew back my foot, which was thrust forward, and athwart the barely penetrable gloom of night I descried, far down beneath me, a vast ravine. A broad river swept around it in a semicircle which swerved away from me; steely gleams of water, flashing forth rarely and dimly, designated its course. The hill on which I found myself descended in an almost perpendicular precipice; its huge outlines stood out, darkling, against the bluish aërial waste, and directly beneath me, in the angle formed by the precipice and the level plain, beside the river, which, at that point, stood like a dark, motionless mirror, beneath the very steep face of the hill, burned and smoked, side by side, two fires. Around them people were swarming, shadows were flickering, the front half a small, curly head was at times brilliantly illuminated. . . .

I recognised, at last, whither I had come. This meadow is renowned in our vicinity under the name of the Byézhin Meadow. . . . But there was no possibility of getting home, especially by night; my legs were giving way beneath me with weariness. I made up my mind to approach the fires, and, in the company of the people, whom I took for drovers, to await the dawn. I made a successful descent, but before I could release from my hand the last bough I had clutched, two large, white, shaggy dogs flew at me, barking viciously. Ringing childish voices resounded around the fires; two or three little boys rose hastily from the ground. They ran toward me, called off the dogs, who had been particularly surprised by the appearance of my Dianka, and I approached them.

I had made a mistake in taking the persons who were sitting round those fires for drovers. They were simply peasant children from the neighbouring village, who were herding the horses. In our parts, during the hot summer weather, the horses are driven out to graze in the fields at night: by day, the flies and gadflies would give them no peace. It is a great treat for the peasant lads to drive the herd out at eventide and drive them home at dawn. Seated, capless, and in old half-coats, on the most restive nags, they dash on with merry whoops and shouts, with dangling arms and legs, bouncing high aloft, with ringing laughter. The light dust rises in a column and blows along the road; far away, the vigorous trampling of hoofs is borne on the air, the horses race onward, pricking up their ears; in front of all, flirting its tail, and incessantly changing foot, gallops a shaggy reddish-yellow beast, with burdock burs in its tangled mane.

I told the little lads that I had lost my way, and sat down with them. They asked me whence I had come, fell silent, drew aside. We chatted a little. I lay down under a gnawed bush, and began to look about me. It was as wonderful picture; around the fires quivered, and, as it were, flickered, resting against the darkness, a round, reddish reflection; the flame, flashing up now and then, cast swift gleams beyond the limit of that circle; a thin tongue of light would lick the bare boughs of the scrub-willows and instantly vanish;—long, sharp-pointed shadows, breaking forth, for a moment, in their turn, rushed up to the very fires: the gloom wrestled with the light. Sometimes, when the flame burned more feebly, and the circle of light contracted, a horse's head would suddenly thrust itself forward out of the invading gloom,—a brown horse, with a sinuous white mark on the forehead, or all white,—and gaze attentively and dully at us, briskly chewing a long tuft of grass the while, and, lowering again, immediately disappear. All that was audible was, that it continued to chew and snort. From the illuminated place, it was difficult to discern what was going on in the darkness, and, consequently, everything near at hand seemed enveloped in an almost black curtain; but further away, toward the horizon, hills and forests could be dimly descried, in long splashes. The dark, pure sky stood solemnly and boundlessly high above us, with all its mysterious majesty. The breast felt sweet oppression as it inhaled that peculiar, fresh and enervating fragrance—the fragrance of a Russian summer night. Hardly a sound was audible round about. . . . Only now and then, in the near-by river, a large fish would splash with sudden sonorousness, and the reeds upon the banks would rustle faintly, barely rocked by a truant wave. . . . The fires alone crackled softly.

The little boys sat around them; there, also, sat the two dogs, who would have liked to devour me. For a long time, they could not reconcile themselves to my presence, and, sleepily screwing up their eyes, and casting sidelong glances at the fire, they growled, now and then, with the consciousness of their own dignity; first they growled, and then whined faintly, as though they regretted the impossibility of fulfilling their desire. There were five lads in all: Fédya, Pavlúsha, Iliúsha, Kóstya, and Ványa. (I learned their names from their conversation, and intend to introduce them at once to the reader.)

You would have said that the first, the oldest of them all, Fédya, was fourteen. He was a graceful lad, with handsome, delicate, and rather small features, curly fair hair, light eyes, and a constant, half-merry, half-abstracted smile. He belonged, by all the tokens, to a rich family, and went out thus into the fields, not through necessity, but because he wished it, for amusement. He wore a gay print shirt with a yellow border; a small, new peasant's long-coat, hanging from his shoulders, the sleeves unused, hardly held in place on his narrow shoulders; from his sky-blue girdle hung a small comb. His boots, with narrow leg-pieces, were really his boots—not his father's. The second lad, Pavlúsha, had tangled, black hair, grey eyes, broad cheek-bones, a pale, pockmarked face, a large, but regular mouth; his whole head was huge as a beer-kettle, as the expression is, his body stubby, uncouth. He was a homely little fellow,—there's no denying that!—but, nevertheless, he pleased me: his gaze was very sensible and direct, and power resounded in his voice. His garments were nothing to boast of: they consisted of a plain hemp-cloth shirt and patched trousers. The face of the third, Iliúsha, was rather insignificant; hook-nosed, long, mole-eyed, it expressed a sort of stupid, sickly anxiety; his tightly compressed lips did not move, his knitted brows did not unbend,—he seemed to be always screening his eyes from the fire. His yellow, almost white hair stuck out in pointed tufts from beneath a low-crowned, felt cap, which he was incessantly pulling down over his ears with both hands. He wore new linden-bark slippers and leg-cloths; a thick cord, wound thrice around his body, carefully confined his neat, black coat. He and Pavlúsha were, apparently, not over twelve years of age. The fourth, Kóstya, a little lad of ten, excited my curiosity by his thoughtful and melancholy gaze. His whole face was small, thin, freckled, pointed below, like that of a squirrel; his lips were hardly discernible; but his large, black eyes, shining with a liquid gleam, produced a strange impression: they seemed to want to express something for which the tongue—his tongue, at all events—had no words. He was short of stature, of fragile build, and dressed quite poorly. At first, I came near not noticing the last one, Ványa: he was lying

on the ground, peaceably curled up under an angular rug, and only now
and then did he thrust out from beneath it his curly chestnut head. This boy
was, at most, seven years of age.

So I lay there under a bush, apart, and surveyed the little lads. A small
kettle hung over one of the fires: in it they were boiling " 'taties." Pavlúsha
was watching it, and, kneeling, thrust a chip into the frothing water. Fédya
was lying propped on his elbow, with the tails of his coat spread apart.
Iliúsha was sitting beside Kóstya, and also screwing up his eyes intently.
Kóstya had dropped his head a little, and was gazing off somewhere into
the distance. Ványa did not stir under his rug. I pretended to be asleep.
Gradually, the boys began to talk again.

At first they prattled about one thing and another, about the toils of the
morrow, about the horses; but, all of a sudden, Fédya turned to Iliúsha and,
as though renewing an interrupted conversation, asked him:

"Well, and what wert thou saying—hast thou seen the domovóy?" [1]

"No, I have not seen him, and it isn't possible to see him,"—replied
Iliúsha, in a hoarse, weak voice, whose sound precisely matched the expression of his face. "I heard him. . . . And I wasn't the only one."

"And whereabouts on your premises does he haunt?"—inquired Pavlúsha.

"In the old stuff-chest room." [2]

"But do you go to the mill?"

"Of course we do. My brother Avdiúshka and I are plater-boys."

"See there, now—you are mill-hands!" . . .

"Well, and how didst thou come to hear him?"—asked Fédya.

"Why, this way. It happened that brother Avdiúshka and I, along with
Feódor Mikhyéevsky and the squint-eyed Iváshka, and another Iváshka, who
is from the Red Hills, and still another Iváshka Sukhorúkoff, and other boys
also; there were ten of us lads in all,—the whole gang, that is to say; well,
and it happened that we had to pass the night in the stuff-chest room,—that
is to say, it didn't happen so, but Nazároff, the overseer, forbade us to go
home: says he: 'What's the good,' says he, 'of you boys trudging home; there's
a lot of work for to-morrow, so don't you go home, my lads.' And so we
stayed, and all lay down together, and Avdiúshka says, 'Well, boys, and what
if the domovóy should come?' . . . And before he, Avdyéi that is, had
finished speaking, some one suddenly walked across over our heads; but we
were lying down-stairs, and he was walking up-stairs, by the wheel. We hear
him walking, and the boards fairly bend under him, and crack; now he
has passed over our heads; the water suddenly begins to roar and roar against
the wheel; the wheel begins to bang and bang, and to turn; but the sluice-
gate is shut. We wonder:—who can have raised it, so that the water comes
through? But the wheel went on turning and turning, and then stopped.

[1] House-sprite, like the banshee.—TRANSLATOR.
[2] The building, in paper-mills, where the paper is bailed out of the stuff-chests. It is close
to the dam, under the wheel.

Then that person went to the door up-stairs again, and began to descend the stairs, and came down as though he were in no hurry; the steps fairly groaned beneath him. . . . Well, the person came to our door, waited, waited,—and suddenly the door flew wide open. We started up in terror, we looked— nothing! . . . All of a sudden, behold, the mould at one of the stuff-chests began to move, rose up, tipped, and floated, floated like that, through the air, as though some one were rinsing with it, and then went back to its place. Then, at another chest, the hook was taken from the nail, and put back on the nail again; then some one seemed to go to the door, and suddenly began to cough and hawk, like some sort of sheep, and so noisily. . . . We all tumbled together in a heap, and crawled under one another. . . . How scared we were that time!"

"You don't say so!"—remarked Pável.—"What made him cough?"

"I don't know; the dampness, perhaps."

All relapsed into silence.

"Well,"—inquired Fédya:—"are the 'taties done?"

Pavlúsha felt of them.

"No, they're still raw. . . . Whew, what a splash,"—he added, turning his face in the direction of the river:—"it must be a pike . . . and yonder is a shooting star."

"See here, fellows, I'll tell you something,"—began Kóstya, in a thin little voice:—"Listen to what daddy told me the other day."

"Come on, we're listening,"—said Fédya, with a patronising mien.

"Of course, you know Gavrílo, the village carpenter?"

"Well, yes; we do."

"But do you know why he is always such a melancholy man: always silent, you know? This is why he is so melancholy: Once on a time, fellows, says my daddy, he went to the forest for nuts. So he went to the forest for nuts, and got lost; God knows where he came out. So he walked and walked, fellows,—but no! he couldn't find the road! and night was already at hand. So he sat down under a tree; 'I'll just wait until morning,' says he to himself, —so he sat down, and fell into a doze. And while he was sleeping, he suddenly heard some one calling him. He looks—no one. Again he fell asleep, —again came the call. Again he looks and looks around: and in front of him, on a bough, sits a water-nymph; she rocks to and fro, and calls him to her, while she herself is dying with laughter. And she laughs so! . . . And the moon was shining strongly,—so strongly, clearly is the moon shining, that everything is visible, my boys. So she calls him, and sits there on the bough, all brilliant, and white, just like a roach or a gudgeon,—or a carp, also, is whitish and silvery like that. . . . Gavrílo the carpenter fairly fell back in a swoon, fellows; but she, you know, shrieked with laughter, and kept beckoning him to her with her hand, like this. Gavrílo tried to rise, tried to obey the water-nymph, fellows, but, you see, the Lord suggested something to him: he just made the sign of the cross over himself. . . . And how hard he found it to make that sign of the cross, fellows! He says:

'My hand was simply like stone, it wouldn't move. . . . Akh, thou wicked nymph, ah!'—So, fellows, when he made the sign of the cross, that water-sprite ceased to laugh, and suddenly began to weep, as it were. . . . She weeps, fellows, and wipes her eyes with her hair, and her hair is as green as thy hemp. So Gavrílo stared and stared at her, and began to question her: 'Why weepest thou, thou imp of the forest?' But the water-sprite says to him: 'Thou shouldst not have crossed thyself, O man,' says she; 'thou mightest have lived with me to the end of thy days; and I am weeping, I am pining away, because thou hast crossed thyself; and 'tis not I alone, who shall pine: pine thou, also, until the end of thy days.' Then she vanished, fellows, and Gavrílo immediately understood how he was to get out of the forest. . . . Only, from that time forth, he goes about always in that melancholy way."

"Ekha!"—remarked Fédya, after a brief silence:—"but how can such a wicked forest demon spoil a Christian soul,—he oughtn't to have listened to her!"

"Oh, go along with you!"—said Kóstya.—"And Gavrílo said she had such a thin, wailing voice, like a toad's."

"Did thy dad narrate that himself?"—went on Fédya.

"Yes, he did. I was lying on the platform over the oven, and heard everything."

"A wonderful affair! Why should he be melancholy? . . . Why, you know, if she called him, 'twas because 'she had taken a fancy to him.'"

"Yes, she had taken a fancy to him!"—put in Iliúsha.—"Of course, she wanted to tickle him,—that's what she wanted. That's what they do, those water-nymphs."

"Why, and there must be water-nymphs here, too,"—remarked Fédya.

"No,"—replied Kóstya:—"this is a clean place, a free place; for one thing, the river is hard by."

All fell silent. Suddenly, somewhere in the far distance, there rang out a long-drawn, sonorous, almost moaning sound, one of those incomprehensible nocturnal noises, which sometimes well up in the midst of profound stillness, rise aloft, hang suspended in the air, and slowly disperse, at last, as though they died away. You strain your ear,—and it seems as though there were nothing, yet it is tinkling. It seemed as though some one had shouted for a long, long time, at the very horizon, and some one else had answered his shout from the forest with a thin, shrill laugh, and a weak, hissing whistle flew with lightning speed along the river. The little lads exchanged glances, and shuddered.

"The power of the cross be with us!"—whispered Ilyá.

"Ekh, you simpletons!"—cried Pável: "what are you frightened at? Look here, the 'taties are boiled soft." (They moved up round the little kettle, and began to eat the smoking-hot potatoes; Ványa alone did not stir.) "What's the matter with thee?"—said Pável.

But he did not crawl forth from under his linden-bast rug. The little kettle was speedily emptied completely.

"But have you heard, my lads,"—began Iliúsha:—"what happened the other day at Varnávitzy?"

"On the dam, thou meanest?"—asked Fédya.

"Yes, yes, on the dam, the broken dam. 'Tis an unhallowed place, you know, so unhallowed, and so God-forsaken. Everywhere around there are such ravines and precipices, and down the precipices snakes breed."

"Well, what happened? Go ahead and tell us."

"Why, this is what happened. Perhaps thou dost not know it, Fédya, but we have a drowned man buried there, and he was drowned long, long ago, when the pond was still deep; only his grave is still visible, and even that is barely visible: 'tis just a tiny mound. . . . Well, the other day, the manager calls up Ermíl the dog-keeper; says he: 'Go to the post-office, Ermíl.' Ermíl always does ride to the post-office: he has starved off all his dogs: that's why they don't live with him, and they never did live with him, any-way, but he's a fine whipper-in, he has all the gifts. So Ermíl rode off for the mail, and he lagged in the town, and he was drunk when he started to ride back. And the night was a bright night: the moon was shining. . . . So Ermíl is riding across the dam: his road lay that way. And as he is riding along, huntsman Ermíl sees, on the drowned man's grave, a young ram strolling about,—such a white, curly, pretty little ram. So Ermíl thinks to himself: 'I'll catch him,—why should he be wasted like this?'—so he slipped off his horse, and took him in his hands. . . . But the ram didn't mind it at all. So Ermíl goes to his horse, but the horse opens his eyes wide and stares, and neighs and tosses his head; but he untied it, mounted, and the ram with him, and started off again: he held the young ram in front of him. He looked at it, and the ram just stared him straight in the eye. He began to feel uneasy, did Ermíl the hunstman: 'I don't remember ever to have heard,' says he, 'that rams stared folks in the eye in this fashion'; how-ever, he didn't mind; he began to stroke its fur,—and says he: 'Ba-a, ba-a!' And all of a sudden, the ram showed his teeth, and says to him the same: 'Ba-a, ba-a! . . .'"

Before the narrator could utter this last word, the two dogs suddenly rose with one impulse, rushed away from the fire, barking convulsively, and vanished into the darkness. All the boys were thoroughly frightened. Ványa jumped out from under his mat. Pavlúsha flew after the dogs with a yell. Their barking swiftly retreated into the distance. . . . The uneasy running to and fro of the startled herd of horses was audible. Pavlúsha shouted loudly: "Grey! Beetle!" . . . In a few moments, the barking ceased; Pável's voice was already wafted to us from afar. . . . A little more time elapsed; the boys exchanged glances of bewilderment, as though anticipating that something was about to happen. . . . Suddenly the hoof-beats of a galloping horse became audible; it stopped abruptly at the very fire, and Pavlúsha, who had been clinging to its mane, leaped from its back. The two dogs also sprang into the circle of light, and immediately sat down, lolling out their red tongues.

"What was it yonder? What was the matter?"—asked the boys.

"Nothing,"—replied Pável, waving his hand toward the horse:—" 'twas just that the dogs scented something. I thought it was a wolf,"—he added in an indifferent voice, breathing fast, with the full capacity of his chest.

I involuntarily admired Pavlúsha. He was very handsome at that moment. His ugly face, animated by the swift ride, blazed with dashing gallantry and firm resolution. Without even a switch in his hand, he had darted off alone, by night, without the slightest hesitation, to encounter a wolf. . . . "What a splendid boy!" I thought, as I gazed at him.

"And have you seen them,—the wolves, I mean?"—asked cowardly Kóstya.

"There are always a lot of them here,"—replied Pável:—"but they are uneasy only in winter."

Again he curled up in front of the fire. As he seated himself on the ground, he dropped his hand on the shaggy neck of one of the dogs, and for a long time the delighted animal did not turn its head, as it gazed sidelong, with grateful pride, at Pavlúsha.

Ványa cuddled up under his mat again.

"What were those horrors thou wert narrating to us, Iliúsha?"—began Fédya, to whose lot, as the son of a wealthy peasant, it fell to act the part of leader (he himself said very little, as though he were afraid of lowering his dignity).—"And 'twas the Evil One who prompted the dogs to set up that barking. . . . But, in fact, I have heard that that locality of yours is unhallowed."

"Varnávitzy? . . . I should say so! unhallowed the worst way! The old master has been seen there more than once, they say—the deceased master. He wears a long-skirted dressing-gown, they say, and keeps sighing all the while, as though he were hunting for something on the ground. Grandaddy Trofímitch met him once.—'What is it, dear little father, Iván Ivánitch,' says he, 'that thou art searching for on the ground?'"

"He asked him that?"—interrupted the astounded Fédya.

"Yes, he asked him."

"Well, Trofímitch is a gallant fellow to do that. . . . Well, and what happened?"

" 'I'm looking for the saxifrage,' says he. And he talks in such a dull, dull voice:—'The saxifrage.'[1]—'And what dost thou want of saxifrage, dear little father, Iván Ivánitch?'—'My grave is crushing me, crushing me, Trofímitch; I want to get out, to get out. . . .'"

"What a fellow!"—remarked Fédya;—"Probably he hadn't lived long enough."

[1] Literally, rend-rock—the rock-splitting plant.—TRANSLATOR.

"What a marvel!" said Kótya:—"I thought dead folks could be seen only on Relatives' Saturday." [2]

"Dead folks can be seen at any hour,"—confidently put in Iliúsha, who, so far as I was able to observe, was better acquainted than the rest with all the rural superstitions. . . . "But on Relatives' Saturday you can also see the living person whose turn it is to die that year. All you have to do is to sit on the church porch, and keep staring at the road; and those who are destined to die that year will pass by. Peasant-wife Uliyána, of our village, went and sat on the church porch last year."

"Well, and did she see any one?"—inquired Kóstya, with interest.

"Of course she did. At first, she sat there a long, long time, without seeing or hearing anybody . . . but a dog seemed to keep barking and barking somewhere or other. . . . All at once, she looks, and a little boy, with nothing on but his shirt, comes walking along the path. She looked closely—'twas Iváshka Feodósyeff . . ."

"The one who died last spring?"—interrupted Fédya.

"The very same. He was walking along, without raising his little head. . . . And Uliyána recognised him. . . . But then she looked again, and a woman was coming along. She stared and stared,—akh, O Lord!—'twas she herself, Uliyána herself, who was coming along the road."

"Was it really she herself?"—asked Fédya.

"God is my witness, it was."

"Well, what of it?—she isn't dead yet, you know."

"But the year isn't over yet. Just take a look at her: she's on the point of death."

All relapsed into silence again. Pável flung a handful of dry twigs on the fire. They turned sharply black with the suddenly upflaring flame, crackled, began to smoke, and set to writhing, thrusting upward their singed tips. The reflection of the fire darted out in all directions, with abrupt flickerings, especially upward. All at once, from somewhere or other, a white pigeon flew straight into this reflection, circled with affright in one spot, all flooded with the hot glare, and disappeared, with flapping wings.

"It must have escaped from home,"—remarked Pável.—"Now it will fly until it hits against something, and it will spend the night, until daybreak, on whatever it hits against."

"See here, Pavlúsha,"—said Kóstya:—"isn't it true, that it was a spirit flying to heaven, hey?"

Pável tossed another handful of twigs on the fire.

"Perhaps so,"—he said at last.

---

[2] Certain Saturdays in the year, on which requiem services are held for dead relatives. One such Saturday occurs in Lent; another in the autumn, called "Dmítry's Day," when dead ancestors in general, and in particular those who fell on that day in the battle of Kulikovo, 1380, under prince Dmítry 'Donskóy' (of the Don), which broke the Tatár yoke, are commemorated. But the one particularly referred to here is that which precedes Pentecost (Trinity Sunday and the Day of the Spirit, Monday).—TRANSLATOR.

"But tell me, please, Pavlúsha,"—began Fédya:—"was the heavenly vision [1] visible also with you in Shalámovo?"

"When the sun was invisible? Certainly."

"You must have been frightened too, I think?"

"Well, we weren't the only ones. Our master, although he had explained to us beforehand that we should see a vision, was so scared himself, they say, when it began to grow dark, that he was beside himself with fear. And in the house-serfs' cottage, the peasant-wife cook, just as soon as it began to grow dark, I hear, took and smashed all the pots in the oven with the oven-fork. 'Who wants to eat now?' says she: 'the day of judgment has come.' And such rumours were circulating in our village, brother,—to the effect that white wolves would overrun the earth, and eat up the people, a bird of prey would swoop down, and then Tríshka himself would be seen." [2]

"What is that Tríshka?"—asked Kóstya.

"Dost not thou know?"—put in Iliúsha hotly:—"well, brother, whence comest thou that thou dost not know about Tríshka? You're great stay-at-homes in your village, that's what you are! Tríshka will be a wonderful man who will come, and he will be such a wonderful man that it will be impossible to catch him, and no one will be able to do anything to him: so wonderful will the man be. The peasants will want to seize him, for example: they will go out against him with cudgels, they will surround him, but he will avert their eyes,—he will avert their eyes in such a way, that they will slay each other. They will put him in prison, for example,—he will ask for a drink of water in a dipper: they will fetch him the dipper, and he will dive down into it, and that's the last they will ever see of him. They will put chains on him, but he will shake his hands and they will fall off him. Well, and that Tríshka will go through the villages and the towns; and that Tríshka, the cunning fellow, will lead astray the Christian race . . . well, and they will not be able to do anything to him. . . . He will be such a wonderful, such a crafty man."

"Well, yes,"—went on Pavlúsha, in his drawling voice:—"that's the man. They've been expecting him in our village too. The old folks said, that as soon as the heavenly vision began, Tríshka would come. So the vision began. All the people scattered out into the street, into the fields, to wait and see what would happen. And we have a conspicuous, extensive site, you know. They are gazing when, suddenly, down-hill from the town, comes some man or other, such a peculiar man, with such a wonderful head . . they all shout out at once: 'Oï, Tríshka's coming! óï, Tríshka's coming!' but 'twas nothing of the sort. Our elder crawled into the ditch; his wife got stuck fast in the board at the bottom of the gate, and yelled at the top of her voice; she scared her watch-dog so that it broke loose from its chain, and leaped over the wattled hedge, and fled off to the forest; and Kúzka's father, Dorofyéitch, sprang into the oats, and squatted down, and set to piping like a quail: he

[1] That is what our peasants call an eclipse of the sun.
[2] The belief in "Tríshka" is, probably, a reflection of the legend about Antichrist.

thought, perhaps, the enemy, the soul-spoiler, would have mercy on a mere bird. So they all set up a rumpus! . . . But the man who was coming was our cooper, Vavíla; he had bought himself a new tub with handles, and had put the empty tub on his head."

All the boys burst out laughing, and again became silent for a moment, as it often happens with people who are conversing in the open air. I cast a glance around: the night reigned, sovereign, triumphant; the damp chill of late evening had given way to the dry warmth of midnight, and it still had long to lie like a soft coverlet over the slumbering fields; a long time still remained before the first lisp, the first fine dews of dawn. There was no moon in the sky: at that time it rose late. Innumerable golden stars seemed all to have glided softly, twinkling in emulation of one another, in the direction of the Milky Way, and, in truth, as you gazed at them, you yourself began to feel the headlong, uninterrupted onward flight of the earth. . . . A strange, sharp, wailing cry suddenly rang out twice in succession over the river, and, after the lapse of a few seconds, was repeated farther away. . . .

Kóstya shuddered: . . . "What's that?"

"That's a heron screaming,"—returned Pável, composedly.

"A heron,"—repeated Kóstya. . . . "But what was it, Pavlúsha, that I heard last night,"—he added, after a short silence:—"perhaps thou knowest . . ."

"What didst thou hear?"

"Why, this is what I heard. I was going from Kámennaya-Grýada [Stone-Ridge] to Sháshkino. First I kept altogether in our hazel-copse, and then went by the pool—thou knowest, at the place where it makes a sharp turn into the cliff,—there's a deep pit there, you see, made by the spring freshets, which never dries up; it's still all overgrown with reeds, you know; so, as I was walking past that water-hole, boys, somebody began to groan from that same hole, and so pitifully, so pitifully . . . 'Oo-oo . . . oo-oo . . . oo-oo!' I was seized with such terror, my brothers: the hour was late, and the voice was so painful.—What could it have been? hey?"

"Thieves drowned Akím the forester in that pool the year before last,"—remarked Pavlúsha;—"so, perhaps, it was his soul wailing."

"Why, that must have been it, my brothers,"—returned Kóstya, opening wide his eyes, which were huge already. . . . "I didn't know that they had drowned Akím in that pool: I would have been scared much worse."

"But they say there are small frogs,"—went on Pavlúsha,—"which cry out in that pitiful way."

"Frogs? well, no, it wasn't frogs . . . which made that . . ." (The heron screamed again above the river).—"Deuce take it!"—ejaculated Kóstya, involuntarily:—"it shrieks like the forest-demon."

"The forest-demon doesn't shriek,—he's dumb,"—put in Iliúsha:—"he only claps his hands and cracks . . ."

"And hast thou seen him,—the forest-demon? I'd like to know,"—Fédya interrupted him, sneeringly.

"No, I haven't, and God forbid that I should see him; but other folks have seen him. The other day now, he tricked a peasant; he led him on and on through the forest, and all the while round one and the self-same meadow. . . . He barely got home by daylight."

"Well, and did he see him?"

"Yes. He says he stands so big, so big, and dark, and muffled up, behind a tree, as it were, so that you can't get a good look at him, as though he were hiding from the moon, and he stares and stares with his little eyes, and blinks them, and blinks . . ."

"Do stop that!"—exclaimed Fédya, with a slight shudder, and a twitch of his shoulders:—"Pfu! . . ."

"And why is this nasty crew distributed over the world?"—remarked Pável:—"really now, why?"

Again a pause ensued.

"Look, look, boys,"—suddenly rang out Ványa's childish voice:—"Look at God's little stars, like bees swarming!"

He poked his fresh little face out from under the mat, propped himself on his little fist, and slowly raised on high his large, tranquil eyes. The eyes of all the little lads were raised to the sky, and were not soon lowered.

"Well, Ványa,"—began Fédya, affectionately:—"how about thy sister Aniútka,—is she well?"

"Yes,"—replied Ványa, with a slight lisp.

"Tell her, we want to know why she doesn't come to see us."

"I don't know."

"Tell her that she must come."

"I'll tell her."

"Tell her that I'll give her a present."

"And wilt thou give me one too?"

"Yes, I'll give thee one too."

Ványa sighed.

"Well, no, I don't want it. Better give it to her: she's such a good girl."

And again Ványa laid his head on the ground. Pável rose, and took the empty kettle in his hand.

"Where art thou going?"—Fédya asked him.

"To the river to dip up some water. I want a drink of water."

The dogs rose and followed him.

"Look out, don't tumble into the river!"—shouted Iliúsha after him.

"Why should he tumble in?"said Fédya:—"He'll take care of himself."

"Yes, so he will. All sorts of things happen: he'll stoop down and begin to dip up the water, and the water-sprite will grab him by the hand and pull him in to himself. Then people will begin to say: 'The little fellow tumbled into the water. . . .' Much he did! . . . Yo-onder, he has made his way in among the rushes," he added, listening.

The rushes, in fact, were moving,—"whispering," as they express it among us.

"And is it true,"—asked Kóstya:—"that Akulína the fool has been crazy ever since the time she was in the water?"

"Yes, ever since then. . . . Just look at her now! But they say that before that, she used to be a beauty. The water-sprite spoiled her. He didn't expect, you see, that they would pull her out so soon. So he spoiled her, down on the bottom, at his own place."

(I had met that Akulína more than once myself. Covered with rags, frightfully thin, with a face as black as a coal, a confused look, and teeth eternally exposed in a grin, she would stamp up and down for hours in one and the self-same spot, somewhere on the highway, with her bony arms pressed tightly to her breast, and slowly shifting from one foot to the other, like a wild beast in a cage. She understood nothing that was said to her, and only laughed convulsively from time to time.)

"But they say,"—went on Kóstya,—"that Akulína threw herself into the river, because her lover deceived her."

"That's exactly why she did it."

"And dost thou remember Vásya?"—added Kóstya, sadly.

"What Vásya?"—inquired Fédya.

"Why, the one who was drowned,"—replied Kóstya. "What a boy he was! i-ikh, what a boy he was! His mother, Feklísta, how she did love him, that Vásya! And she seemed to have a presentiment, did Feklísta, that water would be his ruin. When Vásya used to go to the river with us boys, to bathe, in summer, she would just quiver all over. The other women didn't mind: they would go past with their wash-troughs themselves, waddling along, but Feklísta would set her trough [1] on the ground and begin to call to him. 'Come back,' says she, 'come back, light of my eyes! Okh, come back, my dear little falcon!'—And how he came to get drowned, the Lord knows. He was playing on the shore, and his mother was there also, raking up the hay; all at once, she heard some one making bubbles in the water,—and behold, nothing but Vásya's little cap was floating on the water. Alas, ever since then, Feklísta has not been in her right mind:—she'll come and lie down on that spot where he was drowned; she'll lie there, brothers, and strike up a song,—you remember, Vásya always sang the same song,—so she will strike up that song, and weep, and weep, and complain bitterly to God . . ."

"Yonder comes Pavlúsha,"—said Fédya.

Pavlúsha came up to the fire with a full kettle in his hand.

"Well, boys,"—he began, after a brief pause:—"something is wrong."

"Why, what's the matter?"—asked Kóstya, hastily.

"I have heard Vásya's voice."

All fairly shuddered.

"What dost thou mean, what dost thou mean?"—stammered Kóstya.

"God is my witness. No sooner had I begun to stoop down to the water, than suddenly I heard myself called by Vásya's little voice, and from under

---

[1] The Russian peasant wash-tub is like a long, shallow trough, or chopping-tray, made of a halved and hollowed log.—TRANSLATOR.

the water, as it were: 'Pavlúsha, hey there, Pavlúsha, come hither.' I went away. But I dipped up the water all the same."

"Akh, O my Lord! akh, O Lord!"—cried the little lads, crossing themselves.

"That was the water-sprite calling thee, for sure, Pável,"—added Fédya. . . . "And we have just been talking about him,—about Vásya."

"Akh, 'tis a bad omen,"—faltered Iliúsha.

"Come, 'tis nothing, drop it!"—said Pável, decisively, and sat down again:—"you can't escape your fate."

The boys subsided into silence. It was evident that Pável's words had produced a profound impression upon them. They began to stretch themselves out in front of the fire, as though preparing to go to sleep.

"What's that?"—asked Kóstya, suddenly, raising his head.

Pável listened intently.

" 'Tis the woodcock flying,—they are whistling."

"But whither are they flying?"

"Away yonder, where, they say, there is no winter."

"And is it possible that there is such a country?"

"There is."

"Is it far away?"

"Yes, far, far away, beyond the warm seas."

Kóstya sighed, and closed his eyes.

More than three hours had already elapsed since I had joined the boys. The moon rose at last: I did not immediately observe it, it was so small and slender. This moonless night, apparently, was as magnificent as before. . . . But many stars which had but lately stood high in the heavens, were already sinking toward the dark rim of the earth; everything round about had become perfectly quiet, as things generally do only toward dawn: everything was sleeping, with the deep, motionless slumber which precedes the break of day. The air was no longer so strongly perfumed,—it seemed to have again become impregnated with moisture. . . . Summer nights are not long! . . . The prattle of the little lads had died down with the bonfires. . . . The dogs, too, were sleeping; the horses, so far as I was able to make out by the barely-shining, faintly-spreading light of the stars, were also lying down, with drooping heads. . . . A light forgetfulness descended upon me; it passed into slumber.

A fresh current of air blew across my face. I opened my eyes:—morning was breaking. The dawn was not, as yet, glowing red anywhere, but the east was already beginning to grow white. Everything had become visible, though dimly visible, all around. The pale-gray sky was lighting up, turning cold and blue; the stars now twinkled with a faint light, now disappeared; the earth had grown damp, the foliage had begun to sweat; here and there living sounds, voices, were beginning to resound, and a thin, early breeze had begun to stray abroad and flutter over the earth. My body responded to it with a slight, cheerful shiver. I rose briskly to my feet, and walked toward the little boys. They were all sleeping like dead men around the smouldering bonfire; Pável alone half-rose, and gazed silently at me.

I nodded my head to him and went my way, along the mist-wreathed river. Before I had proceeded two versts, there had streamed forth all around me over the wide, wet meadow, ahead of me, over the hills which were beginning to gleam green, from forest to forest, and behind me, over the long, dusty highway, over the glittering, crimson-tinted bushes, and the river, shyly glinting blue from beneath the dispersing fog—there had streamed forth first scarlet, then red, then golden torrents of young, blazing light. . . . Everythin began to stir, awoke, began to sing, to make a noise, to chatter. Everywhere, like radiant brilliants, glowed great dew drops; the sounds of a bell were wafted toward me, pure and clear, as though they, also, had been washed by the morning freshness, and, suddenly, the rested herd of horses dashed headlong past me, driven by the lads I have mentioned. . . .

Unfortunately, I am bound to add that Pável died that same year. He was not drowned; he was killed by falling from a horse. 'Tis a pity, for he was a splendid young fellow!

Nikolay Gogol

OLD-WORLD LANDOWNERS

I AM VERY fond of the modest manner of life of those solitary owners of remote villages, who in Little Russia are commonly called "old-fashioned," who are like tumbledown picturesque little houses, delightful in their simplicity and complete unlikeness to the new smooth buildings whose walls have not yet been discolored by the rain, whose roofs are not yet covered with green lichen, and whose porch does not display its red bricks through the peeling stucco. I like sometimes to enter for a moment into that extraordinarily secluded life in which not one desire flits beyond the palisade surrounding the little courtyard, beyond the hurdle of the orchard filled with plum and apple trees, beyond the village huts surrounding it, lying all aslant under the shade of willows, elders, and pear trees. The life of their modest owners is so quiet, so quiet, that for a moment one is lost in forgetfulness and imagines that those passions, desires and restless promptings of the evil spirit that trouble the world have no real existence, and that you have only beheld them in some lurid dazzling dream. I can see now the low-pitched little house with the gallery of little blackened wooden posts running right round it, so that in hail or storm they could close the shutters without being wetted by the rain. Behind it a fragrant bird-cherry, rows of dwarf fruit trees, drowned in a sea of red cherries and amethyst plums, covered with lead-colored bloom; a spreading maple in the shade of which a rug is laid to rest on; before the house a spacious courtyard of short fresh grass with a little pathway trodden from the storehouse to the kitchen and from the kitchen to the master's apartments; a long-necked goose drinking water with young goslings soft as down around her; a palisade hung with strings of dried pears and apples and rugs put out to air; a cartful of melons standing by the storehouse; an unharnessed ox lying lazily beside it—they all have an inexpressible charm for me, perhaps because I no longer see them and because everything from which we are parted is dear to us.

Be that as it may, at the very moment when my chaise was driving up to the steps of that little house, my soul yielded to a wonderfully sweet and serene mood; the horses galloped merrily up to the steps; the coachman very tranquilly clambered down from the box and filled his pipe as though he had reached home; even the barking set up by phlegmatic Rovers, Pontos and Neros was pleasant to my ears. But more than all I liked the owners of these modest little nooks—the little old men and women who came out solicitiously to meet me. I can see their faces sometimes even now among fashionable

Translated by Constance Garnett, reprinted from *A Treasury of Great Russian Short Stories*, copyright 1944 by The Macmillan Company and used with their kind permission.

dress-coats in the noise and crowd, and then I sink into a half-dreaming state, and the past rises up before me. Their faces always betray such kindness, such hospitality and singleheartedness that unconsciously one renounces, for a brief spell at least, all ambitious dreams, and imperceptibly passes with all one's heart into this humble bucolic life.

To this day I cannot forget two old people of a past age, now, alas! no more. To this day I am full of regret, and it sends a strange pang to my heart when I imagine myself going some time again to their old now deserted dwelling, and seeing the heap of ruined huts, the pond choked with weeds, an overgrown ditch on the spot where the little house stood—and nothing more. It is sad! I am sad at the thought! But let me turn to my story.

Afanasy Ivanovich Tovstogub and his wife Pulherya Ivanovna Tovstogubiha, as the surrounding peasants called her, were the old people of whom I was beginning to tell you. If I were a painter and wanted to portray Philemon and Baucis on canvas, I could choose no other models. Afanasy Ivanovich was sixty. Pulherya Ivanovna was fifty-five. Afanasy Ivanovich was tall, always wore a camlet-covered sheepskin, used to sit bent up, and was invariably almost smiling, even though he were telling a story or simply listening. Pulherya Ivanovna was rather grave and scarcely ever laughed; but in her face and eyes there was so much kindness, so much readiness to regale you with the best of all they had, that you would certainly have found a smile superfluously sweet for her kind face. The faint wrinkles on their faces were drawn so charmingly that an artist would surely have stolen them; it seemed as though one could read in them their whole life, clear and serene —the life led by the old typically Little Russian, simple-hearted and at the same time wealthy families, always such a contrast to the meaner sort of Little Russians who, struggling up from making tar and petty trading, swarm like locusts in the law courts and public offices, fleece their fellow-villagers of their last farthing, inundate Petersburg with pettifogging attorneys, make their pile at last and solemnly add *v* to surnames ending in *o* [by way of giving them a Great Russian aspect]. No, they, like all the old-fashioned primitive Little Russian families, were utterly different from such paltry contemptible creatures.

One could not look without sympathy at their mutual love. They never addressed each other familiarly, but always with formality. "Was it you who broke the chair, Afanasy Ivanovich?" "Never mind, don't be cross, Pulherya Ivanovna, it was I." They had had no children, and so all their affection was concentrated on each other. At one time in his youth Afanasy Ivanovich was in the service and had been lieutenant-major; but that was very long ago, that was all over, Afanasy Ivanovich himself scarcely ever recalled it. Afanasy Ivanovich was married at thirty when he was a fine young fellow and wore an embroidered waistcoat; he even eloped rather neatly with Pulherya Ivanovna, whose relations opposed their marriage; but he thought very little about that either now, at any rate he never spoke of it.

All these far-away extraordinary adventures had been followed by a peaceful and secluded life, by the soothing and harmonious dreams that you enjoy when you sit on a wooden balcony overlooking the garden, while a delicious rain keeps up a luxurious sound, pattering on the leaves, flowing in gurgling streams and inducing a drowsiness in your limbs, while a rainbow hides behind the trees and in the form of a half-broken arch gleams in the sky with seven soft colors—or when you are swayed in a carriage that drives between green bushes while the quail of the steppes calls and the fragrant grass mingled with ears of corn and wild flowers thrusts itself in at the carriage doors, flicking you pleasantly on the hands and face.

Afanasy Ivanovich always listened with a pleasant smile to the guests who visited him; sometimes he talked himself, but more often he asked questions. He was not one of those old people who bore one with everlasting praises of old days or denunciations of the new: on the contrary, as he questioned you, he showed great interest and curiosity about the circumstances of your own life, your failures and successes, in which all kind-hearted old people show an interest, though it is a little like the curiosity of a child who examines the seal on your watch at the same time as he talks to you. Then his face, one may say, was breathing kindliness.

The rooms of the little house in which our old people lived were small and low-pitched, as they usually are in the houses of old-world folk. In each room there was an immense stove which covered nearly a third of the floor space. These rooms were terribly hot, for both Afanasy Ivanovich and Pulherya Ivanovna liked warmth. The stoves were all heated from the outer room, which was always filled almost up to the ceiling with straw, commonly used in Little Russia instead of firewood. The crackle and flare of this burning straw made the outer room exceedingly pleasant on a winter's evening when ardent young men, chilled with the pursuit of some pretty brunette, run in, clapping their hands. The walls of the room were adorned with a few pictures in old-fashioned narrow frames. I am convinced that their owners had themselves long ago forgotten what they represented, and if some of them had been taken away they would probably not have noticed it. There were two big portraits painted in oils. One depicted a bishop, the other Peter III.; a flyblown Duchesse de La Vallière looked out from a narrow frame. Round the windows and above the doors there were numbers of little pictures which one grew used to looking upon as spots on the wall and so never examined them. In almost all the rooms the floor was of clay, but cleanly painted and kept with a neatness with which probably no parquet floor in a wealthy house, lazily swept by a sleepy gentleman in livery, has ever been kept.

Pulherya Ivanovna's room was all surrounded with chests and boxes, big and little. Numbers of little bags and sacks of flower seeds, vegetable seeds, and melon seeds hung on the walls. Numbers of balls of different colored wools and rags of old-fashioned gowns made half a century ago were stored in the little chests and between the little chests in the corners. Pulherya

Ivanovna was a notable housewife and stored everything, though sometimes she could not herself have said to what use it could be put afterwards.

But the most remarkable thing in the house was the singing of the doors. As soon as morning came the singing of the doors could be heard all over the house. I cannot say why it was they sang: whether the rusty hinges were to blame for it or whether the mechanic who made them had concealed some secret in them; but it was remarkable that each door had its own voice; the door leading to the bedroom sang in the thinnest falsetto and the door into the dining-room in a husky bass; but the one on the outer room gave out a strange cracked and at the same time moaning sound, so that as one listened to it one heard distinctly: "Holy Saints! I am freezing!" I know that many people very much dislike this sound; but I am very fond of it, and if here I sometimes happen to hear a door creak, it seems at once to bring me a whiff of the country: the low-pitched little room lighted by a candle in an old-fashioned candlestick; supper already on the table; a dark May night peeping in from the garden through the open window at the table laid with knives and forks; the nightingale flooding garden, house, and far-away river with its trilling song; the tremor and rustle of branches and, my God! what a long string of memories stretches before me then! . . .

The chairs in the room were massive wooden ones such as were common in old days; they all had high carved backs and were without any kind of varnish or stain; they were not even upholstered, and were rather like the chairs on which bishops sit to this day. Little triangular tables in the corners and square ones before the sofa, and the mirror in its thin gold frame carved with leaves which the flies had covered with black spots; in front of the sofa a rug with birds on it that looked like flowers and flowers that looked like birds: that was almost all the furnishing of the unpretentious little house in which my old people lived. The maids' room was packed full of young girls, and girls who were not young, in striped petticoats; Pulherya Ivanovna sometimes gave them some trifling sewing or set them to prepare the fruit, but for the most part they ran off to the kitchen and slept. Pulherya Ivanovna thought it necessary to keep them in the house and looked strictly after their morals; but to her great surprise many months never passed without the waist of some girl or other growing much larger than usual. This seemed the more surprising as there was scarcely a bachelor in the house with the exception of the houseboy, who used to go about barefoot in a gray tail coat, and if he were not eating was sure to be asleep. Pulherya Ivanovna usually scolded the erring damsel and punished her severely that it might not happen again.

A terrible number of flies were always buzzing on the windowpanes, above whose notes rose the deep bass of a bumblebee, sometimes accompanied by the shrill plaint of a wasp; then as soon as candles were brought all the swarm went to bed and covered the whole ceiling with a black cloud.

Afanasy Ivanovich took very little interest in farming his land, though he did drive out sometimes to the mowers and reapers and watched their labors rather attentively; the whole burden of management rested upon Pulherya Ivanovna. Pulherya Ivanovna's housekeeping consisted in continually locking up and unlocking the storeroom, and in salting, drying and preserving countless masses of fruits and vegetables. Her house was quite like a chemical laboratory. There was everlastingly a fire built under an apple tree; and a caldron or a copper pan of jam, jelly, or a sweetmeat made with fruit, honey, sugar and I don't remember what else, was scarcely ever taken off the iron tripod on which it stood. Under another tree the coachman was for ever distilling in a copper retort vodka with peach leaves, or bird-cherry flowers or centaury or cherry stones, and at the end of the process was utterly unable to control his tongue, jabbered such nonsense that Pulherya Ivanovna could make nothing of it, and had to go away to sleep it off in the kitchen. Such a quantity of all this stuff was boiled, salted and dried that the whole courtyard would probably have been drowned in it at last (for Pulherya Ivanovna always liked to prepare a store for the future in addition to all that was reckoned necessary for use), if the larger half of it had not been eaten up by the serf-girls who, stealing into the storeroom, would overeat themselves so frightfully that they were moaning and complaining of stomachache all day.

Pulherya Ivanovna had little chance of looking after the tilling of the fields or other branches of husbandry. The steward, in conjunction with the village elder, robbed them in a merciless fashion. They had adopted the habit of treating their master's forest-land as though it were their own; they made numbers of sledges and sold them at the nearest fair; moreover, all the thick oaks they sold to the neighboring Cossacks to be cut down for mills. Only on one occasion Pulherya Ivanovna had desired to inspect her forests. For this purpose a chaise was brought out with immense leather aprons which, as soon as the coachman shook the reins and the horses, who had served in the militia, set off, filled the air with strange sounds, so that a flute and a tambourine and a drum all seemed suddenly audible; every nail and iron bolt clanked so loudly that even at the mill it could be heard that the mistress was driving out of the yard, though the distance was fully a mile and a half. Pulherya Ivanovna could not help noticing the terrible devastation in the forest and the loss of the oaks, which even in childhood she had known to be a hundred years old.

"Why is it, Nichipor," she said, addressing her steward who was on the spot, "that the oaks have been so thinned? Mind that the hair on your head does not grow as thin."

"Why is it?" the steward said. "They have fallen down! They have simply fallen: struck by lightning, gnawed by maggots—they have fallen, lady." Pulherya Ivanovna was completely satisfied with this answer, and on arriving home merely gave orders that the watch should be doubled in the garden near the Spanish cherry trees and the big winter pears.

These worthy rulers, the steward and the elder, considered it quite superfluous to take all the flour to their master's granaries; they thought that the latter would have quite enough with half, and what is more they took to the granaries the half that had begun to grow moldy or had got wet and been rejected at the fair. But however much the steward and the elder stole; however gluttonously everyone on the place ate, from the housekeeper to the pigs, who guzzled an immense number of plums and apples and often pushed the tree with their snouts to shake a perfect rain of fruit down from it; however much the sparrows and crows pecked; however many presents all the servants carried to their friends in other villages, even hauling off old linen and yarn from the storerooms, all of which went into the ever-flowing stream, that is, to the pothouse; however much was stolen by visitors, phlegmatic coachmen and flunkies, yet the blessed earth produced everything in such abundance, and Afanasy Ivanovich and Pulherya Ivanovna wanted so little, that all this terrible robbery made no perceptible impression on their prosperity.

Both the old people were very fond of good fare, as was the old-fashioned tradition of old-world landowners. As soon as the sun had risen (they always got up early) and as soon as the doors set up their varied concert, they were sitting down to a little table, drinking coffee. When he had finished his coffee Afanasy Ivanovich would go out into the porch and, shaking his handkerchief, say: 'Kish, kish! Get off the steps, geese!" In the yard he usually came across the steward. As a rule he entered into conversation with him, questioned him about the field labors with the greatest minuteness, made observations and gave orders which would have impressed anyone with his extraordinary knowledge of farming; and no novice would have dared to dream that he could steal from such a sharp-eyed master. But the steward was a wily old bird: he knew how he must answer, and, what is more, he knew how to manage the land.

After this Afanasy Ivanovich would go back indoors, and going up to his wife would say: "Well, Pulherya Ivanovna, isn't it time perhaps for a snack of something?"

"What would you like to have now, Afanasy Ivanovich? Would you like lard cakes or poppy-seed pies, or perhaps salted mushrooms?"

"Perhaps mushrooms or pies," answered Afanasy Ivanovich; and the table would at once be laid with a cloth, pies and mushrooms.

An hour before dinner Afanasy Ivanovich would have another snack, would empty an old-fashioned silver goblet of vodka, would eat mushrooms, various sorts of dried fish and so on. They sat down to dinner at twelve o'clock. Besides the dishes and sauce-boats, there stood on the table numbers of pots with closely-covered lids that no appetizing masterpiece of old-fashioned cookery might be spoilt. At dinner the conversation usually turned on subjects closely related to the dinner. "I fancy this porridge," Afanasy Ivanovich would say, "is a little bit burnt. Don't you think so, Pulherya Ivanovna?" "No, Afanasy Ivanovich. You put a little more butter to it, then it won't taste burnt, or have some of this mushroom sauce; pour that over it!" "Perhaps," said Afanasy Ivanovich, passing his plate: "Let us try how it would be."

After dinner Afanasy Ivanovich went to lie down for an hour, after which Pulherya Ivanovna would take a sliced watermelon and say: "Taste what a nice melon, Afanasy Ivanovich."

"Don't you be so sure of it, Pulherya Ivanovna, because it is red in the middle," Afanasy Ivanovich would say, taking a good slice. "There are some that are red and are not nice."

But the melon quickly disappeared. After that Afanasy Ivanovich would eat a few pears and go for a walk in the garden with Pulherya Ivanovna. On returning home Pulherya Ivanovna would go to look after household affairs, while he sat under an awning turned towards the courtyard and watched the storeroom continually displaying and concealing its interior and the serf-girls pushing one another as they brought in or carried out heaps of trifles of all sorts in wooden boxes, sieves, trays and other receptacles for holding fruit. A little later he sent for Pulherya Ivanovna, or went himself to her and said: "What shall I have to eat, Pulherya Ivanovna?"

"What would you like?" Pulherya Ivanovna would say. "Shall I go and tell them to bring you the fruit-dumpling I ordered them to keep on purpose for you?"

"That would be nice," Afanasy Ivanovich answered.

"Or perhaps you would like some jelly?"

"That would be good too," Afanasy Ivanovich would answer. Then all this was promptly brought him and duly eaten.

Before supper Afanasy Ivanovich would have another snack of something. At half past nine they sat down to supper. After supper they at once went to bed, and a universal stillness reigned in this active and at the same time tranquil home.

The room in which Afanasy Ivanovich and Pulherya Ivanovna slept was so hot that not many people could have stayed in it for several hours; but Afanasy Ivanovich, in order to be even hotter, used to sleep on the platform of the stove, though the intense heat made him get up several times in the night and walk about the room. Sometimes Afanasy Ivanovich would moan as he walked about the room. Then Pulherya Ivanovna would ask: "What are you groaning for, Afanasy Ivanovich?"

"Goodness only knows, Pulherya Ivanovna; I feel as though I had a little stomach-ache," Afanasy Ivanovich would say.

"Hadn't you better eat something, Afanasy Ivanovich?"

"I don't know whether it would be good, Pulherya Ivanovna! What should I eat, though?"

"Sour milk or some dried pears stewed."

"Perhaps I might have just a taste, anyway," said Afanasy Ivanovich.

A sleepy serf-girl went off to rummage in the cupboards, and Afanasy Ivanovich would eat a plateful, after which he commonly said: "Now it does seem to be better."

Sometimes, if it was fine weather and rather warm indoors, Afanasy Ivanovich being in good spirits liked to make fun of Pulherya Ivanovna and talk of something.

"Pulherya Ivanovna," he would say, "what if our house were suddenly burnt down, where should we go?"

"Heaven forbid!" Pulherya Ivanovna would say, crossing herself.

"But suppose our house were burnt down, where should we go then?"

"God knows what you are saying, Afanasy Ivanovich! How is it possible that our house could be burnt down? God will not permit it."

"Well, but if it were burnt down?"

"Oh, then we would move into the kitchen. You should have for the time the little room that the housekeeper has now."

"But if the kitchen were burnt too?"

"What next! God will preserve us from such a calamity as both house and kitchen burnt down all at once! Well, then we would move into the storeroom while a new house was being built."

"And if the storeroom were burnt?"

"God knows what you are saying! I don't want to listen to you! It's a sin to say it, and God will punish you for saying such things!"

And Afanasy Ivanovich, pleased at having made fun of Pulherya Ivanovna, sat smiling in his chair.

But the old couple seemed most of all interesting to me on the occasions when they had guests. Then everything in their house assumed a different aspect. These good-natured people lived, one may say, for visitors. The best of everything they had was all brought out. They vied with each other in trying to regale you with everything their husbandry produced. But what pleased me most of all was that in their solicitude there was no trace of unctuousness. This hospitality and readiness to please was so gently expressed in their faces, was so in keeping with them, that the guests could not help falling in with their wishes, which were the expression of the pure serene simplicity of their kindly guileless souls. This hospitality was something quite different from the way in which a clerk of some government office who has been helped in his career by your efforts entertains you, calling you his benefactor and cringing at your feet. The visitor was on no account to leave on the same day: he absolutely had to stay the night. "How could you set off on such a long journey at so late an hour!" Pulherya Ivanovna always said. (The guest usually lived two or three miles away.)

"Of course not," Afanasy Ivanovich said. "You never know what may happen: robbers or other evil-minded men may attack you."

"God preserve us from robbers!" said Pulherya Ivanovna. "And why talk of such things at night? It's not a question of robbers, but it's dark, it's not fit for driving at all. Besides, your coachman . . . I know your coachman, he is so frail, and such a little man, any horse would be too much for him; and besides he has probably had a drop by now and is asleep somewhere." And the guest was forced to remain; but the evening spent in the low-pitched hot room, the kindly, warming and soporific talk, the steam rising from the food on the table, always nourishing and cooked in first-class fashion, was compensation for him. I can see as though it were to-day Afanasy Ivanovich sitting bent in his chair with his invariable smile, listening to his visitor with attention and even delight! Often the talk touched on politics. The guest, who also very rarely left his village, would often with a significant air and a mysterious expression trot out his conjectures, telling them that the French had a secret agreement with the English to let Bonaparte out again in order to attack Russia, or would simply prophesy war in the near future; and then Afanasy Ivanovich, pretending not to look at Pulherya Ivanovna, would often say: "I think I shall go to the war myself; why shouldn't I go to the war?"

"There he goes again!" Pulherya Ivanovna interrupted. "Don't you believe him," she said, turning to the guest. "How could an old man like him go to the war! The first soldier would shoot him! Yes, indeed he would! He'd simply take aim and shoot him."

"Well," said Afanasy Ivanovich, "and I'll shoot him."

"Just hear how he talks!" Pulherya Ivanovna caught him up. "How could he go to the war! And his pistols have been rusty for years and are lying in the cupboard. You should just see them: why, they'd explode with the gunpowder before they'd fire a shot. And he'd blow off his hands and disfigure his face and be wretched for the rest of his days!"

"Well," said Afanasy Ivanovitch, "I'd buy myself new weapons. I'll take my sabre or a Cossack lance."

"That's all nonsense. An idea comes into his head and he begins talking!" Pulherya Ivanovna interrupted with vexation. "I know he is only joking, but yet I don't like to hear it. That's the way he always talks; sometimes one listens and listens till it frightens one."

But Afanasy Ivanovich, pleased at having scared Pulherya Ivanovna a little, laughed sitting bent up in his chair. Pulherya Ivanovna was most attractive to me when she was taking a guest in to lunch. "This," she would say, taking a cork out of a bottle, "is vodka distilled with milfoil and sage— if anyone has a pain in the shoulder blades or loins, it is very good; now this is distilled with centaury—if anyone has a ringing in the ears or a rash on the face, it is very good; and this now is distilled with peach stones—take a glass, isn't it a delicious smell? If anyone getting up in the morning knocks his head against a corner of the cupboard or a table and a bump comes up on his forehead, he has only to drink one glass of it before dinner and it takes it away entirely; it all passes off that very minute, as though it had never been there at all."

Then followed a similar account of the other bottles, which all had some healing properties. After burdening the guest with all these remedies she would lead him up to a number of dishes. "These are mushrooms with wild thyme! These are with cloves and hazelnuts! A Turkish woman taught me to salt them in the days when we still had Turkish prisoners here. She was such a nice woman, and it was not noticeable at all that she professed the Turkish religion: she went about almost exactly as we do; only she wouldn't eat pork; she said it was forbidden somewhere in their law. And these are mushrooms prepared with black currant leaves and nutmeg! And these are big pumpkins: it's the first time I have pickled them in vinegar; I don't know what they'll be like! I learnt the secret from Father Ivan; first of all you must lay some oak leaves in a tub and then sprinkle with pepper and saltpeter and then put in the flower of the hawkweed, take the flowers and strew them in with stalks uppermost. And here are the little pies; these are cheese pies. And those are the ones Afanasy Ivanovich is very fond of, made with cabbage and buckwheat."

"Yes," Afanasy Ivanovich would add, "I am very fond of them; they are soft and a little sourish."

As a rule Pulherya Ivanovna was in the best of spirits when she had guests. Dear old woman! She was entirely given up to her visitors. I liked staying with them, and although I overate fearfully, as indeed all their visitors did, and though that was very bad for me, I was always glad to go and see them. But I wonder whether the very air of Little Russia has not some peculiar property that promotes digestion; for if anyone were to venture to eat in that way here, there is no doubt he would find himself lying in his coffin instead of his bed.

Good old people! But my account of them is approaching a very melancholy incident which transformed for ever the life of that peaceful nook. This incident is the more impressive because it arose from such an insignificant cause. But such is the strange order of things; trifling causes have always given rise to great events, and on the other hand great undertakings frequently end in insignificant results. Some military leader rallies all the forces of his state, carries on a war for several years, his generals cover themselves with glory, and in the end it all results in gaining a bit of land in which there is not room to plant a potato; while sometimes two sausage-makers of two towns quarrel over some nonsense, and in the end the towns are drawn into the quarrel, then villages, and then the whole kingdom. But let us abandon these reflections: they are out of keeping here; besides I am not fond of reflections, so long as they get no further than being reflections.

Pulherya Ivanovna had a little gray cat, which almost always lay curled up at her feet. Pulherya Ivanovna sometimes stroked her and with one finger scratched her neck, which the spoilt cat stretched as high as she could. I cannot say that Pulherya Ivanovna was excessively fond of her, she was simply attached to her from being used to seeing her about. Afanasy Ivanovich, however, often teased her about her affection for it.

"I don't know, Pulherya Ivanovna, what you find in the cat: what use is she? If you had a dog, then it would be a different matter: one can take a dog out shooting, but what use is a cat?"

"Oh, be quiet, Afanasy Ivanovich," said Pulherya Ivanovna. "You are simply fond of talking and nothing else. A dog is not clean, a dog makes a mess, a dog breaks everything, while a cat is a quiet creature: she does no harm to anyone."

Cats and dogs were all the same to Afanasy Ivanovich, however; he only said it to tease Pulherya Ivanovna a little.

Beyond their garden they had a big forest which had been completely spared by the enterprising steward, perhaps because the sound of the axe would have reached the ears of Pulherya Ivanovna. It was wild and neglected, the old tree stumps were covered with overgrown hazel-bushes and looked like the feathered legs of trumpeter pigeons. Wild cats lived in this forest. Wild forest cats must not be confounded with the bold rascals who run about on the roofs of houses; in spite of their fierce disposition the latter, being in cities, are far more civilized than the inhabitants of the forest. Unlike the town cats the latter are for the most part shy and gloomy creatures; they are always gaunt and lean, they mew in a coarse uncultured voice. They sometimes scratch their way underground into the very store-houses and steal bacon; they even penetrate into the kitchen, springing suddenly in at the open window when they see that the cook has gone off into the high grass.

In fact they are unacquainted with any noble sentiments; they live by plunder, and murder little sparrows in their nests. These cats had for a long time past sniffed through a hole under the storehouse at Pulherya's Ivanovna's gentle little cat and at last they enticed her away, as a company of soldiers entices a silly peasant girl. Pulherya Ivanovna noticed the disappearance of the cat and sent to look for her; but the cat was not found. Three days passed; Pulherya Ivanovna was sorry to lose her, but at last forgot her. One day when she was inspecting her vegetable garden and was returning with fresh green cucumbers plucked by her own hands for Afanasy Ivanovich, her ear was caught by a most pitiful mew. As though by instinct she called, "Puss, puss!" and all at once her gray cat, lean and skinny, came out from the high grass; it was evident that she had not tasted food for several days. Pulherya Ivanovna went on calling her, but the cat stood mewing and did not venture to come close; it was clear that she had grown very wild during her absence. Pulherya Ivanovna went on still calling the cat, who timidly followed her right up to the fence. At last, seeing the old familiar places, she even went indoors. Pulherya Ivanovna at once ordered milk and meat to be brought her and, sitting before her, enjoyed the greediness with which her poor little favorite swallowed piece after piece and lapped up the milk. The little gray fugitive grew fatter almost before her eyes and soon did not eat so greedily. Pulherya Ivanovna stretched out her hand to stroke her, but the ungrateful creature had evidently grown too much accustomed to the ways of wild cats, or had adopted the romantic principle that poverty with love is better than a palace, and, indeed, the wild cats were as poor as church mice; anyway, she sprang out of a window and no one of the house-serfs could catch her.

The old lady sank into thought. "It was my death coming for me!" she said to herself, and nothing could distract her mind. All day she was sad.

In vain Afanasy Ivanovich joked and tried to find out why she was so melancholy all of a sudden. Pulherya Ivanovna made no answer, or answered in a way that could not possibly satisfy Afanasy Ivanovich. Next day she was perceptibly thinner.

"What is the matter with you, Pulherya Ivanovna? You must be ill."

"No, I am not ill, Afanasy Ivanovich! I want to tell you something strange; I know that I shall die this summer: my death has already come to fetch me!"

Afanasy Ivanovich's lips twitched painfully. He tried, however, to overcome his gloomy feeling and with a smile said: "God knows what you are saying, Pulherya Ivanovna! You must have drunk some peach vodka instead of the decoction you usually drink."

"No, Afanasy Ivanovich, I have not drunk peach vodka," said Pulherya Ivanovna. And Afanasy Ivanovich was sorry that he had so teased her; he looked at her and a tear hung on his eyelash.

"I beg you, Afanasy Ianovich, to carry out my wishes," said Pulherya Ivanovna; "when I die, bury me by the church fence. Put my gray dress on me, the one with the little flowers on a brown ground. Don't put on me my satin dress with the crimson stripes: a dead woman has no need of a dress—what use is it to her?—while it will be of use to you: have a fine dressing-gown made of it, so that when visitors are here you can show yourself and welcome them, looking decent."

"God knows what you are saying, Pulherya Ivanovna!" said Afanasy Ivanovich. "Death may be a long way off, but you are frightening me already with such sayings."

"No, Afanasy Ivanovich, I know now when my death will come. Don't grieve for me, though: I am an old woman and have lived long enough, and you are old, too; we shall soon meet in the other world."

But Afanasy Ivanovich was sobbing like a child.

"It is a sin to weep, Afanasy Ivanovich! Do not be sinful and anger God by your sorrow. I am not sorry that I am dying; there is only one thing I am sorry about"—a heavy sigh interrupted her words for a minute. "I am sorry that I do not know in whose care to leave you, who will look after you when I am dead. You are like a little child. You need somebody who loves you to look after you."

At these words there was an expression of such deep, such distressed heartfelt pity on her face that I doubt whether anyone could have looked at her at that moment unmoved.

"Mind, Yavdoha," she said, turning to the housekeeper for whom she had purposely sent, "that when I die you look after your master, watch over him like the apple of your eye, like your own child. Mind that what he likes is always cooked for him in the kitchen; that you always give him clean linen and clothes; that when visitors come you dress him in his best, or else maybe he will sometimes come out in his old dressing-gown, because even now he often forgets when it's a holiday and when it's a working day.

Don't take your eyes off him, Yavdoha; I will pray for you in the next world and God will reward you. Do not forget, Yavdoha, you are old, you have not long to live—do not take a sin upon your soul. If you do not look after him you will have no happiness in life. I myself will beseech God not to give you a happy end. And you will be unhappy yourself and your children will be unhappy, and all your family will not have the blessing of God in anything."

Poor old woman! At that minute she was not thinking of the great moment awaiting her, nor of her soul, nor of her own future life: she was thinking only of her poor companion with whom she had spent her life and whom she was leaving helpless and forlorn. With extraordinary efficiency she arranged everything, so that Afanasy Ivanovich should not notice her absence when she was gone. Her conviction that her end was at hand was so strong, and her state of mind was so attuned to it, that she did in fact take to her bed a few days later and could eat nothing. Afanasy Ivanovich never left her bedside and was all solicitude. "Perhaps you would eat a little of something, Pulherya Ivanovna," he said, looking with anxiety into her eyes. But Pulherya Ivanovna said nothing. At last, after a long silence she seemed trying to say something, her lips stirred—and her breathing ceased.

Afanasy Ivanovich was absolutely overwhelmed. It seemed to him so uncanny that he did not even weep; he looked at her with dull eyes as though not grasping the significance of the corpse.

The dead woman was laid on the table dressed in the gown she had herself fixed upon, her arms were crossed and a wax candle put in her hand— he looked at all this apathetically. Numbers of people of all kinds filled the courtyard; numbers of guests came to the funeral; long tables were laid out in the courtyard; they were covered with masses of funeral rice, of home-made beverages and pies. The guests talked and wept, gazed at the dead woman, discussed her qualities and looked at him; but he himself looked queerly at it all. The coffin was carried out at last, the people crowded after it and he followed it. The priests were in full vestments, the sun was shining, babies were crying in their mothers' arms, larks were singing and children raced and skipped about the road. At last the coffin was put down above the grave, he was bidden approach and kiss the dead woman for the last time. He went up and kissed her; there were tears in his eyes, but they were somehow apathetic tears. The coffin was lowered, the priest took the spade and first threw in a handful of earth; the deep rich voices of the deacon and the two sacristans sang "Eternal Memory" under the pure cloudless sky; the laborers took up their spades and soon the earth covered the grave and made it level. At that moment he pressed forward, everyone stepped aside and made way for him, anxious to know what he meant to do. He raised his eyes, looked at them vacantly and said: "So you have buried her already! What for?" He broke off and said no more.

But when he was home again, when he saw that his room was empty, that even the chair Pulherya Ivanova used to sit on had been taken away—

he sobbed, sobbed violently, inconsolably, and tears flowed from his lusterless eyes like a river.

Five years have passed since then. What grief does not time bear away? What passion survives in the unequal combat with it? I knew a man in the flower of his youth and strength, full of true nobility of character. I knew him in love, tenderly, passionately, madly, fiercely, humbly; and before me, and before my eyes almost, the object of his passion, a tender creature, lovely as an angel, was struck down by merciless death. I have never seen such awful depths of spiritual suffering, such frenzied poignant grief, such devouring despair as overwhelmed the luckless lover. I had never imagined that a man could create for himself such a hell with no shadow, no shape, no semblance of hope. . . . People tried not to leave him alone; all weapons with which he might have killed himself were hidden from him. A fortnight later he suddenly mastered himself, and began laughing and jesting; he was given his freedom, and the first use he made of it was to buy a pistol. One day his family were terrified by the sudden sound of a shot; they ran into the room and saw him stretched on the floor with a shattered skull. A doctor, who happened to be there at the time and whose skill was famous, saw signs of life in him, found that the wound was not absolutely fatal and, to the amazement of everyone, the young man recovered. The watch kept on him was stricter than ever. Even at dinner a knife was not laid for him and everything was removed with which he could have hurt himself; but in a short time he found another opportunity and threw himself under the wheels of a passing carriage. An arm and a leg were broken; but again he recovered. A year after that I saw him in a roomful of people; he was sitting at a table saying gayly "petite ouverte," as he covered a card, and behind him, with her elbows on the back of his chair, was standing his young wife, turning over his counters.

At the end of the five years after Pulherya Ivanovna's death I was in those parts and drove to Afanasy Ivanovich's little farm to visit my old neighbor, in whose house I used at one time to spend the day pleasantly and always to overeat myself with the choicest masterpieces of its hospitable mistress.

As I approached the courtyard the house seemed to me twice as old as it had been: the peasants' huts were lying completely on one side, as no doubt their owners were too; the palisade and the hurdle round the yard were completely broken down, and I myself saw the cook pull sticks out of it to heat the stove, though she need have only taken two steps further to reach the faggot-stack. Sadly I drove up to the steps; the same old dogs, by now blind or lame, barked, wagging their fluffy tails covered with burdocks. An old man came out to greet me. Yes, it was he! I know him at once; but he stooped twice as much as before. He knew me and greeted me with the old familiar smile. I followed him indoors. It seemed as though everything was as before. But I noticed a strange disorder in everything, an unmistakable absence of something. In fact I experienced the strange feel-

ings which come upon us when for the first time we enter the house of a
widower whom we have known in old days inseparable from the wife who
has shared his life. The feeling is the same when we see a man crippled
whom we have always known in health. In everything the absence of careful
Pulherya Ivanovna was visible: at table a knife was laid without a handle;
the dishes were not cooked with the same skill. I did not want to ask about
the farm, I was afraid even to look at the farm buildings. When we sat down
to dinner, a maid tied a napkin round Afanasy Ivanovich, and it was well
she did so, as without it he would have spilt sauce all over his dressing-gown.
I tried to entertain him and told him various items of news; he listened with
the same smile, but from time to time his eyes were completely vacant, and
his thoughts did not stray, but vanished. Often he lifted a spoonful of
porridge and instead of putting it to his mouth put it to his nose; instead of
sticking his fork into a piece of chicken, he prodded the decanter, and then
the maid, taking his hand, brought it back to the chicken. We sometimes
waited several minutes for the next course.

Afanasy Ivanovich himself noticed it and said: "Why is it they are so
long bringing the food?" But I saw through the crack of the door that the
boy who carried away our plates was asleep and nodding on a bench, not
thinking of his duties at all.

"This is the dish," said Afanasy Ivanovich, when we were handed curd-
cakes with sour cream. "This is the dish," he went on, and I noticed that his
voice began quivering and a tear was ready to drop from his leaden eyes,
but he did his utmost to restrain it. "This is the dish which my . . . my . . .
dear . . . my dear . . ." And all at once he burst into tears; his hand fell
on the plate, the plate turned upside down, slipped and was smashed, and
the sauce was spilt all over him. He sat vacantly, vacantly held the spoon;
and tears like a stream, like a ceaselessly flowing fountain, flowed and flowed
on the napkin that covered him.

"My God!" I thought, looking at him, "five years of all-destroying
time—an old man already apathetic, an old man whose life one would have
thought had never once been stirred by a strong feeling, whose whole life
seemed to consist in sitting on a high chair, in eating dried fish and pears,
in telling good-natured stories—and such long, such bitter grief! What is
stronger in us—passion or habit? Or are all the violent impulses, all the
whirl of our desires and boiling passions only the consequences of our
ardent age, and is it only through youth that they seem deep and shattering?"

Be that as it may, at that moment all our passions seemed like child's
play beside this effect of long, slow, almost insensible habit. Several times
he struggled to utter his wife's name, but halfway through the word, his
quiet and ordinary face worked convulsively and his childish weeping cut
me to the very heart. No, those were not the tears of which old men are
usually so lavish, as they complain of their pitiful position and their troubles;
they were not the tears which they drop over a glass of punch either. No!

they were tears which brimmed over uninvited from the accumulated rankling pain of a heart already turning cold.

He did not live long after that. I heard lately of his death. It is strange, though, that the circumstances of his end had some resemblance to those of Pulherya Ivanovna's death. One day Afanasy Ivanovich ventured to take a little walk in the garden. As he was pacing slowly along a path with his usual absent-mindedness, without a thought of any kind in his head, he had a strange adventure. He suddenly heard someone behind him pronounce in a fairly distinct voice: "Afanasy Ivanovich!" He turned round but there was absolutely nobody there; he looked in all directions, he peered into the bushes—no one anywhere. It was a still day and the sun was shining. He pondered for a minute; his face seemed to brighten and he brought out at last: "It's Pulherya Ivanovna calling me!"

It has happened to you doubtless some time or other to hear a voice calling you by name, which simple people explain as a soul grieving for a human being and calling him, and after that, they say, death follows inevitably. I must own I was always frightened by that mysterious call. I remember that in childhood I often heard it. Sometimes suddenly someone behind me distinctly uttered my name. Usually on such occasions it was a very bright and sunny day; not one leaf in the garden was stirring, the stillness was deathlike; even the grasshopper left off churring for the moment; there was not a soul in the garden. But I confess that if the wildest and most tempestuous night had lashed me with all the fury of the elements, alone in the middle of an impenetrable forest, I should not have been so terrified as by that awful stillness in the midst of a cloudless day. I usually ran out of the garden in a great panic, hardly able to breathe, and was only reassured when I met some person, the sight of whom dispelled the terrible spiritual loneliness.

Afanasy Ivanovich surrendered completely to his inner conviction that Pulherya Ivanovna was calling him; he submitted with the readiness of an obedient child, wasted away, coughed, melted like a candle and at last flickered out, as it does when there is nothing left to sustain its feeble flame. "Lay me beside Pulherya Ivanovna" was all he said before his end.

His desire was carried out and he was buried near the church beside Pulherya Ivanovna's grave. The guests were fewer at the funeral, but there were just as many beggars and peasants. The little house was now completely emptied. The enterprising steward and the elder hauled away to their huts all that was left of the old-fashioned goods and furniture, which the housekeeper had not been able to carry off. Soon there arrived, I cannot say from where, a distant kinsman, the heir to the estate, who had been a lieutenant, I don't know in what regiment, and was a terrible reformer. He saw at once the great slackness and disorganization in the management of the land; he made up his mind to change all that radically, to improve things and bring everything into order. He bought six splendid English sickles, pinned a special number on each hut, and managed so well that within six months his estate was put under the supervision of a board of trustees.

The sage trustees (consisting of an ex-assessor and a lieutenant in a faded uniform) had within a very short time left no fowls and eggs. The huts, which were almost lying on the earth, fell down completely; the peasants gave themselves up to drunkenness and most of them ran away. The real owner, who got on, however, pretty comfortably with his trustees and used to drink punch with them, very rarely visited his estate and never stayed long. To this day he drives about to all the fairs in Little Russia, carefully inquiring the prices of all sorts of produce sold wholesale, such as flour, hemp, honey and so on; but he only buys some trifles such as flints, a nail to clean out his pipe, in fact nothing which exceeds at the utmost a rouble in price.

1835

Anton Chekhov

ON THE ROAD

"Upon the breast of a gigantic crag,
A golden cloudlet rested for one night."
—LERMONTOV.

IN THE room which the tavern keeper, the Cossack Semyon Tchistopluy, called the "travellers' room," that is kept exclusively for travellers, a tall, broad-shouldered man of forty was sitting at the big unpainted table. He was asleep with his elbows on the table and his head leaning on his fist. An end of tallow candle, stuck into an old pomatum pot, lighted up his light brown beard, his thick, broad nose, his sunburnt cheeks, and the thick, black eyebrows overhanging his closed eyes. . . . The nose and the cheeks and the eyebrows, all the features, each taken separately, were coarse and heavy, like the furniture and the stove in the "travellers' room," but taken all together they gave the effect of something harmonious and even beautiful. Such is the lucky star, as it is called, of the Russian face: the coarser and harsher its features the softer and more good-natured it looks. The man was dressed in a gentleman's reefer jacket, shabby, but bound with wide new braid, a plush waistcoat, and full black trousers thrust into big high boots.

On one of the benches, which stood in a continuous row along the wall, a girl of eight, in a brown dress and long black stockings, lay asleep on a coat lined with fox. Her face was pale, her hair was flaxen, her shoulders were narrow, her whole body was thin and frail, but her nose stood out as thick and ugly a lump as the man's. She was sound asleep, and unconscious that her semi-circular comb had fallen off her head and was cutting her cheek.

The "travellers' room" had a festive appearance. The air was full of the smell of freshly scrubbed floors, there were no rags hanging as usual on the line that ran diagonally across the room, and a little lamp was burning in the corner over the table, casting a patch of red light on the ikon of St. George the Victorious. From the ikon stretched on each side of the corner a row of cheap oleographs, which maintained a strict and careful gradation in the transition from the sacred to the profane. In the dim light of the candle end and the red ikon lamp the pictures looked like one continuous stripe, covered with blurs of black. When the tiled stove, trying to sing in unison with the weather, drew in the air with a howl, while the logs, as though waking up, burst into bright flame and hissed angrily, red patches began dancing on the log walls, and over the head of the sleeping man could be seen first the Elder Seraphim, then the Shah Nasir-ed-Din, then a fat, brown baby with goggle eyes, whispering in the ear of a young girl with an extraordinarily blank, and indifferent face. . . .

Outside a storm was raging. Something frantic and wrathful, but profoundly unhappy, seemed to be flinging itself about the tavern with the ferocity of a wild beast and trying to break in. Banging at the doors, knocking at the windows and on the roof, scratching at the walls, it alternately threatened and besought, then subsided for a brief interval, and then with a gleeful, treacherous howl burst into the chimney, but the wood flared up, and the fire, like a chained dog, flew wrathfully to meet its foe, a battle began, and after it—sobs, shrieks, howls of wrath. In all of this there was the sound of angry misery and unsatisfied hate, and the mortified impatience of something accustomed to triumph.

Bewitched by this wild, inhuman music the "travellers' room" seemed spellbound for ever, but all at once the door creaked and the potboy, in a new print shirt, came in. Limping on one leg, and blinking his sleepy eyes, he snuffed the candle with his fingers, put some more wood on the fire and went out. At once from the church, which was three hundred paces from the tavern, the clock struck midnight. The wind played with the chimes as with the snowflakes; chasing the sounds of the clock it whirled them round and round over a vast space, so that some strokes were cut short or drawn out in long, vibrating notes, while others were completely lost in the general uproar. One stroke sounded as distinctly in the room as though it had chimed just under the window. The child, sleeping on the foxskin, started and raised her head. For a minute she stared blankly at the dark window, at Nasir-ed-Din over whom a crimson glow from the fire flickered at that moment, then she turned her eyes upon the sleeping man.

"Daddy," she said.

But the man did not move. The little girl knitted her brow angrily, lay down, and curled up her legs. Someone in the tavern gave a loud, prolonged yawn. Soon afterwards there was the squeak of the swing door and the sound of indistinct voices. Someone came in, shaking the snow off, and stamping in felt boots which made a muffled thud.

"What is it?" a woman's voice asked languidly.

"Mademoiselle Ilovaisky has come, . . ." answered a bass voice.

Again there was the squeak of the swing door. Then came the roar of the wind rushing in. Someone, probably the lame boy, ran to the door leading to the "travellers' room," coughed deferentially, and lifted the latch.

"This way, lady, please," said a woman's voice in dulcet tones. "It's clean in here, my beauty. . . ."

The door was opened wide and a peasant with a beard appeared in the doorway, in the long coat of a coachman, plastered all over with snow from head to foot, and carrying a big trunk on his shoulder. He was followed into the room by a feminine figure, scarcely half his height, with no face and no arms, muffled and wrapped up like a bundle and also covered with snow. A damp chill, as from a cellar, seemed to come to the child from the coachman and the bundle, and the fire and the candles flickered.

"What nonsense!" said the bundle angrily. "We could go perfectly well. We have only nine more miles to go, mostly by the forest, and we should not get lost. . . ."

"As for getting lost, we shouldn't, but the horses can't go on, lady!" answered the coachman. "And it is Thy Will, O Lord! As though I had done it on purpose!"

"God knows where you have brought me. . . . Well, be quiet. . . . There are people asleep here, it seems. You can go. . . ."

The coachman put the portmanteau on the floor, and as he did so, a great lump of snow fell off his shoulders. He gave a sniff and went out.

Then the little girl saw two little hands come out from the middle of the bundle, stretch upwards and begin angrily disentangling the network of shawls, kerchiefs, and scarves. First a big shawl fell on the ground, then a hood, then a white knitted kerchief. After freeing her head, the traveller took off her pelisse and at once shrank to half the size. Now she was in a long, grey coat with big buttons and bulging pockets. From one pocket she pulled out a paper parcel, from the other a bunch of big, heavy keys, which she put down so carelessly that the sleeping man started and opened his eyes. For some time he looked blankly round him as though he didn't know where he was, then he shook his head, went to the corner and sat down. . . . The newcomer took off her greatcoat, which made her shrink to half her size again, she took off her big felt boots, and sat down, too.

By now she no longer resembled a bundle: she was a thin little brunette of twenty, as slim as a snake, with a long white face and curly hair. Her nose was long and sharp, her chin, too, was long and sharp, her eyelashes were long, the corners of her mouth were sharp, and, thanks to this general sharpness, the expression of her face was biting. Swathed in a closely fitting black dress with a mass of lace at her neck and sleeves, with sharp elbows and long pink fingers, she recalled the portraits of mediaeval English ladies. The grave concentration of her face increased this likeness.

The lady looked round at the room, glanced sideways at the man and the little girl, shrugged her shoulders, and moved to the window. The dark windows were shaking from the damp west wind. Big flakes of snow glistening in their whiteness lay on the window frame, but at once disappeared, borne away by the wind. The savage music grew louder and louder. . . .

After a long silence the little girl suddenly turned over, and said angrily, emphasizing each word:

"Oh, goodness, goodness, how unhappy I am! Unhappier than anyone!'

The man got up and moved with little steps to the child with a guilty air, which was utterly out of keeping with his huge figure and big beard.

"You are not asleep, dearie?" he said, in an apologetic voice. "What do you want?"

"I don't want anything, my shoulder aches! You are a wicked man, Daddy, and God will punish you! You'll see He will punish you."

"My darling, I know your shoulder aches, but what can I do, dearie?" said the man, in the tone in which men who have been drinking excuse themselves to their stern spouses. "It's the journey has made your shoulder ache, Sasha. To-morrow we shall get there and rest, and the pain will go away. . . ."

"To-morrow, to-morrow. . . . Every day you say to-morrow. We shall be going on another twenty days."

"But we shall arrive to-morrow, dearie, on your father's word of honour. I never tell a lie, but if we are detained by the snowstorm it is not my fault."

"I can't bear any more, I can't, I can't!"

Sasha jerked her leg abruptly and filled the room with an unpleasant wailing. Her father made a despairing gesture, and looked hopelessly towards the young lady. The latter shrugged her shoulders, and hesitatingly went up to Sasha.

"Listen, my dear," she said, "it is no use crying. It's really naughty; if your shoulder aches it can't be helped."

"You see, Madam," said the man quickly, as though defending himself, "we have not slept for two nights, and have been travelling in a revolting conveyance. Well, of course, it is natural she should be ill and miserable, . . . and then, you know, we had a drunken driver, our portmanteau has been stolen . . . the snowstorm all the time, but what's the use of crying, Madam? I am exhausted, though, by sleeping in a sitting position, and I feel as though I were drunk. Oh, dear! Sasha, and I feel sick as it is, and then you cry!"

The man shook his head, and with a gesture of despair sat down.

"Of course you mustn't cry," said the young lady. "It's only little babies cry. If you are ill, dear, you must undress and go to sleep. . . . Let us take off your things!"

When the child had been undressed and pacified a silence reigned again. The young lady seated herself at the window, and looked round wonderingly at the room of the inn, at the ikon, at the stove. . . . Apparently the room and the little girl with the thick nose, in her short boy's nightgown, and the child's father, all seemed strange to her. This strange man was sitting in a corner; he kept looking about him helplessly, as though he were drunk, and rubbing his face with the palm of his hand. He sat silent, blinking, and judging from his guilty-looking figure it was difficult to imagine that he would soon begin to speak. Yet he was the first to begin. Stroking his knees, he gave a cough, laughed, and said:

"It's a comedy, it really is. . . . I look and I cannot believe my eyes: for what devilry has destiny driven us to this accursed inn? What did she want to show by it? Life sometimes performs such 'salto mortale,' one can only stare and blink in amazement. Have you come from far, Madam?"

"No, not from far," answered the young lady. "I am going from our estate, fifteen miles from here, to our farm, to my father and brother. My name is Ilovaisky, and the farm is called Ilovaiskoe. It's nine miles away. What unpleasant weather!"

"It couldn't be worse."

The lame boy came in and stuck a new candle in the pomatum pot.

"You might bring us the samovar, boy," said the man, addressing him.

"Who drinks tea now?" laughed the boy. "It is a sin to drink tea before mass. . . ."

"Never mind, boy, you won't burn in hell if we do. . . ."

Over the tea the new acquaintances got into conversation.

Mlle. Ilovaisky learned that her companion was called Grigory Petrovitch Liharev, that he was the brother of the Liharev who was Marshal of Nobility in one of the neighbouring districts, and he himself had once been a landowner, but had "run through everything in his time." Liharev learned that her name was Marya Mihailovna, that her father had a huge estate, but that she was the only one to look after it as her father and brother looked at life through their fingers, were irresponsible, and were too fond of harriers.

"My father and brother are all alone at the farm," she told him, brandishing her fingers (she had the habit of moving her fingers before her pointed face as she talked, and after every sentence moistened her lips with her sharp little tongue). "They, I mean men, are an irresponsible lot, and don't stir a finger for themselves. I can fancy there will be no one to give them a meal after the fast! We have no mother, and we have such servants that they can't lay the tablecloth properly when I am away. You can imagine their condition now! They will be left with nothing to break their fast, while I have to stay here all night. How strange it all is."

She shrugged her shoulders, took a sip from her cup, and said:

"There are festivals that have a special fragrance: at Easter, Trinity and Christmas there is a peculiar scent in the air. Even unbelievers are fond of those festivals. My brother, for instance, argues that there is no God, but he is the first to hurry to Matins at Easter."

Liharev raised his eyes to Mlle. Ilovaisky and laughed.

"They argue that there is no God," she went on, laughing too, "but why is it, tell me, all the celebrated writers, the learned men, clever people generally, in fact, believe towards the end of their life?"

"If a man does not know how to believe when he is young, Madam, he won't believe in his old age if he is ever so much of a writer."

Judging from Liharev's cough he had a bass voice, but, probably from being afraid to speak aloud, or from exaggerated shyness, he spoke in a tenor. After a brief pause he heaved a sigh and said:

"The way I look at it is that faith is a faculty of the spirit. It is just the same as a talent, one must be born with it. So far as I can judge by myself, by the people I have seen in my time, and by all that is done around us, this faculty is present in Russians in its highest degree. Russian life presents us with an uninterrupted succession of convictions and aspirations, and if you care to know, it has not yet the faintest notion of lack of faith or scepticism. If a Russian does not believe in God, it means he believes in something else."

Liharev took a cup of tea from Mlle. Ilovaisky, drank off half in one gulp, and went on:

"I will tell you about myself. Nature has implanted in my breast an extraordinary faculty for belief. Whisper it not to the night, but half my life I was in the ranks of the Atheists and Nihilists, but there was not one hour in my life in which I ceased to believe. All talents, as a rule, show themselves in early childhood, and so my faculty showed itself when I could still walk upright under the table. My mother liked her children to eat a great deal, and when she gave me food she used to say: 'Eat! Soup is the great thing in life!' I believed, and ate the soup ten times a day, ate like a shark, ate till I was disgusted and stupefied. My nurse used to tell me fairy tales, and I believed in house-spirits, in wood-elves, and in goblins of all kinds. I used sometimes to steal corrosive sublimate from my father, sprinkle it on cakes, and carry them up to the attic that the house-spirits, you see, might eat them and be killed. And when I was taught to read and understand what I read, then there was a fine to-do. I ran away to America and went off to join the brigands, and wanted to go into a monastery, and hired boys to torture me for being a Christian. And note that my faith was always active, never dead. If I was running away to America I was not alone, but seduced someone else, as great a fool as I was, to go with me, and was delighted when I was nearly frozen outside the town gates and when I was thrashed; if I went to join the brigands I always came back with my face battered. A most restless childhood, I assure you! And when they sent me to the high school and pelted me with all sorts of truths—that is, that the earth goes round the sun, or that white light is not white, but is made up of seven colours—my poor little head began to go round! Everything was thrown into a whirl in me: Navin who made the sun stand still, and my mother who in the name of the Prophet Elijah disapproved of lightning conductors, and my father who was indifferent to the truths I had learned. My enlightenment inspired me. I wandered about the house and stables like one possessed, preaching my truths, was horrified by ignorance, glowed with hatred for anyone who saw in white light nothing but white light. . . . But all that's nonsense and childishness. Serious, so to speak, manly enthusiasms began only at the university. You have, no doubt, Madam, taken your degree somewhere?"

"I studied at Novotcherkask at the Don Institute."

"Then you have not been to a university? So you don't know what science means. All the sciences in the world have the same passport, without which they regard themselves as meaningless . . . the striving towards truth! Every one of them, even pharmacology, has for its aim not utility, not the alleviation of life, but truth. It's remarkable! When you set to work to study any science, what strikes you first of all is its beginning. I assure you there is nothing more attractive and grander, nothing is so staggering, nothing takes a man's breath away like the beginning of any science. From the first five or six lectures you are soaring on wings of the brightest hopes, you already seem to yourself to be welcoming truth with open arms. And I gave myself up to science, heart and soul, passionately, as to the woman one loves. I was its slave; I found it the sun of my existence, and asked for no other. I studied day and night without rest, ruined myself over books, wept when before my eyes men exploited science for their own personal ends. But my enthusiasm did not last long. The trouble is that every science has a beginning but not an end, like a recurring decimal. Zoology has discovered 35,000 kinds of insects, chemistry reckons 60 elements. If in time tens of noughts can be written after these figures, zoology and chemistry will be just as far from their end as now, and all contemporary scientific work consists in increasing these numbers. I saw through this trick when I discovered the 35,001st and felt no satisfaction. Well, I had no time to suffer from disillusionment, as I was soon possessed by a new faith. I plunged into Nihilism, with its manifestoes, its 'black divisions,' and all the rest of it. I 'went to the people,' worked in factories, worked as an oiler, as a barge hauler. Afterwards, when wandering over Russia, I had a taste of Russian life, I turned into a fervent devotee of that life. I loved the Russian people with poignant intensity; I loved their God and believed in Him, and in their language, their creative genius. . . . And so on, and so on. . . . I have been a Slavophile in my time, I used to pester Aksakov with letters, and I was a Ukrainophile, and an archaeologist, and a collector of specimens of peasant art. . . . I was enthusiastic over ideas, people, events, places . . . my enthusiasm was endless! Five years ago I was working for the abolition of private property; my last creed was non-resistance to evil."

Sasha gave an abrupt sigh and began moving. Liharev got up and went to her.

"Won't you have some tea, dearie?" he asked tenderly.

"Drink it yourself," the child answered rudely.

Liharev was disconcerted, and went back to the table with a guilty step.

"Then you have had a lively time," said Mlle. Ilovaisky; "you have something to remember."

"Well, yes, it's all very lively when one sits over tea and chatters to a kind listener, but you should ask what that liveliness has cost me! What price have I paid for the variety of my life? You see, Madam, I have not held my convictions like a German doctor of philosophy, *zierlichmännerlich,* I have not lived in solitude, but every conviction I have had has bound my back to the yoke, has torn my body to pieces. Judge, for yourself. I was wealthy like my brothers, but now I am a beggar. In the delirium of my enthusiasm I smashed up my own fortune and my wife's—a heap of other people's money. Now I am forty-two, old age is close upon me, and I am homeless, like a dog that has dropped behind its waggon at night. All my life I have not known what peace meant, my soul has been in continual agitation, distressed even by its hopes . . . I have been wearied out with heavy irregular work, have endured privation, have five times been in prison, have dragged myself across the provinces of Archangel and of Toblosk . . . it's painful to think of it! I have lived, but in my fever I have not even been conscious of the process of life itself. Would you believe it, I don't remember a single spring, I never noticed how my wife loved me, how my children were born. What more can I tell you? I have been a misfortune to all who have loved me. . . . My mother has worn mourning for me all these fifteen years, while my proud brothers, who have had to wince, to blush, to bow their heads, to waste their money on my account, have come in the end to hate me like poison."

Liharev got up and sat down again.

"If I were simply unhappy I should thank God," he went on without looking at his listener. "My personal unhappiness sinks into the background when I remember how often in my enthusiasms I have been absurd, far from the truth, unjust, cruel, dangerous! How often I have hated and despised those whom I ought to have loved, and *vice versa*. I have changed a thousand times. One day I believe, fall down and worship, the next I flee like a coward from the gods and friends of yesterday, and swallow in silence the 'scoundrel!' they hurl after me. God alone has seen how often I have wept and bitten my pillow in shame for my enthusiasms. Never once in my life have I intentionally lied or done evil, but my conscience is not clear! I cannot even boast, Madam, that I have no one's life upon my conscience, for my wife died before my eyes, worn out by my reckless activity. Yes, my wife! I tell you they have two ways of treating women nowadays. Some measure women's skulls to prove woman is inferior to man, pick out her defects to mock at her, to look original in her eyes, and to justify their sensuality. Others do their utmost to raise women to their level, that is, force them to learn by heart the 35,000 species, to speak and write the same foolish things as they speak and write themselves."

Liharev's face darkened.

"I tell you that woman has been and always will be the slave of man," he said in a bass voice, striking his fist on the table. "She is the soft, tender wax which a man always moulds into anything he likes. . . . My God! for the sake of some trumpery masculine enthusiasm she will cut off her hair, abandon her family, die among strangers! . . . among the ideas for which she has sacrificed herself there is not a single feminine one. . . . An unquestioning, devoted slave! I have not measured skulls, but I say this from hard, bitter experience: the proudest, most independent women, if I have succeeded in communicating to them my enthusiasm, have followed me without criticism, without question, and done anything I chose; I have turned a nun into a Nihilist who, as I heard afterwards, shot a gendarme; my wife never left me for a minute in my wanderings, and like a weather-cock changed her faith in step with my changing enthusiasms."

Liharev jumped up and walked up and down the room.

"A noble, sublime slavery!" he said, clasping his hands. "It is just in it that the highest meaning of woman's life lies! Of all the fearful medley of thoughts and impressions accumulated in my brain from my association with women my memory, like a filter, has retained no ideas, no clever saying, no philosophy, nothing but that extraordinary resignation to fate, that wonderful mercifulness, forgiveness of everything."

Liharev clenched his fists, stared at a fixed point, and with a sort of passionate intensity, as though he were savouring each word as he uttered it, hissed through his clenched teeth:

"That . . . that great-hearted fortitude, faithfulness unto death, poetry of the heart. . . . The meaning of life lies in just that unrepining martyrdom, in the tears which would soften a stone, in the boundless, all-forgiving love which brings light and warmth into the chaos of life. . . ."

Mlle. Ilovaisky got up slowly, took a step towards Liharev, and fixed her eyes upon his face. From the tears that glittered on his eyelashes, from his quivering, passionate voice, from the flush on his cheeks, it was clear to her that women were not a chance, not a simple subject of conversation. They were the object of his new enthusiasm, or, as he said himself, his new faith! For the first time in her life she saw a man carried away, fervently believing. With his gesticulations, with his flashing eyes he seemed to her mad, frantic, but there was a feeling of such beauty in the fire of his eyes, in his words, in all the movements of his huge body, that without noticing what she was doing she stood facing him as though rooted to the spot, and gazed into his face with delight.

"Take my mother," he said, stretching out his hand to her with an imploring expression on his face, "I poisoned her existence, according to her ideas disgraced the name of Liharev, did her as much harm as the most malignant enemy, and what do you think? My brothers give her little sums for holy bread and church services, and outraging her religious feelings, she saves that money and sends it in secret to her erring Grigory. This trifle alone elevates and ennobles the soul far more than all the theories, all the clever sayings and the 35,000 species. I can give you thousands of instances. Take you, even, for instance! With tempest and darkness outside you are going to your father and your brother to cheer them with your affection in the holiday, though very likely they have forgotten and are not thinking of you. And, wait a bit, and you will love a man and follow him to the North Pole. You would, wouldn't you?"

"Yes, if I loved him."

"There, you see," cried Liharev delighted, and he even stamped with his foot. "Oh dear! How glad I am that I have met you! Fate is kind to me, I am always meeting splendid people. Not a day passes but one makes

acquaintance with somebody one would give one's soul for. There are ever so
many more good people than bad in this world. Here, see, for instance, how
openly and from our hearts we have been talking as though we had known
each other a hundred years. Sometimes, I assure you, one restrains oneself for
ten years and holds one's tongue, is reserved with one's friends and one's
wife, and meets some cadet in a train and babbles one's whole soul out to
him. It is the first time I have the honour of seeing you, and yet I have
confessed to you as I have never confessed in my life. Why is it?"

Rubbing his hands and smiling good-humouredly Liharev walked up
and down the room, and fell to talking about women again. Meanwhile they
began ringing for matins.

"Goodness," wailed Sasha. "He won't let me sleep with his talking!"

"Oh, yes!" said Liharev, startled. "I am sorry, darling, sleep, sleep. . . .
I have two boys besides her," he whispered. "They are living with their uncle,
Madam, but this one can't exist a day without her father. She's wretched, she
complains, but she sticks to me like a fly to honey. I have been chattering
too much, Madam, and it would do you no harm to sleep. Wouldn't you like
me to make up a bed for you?"

Without waiting for permission he shook the wet pelisse, stretched it
on a bench, fur side upwards, collected various shawls and scarves, put the
overcoat folded up into a roll for a pillow, and all this he did in silence with
a look of devout reverence, as though he were not handling a woman's rags,
but the fragments of holy vessels. There was something apologetic, embarrassed about his whole figure, as though in the presence of a weak creature
he felt ashamed of his height and strength. . . .

When Mlle. Ilovaisky had lain down, he put out the candle and sat down
on a stool by the stove.

"So, Madam," he whispered, lighting a fat cigarette and puffing the
smoke into the stove. "Nature has put into the Russian an extraordinary
faculty for belief, a searching intelligence, and the gift of speculation, but all
that is reduced to ashes by irresponsibility, laziness, and dreamy frivolity.
. . . Yes. . . ."

She gazed wonderingly into the darkness, and saw only a spot of red on
the ikon and the flicker of the light of the stove on Liharev's face. The darkness, the chime of the bells, the roar of the storm, the lame boy, Sasha with
her fretfulness, unhappy Liharev and his sayings—all this was mingled
together, and seemed to grow into one huge impression, and God's world
seemed to her fantastic, full of marvels and magical forces. All that she had
heard was ringing in her ears, and human life presented itself to her as a
beautiful poetic fairy tale without an end.

The immense impression grew and grew, clouded consciousness, and
turned into a sweet dream. She was asleep, though she saw the little ikon
lamp and a big nose with the light playing on it.

She heard the sound of weeping.

"Daddy, darling," a child's voice was tenderly entreating, "let's go back to uncle! There is a Christmas-tree there! Styopa and Kolya are there!"

"My darling, what can I do?" a man's bass persuaded softly. "Understand me! Come, understand!"

And the man's weeping blended with the child's. This voice of human sorrow, in the midst of the howling of the storm, touched the girl's ear with such sweet human music that she could not bear the delight of it, and wept too. She was conscious afterwards of a big, black shadow coming softly up to her, picking up a shawl that had dropped on to the floor and carefully wrapping it round her feet.

Mlle. Ilovaisky was awakened by a strange uproar. She jumped up and looked about her in astonishment. The deep blue dawn was looking in at the window half-covered with snow. In the room there was a grey twilight, through which the stove and the sleeping child and Nasir-ed-Din stood out distinctly. The stove and the lamp were both out. Through the wide-open door she could see the big tavern room with a counter and chairs. A man, with a stupid, gipsy face and astonished eyes, was standing in the middle of the room in a puddle of melting snow, holding a big red star on a stick. He was surrounded by a group of boys, motionless as statues, and plastered over with snow. The light shone through the red paper of the star, throwing a glow of red on their wet faces. The crowd was shouting in disorder, and from its uproar Mlle. Ilovaisky could make out only one couplet:

> "Hi, you little Russian lad,
> Bring your sharp knife,
> We will kill the Jew, we will kill him,
> The son of tribulation. . . ."

Liharev was standing near the counter, looking feeelingly at the singers and tapping his feet in time. Seeing Mlle. Ilovaisky, he smiled all over his face and came up to her. She smiled too.

"A happy Christmas!" he said. "I saw you slept well."

She looked at him, said nothing, and went on smiling.

After the conversation in the night he seemed to her not tall and broad shouldered, but little, just as the biggest steamer seems to us a little thing when we hear that it has crossed the ocean.

"Well, it is time for me to set off," she said. "I must put on my things. Tell me where you are going now?"

"I? To the station of Klinushki, from there to Sergievo, and from Sergievo, with horses, thirty miles to the coal mines that belong to a horrid man, a general called Shashkovsky. My brothers have got me the post of superintendent there. . . . I am going to be a coal miner."

"Stay, I know those mines. Shashkovsky is my uncle, you know. But . . . what are you going there for?" asked Mlle. Ilovaisky, looking at Liharev in surprise.

"As superintendent. To superintend the coal mines."

"I don't understand!" she shrugged her shoulders. "You are going to the mines. But you know, it's the bare steppe, a desert, so dreary that you couldn't exist a day there! It's horrible coal, no one will buy it, and my uncle's a maniac, a despot, a bankrupt. . . . You won't get your salary!"

"No matter," said Liharev, unconcernedly, "I am thankful even for coal mines."

She shrugged her shoulders, and walked about the room in agitation.

"I don't understand, I don't understand," she said, moving her fingers before her face. "It's impossible, and . . . and irrational! You must understand that it's . . . it's worse than exile. It is a living tomb! O Heavens!" she said hotly, going up to Liharev and moving her fingers before his smiling face; her upper lip was quivering, and her sharp face turned pale, "Come, picture it, the bare steppe, solitude. There is no one to say a word to there, and you . . . are enthusiastic over women! Coal mines . . . and women!"

Mlle. Ilovaisky was suddenly ashamed of her heat and, turning away from Liharev, walked to the window.

"No, no, you can't go there," she said, moving her fingers rapidly over the pane.

Not only in her heart, but even in her spine she felt that behind her stood an infinitely unhappy man, lost and outcast, while he, as though he were unaware of his unhappiness, as though he had not shed tears in the night, was looking at her with a kindly smile. Better he should go on weeping! She walked up and down the room several times in agitation, then stopped short in a corner and sank into thought. Liharev was saying something, but she did not hear him. Turning her back on him she took out of her purse a money note, stood for a long time crumpling it in her hand, and looking round at Liharev, blushed and put it in her pocket.

The coachman's voice was heard through the door. With a stern concentrated face she began putting on her things in silence. Liharev wrapped her up, chatting gaily, but every word he said lay on her heart like a weight. It is not cheering to hear the unhappy or the dying jest.

When the transformation of a live person into a shapeless bundle had been completed, Mlle. Ilovaisky looked for the last time round the "travellers' room," stood a moment in silence, and slowly walked out. Liharev went to see her off. . . .

Outside, God alone knows why, the winter was raging still. Whole clouds of big soft snowflakes were whirling restlessly over the earth, unable to find a resting-place. The horses, the sledge, the trees, a bull tied to a post, all were white and seemed soft and fluffy.

"Well, God help you," muttered Liharev, tucking her into the sledge. "Don't remember evil against me. . . ."

She was silent. When the sledge started, and had to go round a huge snowdrift, she looked back at Liharev with an expression as though she wanted to say something to him. He ran up to her, but she did not say a word to him, she only looked at him through her long eyelashes with little specks of snow on them.

Whether his finely intuitive soul were really able to read that look, or whether his imagination deceived him, it suddenly began to seem to him that with another touch or two that girl would have forgiven him his failures, his age, his desolate position, and would have followed him without question or reasonings. He stood a long while as though rooted to the spot, gazing at the tracks left by the sledge runners. The snowflakes greedily settled on his hair, his beard, his shoulders. . . . Soon the track of the runners had vanished, and he himself covered with snow, began to look like a white rock, but still his eyes kept seeking something in the clouds of snow.

COMMENTARY

In March, 1886, when Anton Chekhov was paying his way through medical school by writing humorous sketches and feuilletons under the pseudonym, A. Tchekhonte, he received a letter from D. V. Grigorovich, one of the leading critics of the day. Grigorovich had read "The Sportsman" in the Petersburg *Gazette* and wrote Chekhov: "You have real talent, a talent that puts you far above the circle of writers of the new generation."

This letter made a great impression on Chekhov. "It had the effect on me," he wrote Grigorovich, "of a governor-general's order to leave the city within twenty-four hours! . . . that is, I suddenly felt the imperative need to hurry, to make haste in getting out of the place where I was stuck. . . . Up till now I have taken my literary work extremely lightly, carelessly, casually. I don't remember a single story at which I worked for more than a day, and 'The Sportsman,' which you liked, I wrote in a bathing-shed! As reporters write their notes on fires, so I wrote my stories; mechanically, half consciously, without caring a bit about the reader or myself. . . . All my hope is for the future. I am only twenty-six. Perhaps I shall succeed in doing something although time runs swiftly."

In April, 1889, he wrote his friend Souvorin: "I think that if I could live another forty years and read, read, read and learn to write talentedly—that is, concisely—at the end of that time I would fire on you all with so great a cannon that the heavens would shake. But now I am but a Lilliputian, like all the rest."

Chekhov died on July 2, 1904, but in the years between his "awakening" and his death he had learned to write so "talentedly" that he was able not long before he died to sum up and in a measure appraise his life work. "All that I have written," he wrote S. S. Koteliansky, "will be forgotten in five or ten years; but the paths, paved by me, will remain safe and sound—therein is my only merit."

The paths he paved have opened up into avenues, broader perhaps than he envisioned. Most contemporary writers have felt his influence. Those who have not come into direct contact with it have been influenced by his disciples, such as Katherine Mansfield. His greatest disciple is James Joyce. Joyce's masterpiece, "The Dead," may be taken as the supreme example to date of what the Chekhovian method will yield in the hands of a master capable of exploring its ultimate possibilities (see pp. 279–282).

However, in spite of Chekhov's enormous influence, so widespread as to have reached "the man in the street"—in this case the women's magazines— there are still critics who maintain that Chekhov's stories are essentially vignettes, or character sketches, rather than true tales. Somerset Maugham says:

> If you try to tell one of his stories you will find that there is nothing to tell. The anecdote, stripped of its trimmings, is insignificant and often inane. It was grand for people who wanted to write a story and couldn't think of a plot to discover that you could very well manage without one. If you could take two or three persons, describe their mutual relations and leave it at that, why then it wasn't hard to write a story: and if you could flatter yourself that this really was art, what could be more charming?

This passage reveals a fundamental misunderstanding of Chekhov's effects, as well as his method. Chekhov himself says in this connection:

> Why write about a man getting into a submarine and going to the North Pole to reconcile himself to the world, while his beloved at that moment throws herself with a hysterical shriek from the belfry? All this is untrue and does not happen in real life. One must write about simple things: how Peter Semionovich married Maria Ivanovna. That is all.

In "On the Road" Chekhov shows us—he never tells us anything!— how Grigory Petrovich Liharev did not marry Mlle. Ilovaisky. He also shows us what the past lives of these two persons, who might have been lovers, has been, as well as what their future lives will be like, and explains, in terms of compelling symbolism (see Appendix A, p. 633), why they, and all men and women, are as they are. It is hard to see how a short story could accomplish more.

In this story, as in "The Dead," the controlling image is the snowstorm. It appears almost as soon as the stage is set in the "travellers' room" of the inn. Here it is well to recall one of Chekhov's admonitions, to the effect that if a gun hangs on the wall in the first part of a story it must be discharged before the story is over. In this story every "gun" has its little explosion into action; there is hardly a detail which does not contribute to the action, and the details are selected with the sure hand of genius.

A "tall, broad shouldered man of forty" is asleep in a room which is so dimly lit that the holy pictures on the wall "looked like one continuous stripe, covered with blurs of black." Grigory Liharev is a man who all his life has lived only by faith, as he reveals later to his fellow traveller—a succession of faiths which range from his infantile faith in the powers of soup to his latest creed: non-resistance to violence. It is therefore fitting that we see him first, surrounded by emblems of faith, although the light is so dim that he could hardly see them if he were awake; that is to say, they have very little influence on his conduct. Nevertheless, they exist, and the storm—the perturbations and obfuscations of mortal life—finally penetrates into this secluded spot and attacks his faith. "Something frantic and wrathful, but profoundly unhappy, seemed to be flinging itself about the tavern with the ferocity of a wild beast and trying to break in . . . and then with a gleeful, treacherous howl burst into the chimney."

It may be noted here how Chekhov's manner of handling nature, land-scapes, storms, pastoral scenes, sea-scapes, differs from James'. In James, the landscape exists only as reflected in the eyes of the observer, the Central Intelligence (see Appendix A, p. 626). The French countryside which Lambert Strether sees on his day's excursion from Paris is presented to us through Strether's eyes, in fact, through his double vision of it, for he sees it as a picture that somebody has painted, like the "little Lambinet," the picture he wanted so much but did not buy. But with Chekhov, nature, a storm, a landscape, the climate functions as an actor which at any moment may assume a leading rôle, as in "On the Road."

The proportions and timing of the action are exquisitely executed. The holy pictures, the storm, the pot boy, the grumbling little girl, all contribute exactly the amount of action necessary to make the dynamic whole. Against this living, vibrating background the figures of the two protagonists move in a slow, intricate dance. Into this room steps what looks like a shapeless bundle, which, when divested of its wrappings, proves to be "a thin little brunette of twenty . . . with a long white face and curly black hair. Her nose long and sharp, her chin, too, was long and sharp, her eyelashes were long, the corners of her mouth were sharp, and, thanks to this general sharp-ness, the expression of her face was biting." Liharev, however, has the power to change all this sharpness into sweetness. He tells her the story of his life between gulps of hot tea, but one does not have the impression of one person listening to a narrative told by another, but rather of two persons taking part in some action of absorbing interest. Her actions complement and crown his. It is she, not he, who realizes and announces that women are for him not "a simple subject of conversation" but his new faith. But she is as much a child of the mortal storm as he, and for all her quick response does not see him truly. When he has talked himself out and she lies down on the bench she goes to sleep with all he has said ringing in her ears "and human life pre-sented itself to her as a beautiful fairy tale without an end."

In the morning when she wakes she acts as Liharev has said women act, "with great-hearted fortitude," but Liharev will not give her the oppor-tunity to live out "the poetry of her heart." She, playing somewhat the same rôle as May Bartram in James' "The Beast in the Jungle," all but proposes marriage to him in her effort to save him. But Liharev, even after she has told him of the horrors of the coal mines for which he is bound, says unconcernedly that it does not much matter where he goes. As he wraps her up (completing the transformation of a live person into a shapeless bundle) he chatters gaily. Mlle. Ilovaisky hears him in stern silence: "It is not cheering to hear the unhappy or the dying jest." Just before she drives off she looks at him through her long eyelashes, which already have little specks of snow on them and "it suddenly began to seem to him that with another touch or two this girl would have forgiven him his failures, his age, his desolate position and would have followed him without question or reasonings." But the storm (symbolic of mortal life) which has been howling about them all night now overwhelms them both; snowflakes are "greedily" settling on his hair, beard and shoulders and he only stands, gazing at the tracks left by her sledge runners.

It is possible that some of Chekhov's critics are baffled by the abundance of life in his scenes. Every masterpiece demands collaboration from the beholder. When Puvis de Chavannes first saw Seurat's "La Grande Jatte" he did not realize its grandeur; the salon authorities, like the authorities in the Chicago Institute, had hung it so that it could not be seen in proper perspective. Chekhov presented difficulties to his first English readers. Imaginations "conditioned" by the Victorian novelists' leisurely pace were not athletic enough for the collaboration he demanded. And, indeed, his achievements surpassed anything the Victorians had imagined. He may well be compared to the great Pointillist painter, Seurat, on whose canvas every fleck of paint, when viewed in the proper perspective, unites with a neighboring fleck of paint to make the color the artist had in mind. There are no "dead" spots on Chekhov's canvases. Each detail not only vibrates with a life of its own but "acts" upon the neighboring detail. The result is a scene of extraordinary animation. The actors' speeches and gestures are lifelike in the extreme and they move through their rôles with consistent boldness, but in addition, the whole scene seems to be bathed in a living air. Reading a Chekhov story one feels often as one does on an early autumn day when fields, woods, mountains, lakes and rivers show more brilliantly for the luminous light which shimmers between us and them.

Guy de Maupassant

THE STORY OF A FARM GIRL

i

S THE WEATHER was very fine, the people on the farm had
dined more quickly than usual, and had returned to the fields.
The female servant, Rose, remained alone in the large
kitchen, where the fire on the hearth was dying out, under the
large boiler of hot water. From time to time she took some
water out of it, and slowly washed her plates and dishes, stopping occasionally
to look at the two streaks of light which the sun threw onto the long table
through the window, and which showed the defects in the glass.

Three venturesome hens were picking up the crumbs under the chairs,
while the smell of the poultry yard and the warmth from the cow-stall came
in through the half open door, and a cock was heard crowing in the distance.

When she had finished her work, wiped down the table, dusted the
mantelpiece, and put the plates on the high dresser, close to the wooden clock,
with its enormous pendulum, she drew a long breath, as she felt rather oppressed, without exactly knowing why. She looked at the black clay walls,
the rafters that were blackened with smoke, from which spiders' webs were
hanging amid pickled herrings and strings of onions, and then she sat down,
rather overcome by the stale emanations from the floor, on which so many
things had been spilled. With these was mingled the smell of the pans of
milk, which were set out to raise the cream in the adjoining dairy.

She wanted to sew, as usual, but she did not feel strong enough for it,
and so she went to get a mouthful of fresh air at the door, which seemed to
do her good.

The fowls were lying on the smoking dung-hill; some of them were
scratching with one claw in search of worms, while the cock stood up proudly
among them. Now and then he selected one of them, and walked round her
with a slight cluck of amorous invitation. The hen got up in a careless way as
she received his attentions, supported herself on her legs and spread out her
wings; then she shook her feathers to shake out the dust, and stretched
herself out on the dung-hill again, while he crowed, in sign of triumph, and
the cocks in all the neighboring farmyards replied to him, as if they were
uttering amorous challenges from farm to farm.

The girl looked at them without thinking; then she raised her eyes and
was almost dazzled at the sight of the apple-trees in blossom, which looked
almost like powdered heads. Just then, a colt, full of life and friskiness, gal-

loped past her. Twice he jumped over the ditches, and then stopped suddenly, as if surprised at being alone.

She also felt inclined to run; she felt inclined to move and to stretch her limbs, and to repose in the warm, breathless air. She took a few undecided steps, and closed her eyes, for she was seized with a feeling of animal comfort; then she went to look for the eggs in the hen loft. There were thirteen of them, which she took in and put into the storeroom; but the smell from the kitchen disgusted her again, and she went out to sit on the grass for a time.

The farmyard, which was surrounded by trees, seemed to be asleep. The tall grass, among which the tall yellow dandelions rose up like streaks of yellow light, was of a vivid green, the fresh spring green. The apple-trees threw their shade all round them, and the thatched houses, on which the blue and yellow iris flowers, with their sword-like leaves, grew, smoked as if the moisture of the stables and barns was coming through the straw.

The girl went to the shed where the carts and traps were kept. Close to it, in a ditch, there was a large patch of violets whose scent was perceptible all round, while beyond it could be seen the open country where the corn was growing, with clumps of trees in the distance, and groups of laborers here and there, who looked as small as dolls, and white horses like toys, who were pulling a child's cart, driven by a man as tall as one's finger.

She took up a bundle of straw, threw it into the ditch and sat down upon it; then, not feeling comfortable, she undid it, spread it out and lay down upon it at full length, on her back, with both arms under her head, and her limbs stretched out.

. Gradually her eyes closed, and she was falling into a state of delightful languor. She was, in fact, almost asleep, when she felt two hands on her bosom, and then she sprang up at a bound. It was Jacques, one of the farm laborers, a tall fellow from Picardy, who had been making love to her for a long time. He had been looking after the sheep, and seeing her lying down in the shade, he had come stealthily, and holding his breath, with glistening eyes, and bits of straw in his hair.

He tried to kiss her, but she gave him a smack in the face, for she was as strong as he, and he was shrewd enough to beg her pardon: so they sat down side by side and talked amicably. They spoke about the favorable weather, of their master, who was a good fellow, then of their neighbors, of all the people in the country round, of themselves, of their village, of their youthful days, of their recollections, of their relatives, whom they had not seen for a long time, and might not see again. She grew sad, as she thought of it, while he, with one fixed idea in his head, rubbed against her with a kind of a shiver, overcome by desire.

"I have not seen my mother for a long time," she said. "It is very hard to be separated like that." And she directed her looks into the distance, toward the village in the North, which she had left.

Suddenly, however, he seized her by the neck and kissed her again! but she struck him so violently in the face with her clenched fist, that his nose began to bleed, and he got up and laid his head against the branch of a tree. When she saw that, she was sorry, and going up to him, she said:

"Have I hurt you?"

He, however, only laughed. "No, it was a mere nothing"; though she had hit him right on the middle of the nose. "What a devil!" he said, and he looked at her with admiration, for she had inspired him with a feeling of respect and of a very different kind of admiration, which was the beginning of real love for that tall, strong wench.

When the bleeding had stopped, he proposed a walk, as he was afraid of his neighbor's heavy hand, if they remained side by side like that much longer; but she took his arm of her own accord, in the avenue, as if they had been out for an evening walk, and said: "It is not nice of you to despise me like that, Jacques."

He protested, however. No, he did not despise her. He was in love with her, that was all.

"So you really want to marry me?" she asked.

He hesitated, and then looked at her aside, while she looked straight ahead of her. She had fat, red cheeks, a full, protuberant bust under her muslin dress, thick, red lips, and her neck, which was almost bare, was covered with small beads of perspiration. He felt a fresh access of desire, and putting his lips to her ear, he murmured: "Yes, of course I do."

Then she threw her arms round his neck, and kissed him for such a long time that both of them lost their breath. From that moment the eternal story of love began between them. They plagued each other in corners; they met in the moonlight under a haystack, and gave each other bruises on the legs, with their heavy nailed boots. By degrees, however, Jacques seemed to grow tired of her: he avoided her; scarcely spoke to her, and did not try any longer to meet her alone, which made her sad and anxious, especially when she found that she was pregnant.

At first, she was in a state of consternation; then she got angry, and her rage increased every day, because she could not meet him, as he avoided her most carefully. At last, one night when everyone in the farmhouse was asleep, she went out noiselessly in her petticoat, with bare feet, crossed the yard and opened the door of the stable where Jacques was lying in a large box of straw, over his horses. He pretended to snore when he heard her coming, but she knelt down by his side and shook him until he sat up.

"What do you want?" he then asked of her. And she with clenched teeth, and trembling with anger, replied:

"I want—I want you to marry me, as you promised."

But he only laughed, and replied: "Oh! If a man were to marry all the girls with whom he has made a slip, he would have more than enough to do."

Then she seized him by the throat, threw him onto his back, so that he could not disengage himself from her, and half strangling him, she shouted into his face: "I am *enceinte,* do you hear? I am *enceinte!*"

He gasped for breath, as he was nearly choked, and so they remained, both of them, motionless and without speaking, in the dark silence, which was only broken by the noise that a horse made as he pulled the hay out of the manger, and then slowly chewed it.

When Jacques found that she was the stronger, he stammered out: "Very well, I will marry you, as that is the case."

But she did not believe his promises. "It must be at once," she said. "You must have the banns put up."

"At once," he replied.

"Swear solemnly that you will."

He hesitated for a few moments, and then said: "I swear it, by heaven."

Then she released her grasp, and went away without another word.

She had no chance of speaking to him for several days, and as the stable was now always locked at night, she was afraid to make any noise, for fear of creating a scandal. One day, however, she saw another man come in at dinner-time, and so she said: "Has Jacques left?"

"Yes," the man replied; "I have got his place."

This made her tremble so violently that she could not take the saucepan off the fire; and later when they were all at work, she went up into her room and cried, burying her head in her bolster, so that she might not be heard. During the day, however, she tried to obtain some information without exciting any suspicions, but she was so overwhelmed by the thoughts of her misfortune she fancied that all the people whom she asked laughed maliciously. All she learned, however, was that he had left the neighborhood altogether.

ii

Then a cloud of constant misery began for her. She worked mechanically, without thinking of what she was doing, with one fixed idea in her head: "Suppose people were to know."

This continual feeling made her so incapable of reasoning that she did not even try to think of any means of avoiding the disgrace that she knew must ensue, which was irreparable, and drawing nearer every day, and which was as sure as death itself. She got up every morning long before the others, and persistently tried to look at her figure in a piece of broken looking-glass at which she did her hair, as she was very anxious to know whether anybody would notice a change in her, and during the day she stopped working every few minutes to look at herself from top to toe, to see whether the size of her abdomen did not make her apron look too short.

The months went on. She scarcely spoke now, and when she was asked a question, she did not appear to understand. She had a frightened look, with haggard eyes and trembling hands, which made her master say to her occasionally: "My poor girl, how stupid you have grown lately."

In church, she hid behind a pillar, and no longer ventured to go to confession. She feared to face the priest, to whom she attributed a superhuman power, which enabled him to read people's consciences; and at meal times, the looks of her fellow-servants almost made her faint with mental agony She was always fancying that she had been found out by the cowherd, a precocious and cunning little lad, whose bright eyes seemed always to be watching her.

One morning the postman brought her a letter, and as she had never received one in her life before, she was so upset by it that she was obliged to sit down. Perhaps it was from him? But as she could not read, she sat anxious and trembling with that piece of paper covered with ink in her hand; after a time, however, she put it into her pocket, as she did not venture to confide her secret to anyone. She often stopped in her work to look at the lines, written at regular intervals, and terminating in a signature, imagining vaguely that she would suddenly discover their meaning. At last, as she felt half mad with impatience and anxiety, she went to the schoolmaster, who told her to sit down, and read the letter to her, as follows:

> "My Dear Daughter: I write to tell you that I am very ill. Our neighbor, Monsieur Dentu, begs you to come, if you can,
> > "For your affectionate mother.
> > > "Césaire Dentu,
> > > > "Deputy Mayor."

She did not say a word, and went away, but as soon as she was alone, her legs gave way, and she fell down by the roadside, and remained there till night.

When she got back, she told the farmer her trouble. He allowed her to go home for as long as she wanted, promised to have her work done by a charwoman, and to take her back when she returned.

Her mother died soon after she got there, and the next day Rose gave birth to a seven months' child, a miserable little skeleton, thin enough to make anybody shudder. It seemed to be suffering continually, to judge from the painful manner in which it moved its poor little limbs, which were as thin as a crab's legs, but it lived, for all that. She said that she was married, but that she could not saddle herself with the child, so she left it with some neighbors, who promised to take great care of it, and she went back to the farm.

But then, in her heart, which had been wounded so long, there arose something like brightness, an unknown love for that frail little creature which she had left behind her, but there was fresh suffering in that very love, suffering which she felt every hour and every minute, because she was parted from the child. What pained her most, however, was a mad longing to kiss it, to press it in her arms, to feel the warmth of its little body against her skin. She could not sleep at night; she thought of it the whole day long, and in the evening, when her work was done, she used to sit in front of the fire and look at it intently, as people do whose thoughts are far away.

They began to talk about her, and to tease her about her lover. They asked her whether he was tall, handsome, and rich. When was the wedding to be, and the christening? And often she ran away to cry by herself, for these questions seemed to hurt her, like the prick of a pin, and in order to forget their jokes, she began to work still more energetically, and still thinking of her child, she sought for the means of saving up money for it, and determined to work so that her master would be obliged to raise her wages.

Then, by degrees, she almost monopolized the work, and persuaded him to get rid of one servant girl, who had become useless since she had taken to working like two; she economized in the bread, oil, and candles, in the corn which they gave to the fowls too extravagantly, and in the fodder for the horses and cattle, which was rather wasted. She was as miserly about her master's money as if it had been her own, and by dint of making good bargains, of getting high prices for all their produce, and by baffling the peasants' tricks when they offered anything for sale, he at last intrusted her with buying and selling everything, with the direction of all the laborers, and with the quantity of provisions necessary for the household, so that in a short time she became indispensable to him. She kept such a strict eye on everything about her that under her direction the farm prospered wonderfully, and for five miles round people talked of "Master Vallin's servant," and the farmer himself said everywhere: "That girl is worth more than her weight in gold."

But time passed by, and her wages remained the same. Her hard work was accepted as something that was due from every good servant, and as a mere token of her good-will; and she began to think rather bitterly that if the farmer could put fifty or a hundred crowns extra into the bank every month, thanks to her, she was still only earning her two hundred francs a year, neither more nor less, and so she made up her mind to ask for an increase of wages. She went to see the schoolmaster three times about it, but when she got there, she spoke about something else. She felt a kind of modesty in asking for money, as if it were something disgraceful; but at last, one day, when the farmer was having breakfast by himself in the kitchen, she said to him, with some embarrassment, that she wished to speak to him particularly. He raised his head in surprise, with both his hands on the table, holding his knife, with its point in the air, in one, and a piece of bread in the other. He looked fixedly at the girl, who felt uncomfortable under his gaze, but asked for a week's holiday, so that she might get away, as she was not very well. He acceded to her request immediately, and then added, in some embarrassment, himself:

"When you come back, I shall have something to say to you, myself."

iii

The child was nearly eight months old. It had grown rosy and chubby all over like a little bundle of living fat. She threw herself onto it as if it had been some prey, and kissed it so violently that it began to scream with terror, and then she began to cry herself, because it did not know her, and stretched out its arms to its nurse, as soon as it saw her. But the next day, it began to get used to her, and laughed when it saw her, and she took it into the fields and ran about excitedly with it, and sat down under the shade of the trees, and then, for the first time in her life, she opened her heart to somebody and told the infant her toubles, how hard her work was, her anxieties and her hopes, and she quite tired the child with the violence of her caresses.

She took the greatest pleasure in handling it, in washing and dressing it, for it seemed to her that all this was the confirmation of her maternity, and she would look at it, almost feeling surprised that it was hers, and she used to say to herself in a low voice, as she danced it in her arms: "It is my baby, it is my baby."

She cried all the way home as she returned to the farm, and had scarcely got in, before her master called her into his room. She went in, feeling astonished and nervous, without knowing why.

"Sit down there," he said.

She sat down, and for some moments they remained side by side, in some embarrassment, with their arms hanging at their sides, as if they did not know what to do with them, and looking each other in the face, after the manner of peasants.

The farmer, a stout, jovial, obstinate man of forty-five, who had lost two wives, evidently felt embarrassed, which was very unusual with him. But at last he made up his mind, and began to speak vaguely, hesitating a little, and looking out of the window as he talked.

"How is it, Rose," he said, "that you have never thought of settling in life?"

She grew as pale as death, and seeing that she gave him no answer, he went on:

"You are a good, steady, active, and economical girl, and a wife like you would make a man's fortune."

She did not move, but looked frightened; she did not even try to comprehend his meaning, for her thoughts were in a whirl, as if at the approach of some great danger; so after waiting for a few seconds, he went on:

"You see, a farm without a mistress can never succeed, even with a servant like you are."

Then he stopped, for he did not know what else to say, and Rose looked at him with the air of a person who thinks that he is face to face with a murderer, and ready to flee at the slightest movement he may make; but after waiting for about five minutes, he asked her:

"Well, will it suit you?"

"Will what suit me, master?"

And he said, quickly: "Why, to marry me, by Jove!"

She jumped up, but fell back on to her chair as if she had been struck, and there she remained motionless, like a person who is overwhelmed by some great misfortune. But at last the farmer grew impatient, and said: "Come, what more do you want?"

She looked at him almost in terror; then suddenly the tears came into her eyes, and she said twice, in a choking voice: "I cannot, I cannot!"

"Why not?" he asked. "Come, don't be silly; I will give you until tomorrow to think it over."

And he hurried out of the room, very glad to have finished a matter which had troubled him a good deal. He had no doubt that she would the next morning accept a proposal which she could never have expected, and which would be a capital bargain for him, as he thus bound a woman to himself who would certainly bring him more than if she had the best dowry in the district.

Neither could there be any scruples about an unequal match between them, for in the country everyone is very nearly equal. The farmer works just as his laborers do; the latter frequently become masters in their turn, and the female servants constantly become the mistresses of the establishment, without making any change in their life or habits.

Rose did not go to bed that night. She threw herself, dressed as she was, onto her bed, and she had not even strength to cry left in her, she was so thoroughly astonished. She remained quite inert, scarcely knowing that she had a body, and without being at all able to collect her thoughts, though at moments she remembered a part of what had happened, and then she was frightened at the idea of what might happen. Her terror increased, and every time the great kitchen clock struck the hour, she broke into a perspiration from grief. She lost her head, and had a nightmare; her candle went out, and then she began to imagine that some one had thrown a spell over her, as country people so often fancy, and she felt a mad inclination to run away, to escape and flee before her misfortune, as a ship scuds before the wind.

An owl hooted, and she shivered, sat up, put her hands to her face, into her hair, and all over her body, and then she went downstairs, as if she were walking in her sleep. When she got into the yard, she stooped down, so as not to be seen by any prowling scamp, for the moon, which was setting, shed a bright light over the fields. Instead of opening the gate, she scrambled over the fence, and as soon as she was outside, she started off. She went on straight before her, with a quick, elastic trot, and from time to time, she unconsciously uttered a piercing cry. Her long shadow accompanied her, and now and then some night-bird flew over her head, while the dogs in the farmyards barked, as they heard her pass. One even jumped over the ditch, followed her, and tried to bite her, but she turned round at it, and gave such a terrible yell that the frightened animal ran back, and cowered in silence in its kennel.

The stars grew dim, and the birds began to twitter; day was breaking.

The girl was worn out and panting, and when the sun rose in the purple sky, she stopped, for her swollen feet refused to go any further. But she saw a pond in the distance, a large pond whose stagnant water looked like blood under the reflection of this new day, and she limped on with short steps and with her hand on her heart, in order to dip both her feet in it.

She sat down on a tuft of grass, took off her sabots which were full of dust, pulled off her stockings and plunged her legs into the still water, from which bubbles were rising here and there.

A feeling of delicious coolness pervaded her from head to foot, and suddenly, while she was looked fixedly at the deep pool, she was seized with giddiness, and with a mad longing to throw herself into it. All her sufferings would be over in there; over forever. She no longer thought of her child; she only wanted peace, complete rest, and to sleep forever, and she got up with raised arms and took two steps forward. She was in the water up to her thighs, and she was just about to throw herself in, when sharp, pricking pains in her ankles made her jump back. She uttered a cry of despair, for, from her knees to the tips of her feet, long, black leeches were sucking in her life blood, and were swelling, as they adhered to her flesh. She did not dare to touch them, and screamed with horror, so that her cries of despair attracted a peasant, who was driving along at some distance, to the spot. He pulled off the leeches one by one, applied herbs to the wounds, and drove the girl to her master's farm, in his gig.

She was in bed for a fortnight, and as she was sitting outside the door on the first morning that she got up, the farmer suddenly came and planted himself before her.

"Well," he said, "I suppose the affair is settled, isn't it?"

She did not reply at first, and then, as he remained standing and looking at her intently with his piercing eyes, she said with difficulty: "No, master, I cannot."

But he immediately flew into a rage. "You cannot, girl; you cannot? I should just like to know the reason why?"

She began to cry, and repeated: "I cannot."

He looked at her, and then exclaimed, angrily: "Then I suppose you have a lover?"

"Perhaps that is it," she replied, trembling with shame.

The man got as red as a poppy, and stammered out in a rage: "Ah! So you confess it, you slut! And pray who is the fellow? Some penniless, half-starved ragamuffin, without a roof to his head, I suppose? Who is it, I say?"

And as she gave him no answer, he continued: "Ah! So you will not tell me. Then I will tell you; it is Jean Bauda!"

"No, not he," she exclaimed.

"Then it is Pierre Martin?"

"Oh! no, master."

And he angrily mentioned all the young fellows in the neighborhood, while she denied that he had hit upon the right one, and every moment wiped her eyes with the corner of her blue apron. But he still tried to find it out, with his brutish obstinacy, and, as it were, scratched her heart to discover her secret, as a terrier scratches at a hole to try and get at the animal which he scents in it. Suddenly, however, the man shouted: "By George! It is Jacques, the man who was here last year. They used to say that you were always talking together, and that you thought about getting married."

Rose was choking, and she grew scarlet, while her tears suddenly stopped, and dried up on her cheeks, like drops of water on hot iron, and she exclaimed: "No, it is not he, it is not he!"

"Is that really a fact?" asked the cunning farmer, who partly guessed the truth, and she replied hastily:

"I will swear it; I will swear it to you." She tried to think of something by which to swear, as she did not dare to invoke sacred things.

But he interrupted her: "At any rate, he used to follow you into every corner, and devoured you with his eyes at meal times. Did you ever give him your promise, eh?"

This time she looked her master straight in the face. "No, never, never; I will solemnly swear to you that if he were to come today and ask me to marry him, I would have nothing to do with him."

She spoke with such an air of sincerity that the farmer hesitated, and then he continued, as if speaking to himself: "What, then? You have not had a *misfortune,* as they call it, or it would have been known, and as it has no consequences, no girl would refuse her master on that account. There must be something at the bottom of it, however."

She could say nothing; she had not the strength to speak, and he asked her again: "You will not?"

"I cannot, master," she said, with a sigh, and he turned on his heel.

She thought she had got rid of him altogether, and spent the rest of the day almost tranquilly, but as worn out as if she, instead of the old white horse, had been turning the threshing machine all day. She went to bed as soon as she could, and fell asleep immediately. In the middle of the night, however, two hands touching the bed woke her. She trembled with fear, but she immediately recognized the farmer's voice, when he said to her: "Don't be frightened, Rose; I have come to speak to you."

She was surprised at first, but when he tried to take liberties with her, she understood what he wanted, and began to tremble violently. She felt quite alone in the darkness, still heavy from sleep, and quite unprotected, by the side of the man who stood near her. She certainly did not consent, but resisted carelessly, herself struggling against that instinct which is always strong in simple natures, and very imperfectly protected, by the undecided will of an exhausted body. She turned her head now to the wall, and now toward the room, in order to avoid the attentions which the farmer tried to press on her, and her body writhed under the coverlet, weakened as she was by the fatigue of the struggle, while he became brutal, intoxicated by desire.

They lived together as man and wife, and one morning he said to her: "I have put up our banns, and we will get married next month."

She did not reply, for what could she say? She did not resist, for what could she do?

iv

She married him. She felt as if she were in a pit with inaccessible edges, from which she could never get out, and all kinds of misfortunes remained hanging over her head, like huge rocks, which would fall on the first occasion. Her husband gave her the impression of a man whom she had stolen, and who would find it out some day or other. And then she thought of her child, who was the cause of her misfortunes, but was also the cause of all her happiness on earth. She went to see him twice a year, and she came back more unhappy each time.

But she gradually grew accustomed to her life, her fears were allayed, her heart was at rest, and she lived with an easier mind, though still with some vague fear floating in her mind. So years went on, and the child was six. She was almost happy now, when suddenly the farmer's temper grew very bad.

For two or three years, he seemed to have been nursing some secret anxiety, to be troubled by some care, some mental disturbance, which was gradually increasing. He remained at table a long time after dinner, with his head in his hands, sad and devoured by sorrow. He always spoke hastily, sometimes even brutally, and it even seemed as if he bore a grudge against his wife, for at times he answered her roughly, almost angrily.

One day, when a neighbor's boy came for some eggs, and she spoke rather crossly to him, for she was very busy, her husband suddenly came in, and said to her in his unpleasant voice: "If that were your own child, you would not treat him so."

She was hurt and did not reply, and then she went back into the house with all her grief awakened afresh. At dinner, the farmer neither spoke to her nor looked at her, and seemed to hate her, to despise her, to know something about the affair at last. In consequence, she lost her head and did not venture to remain alone with him after the meal was over, but left the room and hastened to the church.

It was getting dusk; the narrow nave was in total darkness, but she heard footsteps in the choir, for the sacristan was preparing the tabernacle lamp for the night. That spot of trembling light, which was lost in the darkness of the arches, looked to Rose like her last hope, and with her eyes fixed on it, she fell on her knees. The chain rattled as the little lamp swung up into the air, and almost immediately the small bell rang out the "Angelus" through the increasing mist. She went up to him, as he was going out.

"Is Monsieur le Curé at home?" she asked.

"Of course he is; this is his dinner time."

She trembled as she rang the bell of the parsonage. The priest was just sitting down to dinner, and he made her sit down also. "Yes, yes, I know all about it; your husband has mentioned the matter to me that brings you here."

The poor woman nearly fainted, and the priest continued: "What do you want, my child?" And he hastily swallowed several spoonfuls of soup, some of which dropped on to his greasy cassock. But Rose did not venture to say anything more, but got up to go, while the priest said: "Courage."

So she went out, and returned to the farm, without knowing what she was doing. The farmer was waiting for her, as the laborers had gone away during her absence, and she fell heavily at his feet, and shedding a flood of tears, she said to him: "What have you got against me?"

He began to shout and to swear: "What have I got against you? That I have no children, by God! When a man takes a wife, he does not want to be left alone with her until the end of his days. That is what I have against you. When a cow has no calves, she is not worth anything, and when a woman has no children, she is also not worth anything."

She began to cry, and said: "It is not my fault! It is not my fault!"

He grew rather more gentle when he heard that, and added: "I do not say that it is, but it is very annoying, all the same."

V

From that day forward, she had only one thought—to have a child, another child. She confided her wish to everybody, and in consequence of this, a neighbor told her of an infallible method. This was, to make her husband a glass of water with a pinch of ashes in it, every evening. The farmer consented to try it, but without success; so they said to each other: "Perhaps there are some secret ways?" And they tried to find out. They were told of a shepherd who lived ten leagues off, and so Vallin one day drove off to consult him. The shepherd gave him a loaf on which he had made some marks; it was kneaded up with herbs, and both of them were to eat a piece of it before and after their mutual caresses; but they ate the whole loaf without obtaining any results from it.

Next, a schoolmaster unveiled mysteries and processes of love which were unknown in the country, but infallible, so he declared; but none of them had the desired effect. Then the priest advised them to make a pilgrimage to the shrine at Fécamp. Rose went with the crowd and prostrated herself in the abbey, and mingling her prayers with the coarse wishes of the peasants around her, she prayed that she might be fruitful a second time; but it was in vain, and then she thought that she was being punished for her first fault, and she was seized by terrible grief. She was wasting away with sorrow; her husband was growing old prematurely, and was wearing himself out in useless hopes.

Then war broke out between them; he called her names and beat her.

They quarreled all day long, and when they were in bed together at night he flung insults and obscenities at her, panting with rage, until one night, not being able to think of any means of making her suffer more, he ordered her to get up and go and stand out of doors in the rain, until daylight. As she did not obey him, he seized her by the neck, and began to strike her in the face with his fists, but she said nothing, and did not move. In his exasperation he knelt on her, and with clenched teeth and mad rage began to beat her. Then in her despair she rebelled, and flinging him against the wall with a furious gesture, she sat up, and in an altered voice, she hissed: "I have had a child, I have had one! I had it by Jacques; you know Jacques well. He promised to marry me, but he left this neighborhood without keeping his word."

The man was thunderstruck, and could hardly speak, but at last he stammered out: "What are you saying? What are you saying?"

Then she began to sob, and amid her tears she said: "That was the reason why I did not want to marry you. I could not tell you, for you would have left me without any bread for my child. You have never had any children, so you cannot understand, you cannot understand!"

He said again, mechanically, with increasing surprise: "You have a child? You have a child?"

"You won me by force, as I suppose you know. I did not want to marry you," she said, still sobbing.

Then he got up, lighted the candle, and began to walk up and down, with his arms behind him. She was cowering on the bed and crying, and suddenly he stopped in front of her, and said: "Then it is my fault that you have no children?"

She gave him no answer, and he began to walk up and down again, and then, stopping again, he continued: "How old is your child?"

"Just six," she whispered.

"Why did you not tell me about it?" he asked.

"How could I?" she replied, with a sigh.

He remained standing, motionless. "Come, get up," he said.

She got up, with some difficulty, and then when she was standing on the floor, he suddenly began to laugh, with his hearty laugh of his good days, and seeing how surprised she was, he added: "Very well, we will go and fetch the child, as you and I can have none together."

She was so frightened that if she had the strength she would assuredly have run away, but the farmer rubbed his hands and said: "I wanted to adopt one, and now we have found one. I asked the Curé about an orphan, some time ago."

Then, still laughing, he kissed his weeping and agitated wife on both cheeks, and shouted out, as if she could not hear him: "Come along, mother, we will go and see whether there is any soup left; I should not mind a plateful."

She put on her petticoat, and they went downstairs; and while she was kneeling in front of the fireplace, and lighting the fire under the saucepan, he continued to walk up and down the kitchen with long strides, and said: "Well, I am really glad at this; I am not saying it for form's sake, but I am glad, I am really very glad."

COMMENTARY

Maupassant's "The Story of a Farm Girl" (*L'Histoire d'une Fille de Ferme*) affords the student an excellent opportunity to compare his art with that of his master, Flaubert. Flaubert was, in truth, his master. For seven years Maupassant showed Flaubert everything he wrote. During that time Flaubert did not allow him to publish anything. He was, perhaps, thinking of the seven years in which *he* refused to publish anything, devoting himself to the composition of his masterpiece, *Madame Bovary*. But in writing, as in everything else, one can never raise oneself very far except by one's own boot-straps. Maupassant's achievement is prodigious—it seems scarcely possible that one man could have accomplished as much as he did in his short writing life of nine years. But he was never the disciplined writer that Flaubert was. When one surveys Maupassant's work from the vantage point of the present time it would seem that he apprenticed himself only to Flaubert. Certainly his work declined in artistic value after Flaubert's death.

But he learned his lesson well. Nobody of his own time, except Flaubert, surpassed him in the ability to render a scene in sensuous detail. His eye is keen, his choice of detail unerring. A story like "Boule de Suif," for instance, is so full of masterly strokes that the whole surface seems to sparkle with life. One will never forget the very appearance of the basket which Boule de Suif draws out from under her capacious skirts. Maupassant appears to have the same gift for vivid rendition which Flaubert had (for hard work alone could never have accomplished Flaubert's triumphs), and he had other gifts which his master did not have. Flaubert's powers of invention seem meager compared to his. One feels that no matter how long Flaubert lived or how hard he worked he could never have developed Maupassant's adroitness in constructing plots. He did not handle action easily enough. He could never have contrived for his stories the kind of Resolution of which Maupassant became a past master, in which the climax seems to explode like fireworks out of the action, leaving behind a lingering trail of brilliance.

Maupassant felt the same attraction and repulsion for his native province, Normandy, which Flaubert felt for his native city, Rouen. He is at his best when he is writing about Normandy. He brings its sights and smells and sounds before us so vividly that we feel that we ourselves have visited the places he describes:

> The farmyard, which was surrounded by trees, seemed to be asleep. The tall grass, amid which the tall yellow dandelions rose up like streaks

of yellow light, was of a vivid, fresh spring green. The apple trees cast their shade all round them, and the thatched roofs, on which grew blue and yellow irises, with their sword-like leaves, steamed as if the moisture of the stables and barns were coming through the straw.

"The Story of a Farm Girl" has no Enveloping Action. There is no superior or ironic intelligence playing over the incidents, as in *Madame Bovary* or "A Simple Heart," or if there is, it makes its commentary merely by juxtaposing one event with another. In the introduction Maupassant shows himself inferior to his master. The passage does not have the tone or the inevitability of the opening of "A Simple Heart." Indeed, the alternation of Long and Short Views (see Appendix A, p. 627) is poorly managed throughout the story. Maupassant never learned, perhaps saw no necessity for learning, how to time a Long View so that it would have the dramatic impact of a Short View, and in some of his best stories these alternations are carelessly handled, as in the first pages of "Boule de Suif."

The heroine of "The Story of a Farm Girl," Rose, reminds us of Félicité in "A Simple Heart." Like Félicité she spends her life in hard labor among people who do not appreciate her, and like Félicité she has a lover who deserts her. But the Complication and Resolution (see Appendix A, p. 630) of the two stories are very different. On the surface "L'Histoire" has a happier ending. Félicité dies old, alone and almost deserted, while Rose gets what she wants, marriage, security and the privilege of bringing up her own child. Rose's love for her child, the noblest emotion of her life, is a blind, almost animal love, like the love of a cat for her kitten. Félicité, on the other hand, though she is capable of strong affection (she loves Virginie and Paul and her nephew devotedly) outlives earthly attachments and fixes all her thoughts on Heaven. Rose's reward, which she obtains here on earth, is the kind that might come to any well-disposed, well-behaved young woman.

Flaubert's story has a dimension, a whole plane of action which Maupassant's lacks. This plane of action, which includes some of the deepest and most mysterious mainsprings of human conduct, does not exist in Maupassant's stories. Rose is scarcely more articulate or reflective than the farm animals she tends, but she is fully as articulate, as reflective as the lady heroine of *Une Vie*. It is not the fact that she is a rude peasant that makes her dull. Her creator seems to have decreed that her response to life should be limited. Maupassant himself said in this connection that in his opinion "psychology should be hidden in a book, as it is hidden in reality under the facts of existence." But Flaubert gives us no explanations or comments in "A Simple Heart." Félicité's life is presented with the same bold naturalistic details as Rose's. The fault, after all, seems to lie with her creator. Psychology should be hidden, in a story, as in real life, under the facts of existence, but it must be present. And the author, if he is to engage our deepest interest, must see further into life than the next man. Henry James, who had great admiration for Maupassant's gifts, was also aware of his limitations. He speaks of the "hard, short, intelligent gaze" which he brings to bear upon life. It expresses, James thinks, a sort of "bird's-eye-view contempt" of life. "He tells us all he knows, all he suspects, and if these things take no account of the moral nature of man, it is because he has no window looking in that direction, and not because any artistic scruples have compelled him to close it up. The very compact mansion in which he dwells presents on that side a perfectly dead wall."

Henry James

THE BEAST IN THE JUNGLE

i

WHAT determined the speech that startled him in the course of their encounter scarcely matters, being probably but some words spoken by himself quite without intention—spoken as they lingered and slowly moved together after their renewal of acquaintance. He had been conveyed by friends, an hour or two before, to the house at which she was staying; the party of visitors at the other house, of whom he was one, and thanks to whom it was his theory, as always, that he was lost in the crowd, had been invited over to luncheon. There had been after luncheon much dispersal, all in the interest of the original motive, a view of Weatherend itself and the fine things, intrinsic features, pictures, heirlooms, treasures of all the arts, that made the place almost famous; and the great rooms were so numerous that guests could wander at their will, hang back from the principal group, and, in cases where they took such matters with the least seriousness, give themselves up to mysterious appreciations and measurements. There were persons to be observed, singly or in couples, bending toward objects in out-of-the-way corners with their hands on their knees and their heads nodding quite as with the emphasis of an excited sense of smell. When they were two they either mingled their sounds of ecstasy or melted into silences of even deeper import, so that there were aspects of the occasion that gave it for Marcher much the air of the "look round," previous to a sale highly advertised, that excites or quenches, as may be, the dream of acquisition. The dream of acquisition at Weatherend would have had to be wild indeed, and John Marcher found himself, among such suggestions, disconcerted almost equally by the presence of those who knew too much and by that of those who knew nothing. The great rooms caused so much poetry and history to press upon him that he needed to wander apart to feel in a proper relation with them, though his doing so was not, as happened, like the gloating of some of his companions, to be compared to the movements of a dog sniffing a cupboard. It had an issue promptly enough in a direction that was not to have been calculated.

It led, in short, in the course of the October afternoon, to his closer meeting with May Bartram, whose face, a reminder, yet not quite a remembrance, as they sat, much separated, at a very long table, had begun merely by troubling him rather pleasantly. It affected him as the sequel of something of which he had lost the beginning. He knew it, and for the time quite welcomed it, as a continuation, but didn't know what it continued, which was an interest, or an amusement, the greater as he was also somehow aware—yet without a direct sign from her—that the young woman herself had not lost the thread. She had not lost it, but she wouldn't give it back to him, he saw, without some putting forth of his hand for it; and he not only saw that, but saw several things more, things odd enough in the light of the fact that at the moment some accident of grouping brought them face to face he was still merely fumbling with the idea that any contact between them in the past would have had no importance. If it had had no importance he scarcely knew why his actual impression of her should so seem to have so much; the answer to which, however, was that in such a life as they all appeared to be leading for the moment one could but take things as they came. He was satisfied, without in the least being able to say why, that this young lady might roughly have ranked in the house as a poor relation; satisfied also that she was not there on a brief visit, but was more or less a part of the establishment —almost a working, a remunerated part. Didn't she enjoy at periods a protection that she paid for by helping, among other services, to show the place and explain it, deal with the tiresome people, answer questions about the dates of the buildings, the styles of the furniture, the authorship of the pictures, the favourite haunts of the ghost? It wasn't that she looked as if you could have given her shillings—it was impossible to look less so. Yet when she finally drifted toward him, distinctly handsome, though ever so much older—older than when he had seen her before—it might have been as an effect of her guessing that he had, within the couple of hours, devoted more imagination to her than to all the others put together, and had thereby penetrated to a kind of truth that the others were too stupid for. She *was* there on harder terms than anyone; she was there as a consequence of things suffered, in one way and another, in the interval of years; and she remembered him very much as she was remembered—only a good deal better.

By the time they at last thus came to speech they were alone in one of the rooms—remarkable for a fine portrait over the chimney-place—out of which their friends had passed, and the charm of it was that even before they had spoken they had practically arranged with each other to stay behind for talk. The charm, happily, was in other things too; it was partly in there being scarce a spot at Weatherend without something to stay behind for. It was in the way the autumn day looked into the high windows as it waned; in the way the red light, breaking at the close from under a low, sombre sky, reached out in a long shaft and played over old wainscots, old tapestry, old gold, old colour. It was most of all perhaps in the way she came to him as if, since she had been turned on to deal with the simpler sort, he might, should he choose to keep the whole thing down, just take her mild attention for a part of her general business. As soon as he heard her voice, however, the gap was filled up and the missing link supplied; the slight irony he divined in her attitude lost its advantage. He almost jumped at it to get there before her. "I met you years and years ago in Rome. I remember all about it." She confessed to disappointment—she had been so sure he didn't; and to prove how well he did he began to pour forth the particular recollections that popped up as he called for them. Her face and her voice, all at his service now, worked the miracle—the impression operating like the torch of a lamp-lighter who touches into flame, one by one, a long row of gas jets. Marcher flattered himself that the illumination was brilliant, yet he was really still more pleased on her showing him, with amusement, that in his haste to make everything right he had got most things rather wrong. It hadn't been at Rome—it had been at Naples; and it hadn't been seven years before—it had been more nearly ten. She hadn't been either with her uncle and aunt, but with her mother and her brother; in addition to which it was not with the Pembles that *he* had been, but with the Boyers, coming down in their com-pany from Rome—a point on which she insisted, a little to his confusion, and as to which she had her evidence in hand. The Boyers she had known, but she didn't know the Pembles, though she had heard of them, and it was the people he was with who had made them acquainted. The incident of the thunderstorm that had raged round them with such violence as to drive them for refuge into an excavation—this incident had not occurred at the Palace of the Cæsars, but at Pompeii, on an occasion when they had been present there at an important find.

He accepted her amendments, he enjoyed her corrections, though the moral of them was, she pointed out, that he *really* didn't remember the least thing about her; and he only felt it as a drawback that when all was made conformable to the truth there didn't appear much of anything left. They lingered together still, she neglecting her office—for from the moment he was so clever she had no proper right to him—and both neglecting the house, just waiting as to see if a memory or two more wouldn't again breathe upon them. It had not taken them many minutes, after all, to put down on the table, like the cards of a pack, those that constituted their respective hands; only what came out was that the pack was unfortunately not perfect—that the past, invoked, invited, encouraged, could give them, naturally, no more than it had. It had made them meet—her at twenty, him at twenty-five; but nothing was so strange, they seemed to say to each other, as that, while so occupied, it hadn't done a little more for them. They looked at each other as with the feeling of an occasion missed; the present one would have been so much better if the other, in the far distance, in the foreign land, hadn't been so stupidly meagre. There weren't apparently, all counted, more than a dozen little old things that had succeeded in coming to pass between them; trivialities of youth, simplicities of freshness, stupidities of ignorance, small possible germs, but too deeply buried—too deeply (didn't it seem?) to sprout after so many years. Marcher said to himself that he ought to have rendered her some service—saved her from a capsized boat in the Bay, or at least recovered her dressing-bag, filched from her cab, in the streets of Naples, by a lazzarone with a stiletto. Or it would have been nice if he could have been taken with fever, alone, at his hotel, and she could have come to look after him, to write to his people, to drive him out in convalescence. *Then* they would be in possession of the something or other that their actual show seemed to lack. It yet somehow presented itself, this show, as too good to be spoiled; so that they were reduced for a few minutes more to wondering a little helplessly why—since they seemed to know a certain number of the same people—their reunion had been so long averted. They didn't use that name for it, but their delay from minute to minute to join the others was a kind of confession that they didn't quite want it to be a failure. Their attempted supposition of reasons for their not having met but showed how little they knew of each other. There came in fact a moment when Marcher felt a positive pang. It was vain to pretend she was an old friend, for all the communities were wanting, in spite of which it was as an old friend that he saw she would have suited him. He had new ones enough—was surrounded with them, for instance, at that hour at the other house; as a new one he probably wouldn't have so much as noticed her. He would have liked to invent something, get her to make-believe with him that some passage of a romantic or critical kind *had* originally occurred. He was really almost reaching out in imagination—as against time—for something that would do, and saying to himself that if it didn't come this new incident would simply and rather awkwardly close. They would separate, and now for no second or for no third chance. They would have tried and not succeeded. Then it was, just at the turn, as he afterwards made it out to himself, that, everything else failing, she herself decided to take up the case and, as it were, save the situation. He felt as soon as she spoke that she had been consciously keeping back what she said and hoping to get on without it; a scruple in her that immensely touched him when, by the end of three or four minutes more, he was able to measure it. What she brought out, at any rate, quite cleared the air and supplied the link—the link it was such a mystery he should frivolously have managed to lose.

"You know you told me something that I've never forgotten and that again and again has made me think of you since; it was that tremendously hot day when we went to Sorrento, across the bay, for the breeze. What I allude to was what you said to me, on the way back, as we sat, under the awning of the boat, enjoying the cool. Have you forgotten?"

He had forgotten, and he was even more surprised than ashamed. But the great thing was that he saw it was no vulgar reminder of any "sweet" speech. The vanity of women had long memories, but she was making no claim on him of a compliment or a mistake. With another woman, a totally different one, he might have feared the recall possibly even of some imbecile "offer." So, in having to say that he had indeed forgotten, he was conscious rather of a loss than of a gain; he already saw an interest in the matter of her reference. "I try to think—but I give it up. Yet I remember the Sorrento day."

"I'm not very sure you do," May Bartram after a moment said; "and I'm not very sure I ought to want you to. It's dreadful to bring a person back, at any time, to what he was ten years before. If you've lived away from it," she smiled, "so much the better."

"Ah, if *you* haven't why should I?" he asked.

"Lived away, you mean, from what I myself was?"

"From what *I* was. I was of course an ass," Marcher went on; "but I would rather know from you just the sort of ass I was than—from the moment you have something in your mind—not know anything."

Still, however, she hesitated. "But if you've completely ceased to be that sort——?"

"Why, I can then just so all the more bear to know. Besides, perhaps I haven't."

"Perhaps. Yet if you haven't," she added, "I should suppose you would remember. Not indeed that *I* in the least connect with my impression the invidious name you use. If I had only thought you foolish," she explained, "the thing I speak of wouldn't so have remained with me. It was about yourself." She waited, as if it might come to him; but as, only meeting her eyes in wonder, he gave no sign, she burnt her ships. "Has it ever happened?"

Then it was that, while he continued to stare, a light broke for him and the blood slowly came to his face, which began to burn with recognition. "Do you mean I told you——?" But he faltered, lest what came to him shouldn't be right, lest he should only give himself away.

"It was something about yourself that it was natural one shouldn't forget —that is if one remembered you at all. That's why I ask you," she smiled, "if the thing you then spoke of has ever come to pass?"

Oh, then he saw, but he was lost in wonder and found himself embarrassed. This, he also saw, made her sorry for him, as if her allusion had been a mistake. It took him but a moment, however, to feel that it had not been, much as it had been a surprise. After the first little shock of it her knowledge on the contrary began, even if rather strangely, to taste sweet to him. She was the only other person in the world then who would have it, and she had had it all these years, while the fact of his having so breathed his secret had unaccountably faded from him. No wonder they couldn't have met as if nothing had happened. "I judge," he finally said, "that I know what you mean. Only I had strangely enough lost the consciousness of having taken you so far into my confidence."

"Is it because you've taken so many others as well?"

"I've taken nobody. Not a creature since then."

"So that I'm the only person who knows?"

"The only person in the world."

"Well," she quickly replied, "I myself have never spoken. I've never, never repeated of you what you told me." She looked at him so that he perfectly believed her. Their eyes met over it in such a way that he was without a doubt. "And I never will."

She spoke with an earnestness that, as if almost excessive, put him at ease about her possible derision. Somehow the whole question was a new luxury to him—that is, from the moment she was in possession. If she didn't take the ironic view she clearly took the sympathetic, and that was what he had had, in all the long time, from no one whomsoever. What he felt was that he couldn't at present have begun to tell her and yet could profit perhaps exquisitely by the accident of having done so of old. "Please don't then. We're just right as it is."

"Oh, I am," she laughed, "if you are!" To which she added: "Then you do still feel in the same way?"

It was impossible to him not to take to himself that she was really interested, and it all kept coming as a sort of revelation. He had thought of himself so long as abominably alone, and, lo, he wasn't alone a bit. He hadn't been, it appeared, for an hour—since those moments on the Sorrento boat. It was *she* who had been, he seemed to see as he looked at her—she who had been made so by the graceless fact of his lapse of fidelity. To tell her what he had told her—what had it been but to ask something of her? something that she had given, in her charity, without his having, by a remembrance, by a return of the spirit, failing another encounter, so much as thanked her. What he had asked of her had been simply at first not to laugh at him. She had beautifully not done so for ten years, and she was not doing so now. So he had endless gratitude to make up. Only for that he must see just how he had figured to her. "What, exactly, was the account I gave——?"

"Of the way you did feel? Well, it was very simple. You said you had had from your earliest time, as the deepest thing within you, the sense of being kept for something rare and strange, possibly prodigious and terrible, that was sooner or later to happen to you, that you had in your bones the foreboding and the conviction of, and that would perhaps overwhelm you."

"Do you call that very simple?" John Marcher asked.

She thought a moment. "It was perhaps because I seemed, as you spoke, to understand it."

"You do understand it?" he eagerly asked.

Again she kept her kind eyes on him. "You still have the belief?"

"Oh!" he exclaimed helplessly. There was too much to say.

"Whatever it is to be," she clearly made out, "it hasn't yet come."

He shook his head in complete surrender now. "It hasn't yet come. Only, you know, it isn't anything I'm to *do*, to achieve in the world, to be distinguished or admired for. I'm not such an ass as *that*. It would be much better, no doubt, if I were."

"It's to be something you're merely to suffer?"

"Well, say to wait for—to have to meet, to face, to see suddenly break out in my life; possibly destroying all further consciousness, possibly anni-hilating me; possibly, on the other hand, only altering everything, striking at the root of all my world and leaving me to the consequences, however they shape themselves."

She took this in, but the light in her eyes continued for him not to be that of mockery. "Isn't what you describe perhaps but the expectation—or, at any rate, the sense of danger, familiar to so many people—of falling in love?"

John Marcher thought. "Did you ask me that before?"

"No—I wasn't so free-and-easy then. But it's what strikes me now."

"Of course," he said after a moment, "it strikes you. Of course it strikes *me*. Of course what's in store for me may be no more than that. The only thing is," he went on, "that I think that if it had been that, I should by this time know."

"Do you mean because you've *been* in love?" And then as he but looked at her in silence: "You've been in love, and it hasn't meant such a cataclysm, hasn't proved the great affair?"

"Here I am, you see. It hasn't been overwhelming."

"Then it hasn't been love," said May Bartram.

"Well, I at least thought it was. I took it for that—I've taken it till now. It was agreeable, it was delightful, it was miserable," he explained. "But it wasn't strange. It wasn't what *my* affair's to be."

"You want something all to yourself—something that nobody else knows or *has* known?"

"It isn't a question of what I 'want'— God knows I don't want any-thing. It's only a question of the apprehension that haunts me—that I live with day by day."

He said this so lucidly and consistently that, visibly, it further imposed itself. If she had not been interested before she would have been interested now. "Is it a sense of coming violence?"

Evidently now too, again, he liked to talk of it. "I don't think of it as—when it does come—necessarily violent. I only think of it as natural and as of course, above all, unmistakable. I think of it simply as *the* thing. *The* thing will of itself appear natural."

"Then how will it appear strange?"

Marcher bethought himself. "It won't—to *me*."

"To whom then?"

"Well," he replied, smiling at last, "say to you."

"Oh then, I'm to be present?"

"Why, you *are* present—since you know."

"I see." She turned it over. "But I mean at the catastrophe."

At this, for a minute, their lightness gave way to their gravity; it was as if the long look they exchanged held them together. "It will only depend on yourself—if you'll watch with me."

"Are you afraid?" she asked.

"Don't leave me *now*," he went on.

"Are you afraid?" she repeated.

"Do you think me simply out of my mind?" he pursued instead of answering. "Do I merely strike you as a harmless lunatic?"

"No," said May Bartram. "I understand you. I believe you."

"You mean you feel how my obsession—poor old thing!—may correspond to some possible reality?"

"To some possible reality."

"Then you *will* watch with me?"

She hesitated, then for the third time put her question. "Are you afraid?"

"Did I tell you I was—at Naples?"

"No, you said nothing about it."

"Then I don't know. And I should *like* to know," said John Marcher. "You'll tell me yourself whether you think so. If you'll watch with me you'll see."

"Very good then." They had been moving by this time across the room, and at the door, before passing out, they paused as if for the full wind-up of their understanding. "I'll watch with you," said May Bartram.

ii

The fact that she "knew"—knew and yet neither chaffed him nor betrayed him—had in a short time begun to constitute between them a sensible bond, which became more marked when, within the year that followed their afternoon at Weatherend, the opportunities for meeting multiplied. The event that thus promoted these occasions was the death of the ancient lady, her great-aunt, under whose wing, since losing her mother, she had to such an extent found shelter, and who, though but the widowed mother of the new successor to the property, had succeeded—thanks to a high tone and a high temper—in not forfeiting the supreme position at the great house. The deposition of this personage arrived but with her death, which, followed by many changes, made in particular a difference for the young woman in whom Marcher's expert attention had recognised from the first a dependent with a pride that might ache though it didn't bristle. Nothing for a long time had made him easier than the thought that the aching must have been much soothed by Miss Bartram's now finding herself able to set up a small home in London. She had acquired property, to an amount that made that luxury just possible, under her aunt's extremely complicated will, and when the whole matter began to be straightened out, which indeed took time, she let him know that the happy issue was at last in view. He had seen her again before that day, both because she had more than once accompanied the ancient lady to town and because he had paid another visit to the friends who so conveniently made of Weatherend one of the charms of their own hospitality. These friends had taken him back there; he had achieved there again with Miss Bartram some quiet detachment; and he had

in London succeeded in persuading her to more than one brief absence from
her aunt. They went together, on these latter occasions, to the National
Gallery and the South Kensington Museum, where, among vivid reminders,
they talked of Italy at large—not now attempting to recover, as at first, the
taste of their youth and their ignorance. That recovery, the first day at
Weatherend, had served its purpose well, had given them quite enough;
so that they were, to Marcher's sense, no longer hovering about the head-
waters of their stream, but had felt their boat pushed sharply off and down
the current.

They were literally afloat together; for our gentleman this was marked,
quite as marked as that the fortunate cause of it was just the buried treasure
of her knowledge. He had with his own hands dug up this little hoard,
brought to light—that is to within reach of the dim day constituted by their
discretions and privacies—the object of value the hiding-place of which he
had, after putting it into the ground himself, so strangely, so long forgotten.
The exquisite luck of having again just stumbled on the spot made him
indifferent to any other question; he would doubtless have devoted more
time to the odd accident of his lapse of memory if he had not been moved
to devote so much to the sweetness, the comfort, as he felt, for the future, that
this accident itself had helped to keep fresh. It had never entered into his
plan that anyone should "know," and mainly for the reason that it was not
in him to tell anyone. That would have been impossible, since nothing but
the amusement of a cold world would have waited on it. Since, however, a
mysterious fate had opened his mouth in youth, in spite of him, he would
count that a compensation and profit by it to the utmost. That the right
person *should* know tempered the asperity of his secret more even than his
shyness had permitted him to imagine; and May Bartram was clearly right,
because—well, because there she was. Her knowledge simply settled it; he
would have been sure enough by this time had she been wrong. There was
that in his situation, no doubt, that disposed him too much to see her as a
mere confidant, taking all her light for him from the fact—the fact only—
of her interest in his predicament, from her mercy, sympathy, seriousness,
her consent not to regard him as the funniest of the funny. Aware, in fine,
that her price for him was just in her giving him this constant sense of his
being admirably spared, he was careful to remember that she had, after all,
also a life of her own, with things that might happen to *her*, things that in
friendship one should likewise take account of. Something fairly remarkable
came to pass with him, for that matter, in this connection—something represented by a certain passage of his consciousness, in the suddenest way, from
one extreme to the other.

He had thought himself, so long as nobody knew, the most disinterested
person in the world, carrying his concentrated burden, his perpetual suspense, ever so quietly, holding his tongue about it, giving others no glimpse
of it nor of its effect upon his life, asking of them no allowance and only
making on his side all those that were asked. He had disturbed nobody with

the queerness of having to know a haunted man, though he had had moments
of rather special temptation on hearing people say that they were "unsettled."
If they were as unsettled as he was—he who had never been settled for an
hour in his life—they would know what it meant. Yet it wasn't, all the same,
for him to make them, and he listened to them civilly enough. This was why
he had such good—though possibly such rather colourless—manners; this
was why, above all, he could regard himself, in a greedy world, as decently—
as, in fact, perhaps even a little sublimely—unselfish. Our point is accordingly that he valued this character quite sufficiently to measure his present
danger of letting it lapse, against which he promised himself to be much
on his guard. He was quite ready, none the less, to be selfish just a little,
since, surely, no more charming occasion for it had come to him. "Just a
little," in a word, was just as much as Miss Bartram, taking one day with
another, would let him. He never would be in the least coercive, and he
would keep well before him the lines on which consideration for her—the
very highest—ought to proceed. He would thoroughly establish the heads
under which her affairs, her requirements, her peculiarities—he went so far
as to give them the latitude of that name—would come into their intercourse.
All this naturally was a sign of how much he took the intercourse itself for
granted. There was nothing more to be done about *that*. It simply existed;
had sprung into being with her first penetrating question to him in the
autumn light there at Weatherend. The real form it should have taken on
the basis that stood out large was the form of their marrying. But the devil
in this was that the very basis itself put marrying out of the question. His
conviction, his apprehension, his obsession, in short, was not a condition he
could invite a woman to share; and that consequence of it was precisely
what was the matter with him. Something or other lay in wait for him,
amid the twists and the turns of the months and the years, like a crouching
beast in the jungle. It signified little whether the crouching beast were destined to slay him or to be slain. The definite point was the inevitable spring
of the creature; and the definite lesson from that was that a man of feeling
didn't cause himself to be accompanied by a lady on a tiger-hunt. Such was
the image under which he had ended by figuring his life.

They had at first, none the less, in the scattered hours spent together,
made no allusion to that view of it; which was a sign he was handsomely
ready to give that he didn't expect, that he in fact didn't care always to be
talking about it. Such a feature in one's outlook was really like a hump on
one's back. The difference it made every minute of the day existed quite
independently of discussion. One discussed, of course, *like* a hunchback, for
there was always, if nothing else, the hunchback face. That remained, and
she was watching him; but people watched best, as a general thing, in
silence, so that such would be predominantly the manner of their vigil. Yet
he didn't want, at the same time, to be solemn; solemn was what he imagined
he too much tended to be with other people. The thing to be, with the one
person who knew, was easy and natural—to make the reference rather than

be seeming to avoid it, to avoid it rather than be seeming to make it, and to keep it, in any case, familiar, facetious even, rather than pedantic and portentous. Some such consideration as the latter was doubtless in his mind, for instance, when he wrote pleasantly to Miss Bartram that perhaps the great thing he had so long felt as in the lap of the gods was no more than this circumstance, which touched him so nearly, of her acquiring a house in London. It was the first allusion they had yet again made, needing any other hitherto so little; but when she replied, after having given him the news, that she was by no means satisfied with such a trifle, as the climax to so special a suspense, she almost set him wondering if she hadn't even a larger conception of singularity for him than he had for himself. He was at all events destined to become aware little by little, as time went by, that she was all the while looking at his life, judging it, measuring it, in the light of the thing she knew, which grew to be at last, with the consecration of the years, never mentioned between them save as "the real truth" about him. That had always been his own form of reference to it, but she adopted the form so quietly that, looking back at the end of a period, he knew there was no moment at which it was traceable that she had, as he might say, got inside his condition, or exchanged the attitude of beautifully indulging for that of still more beautifully believing him.

It was always open to him to accuse her of seeing him but as the most harmless of maniacs, and this, in the long run—since it covered so much ground—was his easiest description of their friendship. He had a screw loose for her, but she liked him in spite of it, and was practically, against the rest of the world, his kind, wise keeper, unremunerated, but fairly amused and, in the absence of other near ties, not disreputably occupied. The rest of the world of course thought him queer, but she, she only, knew how, and above all why, queer; which was precisely what enabled her to dispose the concealing veil in the right folds. She took his gaiety from him—since it had to pass with them for gaiety—as she took everything else; but she certainly so far justified by her unerring touch his finer sense of the degree to which he had ended by convincing her. *She* at least never spoke of the secret of his life except as "the real truth about you," and she had in fact a wonderful way of making it seem, as such, the secret of her own life too. That was in fine how he so constantly felt her as allowing for him; he couldn't on the whole call it anything else. He allowed for himself, but she, exactly, allowed still more; partly because, better placed for a sight of the matter, she traced his unhappy perversion through portions of its course into which he could scarce follow it. He knew how he felt, but, besides knowing that, she knew how he *looked* as well; he knew each of the things of importance he was insidiously kept from doing, but she could add up the amount they made, understand how much, with a lighter weight on his spirit, he might have done, and thereby establish how, clever as he was, he fell short. Above all she was in the secret of the difference between the forms he went through—those of his little office under Government, those of caring for his modest patrimony, for his library, for his garden in the country, for the people in London whose invitations he accepted and repaid— and the detachment that reigned beneath them and that made of all behaviour, all that could in the least be called behaviour, a long act of dissimulation. What it had come to was that he wore a mask painted with the social simper, out of the eye-holes of which there looked eyes of an expression not in the least matching the other features. This the stupid world, even after years, had never more than half discovered. It was only May Bartram who had, and she achieved, by an art indescribable, the feat of at once—or perhaps it was only alternately—meeting the eyes from in front and mingling her own vision, as from over his shoulder, with their peep through the apertures.

So, while they grew older together, she did watch with him, and so she let this association give shape and colour to her own existence. Beneath *her* forms as well detachment had learned to sit, and behaviour had become for her, in the social sense, a false account of herself. There was but one account of her that would have been true all the while, and that she could give, directly, to nobody, least of all to John Marcher. Her whole attitude was a virtual statement, but the perception of that only seemed destined to take its place for him as one of the many things necessarily crowded out of his consciousness. If she had, moreover, like himself, to make sacrifices to their real truth, it was to be granted that her compensation might have affected her as more prompt and more natural. They had long periods, in this London time, during which, when they were together, a stranger might have listened to them without in the least pricking up his ears; on the other hand, the real truth was equally liable at any moment to rise to the surface, and the auditor would then have wondered indeed what they were talking about. They had from an early time made up their mind that society was, luckily, unintelligent, and the margin that this gave them had fairly become one of their commonplaces. Yet there were still moments when the situation turned almost fresh—usually under the effect of some expression drawn from herself. Her expressions doubtless repeated themselves, but her intervals were generous. "What saves us, you know, is that we answer so completely to so usual an appearance: that of the man and woman whose friendship has become such a daily habit, or almost, as to be at last indispensable." That, for instance, was a remark she had frequently enough had occasion to make, though she had given it at different times different developments. What we are especially concerned with is the turn it happened to take from her one afternoon when he had come to see her in honour of her birthday. This anniversary had fallen on a Sunday, at a season of thick fog and general outward gloom; but he had brought her his customary offering, having known her now long enough to have established a hundred little customs. It was one of his proofs to himself, the present he made her on her birthday, that he had not sunk into real selfishness. It was mostly nothing more than a small trinket, but it was always fine of its kind, and he was regularly careful to pay for it more than he thought he could afford. "Our habit saves you, at least, don't you see? because it makes you, after all, for the vulgar, indistinguishable from other men. What's the most inveterate mark of men in general? Why, the capacity to spend endless time with dull women—to spend it, I won't say without being bored, but without minding that they are, without being driven off at a tangent by it; which comes to the same thing. I'm your dull woman, a part of the daily bread for which you pray at church. That covers your tracks more than anything."

"And what covers yours?" asked Marcher, whom his dull woman could mostly to this extent amuse. "I see of course what you mean by your saving me, in one way and another, so far as other people are concerned—I've seen it all along. Only, what is it that saves *you?* I often think, you know, of that."

She looked as if she sometimes thought of that too, but in rather a different way. "Where other people, you mean, are concerned?"

"Well, you're really so in with me, you know—as a sort of result of my being so in with yourself. I mean of my having such an immense regard for you, being so tremendously grateful for all you've done for me. I sometimes ask myself if it's quite fair. Fair I mean to have so involved and—since one may say it—interested you. I almost feel as if you hadn't really had time to do anything else."

"Anything else but be interested?" she asked. "Ah, what else does one ever want to be? If I've been 'watching' with you, as we long ago agreed that I was to do, watching is always in itself an absorption."

"Oh, certainly," John Marcher said, "if you hadn't had your curiosity——! Only, doesn't it sometimes come to you, as time goes on, that your curiosity is not being particularly repaid?"

May Bartram had a pause. "Do you ask that, by any chance, because you feel at all that yours isn't? I mean because you have to wait so long."

Oh, he understood what she meant. "For the thing to happen that never does happen? For the beast to jump out? No, I'm just where I was about it. It isn't a matter as to which I can *choose,* I can decide for a change. It isn't one as to which there *can* be a change. It's in the lap of the gods. One's in the hands of one's law—there one is. As to the form the law will take, the way it will operate, that's its own affair."

"Yes," Miss Bartram replied; "of course one's fate is coming, of course it *has* come, in its own form and its own way, all the while. Only, you know, the form and the way in your case were to have been—well, something so exceptional and, as one may say, so particularly *your* own."

Something in this made him look at her with suspicion. "You say 'were to *have* been,' as if in your heart you had begun to doubt."

"Oh!" she vaguely protested.

"As if you believed," he went on, "that nothing will now take place."

She shook her head slowly, but rather inscrutably. "You're far from my thought."

He continued to look at her. "What then is the matter with you?"

"Well," she said after another wait, "the matter with me is simply that I'm more sure than ever my curiosity, as you call it, will be but too well repaid."

They were frankly grave now; he had got up from his seat; had turned once more about the little drawing-room to which, year after year, he brought his inevitable topic; in which he had, as he might have said, tasted their intimate community with every sauce, where every object was as familiar to him as the things of his own house and the very carpets were worn with his fitful walk very much as the desks in old counting-houses are worn by the elbows of generations of clerks. The generations of his nervous moods had been at work there, and the place was the written history of his whole middle life. Under the impression of what his friend had just said he knew himself, for some reason, more aware of these things, which made him, after a moment, stop again before her. "Is it, possibly, that you've grown afraid?"

"Afraid?" He thought, as she repeated the word, that his question had made her, a little, change colour; so that, lest he should have touched on a truth, he explained very kindly. "You remember that that was what you asked *me* long ago—that first day at Weatherend."

"Oh yes, and you told me you didn't know—that I was to see for myself. We've said little about it since, even in so long a time."

"Precisely," Marcher interposed—"quite as if it were too delicate a matter for us to make free with. Quite as if we might find, on pressure, that I *am* afraid. For then," he said, "we shouldn't, should we? quite know what to do."

She had for the time no answer to this question. "There have been days when I thought you were. Only, of course," she added, "there have been days when we have thought almost anything."

"Everything. Oh!" Marcher softly groaned as with a gasp, half spent, at the face, more uncovered just then than it had been for a long while, of the imagination always with them. It had always had its incalculable moments of glaring out, quite as with the very eyes of the very Beast, and, used as he was to them, they could still draw from him the tribute of a sigh that rose from the depths of his being. All that they had thought, first and last, rolled over him; the past seemed to have been reduced to mere barren speculation. This in fact was what the place had just struck him as so full of—the simplification of everything but the state of suspense. That remained only by seeming to hang in the void surrounding it. Even his original fear, if fear it had been, had lost itself in the desert. "I judge, however," he continued, "that you see I'm not afraid now."

"What I see is, as I make it out, that you've achieved something almost unprecedented in the way of getting used to danger. Living with it so long and so closely, you've lost your sense of it; you know it's there, but you're indifferent, and you cease even, as of old, to have to whistle in the dark. Considering what the danger is," May Bartram wound up, "I'm bound to say that I don't think your attitude could well be surpassed."

John Marcher faintly smiled. "It's heroic?"

"Certainly—call it that."

He considered. "I *am*, then, a man of courage?"

"That's what you were to show me."

He still, however, wondered. "But doesn't the man of courage know what he's afraid of—or *not* afraid of? I don't know *that*, you see. I don't focus it. I can't name it. I only know I'm exposed."

"Yes, but exposed—how shall I say?—so directly. So intimately. That's surely enough."

"Enough to make you feel, then—as what we may call the end of our watch—that I'm not afraid?"

"You're not afraid. But it isn't," she said, "the end of our watch. That is, it isn't the end of yours. You've everything still to see."

"Then why haven't *you?*" he asked. He had had, all along, to-day, the sense of her keeping something back, and he still had it. As this was his first impression of that, it made a kind of date. The case was the more marked as she didn't at first answer; which in turn made him go on. "You know something I don't." Then his voice, for that of a man of courage, trembled a little. "You know what's to happen." Her silence, with the face she showed, was almost a confession—it made him sure. "You know, and you're afraid to tell me. It's so bad that you're afraid I'll find out."

All this might be true, for she did look as if, unexpectedly to her, he had crossed some mystic line that she had secretly drawn round her. Yet she might, after all, not have worried; and the real upshot was that he himself, at all events, needn't. "You'll never find out."

iii

It was all to have made, none the less, as I have said, a date; as came out in the fact that again and again, even after long intervals, other things that passed between them wore, in relation to this hour, but the character of recalls and results. Its immediate effect had been indeed rather to lighten insistence—almost to provoke a reaction; as if their topic had dropped by its own weight and as if moreover, for that matter, Marcher had been visited by one of his occasional warnings against egotism. He had kept up, he felt, and very decently on the whole, his consciousness of the importance of not being selfish, and it was true that he had never sinned in that direction without promptly enough trying to press the scales the other way. He often repaired his fault, the season permitting, by inviting his friend to accompany him to the opera; and it not infrequently thus happened that, to show he didn't wish her to have but one sort of food for her mind, he was the cause of her appearing there with him a dozen nights in the month. It even happened that, seeing her home at such times, he occasionally went in with her to finish, as

he called it, the evening, and, the better to make his point, sat down to the
frugal but always careful little supper that awaited his pleasure. His point
was made, he thought, by his not eternally insisting with her on himself;
made for instance, at such hours, when it befell that, her piano at hand and
each of them familiar with it, they went over passages of the opera together.
It chanced to be on one of these occasions, however, that he reminded her of
her not having answered a certain question he had put to her during the talk
that had taken place between them on her last birthday. "What is it that saves
you?"—saved her, he meant, from that appearance of variation from the
usual human type. If he had practically escaped remark, as she pretended, by
doing, in the most important particular, what most men do—find the answer
to life in patching up an alliance of a sort with a woman no better than himself—how had she escaped it, and how could the alliance, such as it was, since
they must suppose it had been more or less noticed, have failed to make her
rather positively talked about?

"I never said," May Bartram replied, "that it hadn't made me talked
about."

"Ah well then, you're not 'saved.'"

"It has not been a question for me. If you've had your woman, I've had,"
she said, "my man."

"And you mean that makes you all right?"

She hesitated. "I don't know why it shouldn't make me—humanly,
which is what we're speaking of—as right as it makes you."

"I see," Marcher returned. "'Humanly,' no doubt, as showing that you're
living for something. Not, that is, just for me and my secret."

May Bartram smiled. "I don't pretend it exactly shows that I'm not living
for you. It's my intimacy with you that's in question."

He laughed as he saw what she meant. "Yes, but since, as you say, I'm
only, so far as people make out, ordinary, you're—aren't you?—no more than
ordinary either. You help me to pass for a man like another. So if I *am,* as I
understand you, you're not compromised. Is that it?"

She had another hesitation, but she spoke clearly enough. "That's it. It's
all that concerns me—to help you to pass for a man like another."

He was careful to acknowledge the remark handsomely. "How kind,
how beautiful, you are to me! How shall I ever repay you?"

She had her last grave pause, as if there might be a choice of ways. But
she chose. "By going on as you are."

It was into this going on as he was that they relapsed, and really for so
long a time that the day inevitably came for a further sounding of their
depths. It was as if these depths, constantly bridged over by a structure that
was firm enough in spite of its lightness and of its occasional oscillation in
the somewhat vertiginous air, invited on occasion, in the interest of their
nerves, a dropping of the plummet and a measurement of the abyss. A difference had been made moreover, once for all, by the fact that she had, all the
while, not appeared to feel the need of rebutting his charge of an idea within

her that she didn't dare to express, uttered just before one of the fullest of their later discussions ended. It had come up for him then that she "knew" something and that what she knew was bad—too bad to tell him. When he had spoken of it as visibly so bad that she was afraid he might find it out, her reply had left the matter too equivocal to be let alone and yet, for Marcher's special sensibility, almost too formidable again to touch. He circled about it at a distance that alternately narrowed and widened and that yet was not much affected by the consciousness in him that there was nothing she could "know," after all, any better than he did. She had no source of knowledge that he hadn't equally—except of course that she might have finer nerves. That was what women had where they were interested; they made out things, where people were concerned, that the people often couldn't have made out for themselves. Their nerves, their sensibility, their imagination, were conductors and revealers, and the beauty of May Bartram was in particular that she had given herself so to his case. He felt in these days what, oddly enough, he had never felt before, the growth of a dread of losing her by some catastrophe—some catastrophe that yet wouldn't at all be *the* catastrophe: partly because she had, almost of a sudden, begun to strike him as useful to him as never yet, and partly by reason of an appearance of uncertainty in her health, coincident and equally new. It was characteristic of the inner detachment he had hitherto so successfully cultivated and to which our whole account of him is a reference, it was characteristic that his complications, such as they were, had never yet seemed so as at this crisis to thicken about him, even to the point of making him ask himself if he were, by any chance, of a truth, within sight or sound, within touch or reach, within the immediate jurisdiction of the thing that waited.

When the day came, as come it had to, that his friend confessed to him her fear of a deep disorder in her blood, he felt somehow the shadow of a change and the chill of a shock. He immediately began to imagine aggravations and disasters, and above all to think of her peril as the direct menace for himself of personal privation. This indeed gave him one of those partial recoveries of equanimity that were agreeable to him—it showed him that what was still first in his mind was the loss she herself might suffer. "What if she should have to die before knowing, before seeing——?" It would have been brutal, in the early stages of her trouble, to put that question to her; but it had immediately sounded for him to his own concern, and the possibility was what most made him sorry for her. If she did "know," moreover, in the sense of her having had some—what should he think?—mystical, irresistible light, this would make the matter not better, but worse, inasmuch as her original adoption of his own curiosity had quite become the basis of her life. She had been living to see what would *be* to be seen, and it would be cruel to her to have to give up before the accomplishment of the vision. These reflections, as I say, refreshed his generosity; yet, make them as he might, he saw himself, with the lapse of the period, more and more disconcerted. It lapsed for him with a strange, steady sweep, and the oddest oddity was that it gave

him, independently of the threat of such inconvenience, almost the only positive surprise his career, if career it could be called, had yet offered him. She
kept the house as she had never done; he had to go to her to see her—she
could meet him nowhere now, though there was scarce a corner of their loved
old London in which she had not in the past, at one time or another, done so;
and he found her always seated by her fire in the deep, old-fashioned chair
she was less and less able to leave. He had been struck one day, after an
absence exceeding his usual measure, with her suddenly looking much older
to him than he had ever thought of her being; then he recognised that the
suddenness was all on his side—he had just been suddenly struck. She looked
older because inevitably, after so many years, she *was* old, or almost; which
was of course true in still greater measure of her companion. If she was old,
or almost, John Marcher assuredly was, and yet it was her showing of the
lesson, not his own, that brought the truth home to him. His surprises began
here; when once they had begun they multiplied; they came rather with a
rush: it was as if, in the oddest way in the world, they had all been kept back,
sown in a thick cluster, for the late afternoon of life, the time at which, for
people in general, the unexpected has died out.

One of them was that he should have caught himself—for he *had* so
done—*really* wondering if the great accident would take form now as
nothing more than his being condemned to see this charming woman, this
admirable friend, pass away from him. He had never so unreservedly qualified her as while confronted in thought with such a possibility; in spite of
which there was small doubt for him that as an answer to his long riddle the
mere effacement of even so fine a feature of his situation would be an abject
anticlimax. It would represent, as connected with his past attitude, a drop of
dignity under the shadow of which his existence could only become the most
grotesque of failures. He had been far from holding it a failure—long as he
had waited for the appearance that was to make it a success. He had waited
for a quite other thing, not for such a one as that. The breath of his good
faith came short, however, as he recognised how long he had waited, or how
long, at least, his companion had. That she, at all events, might be recorded
as having waited in vain—this affected him sharply, and all the more because
of his at first having done little more than amuse himself with the idea. It
grew more grave as the gravity of her condition grew, and the state of mind
it produced in him, which he ended by watching, himself, as if it had been
some definite disfigurement of his outer person, may pass for another of his
surprises. This conjoined itself still with another, the really stupefying consciousness of a question that he would have allowed to shape itself had he
dared. What did everything mean—what, that is, did *she* mean, she and her
vain waiting and her probable death and the soundless admonition of it all—
unless that, at this time of day, it was simply, it was overwhelmingly too late?
He had never, at any stage of his queer consciousness, admitted the whisper
of such a correction; he had never, till within these last few months, been so
false to his conviction as not to hold that what was to come to him had time,

whether *he* struck himself as having it or not. That at last, at last, he certainly hadn't it, to speak of, or had it but in the scantiest measure—such, soon enough, as things went with him, became the inference with which his old obsession had to reckon: and this it was not helped to do by the more and more confirmed appearance that the great vagueness casting the long shadow in which he had lived had, to attest itself, almost no margin left. Since it was in Time that he was to have met his fate, so it was in Time that his fate was to have acted; and as he waked up to the sense of no longer being young, which was exactly the sense of being stale, just as that, in turn, was the sense of being weak, he waked up to another matter beside. It all hung together; they were subject, he and the great vagueness, to an equal and indivisible law. When the possibilities themselves had, accordingly, turned stale, when the secret of the gods had grown faint, had perhaps even quite evaporated, that, and that only, was failure. It wouldn't have been failure to be bankrupt, dishonoured, pilloried, hanged; it was failure not to be anything. And so, in the dark valley into which his path had taken its unlooked-for twist, he wondered not a little as he groped. He didn't care what awful crash might overtake him, with what ignominy or what monstrosity he might yet be associated—since he wasn't, after all, too utterly old to suffer—if it would only be decently proportionate to the posture he had kept, all his life, in the promised presence of it. He had but one desire left—that he shouldn't have been "sold."

iv

Then it was that one afternoon, while the spring of the year was young and new, she met, all in her own way, his frankest betrayal of these alarms. He had gone in late to see her, but evening had not settled, and she was presented to him in that long, fresh light of waning April days which affects us often with a sadness sharper than the greyest hours of autumn. The week had been warm, the spring was supposed to have begun early, and May Bartram sat, for the first time in the year, without a fire, a fact that, to Marcher's sense, gave the scene of which she formed part a smooth and ultimate look, an air of knowing, in its immaculate order and its cold, meaningless cheer, that it would never see a fire again. Her own aspect—he could scarce have said why—intensified this note. Almost as white as wax, with the marks and signs in her face as numerous and as fine as if they had been etched by a needle, with soft white draperies relieved by a faded green scarf, the delicate tone of which had been consecrated by the years, she was the picture of a serene, exquisite, but impenetrable sphinx, whose head, or indeed all whose person, might have been powdered with silver. She was a sphinx, yet with her white petals and green fronds she might have been a lily too—only an artificial lily, wonderfully imitated and constantly kept, without dust or stain, though not exempt from a slight droop and a complexity of faint creases, under some clear glass bell. The perfection of household care, of high polish and finish, always reigned in her rooms, but they especially looked to Marcher at present as if everything had been wound up, tucked in, put away, so that she might sit with folded hands and with nothing more to do. She was "out of it," to his vision; her work was over; she communicated with him as across some gulf, or from some island of rest that she had already reached, and it made him feel strangely abandoned. Was it—or, rather, wasn't it—that if for so long she had been watching with him the answer to their question had swum into her ken and taken on its name, so that her occupation was verily gone? He had as much as charged her with this in saying to her, many months before, that she even then knew something she was keeping from him. It was a point he had never since ventured to press, vaguely fearing, as he did, that it might become a difference, perhaps a disagreement, between them. He had in short, in this later time, turned nervous, which was what, in all the other years, he had never been; and the oddity was that his nervousness should have waited till he had begun to doubt, should have held off so long as he was sure. There was something, it seemed to him, that the wrong word would bring down on his head, something that would so at least put an end to his suspense. But he wanted not to speak the wrong word; that would make everything ugly. He wanted the knowledge he lacked to drop on him, if drop it could, by its own august weight. If she was to forsake him it was surely for her to take leave. This was why he didn't ask her again, directly, what she knew; but it was also why, approaching the matter from another side, he said to her in the course of his visit: "What do you regard as the very worst that, at this time of day, *can* happen to me?"

He had asked her that in the past often enough; they had, with the odd, irregular rhythm of their intensities and avoidances, exchanged ideas about it and then had seen the ideas washed away by cool intervals, washed like figures traced in sea-sand. It had ever been the mark of their talk that the oldest allusions in it required but a little dismissal and reaction to come out again, sounding for the hour as new. She could thus at present meet his inquiry quite freshly and patiently. "Oh, yes, I've repeatedly thought, only it always seemed to me of old that I couldn't quite make up my mind. I thought of dreadful things, between which it was difficult to choose; and so must you have done."

"Rather! I feel now as if I had scarce done anything else. I appear to myself to have spent my life in thinking of nothing *but* dreadful things. A great many of them I've at different times named to you, but there were others I couldn't name."

"They were too, too dreadful?"

"Too, too dreadful—some of them."

She looked at him a minute, and there came to him as he met it an inconsequent sense that her eyes, when one got their full clearness, were still as beautiful as they had been in youth, only beautiful with a strange, cold light—a light that somehow was a part of the effect, if it wasn't rather a part of the cause, of the pale, hard sweetness of the season and the hour. "And yet," she said at last, "there are horrors we have mentioned."

It deepened the strangeness to see her, as such a figure in such a picture, talk of "horrors," but she was to do, in a few minutes, something stranger yet—though even of this he was to take the full measure but afterwards—and the note of it was already in the air. It was, for the matter of that, one of the signs that her eyes were having again such a high flicker of their prime. He had to admit, however, what she said. "Oh yes, there were times when we did go far." He caught himself in the act, speaking as if it all were over. Well, he wished it were; and the consummation depended, for him, clearly, more and more on his companion.

But she had now a soft smile. "Oh, far——!"

It was oddly ironic. "Do you mean you're prepared to go further?"

She was frail and ancient and charming as she continued to look at him, yet it was rather as if she had lost the thread. "Do you consider that we went so far?"

"Why, I thought it the point you were just making—that we *had* looked most things in the face."

"Including each other?" She still smiled. "But you're quite right. We've had together great imaginations, often great fears; but some of them have been unspoken."

"Then the worst—we haven't faced that. I *could* face it, I believe, if I knew what you think it. I feel," he explained, "as if I had lost my power to conceive such things." And he wondered if he looked as blank as he sounded. "It's spent."

"Then why do you assume," she asked, "that mine isn't?"

"Because you've given me signs to the contrary. It isn't a question for you of conceiving, imagining, comparing. It isn't a question now of choosing." At last he came out with it. "You know something that I don't. You've showed me that before."

These last words affected her, he could see in a moment, remarkably, and she spoke with firmness. "I've shown you, my dear, nothing."

He shook his head. "You can't hide it."

"Oh, oh!" May Bartram murmured over what she couldn't hide. It was almost a smothered groan.

"You admitted it months ago, when I spoke of it to you as of something you were afraid I would find out. Your answer was that I couldn't, that I wouldn't, and I don't pretend I have. But you had something therefore in mind, and I see now that it must have been, that it still is, the possibility that, of all possibilities, has settled itself for you as the worse. This," he went on, "is why I appeal to you. I'm only afraid of ignorance now—I'm not afraid of knowledge." And then as for a while she said nothing: "What makes me sure is that I see in your face and feel here, in this air and amid these appearances, that you're out of it. You've done. You've had your experience. You leave me to my fate."

Well, she listened, motionless and white in her chair, as if she had in fact a decision to make, so that her whole manner was a virtual confession, though still with a small, fine, inner stiffness, an imperfect surrender. "It *would* be the worst," she finally let herself say. "I mean the thing that I've never said."

It hushed him a moment. "More monstrous than all the monstrosities we've named?"

"More monstrous. Isn't that what you sufficiently express," she asked, "in calling it the worst?"

Marcher thought. "Assuredly—if you mean, as I do, something that includes all the loss and all the shame that are thinkable."

"It would if it *should* happen," said May Bartram. "What we're speaking of, remember, is only my idea."

"It's your belief," Marcher returned. "That's enough for me. I feel your beliefs are right. Therefore if, having this one, you give me no more light on it, you abandon me."

"No, no!" she repeated. "I'm with you—don't you see?—still." And as if to make it more vivid to him she rose from her chair—a movement she seldom made in these days—and showed herself, all draped and all soft, in her fairness and slimness. "I haven't forsaken you."

It was really, in its effort against weakness, a generous assurance, and had the success of the impulse not, happily, been great, it would have touched him to pain more than to pleasure. But the cold charm in her eyes had spread, as she hovered before him, to all the rest of her person, so that it was, for the minute, almost like a recovery of youth. He couldn't pity her for that; he could only take her as she showed—as capable still of helping him. It was as if, at the same time, her light might at any instant go out; wherefore he must make the most of it. There passed before him with intensity the three or four things he wanted most to know; but the question that came of itself to his lips really covered the others. "Then tell me if I shall consciously suffer."

She promptly shook her head. "Never!"

It confirmed the authority he imputed to her, and it produced on him an extraordinary effect. "Well, what's better than that? Do you call that the worst?"

"You think nothing is better?" she asked.

She seemed to mean something so special that he again sharply wondered, though still with the dawn of a prospect of relief. "Why not, if one doesn't *know?*" After which, as their eyes, over his question, met in a silence, the dawn deepened and something to his purpose came, prodigiously, out of her very face. His own, as he took it in, suddenly flushed to the forehead, and he gasped with the force of a perception to which, on the instant, everything fitted. The sound of his gasp filled the air; then he became articulate. "I see—if I don't suffer!"

In her own look, however, was doubt. "You see what?"

"Why, what you mean—what you've always meant."

She again shook her head. "What I mean isn't what I've always meant. It's different."

"It's something new?"

She hesitated. "Something new. It's not what you think. I see what you think."

His divination drew breath then; only her correction might be wrong. "It isn't that I *am* a donkey?" he asked between faintness and grimness. "It isn't that it's all a mistake?"

"A mistake?" she pityingly echoed. *That* possibility, for her, he saw, would be monstrous; and if she guaranteed him the immunity from pain it would accordingly not be what she had in mind. "Oh, no," she declared; "it's nothing of that sort. You've been right."

Yet he couldn't help asking himself if she weren't, thus pressed, speaking but to save him. It seemed to him he should be most lost if his history should prove all a platitude. "Are you telling me the truth, so that I sha'n't have been a bigger idiot than I can bear to know? I *haven't* lived with a vain imagination, in the most besotted illusion? I haven't waited but to see the door shut in my face?"

She shook her head again. "However the case stands *that* isn't the truth. Whatever the reality, it *is* a reality. The door isn't shut. The door's open," said May Bartram.

"Then something's to come?"

She waited once again, always with her cold, sweet eyes on him. "It's never too late." She had, with her gliding step, diminished the distance between them, and she stood nearer to him, close to him, a minute, as if still full of the unspoken. Her movement might have been for some finer emphasis of what she was at once hesitating and deciding to say. He had been standing by the chimney-piece, fireless and sparely adorned, a small, perfect old French clock and two morsels of rosy Dresden constituting all its furniture; and her hand grasped the shelf while she kept him waiting, grasped it a little as for support and encouragement. She only kept him waiting, however; that is, he only waited. It had become suddenly, from her movement and attitude, beautiful and vivid to him that she had something more to give him; her wasted face delicately shone with it, and it glittered, almost as with the white lustre of silver, in her expression. She was right, incontestably, for what he saw in her face was the truth, and strangely, without consequence, while their talk of it as dreadful was still in the air, she appeared to present it as inordinately soft. This, prompting bewilderment, made him but gape the more gratefully for her revelation, so that they continued for some minutes silent, her face shining at him, her contact imponderably pressing, and his stare all kind, but all expectant. The end, none the less, was that what he had expected failed to sound. Something else took place instead, which seemed to consist at first in the mere closing of her eyes. She gave way at the same instant to a slow, fine shudder, and though he remained staring —though he stared, in fact, but the harder—she turned off and regained her chair. It was the end of what she had been intending, but it left him thinking only of that.

"Well, you don't say——?"

She had touched in her passage a bell near the chimney and had sunk back, strangely pale. "I'm afraid I'm too ill."

"Too ill to tell me?" It sprang up sharp to him, and almost to his lips, the fear that she would die without giving him light. He checked himself in time from so expressing his question, but she answered as if she had heard the words.

"Don't you know—now?"

" 'Now'——?" She had spoken as if something that had made a difference had come up within the moment. But her maid, quickly obedient to her bell, was already with them. "I know nothing." And he was afterwards to say to himself that he must have spoken with odious impatience, such an impatience as to show that, supremely disconcerted, he washed his hands of the whole question.

"Oh!" said May Bartram.

"Are you in pain?" he asked, as the woman went to her.

"No," said May Bartram.

Her maid, who had put an arm round her as if to take her to her room, fixed on him eyes that appealingly contradicted her; in spite of which, however, he showed once more his mystification. "What then has happened?"

She was once more, with her companion's help, on her feet, and, feeling withdrawal imposed on him, he had found, blankly, his hat and gloves and had reached the door. Yet he waited for her answer. "What *was* to," she said.

V

He came back the next day, but she was then unable to see him, and as it was literally the first time this had occurred in the long stretch of their acquaintance he turned away, defeated and sore, almost angry—or feeling at least that such a break in their custom was really the beginning of the end—and wandered alone with his thoughts, especially with one of them that he was unable to keep down. She was dying, and he would lose her; she was dying, and his life would end. He stopped in the park, into which he had passed, and stared before him at his recurrent doubt. Away from her the doubt pressed again; in her presence he had believed her, but as he felt his forlornness he threw himself into the explanation that, nearest at hand, had most of a miserable warmth for him and least of a cold torment. She had deceived him to save him—to put him off with something in which he should be able to rest. What could the thing that was to happen to him be, after all, but just this thing that had begun to happen? Her dying, her death, his consequent solitude—*that* was what he had figured as the beast in the jungle, that was what had been in the lap of the gods. He had had her word for it as he left her; for what else, on earth, could she have meant? It wasn't a thing of a monstrous order; not a fate rare and distinguished; not a stroke of fortune that overwhelmed and immortalised; it had only the stamp of the common doom. But poor Marcher, at this hour, judged the common doom sufficient. It would serve his turn, and even as the consummation of infinite waiting he would bend his pride to accept it. He sat down on a bench in the twilight. He hadn't been a fool. Something had *been,* as she had said, to come. Before he rose indeed it had quite struck him that the final fact really matched with the long avenue through which he had had to reach it. As sharing his suspense, and as giving herself all, giving her life, to bring it to an end, she had come with him every step of the way. He had lived by her aid, and to leave her behind would be cruelly, damnably to miss her. What could be more overwhelming than that?

Well, he was to know within the week, for though she kept him a while at bay, left him restless and wretched during a series of days on each of which he asked about her only again to have to turn away, she ended his trial by receiving him where she had always received him. Yet she had been brought out at some hazard into the presence of so many of the things that were, consciously, vainly, half their past, and there was scant service left in the gentleness of her mere desire, all too visible, to check his obsession and wind up his long trouble. That was clearly what she wanted; the one thing more, for her own peace, while she could still put out her hand. He was so affected by her state that, once seated by her chair, he was moved to let everything go; it was she herself therefore who brought him back, took up again, before she dismissed him, her last word of the other time. She showed how she wished to leave their affair in order. "I'm not sure you understood. You've nothing to wait for more. It *has* come."

Oh, how he looked at her! "Really?"

"Really."

"The thing that, as you said, *was* to?"

"The thing that we began in our youth to watch for."

Face to face with her once more he believed her; it was a claim to which he had so abjectly little to oppose. "You mean that it has come as a positive, definite occurrence, with a name and a date?"

"Positive. Definite. I don't know about the 'name,' but, oh, with a date!"

He found himself again too helplessly at sea. "But come in the night—come and passed me by?"

May Bartram had her strange, faint smile. "Oh no, it hasn't passed you by!"

"But if I haven't been aware of it, and it hasn't touched me——?"

"Ah, your not being aware of it," and she seemed to hesitate an instant to deal with this—"your not being aware of it is the strangeness *in* the strangeness. It's the wonder *of* the wonder." She spoke as with the softness almost of a sick child, yet now at last, at the end of all, with the perfect straightness of a sybil. She visibly knew that she knew, and the effect on him was of something co-ordinate, in its high character, with the law that had ruled him. It was the true voice of the law; so on her lips would the law itself have sounded. "It *has* touched you," she went on. "It has done its office. It has made you all its own."

"So utterly without my knowing it?"

"So utterly without your knowing it." His hand, as he leaned to her, was on the arm of her chair, and, dimly smiling always now, she placed her own on it. "It's enough if *I* know it."

"Oh!" he confusedly sounded, as she herself of late so often had done.

"What I long ago said is true. You'll never know now, and I think you ought to be content. You've *had* it," said May Bartram.

"But had what?"

"Why, what was to have marked you out. The proof of your law. It has acted. I'm too glad," she then gravely added, "to have been able to see what it's *not*."

He continued to attach his eyes to her, and with the sense that it was all beyond him, and that *she* was too, he would still have sharply challenged her, had he not felt it an abuse of her weakness to do more than take devoutly what she gave him, take it as hushed as to a revelation. If he did speak, it was out of the foreknowledge of his loneliness to come. "If you're glad of what it's 'not,' it might then have been worse?"

She turned her eyes away, she looked straight before her; with which, after a moment: "Well, you know our fears."

He wondered. "It's something then we never feared?"

On this, slowly, she turned to him. "Did we ever dream, with all our dreams, that we should sit and talk of it thus?"

He tried for a little to make out if they had; but it was as if their dreams, numberless enough, were in solution in some thick, cold mist, in which thought lost itself. "It might have been that we couldn't talk?"

"Well"—she did her best for him—"not from this side. This, you see," she said, "is the *other* side."

"I think," poor Marcher returned, "that all sides are the same to me." Then, however, as she softly shook her head in correction: "We mightn't, as it were, have got across——?"

"To where we are—no. We're *here*"—she made her weak emphasis.

"And much good does it do us!" was her friend's frank comment.

"It does us the good it can. It does us the good that *it* isn't here. It's past. It's behind," said Mary Bartram. "Before——" but her voice dropped.

He had got up, not to tire her, but it was hard to combat his yearning. She after all told him nothing but that his light had failed—which he knew well enough without her. "Before——?" he blankly echoed.

"Before, you see, it was always to *come*. That kept it present."

"Oh, I don't care what comes now! Besides," Marcher added, "it seems to me I liked it better present, as you say, than I can like it absent with *your* absence."

"Oh, mine!"—and her pale hands made light of it.

"With the absence of everything." He had a dreadful sense of standing there before her for—so far as anything but this proved, this bottomless drop was concerned—the last time of their life. It rested on him with a weight he felt he could scarce bear, and this weight it apparently was that still pressed out what remained in him of speakable protest. "I believe you; but I can't begin to pretend I understand. *Nothing,* for me, is past; nothing *will* pass until I pass myself, which I pray my stars may be as soon as possible. Say, however," he added, "that I've eaten my cake, as you contend, to the last crumb—how can the thing I've never felt at all be the thing I was marked out to feel?"

She met him, perhaps, less directly, but she met him unperturbed. "You take your 'feelings' for granted. You were to suffer your fate. That was not necessarily to know it."

"How in the world—when what is such knowledge but suffering?"

She looked up at him a while, in silence. "No—you don't understand."

"I suffer," said John Marcher.

"Don't, don't!"

"How can I help at least *that?*"

"*Don't!*" May Bartram repeated.

She spoke it in a tone so special, in spite of her weakness, that he stared an instant—stared as if some light, hitherto hidden, had shimmered across his vision. Darkness again closed over it, but the gleam had already become for him an idea. "Because I haven't the right——?"

"Don't *know*—when you needn't," she mercifully urged. "You needn't—for we shouldn't."

"Shouldn't?" If he could but know what she meant!

"No—it's too much."

"Too much?" he still asked—but with a mystification that was the next moment, of a sudden, to give way. Her words, if they meant something, affected him in this light—the light also of her wasted face—as meaning *all,* and the sense of what knowledge had been for herself came over him with a rush which broke through into a question. "Is it of that, then, you're dying?"

She but watched him, gravely at first, as if to see, with this, where he was, and she might have seen something, or feared something, that moved her sympathy. "I would live for you still—if I could." Her eyes closed for a little, as if, withdrawn into herself, she were, for a last time, trying. "But I can't!" she said as she raised them again to take leave of him.

She couldn't indeed, as but too promptly and sharply appeared, and he had no vision of her after this that was anything but darkness and doom. They had parted forever in that strange talk; access to her chamber of pain, rigidly guarded, was almost wholly forbidden him; he was feeling now more-over, in the face of doctors, nurses, the two or three relatives attracted doubt-less by the presumption of what she had to "leave," how few were the rights, as they were called in such cases, that he had to put forward, and how odd it might even seem that their intimacy shouldn't have given him more of them. The stupidest fourth cousin had more, even though she had been nothing in such a person's life. She had been a feature of features in *his,* for what else was it to have been so indispensable? Strange beyond saying were the ways of existence, baffling for him the anomaly of his lack, as he felt it to be, of producible claim. A woman might have been, as it were, everything to him, and it might yet present him in no connection that anyone appeared obliged to recognise. If this was the case in these closing weeks it was the case more sharply on the occasion of the last offices rendered, in the great grey London cemetery, to what had been mortal, to what had been precious, in his friend. The concourse at her grave was not numerous, but he saw himself treated as scarce more nearly concerned with it than if there had been a thousand others. He was in short from this moment face to face with the fact that he was to profit extraordinarily little by the interest May Bartram had taken in him. He couldn't quite have said what he expected, but he had somehow not expected this approach to a double privation. Not only had her interest failed him, but he seemed to feel himself unattended—and for a reason he couldn't sound—by the distinction, the dignity, the propriety, if nothing else, of the man markedly bereaved. It was as if, in the view of society, he had not *been* markedly bereaved, as if there still failed some sign or proof of it, and as if, none the less, his character could never be affirmed, nor the deficiency ever made up. There were moments, as the weeks went by, when he would have liked, by some almost aggressive act, to take his stand on the intimacy of his loss, in order that it *might* be questioned and his retort, to the relief of his spirit, so recorded; but the moments of an irritation more helpless followed fast on these, the moments during which, turning things over with a good conscience but with a bare horizon, he found himself wondering if he oughtn't to have begun, so to speak, further back.

He found himself wondering indeed at many things, and this last speculation had others to keep it company. What could he have done, after all, in her lifetime, without giving them both, as it were, away? He couldn't have made it known she was watching him, for that would have published the superstition of the Beast. This was what closed his mouth now—now that the Jungle had been threshed to vacancy and that the Beast had stolen away. It sounded too foolish and too flat; the difference for him in this particular, the extinction in his life of the element of suspense, was such in fact as to surprise him. He could scarce have said what the effect resembled; the abrupt cessation, the positive prohibition, of music perhaps, more than anything else, in some place all adjusted and all accustomed to sonoriety and to attention. If he could at any rate have conceived lifting the veil from his image at some moment of the past (what had he done, after all, if not lift it to *her?*) so to do this to-day, to talk to people at large of the Jungle cleared and confide to them that he now felt it as safe, would have been not only to see them listen as to a goodwife's tale, but really to hear himself tell one. What it presently came to in truth was that poor Marcher waded through his beaten grass, where no life stirred, where no breath sounded, where no evil eye seemed to gleam from a possible lair, very much as if vaguely looking for the Beast, and still more as if missing it. He walked about in an existence that had grown strangely more spacious, and, stopping fitfully in places where the under-growth of life struck him as closer, asked himself yearningly, wondered secretly and sorely, if it would have lurked here or there. It would have at all events *sprung*; what was at least complete was his belief in the truth itself of the assurance given him. The change from his old sense to his new was absolute and final: what was to happen *had* so absolutely and finally hap-pened that he was as little able to know a fear for his future as to know a hope; so absent in short was any question of anything still to come. He was to live entirely with the other question, that of his unidentified past, that of his having to see his fortune impenetrably muffled and masked.

The torment of this vision became then his occupation; he couldn't per-haps have consented to live but for the possibility of guessing. She had told him, his friend, not to guess; she had forbidden him, so far as he might, to know, and she had even in a sort denied the power in him to learn: which were so many things, precisely, to deprive him of rest. It wasn't that he wanted, he argued for fairness, that anything that had happened to him should happen over again; it was only that he shouldn't, as an anticlimax, have been taken sleeping so sound as not to be able to win back by an effort of thought the lost stuff of consciousness. He declared to himself at moments that he would either win it back or have done with consciousness for ever; he made this idea his one motive, in fine, made it so much his passion that none other, to compare with it, seemed ever to have touched him. The lost stuff of consciousness became thus for him as a strayed or stolen child to an unappeasable father; he hunted it up and down very much as if he were knocking at doors and inquiring of the police. This was the spirit in which, inevitably, he set himself to travel; he started on a journey that was to be as long as he could make it; it danced before him that, as the other side of the globe couldn't possibly have less to say to him, it might, by a possibility of suggestion, have more. Before he quitted London, however, he made a pilgrimage to May Bartram's grave, took his way to it through the endless avenues of the grim suburban necropolis, sought it out in the wilderness of tombs, and, though he had come but for the renewal of the act of farewell, found himself, when he had at last stood by it, beguiled into long intensities. He stood for an hour, powerless to turn away and yet powerless to pene-trate the darkness of death; fixing with his eyes her inscribed name and date, beating his forehead against the fact of the secret they kept, drawing his breath, while he waited as if, in pity of him, some sense would rise from the stones. He kneeled on the stones, however, in vain; they kept what they concealed; and if the face of the tomb did become a face for him it was because her two names were like a pair of eyes that didn't know him. He gave them a last long look, but no palest light broke.

vi

He stayed away, after this, for a year; he visited the depths of Asia, spending himself on scenes of romantic interest, of superlative sanctity; but what was present to him everywhere was that for a man who had known what *he* had known the world was vulgar and vain. The state of mind in which he had lived for so many years shone out to him, in reflection, as a light that coloured and refined, a light beside which the glow of the East was garish, cheap and thin. The terrible truth was that he had lost—with everything else—a distinction as well; the things he saw couldn't help being common when he had become common to look at them. He was simply now one of them himself—he was in the dust, without a peg for the sense of difference; and there were hours when, before the temples of gods and the sepulchres of kings, his spirit turned, for nobleness of association, to the barely discriminated slab in the London suburb. That had become for him, and more intensely with time and distance, his one witness of a past glory. It was all that was left to him for proof or pride, yet the past glories of Pharaohs were nothing to him as he thought of it. Small wonder then that he came back to it on the morrow of his return. He was drawn there this time as irresistibly as the other, yet with a confidence, almost, that was doubtless the effect of the many months that had elapsed. He had lived, in spite of himself, into his change of feeling, and in wandering over the earth had wandered, as might be said, from the circumference to the centre of his desert. He had settled to his safety and accepted perforce his extinction; figuring to himself, with some colour, in the likeness of certain little old men he remembered to have seen, of whom, all meagre and wizened as they might look, it was related that they had in their time fought twenty duels or been loved by ten princesses. They indeed had been wondrous for others, while he was but wondrous for himself; which, however, was exactly the cause of his haste to renew the wonder by getting back, as he might put it, into his own presence. That had quickened his steps and checked his delay. If his visit was prompt it was because he had been separated so long from the part of himself that alone he now valued.

It is accordingly not false to say that he reached his goal with a certain elation, and stood there again with a certain assurance. The creature beneath the sod *knew* of his rare experience, so that, strangely now, the place had lost for him its mere blankness of expression. It met him in mildness—not, as before, in mockery; it wore for him the air of conscious greeting that we find, after absence, in things that have closely belonged to us and which seem to confess of themselves to the connection. The plot of ground, the graven tablet, the tended flowers affected him so as belonging to him that he quite felt for the hour like a contented landlord reviewing a piece of property. Whatever had happened—well, had happened. He had not come back this time with the vanity of that question, his former worrying, "What, *what?*" now practically so spent. Yet he would, none the less, never again so cut himself off from the spot; he would come back to it every month, for if he did nothing else by its aid he at least held up his head. It thus grew for him, in the oddest way, a positive resource; he carried out his idea of periodical returns, which took their place at last among the most inveterate of his habits. What it all amounted to, oddly enough, was that, in his now so simplified world, this garden of death gave him the few square feet of earth on which he could still most live. It was as if, being nothing anywhere else for anyone, nothing even for himself, he were just everything here, and if not for a crowd of witnesses, or indeed for any witness but John Marcher, then by clear right of the register that he could scan like an open page. The open page was the tomb of his friend, and *there* were the facts of the past, there the truth of his life, there the backward reaches in which he could lose himself. He did this, from time to time, with such effect that he seemed to wander through the old years with his hand in the arm of a companion who was, in the most extraordinary manner, his other, his younger self; and to wander, which was more extraordinary yet, round and round a third presence—not wandering she, but stationary, still, whose eyes, turning with his revolution, never ceased to follow him, and whose seat was his point, so to speak, of orientation. Thus in short he settled to live—feeding only on the sense that he once *had* lived, and dependent on it not only for a support but for an identity.

It sufficed him, in its way, for months, and the year elapsed; it would doubtless even have carried him further but for an accident, superficially slight, which moved him, in a quite other direction, with a force beyond any of his impressions of Egypt or of India. It was a thing of the merest chance —the turn, as he afterwards felt, of a hair, though he was indeed to live to believe that if light hadn't come to him in this particular fashion it would still have come in another. He was to live to believe this, I say, though he was not to live, I may not less definitely mention, to do much else. We allow him at any rate the benefit of the conviction, struggling up for him at the end, that, whatever might have happened or not happened, he would have come round of himself to the light. The incident of an autumn day had put the match to the train laid from of old by his misery. With the light before him he knew that even of late his ache had only been smothered. It was strangely drugged, but it throbbed; at the touch it began to bleed. And the touch, in the event, was the face of a fellow-mortal. This face, one grey afternoon when the leaves were thick in the alleys, looked into Marcher's own, at the ceme- tery, with an expression like the cut of a blade. He felt it, that is, so deep down that he winced at the steady thrust. The person who so mutely assaulted him was a figure he had noticed, on reaching his own goal, absorbed by a grave a short distance away, a grave apparently fresh, so that the emotion of the visitor would probably match it for frankness. This fact alone forbade further attention, though during the time he stayed he remained vaguely conscious of his neighbour, a middle-aged man apparently, in mourning, whose bowed back, among the clustered monuments and mortuary yews, was constantly presented. Marcher's theory that these were elements in con-

tact with which he himself revived, had suffered, on this occasion, it may
be granted, a sensible though inscrutable check. The autumn day was dire
for him as none had recently been, and he rested with a heaviness he had
not yet known on the low stone table that bore May Bartram's name. He
rested without power to move, as if some spring in him, some spell vouchsafed, had suddenly been broken forever. If he could have done that
moment as he wanted he would simply have stretched himself on the slab
that was ready to take him, treating it as a place prepared to receive his last
sleep. What in all the wide world had he now to keep awake for? He stared
before him with the question, and it was then that, as one of the cemetery
walks passed near him, he caught the shock of the face.

His neighbour at the other grave had withdrawn, as he himself, with
force in him to move, would have done by now, and was advancing along
the path on his way to one of the gates. This brought him near, and his pace
was slow, so that—and all the more as there was a kind of hunger in his
look—the two men were for a minute directly confronted. Marcher felt him
on the spot as one of the deeply stricken—a perception so sharp that nothing
else in the picture lived for it, neither his dress, his age, nor his presumable
character and class; nothing lived but the deep ravage of the features that he
showed. He *showed* them—that was the point; he was moved, as he passed,
by some impulse that was either a signal for sympathy or, more possibly, a
challenge to another sorrow. He might already have been aware of our
friend, might, at some previous hour, have noticed in him the smooth habit
of the scene, with which the state of his own senses so scantly consorted,
and might thereby have been stirred as by a kind of overt discord. What
Marcher was at all events conscious of was, in the first place, that the image
of scarred passion presented to him was conscious too—of something that
profaned the air; and, in the second, that, roused, startled, shocked, he was
yet the next moment looking after it, as it went, with envy. The most
extraordinary thing that had happened to him—though he had given that
name to other matters as well—took place, after his immediate vague stare,
as a consequence of this impression. The stranger passed, but the raw glare
of his grief remained, making our friend wonder in pity what wrong, what
wound it expressed, what injury not to be healed. What had the man *had*
to make him, by the loss of it, so bleed and yet live?

Something—and this reached him with a pang—that *he,* John Marcher,
hadn't; the proof of which was precisely John Marcher's arid end. No passion
had ever touched him, for this was what passion meant; he had survived
and maundered and pined, but where had been *his* deep ravage? The
extraordinary thing we speak of was the sudden rush of the result of this
question. The sight that had just met his eyes named to him, as in letters
of quick flame, something he had utterly, insanely missed, and what he
had missed; made these things a train of fire, made them mark themselves
in an anguish of inward throbs. He had seen *outside* of his life, not learned
it within, the way a woman was mourned when she had been loved for

herself; such was the force of his conviction of the meaning of the stranger's face, which still flared for him like a smoky torch. It had not come to him, the knowledge, on the wings of experience; it had brushed him, jostled him, upset him, with the disrespect of chance, the insolence of an accident. Now that the illumination had begun, however, it blazed to the zenith, and what he presently stood there gazing at was the sounded void of his life. He gazed, he drew breath, in pain; he turned in his dismay, and, turning, he had before him in sharper incision than ever the open page of his story. The name on the table smote him as the passage of his neighbour had done, and what it said to him, full in the face, was that *she* was what he had missed. This was the awful thought, the answer to all the past, the vision at the dread clearness of which he turned as cold as the stone beneath him. Everything fell together, confessed, explained, overwhelmed; leaving him most of all stupefied at the blindness he had cherished. The fate he had been marked for he had met with a vengeance—he had emptied the cup to the lees; he had been the man of his time, *the* man, to whom nothing on earth was to have happened. That was the rare stroke—that was his visitation. So he saw it, as we say, in pale horror, while the pieces fitted and fitted. So *she* had seen it, while he didn't, and so she served at this hour to drive the truth home. It was the truth, vivid and monstrous, that all the while he had waited the wait was itself his portion. This the companion of his vigil had at a given moment perceived, and she had then offered him the chance to baffle his doom. One's doom, however, was never baffled, and on the day she had told him that his own had come down she had seen him but stupidly stare at the escape she offered him.

The escape would have been to love her; then, *then* he would have lived. *She* had lived—who could say now with what passion?—since she had loved him for himself; whereas he had never thought of her (ah, how it hugely glared at him!) but in the chill of his egotism and the light of her use. Her spoken words came back to him, and the chain stretched and stretched. The beast had lurked indeed, and the beast, at its hour, had sprung; it had sprung in that twilight of the cold April when, pale, ill, wasted, but all beautiful, and perhaps even then recoverable, she had risen from her chair to stand before him and let him imaginably guess. It had sprung as he didn't guess; it had sprung as she hopelessly turned from him, and the mark, by the time he left her, had fallen where it *was* to fall. He had justified his fear and achieved his fate; he had failed, with the last exactitude, of all he was to fail of; and a moan now rose to his lips as he remembered she had prayed he mightn't know. This horror of waking—*this* was knowledge, knowledge under the breath of which the very tears in his eyes seemed to freeze. Through them, none the less, he tried to fix it and hold it; he kept it there before him so that he might feel the pain. That at least, belated and bitter, had something of the taste of life. But the bitterness suddenly sickened him, and it was as if, horribly, he saw, in the truth, in the cruelty of his image, what had been appointed and done. He saw the Jungle of his life and saw the lurking Beast; then, while he looked, perceived it, as by a stir of the air, rise, huge and hideous, for the leap that was to settle him. His eyes darkened—it was close; and, instinctively turning, in his hallucination, to avoid it, he flung himself, on his face, on the tomb.

COMMENTARY

James's "The Beast in the Jungle" was first published in a "volume of miscellanies" entitled *The Better Sort* in 1903. It was written at about the same time as Joyce's "The Dead," and although the fables of the two stories differ as profoundly as their techniques, they invite comparison at several levels. Both stories hinge upon climaxes of self-revelation, and both limit the reader's access to the subject to a Central Intelligence (see Appendix A, p. 626); both end with a powerful effect of irony which we may call "classical irony" because its appearance has been predicted by the reader whose interest is thus engaged at a higher level than that of mere surprise. We know that John Marcher and Gabriel Conroy are failing in some fundamental insight into their predicaments: our suspense looks ahead to the revelation of this failure to themselves. It comes, in both stories, in a Short View scene (see Appendix A, p. 627), towards which our interest has been directed in mounting intensity.

Again, as in "The Dead," we have the embodiment of the great contemporary subject: the isolation and the frustration of personality. It is a subject that goes back to Poe in "William Wilson" and "The Fall of the House of Usher" (see pp. 114–117), and to Hawthorne in "The Bosom Serpent" and "Young Goodman Brown" (see pp. 36–39). Poe's method is nearer than Hawthorne's to the modern technique which grounds in psychological realism the symbolic representation (see Appendix A, p. 633) of the hero's egoism. Hawthorne tends to scant the realistic base and to let his symbols become attenuated into allegory. But it is a fact of curious and perhaps of important historical interest that Hawthorne was the first American writer (he may have anticipated anybody in Europe) who was conscious of the failure of modern man to realize his full capacity for moral growth. In four entries in *American Notes* he plays with this problem as the theme of a possible story, and he actually states the theme of "The Beast in the Jungle" some sixty years before the story was written (see p. 37).

To distinguish certain features of the method of "The Beast in the Jungle" we could scarcely do better than to use some of James's own critical terms. The "story," reduced to the slight action through which James develops the values of the situation, can be told very briefly. At a party John Marcher meets May Bartram; they renew a casual acquaintance of ten years before. Miss Bartram reminds him of a remarkable confession that he had made on that occasion: he had seen himself as a man to whom something overwhelming was destined to happen, and his part in life, excluding all other aims, was to await it—something special, even unique, for which he was to hold himself in readiness. He still feels the imminence of his destiny: it may come at any moment. Marcher and Miss Bartram now enter into a long, uncommitted relationship from which she gets nothing and he all that he can allow himself to get, since he must accept nothing short of his supreme moment. What he gets in the long run is her life, but he cannot "use" it since he can give nothing in return. They drift, in this moral stalemate, into middle age. Miss Bartram dies. Marcher feels increasingly empty and abandoned, and forms the habit of haunting her grave (one thinks here of the related story, "The Altar of the Dead"), until one day he looks into the eyes of another man haunting another grave. The man's eyes expose the depths of grief. The revelation forces Marcher into a tragic and ironic awareness. The supreme value for which he had reserved his life he had, of course, killed: it lay in the grave of May Bartram.

The story is laid out in six sections, and the point of view (see Appendix A, pp. 621, 626) is consistently that of Marcher. The two first sections constitute a long foreground or Complication (see Appendix A, p. 630). It may be questioned whether the long Complication is justified, since in it nothing "happens": in only about twice the space James lays the foreground of a very long novel, *The Ambassadors*. There are only two Short View scenes in the story (see Appendix A, p. 627). In slighting the scenic effect it is possible that James has violated one of his primary canons: the importance of rendition over statement. (There is too much of the elaborate voice of James, what Mr. Edmund Wilson has harshly described as the "Jamesian gas.") Yet one can see that he could not allow himself to get too deeply into Marcher's consciousness, at the stage of the Complication, or Marcher himself would have had to examine his illusion too closely, and the story would have collapsed. The reader may well wonder whether the two brief scenic moments, when they finally come, are adequately prepared for, in spite of the length of preparation. James has not, in the first three sections, made either Marcher or Miss Bartram a *visible* character; he has merely presented their Enveloping fate (see Appendix A, p. 631) as it *could* have been seen from Marcher's point of view; but we have seen them not quite credibly.

The excessive foreground is an instance of what James called the Indirect Approach to the objective situation through the trial-and-error of a Central Intelligence; but the Receptive Lucidity of a Strether, in *The Ambassadors,* is not at Marcher's command. Are we to conclude that the very nature of James's problem in "The Beast in the Jungle," the problem of dramatizing the insulated ego, of making active what in its essence is incapable of action, excluded the use of an active and searching intelligence in the main character?

The first of the two scenes appears in part iv when years of waiting have driven May Bartram to something like desperation. She cannot overtly break the frame of their intercourse, which permits her only to affirm and reaffirm her loyalty to the rôle of asking nothing for herself; in the act of a new reaffirmation,

> "No, no!" she repeated. "I'm with you—don't you see—still." And as to make it more vivid to him she rose from her chair—a movement she seldom risked in these days—and showed herself, all draped and all soft, in her fairness and slimness. "I haven't forsaken you."

We return to Marcher's mind, in which this reflection is all that the moment can give him:

> . . . He couldn't pity her for that; he could only take her as she showed —as capable even yet of helping him. It was as if, at the same time, her light might at any instant go out; wherefore he must make the most of it. . . . "Tell me if I shall consciously suffer."

Here we get a special case of James's Operative Irony, which "implies and projects the possible other case." But the "possible other case" is not in the awareness of Marcher, as it always is in Strether; it is manipulated by James himself standing beside Marcher and moving May Bartram up close to imply her virtual offer of herself, her very body—an offer of which Marcher is not aware, so deeply concerned is he with his "problem." As May Bartram stands before him, "all soft," it is Marcher's Beast which has leaped at him from the jungle; and he doesn't know it.

It is a fine scene, unobtrusively arrived at, and it has a certain power. It is perhaps sounder in its structure than the second and climactic scene. Marcher's frequent visits to Miss Bartram's grave are occasions of a developing insight into his loss, his failure to see that his supreme experience had been there for him day after day through many years. But James must have known that, to make the insight dramatically credible, it must reach the reader through a scene; and to have a "scene" there must be at least two persons and an interchange between them. He thus suddenly introduces, at the last moment, what he called in the Prefaces a *ficelle,* a character not in the action but brought in to elicit some essential quality from the involved characters. The stranger haunting the other grave is such a *ficelle;* but not having been "planted" earlier and disguised, he appears with the force of a shock, and could better be described as a *deus ex machina*—a device for ending an action by means of a force outside it; here it serves to render scenically, for the eye and ear, what had otherwise been a reported insight of Marcher's. James could not let himself merely tell us that Marcher had at last seen his tragic flaw; he must contrive to show him seeing it.

If this story is the greatest of the James *nouvelles,* as it probably is, one must reconsider the generally held belief that it is his special form, in which he scored greater triumphs than he ever did in the novels. If we look at it in terms of the visible material—the material *made* visible—it is much too long; the foreground is too elaborate, and the structure suffers from the disproportion (see Appendix B, p. 635) of the Misplaced Middle (James's phrase); that is, he has not been able to render dramatically parts I and II and "confer on the false quantity the brave appearance of the true." If the grief-stricken stranger at the end was to be more than a palpable trick, should not James have planted him (or his equivalent) somewhere in the foreground?

These questions do not exhaust the story, which remains one of the great stories in the language. In the long run its effect is that of tone (see Appendix A, p. 632), even of lyric meditation; and it is closer to the method of Hawthorne than one may at a glance suppose; for in the last scene it is very nearly allegory, though less so than that companion piece, James's great failure in spite of its own great tone, "The Altar of the Dead." In neither of these stories is the naturalistic detail distinct enough to give the situation reality; and the symbolism (see Appendix A, p. 633) tends to allegory because there is not enough detail to support it. We must always return to Joyce's "The Dead" for the great modern example of the *nouvelle*.

Rudyard Kipling

ON GREENHOW HILL

To Love's low voice she lent a careless ear;
Her hand within his rosy fingers lay,
A chilling weight. She would not turn or hear;
But with averted face went on her way.
But when pale Death, all featureless and grim,
Lifted his bony hand, and beckoning
Held out his cypress-wreath, she followed him,
And Love was left forlorn and wondering,
That she who for his bidding would not stay,
At Death's first whisper rose and went away.

Rivals.

"OHE, *Ahmed Din! Shafiz Ulla ahoo!* Bahadur Khan, where are you? Come out of the tents, as I have done, and fight against the English. Don't kill your own kin! Come out to me!"

The deserter from a native corps was crawling round the outskirts of the camp, firing at intervals and shouting invitations to his old comrades. Misled by the rain and the darkness, he came to the English wing of the camp, and with his yelping and rifle-practice disturbed the men. They had been making roads all day, and were tired.

Ortheris was sleeping at Learoyd's feet. "Wot's all that?" he said thickly. Learoyd snored, and a Snider bullet ripped its way through the tent wall. The men swore. "It's that bloomin' deserter from the Aurangabadis," said Ortheris. "Git up, some one, an' tell 'im 'e's come to the wrong shop."

"Go to sleep, little man," said Mulvaney, who was steaming nearest the door. "I can't arise and expaytiate with him. 'Tis rainin' entrenchin' tools outside."

" 'Tain't because you bloomin' can't. It's 'cause you bloomin' won't, ye long, limp, lousy, lazy beggar, you. 'Ark to 'im 'owlin'!"

"Wot's the good of argifying? Put a bullet into the swine! 'E's keepin' us awake!" said another voice.

A subaltern shouted angrily, and a dripping sentry whined from the darkness—

" 'Tain't no good, sir. I can't see 'im. 'E's 'idin' somewhere down 'ill."

Reprinted from *Life's Handicap* by Rudyard Kipling, and used with the kind permission of Doubleday and Co., Inc., Mrs. George Bambridge, A. P. Watt & Son and The Macmillan Company of Canada, Ltd.

Ortheris tumbled out of his blanket. "Shall I try to get 'im, sir?" said he.

"No," was the answer. "Lie down. I won't have the whole camp shooting all round the clock. Tell him to go and pot his friends."

Ortheris considered for a moment. Then, putting his head under the tent wall, he called, as a 'bus conductor calls in a block, "'igher up, there! 'igher up!"

The men laughed, and the laughter was carried down wind to the deserter, who, hearing that he had made a mistake, went off to worry his own regiment half a mile away. He was received with shots; the Aurangabadis were very angry with him for disgracing their colors.

"An' that's all right," said Ortheris, withdrawing his head as he heard the hiccough of the Sniders in the distance. "S'elp me Gawd, tho', that man's not fit to live—messin' with my beauty-sleep this way."

"Go out and shoot him in the morning, then," said the subaltern incautiously. "Silence in the tents now. Get your rest, men."

Ortheris lay down with a happy little sigh, and in two minutes there was no sound except the rain on the canvas and the all-embracing and elemental snoring of Learoyd.

The camp lay on a bare ridge of the Himalayas, and for a week had been waiting for a flying column to make connection. The nightly rounds of the deserter and his friends had become a nuisance.

In the morning the men dried themselves in hot sunshine and cleaned their grimy accoutrements. The native regiment was to take its turn of road-making that day while the Old Regiment loafed.

"I'm goin' to lay for a shot at that man," said Ortheris, when he had finished washing out his rifle. "'E comes up the watercourse every evenin' about five o'clock. If we go and lie out on the north 'ill a bit this afternoon we'll get 'im."

"You're a bloodthirsty little mosquito," said Mulvaney, blowing blue clouds into the air. "But I suppose I will have to come wid you. Fwhere's Jock?"

"Gone out with the Mixed Pickles, 'cause 'e thinks 'isself a bloomin' marksman," said Ortheris, with scorn.

The "Mixed Pickles" were a detachment of picked shots, generally employed in clearing spurs of hills when the enemy were too impertinent. This taught the young officers how to handle men, and did not do the enemy much harm. Mulvaney and Ortheris strolled out of camp, and passed the Aurangabadis going to their road-making.

"You've got to sweat to-day," said Ortheris, genially. "We're going to get your man. You didn't knock 'im out last night by any chance, any of you?"

"No. The pig went away mocking us. I had one shot at him," said a private. "He's my cousin, and *I* ought to have cleared our dishonor. But good luck to you."

They went cautiously to the north hill, Ortheris leading, because, as he explained, "this is a long-range show, an' I've got to do it." His was an almost passionate devotion to his rifle, which, by barrack-room report, he was supposed to kiss every night before turning in. Charges and scuffles he held in contempt, and, when they were inevitable, slipped between Mulvaney and Learoyd, bidding them to fight for his skin as well as their own. They never failed him. He trotted along, questing like a hound on a broken trail, through the wood of the north hill. At last he was satisfied, and threw himself down on the soft pine-needle slope that commanded a clear view of the watercourse and a brown, bare hillside beyond it. The trees made a scented darkness in which an army-corps could have hidden from the sun-glare without.

"'Ere's the tail o' the wood," said Ortheris. "'E's got to come up the watercourse, 'cause it gives 'im cover. We'll lay 'ere. 'Tain't not arf so bloomin' dusty neither."

He buried his nose in a clump of scentless white violets. No one had come to tell the flowers that the season of their strength was long past, and they had bloomed merrily in the twilight of the pines.

"This is something like," he said, luxuriously. "Wot a 'evinly clear drop for a bullet acrost! How much d'you make it, Mulvaney?"

"Seven hunder. Maybe a trifle less, bekaze the air's so thin."

Wop! Wop! Wop! went a volley of musketry in the rear face of the north hill.

"Curse them Mixed Pickles firin' at nothin'! They'll scare 'arf the country."

"Thry a sightin' shot in the middle of the row," said Mulvaney, the man of many wiles. "There's a red rock yonder he'll be sure to pass. Quick!"

Ortheris ran his sight up to six hundred yards and fired. The bullet threw up a feather of dust by a clump of gentians at the base of the rock.

"Good enough!" said Ortheris, snapping the scale down. "You snick your sights to mine or a little lower. You're always firin' high. But remember, first shot to me. O Lordy! but it's a lovely afternoon."

The noise of the firing grew louder, and there was a tramping of men in the wood. The two lay very quiet, for they knew that the British soldier is desperately prone to fire at anything that moves or calls. Then Learoyd appeared, his tunic ripped across the breast by a bullet, looking ashamed of himself. He flung down on the pine-needles, breathing in snorts.

"One o' them damned gardeners o' th' Pickles," said he, fingering the rent. "Firin' to th' right flank, when he knowed I was there. If I knew who he was I'd 'a' rippen the hide offan him. Look at ma tunic!"

"That's the spishil trustability av a marksman. Train him to hit a fly wid a stiddy rest at seven hunder, an' he loose on anythin' he sees or hears up to th' mile. You're well out av that fancy-firin' gang, Jock. Stay here."

"Bin firin' at the bloomin' wind in the bloomin' treetops," said Ortheris, with a chuckle. "I'll show you some firin' later on."

They wallowed in the pine-needles, and the sun warmed them where they lay. The Mixed Pickles ceased firing, and returned to camp, and left the wood to a few scared apes. The watercourse lifted up its voice in the silence, and talked foolishly to the rocks. Now and again the dull thump of a blasting charge three miles away told that the Aurangabadis were in difficulties with their road-making. The men smiled as they listened and lay still, soaking in the warm leisure. Presently Learoyd, between the whiffs of his pipe—

"Seems queer—about 'im yonder—desertin' at all."

" 'E'll be a bloomin' side queerer when I've done with 'im," said Ortheris. They were talking in whispers, for the stillness of the wood and the desire of slaughter lay heavy upon them.

"I make no doubt he had his reasons for desertin'; but, my faith! I make less doubt ivry man has good reason for killin' him," said Mulvaney.

"Happen there was a lass tewed up wi' it. Men do more than more for th' sake of a lass."

"They make most av us 'list. They've no manner av right to make us desert."

"Ah; they make us 'list, or their fathers do," said Learoyd softly, his helmet over his eyes.

Ortheris's brows contracted savagely. He was watching the valley. "If it's a girl I'll shoot the beggar twice over, and second time for bein' a fool. You're blasted sentimental all of a sudden. Thinkin' o' your last near shave?"

"Nay, lad; ah was but thinkin' o' what had happened."

"An fwhat has happened, ye lumberin' child av calamity, that you're lowing like a cow-calf at the back av the pasture, an' suggestin' invidious excuses for the man Stanley's goin' to kill. Ye'll have to wait another hour yet, little man. Spit it out, Jock, an' bellow melojus to the moon. It takes an earthquake or a bullet graze to fetch aught out av you. Discourse, Don Juan! The a-moors av Lotharius Learoyd! Stanley, kape a rowlin' rig'mental eye on the valley."

"It's along o' yon hill there," said Learoyd, watching the bare sub-Himalayan spur that reminded him of his Yorkshire moors. He was speaking more to himself than his fellows. "Ay," said he, "Rumbolds Moor stands up ower Skipton town, an' Greenhow Hill stands up ower Pately Brig. I reckon you've never heeard tell o' Greenhow Hill, but yon bit o' bare stuff if there was nobbut a white road windin' is like ut; strangely like. Moors an' moors an' moors, wi' never a tree for shelter, an' grey houses wi' flagstone rooves, and pewits cryin' an' a windhover goin' to and fro just like these kites. And cold! A wind that cuts you like a knife. You could tell Greenhow Hill folk by the red-apple color o' their cheeks an' nose tips, and their blue eyes, driven into pin-points by the wind. Miners mostly, burrowin' for lead i' th' hillsides, followin' the trail of th' ore vein same as a field-rat. It was the roughest minin' I ever seen. Yo'd come on a bit o' creakin' wood windlass like a wellhead, an' you was let down i' th' bight of a rope, fendin' yoursen off the side wi' one hand, carryin' a candle stuck in a lump o' clay with t'other, an' clickin' hold of a rope with, t'other hand."

"An' that's three of them," said Mulvaney. "Must be a good climate in those parts."

Learoyd took no heed.

"An' then yo' came to a level, where you crept on your hands and knees through a mile o' windin' drift, an' you come out into a cave-place as big as Leeds Townhall, with a engine pumpin' water from workin's 'at went deeper still. It's a queer country, let alone minin', for the hill is full of those natural caves, an' the rivers an' the becks drops into what they call pot-holes, an' come out again miles away."

"Wot was you doin' there?" said Ortheris.

"I was a young chap then, an' mostly went wi' 'osses, leadin' coal and lead ore; but at th' time I'm tellin' on I was drivin' the waggon-team i' th' big sumph. I didn't belong to that country-side by rights. I went there because of a little difference at home, an' at fust I took up wi' a rough lot. One night we'd been drinkin', an' I must ha' hed more than I could stand, or happen th' ale was none so good. Though i' them days, By for God, I never seed bad ale." He flung his arms over his head, and gripped a vast handful of white violets. "Nah," said he, "I never seed the ale I could not drink, the bacca I could not smoke, nor the lass I could not kiss. Well, we mun have a race home, the lot on us. I lost all th' others, an' when I was climbin' ower one of them walls built o' loose stones, I comes down into the ditch, stones and all, an' broke my arm. Not as I knawed much about it, for I fell on th' back of my head, an' was knocked stupid like. An' when I come to mysen it were mornin', an' I were lyin' on the settle i' Jesse Roantree's houseplace, an' 'Liza Roantree was settin' sewin'. I ached all ovver, and my mouth were like a lime-kiln. She gave me a drink out of a china mug wi' gold letters—'A Present from Leeds'—as I looked at many and many a time at after. 'Yo're to lie still while Dr. Warbottom comes, because your arm's broken, and father has sent a lad to fetch him. He found yo' when he was goin' to work, an' carried you here on his back,' sez she. 'Oa!' sez I; an' I shet my eyes, for I felt ashamed o' mysen. 'Father's gone to his work these three hours, an' he said he' tell 'em to get somebody to drive the tram.' The clock ticked, an' a bee comed in the house, an' they rung i' my head like mill-wheels. An' she give me another drink an' settled the pillow. 'Eh, but yo're young to be getten drunk an' such like, but yo' won't do it again, will yo'?'—'Noa,' sez I, 'I wouldn't if she'd not but stop they mill-wheels clatterin'.'"

"Faith, it's a good thing to be nursed by a woman when you're sick!" said Mulvaney. "Dir' cheap at the price av twenty broken heads."

Ortheris turned to frown across the valley. He had not been nursed by many women in his life.

"An' then Dr. Warbottom comes ridin' up, an' Jesse Roantree along with 'im. He was a high-larned doctor, but he talked wi' poor folk same as theirsens. 'What's ta bin agaate on naa?' he sings out. 'Brekkin' tha thick head?' An' he felt me all ovver. 'That's none broken. Tha' nobbut knocked a bit sillier than ordinary, an' that's daaft eneaf.' An' soa he went on, callin' me all the names he could think on, but settin' my arm, wi's Jesse's help, as careful as could be. 'Yo' mun let the big oaf bide here a bit, Jesse,' he says, when he hed strapped me up an' given me a dose o' physic; an' you an' 'Liza will tend him, though he's scarcelins worth the trouble. An' tha'll lose tha' work,' sez he, an' tha'll be upon th' Sick Club for a couple o' months an' more. Doesn't tha think tha's a fool?'"

"But whin was a young man, high or low, the other av a fool, I'd like to know?" said Mulvaney. "Sure, folly's the only safe way to wisdom, for I've thried it."

"Wisdom!" grinned Ortheris, scanning his comrades with uplifted chin. "You're bloomin' Solomons, you two, ain't you?"

Learoyd went calmly on, with a steady eye like an ox chewing the cud.

"And that was how I come to know 'Liza Roantree. There's some tunes as she used to sing—aw, she were always singin'—that fetches Greenhow Hill before my eyes as fair as yon brow across there. And she would learn me to sing bass, an' I was to go to th' chapel wi' 'em where Jesse and she led the singin', th' old man playin' the fiddle. He was a strange chap, old Jesse, fair mad wi' music, an' he made me promise to learn the big fiddle when my arm was better. It belonged to him, and it stood up in a big case alongside o' th' eight-day clock, but Willie Satterthwaite, as played it in the chapel, had getten deaf as a door-post, and it vexed Jesse, as he had to rap him ower his head wi' th' fiddle-stick to make him give ower sawin' at th' right time.

"But there was a black drop in it all, an' it was a man in a black coat that brought it. When th' primitive Methodist preacher came to Greenhow, he would always stop wi' Jesse Roantree, an' he laid hold of me from th' beginning. It seemed I wor a soul to be saved, and he meaned to do it. At th' same time I jealoused 'at he were keen o' savin' 'Liza Roantree's soul as well, and I could ha' killed him many a time. An' this went on till one day I broke out, an' borrowed th' brass for a drink from 'Liza. After fower days I come back, wi' my tail between my legs, just to see 'Liza again. But Jesse were at home an' th' preacher—th' Rev. Amos Barraclough. 'Liza said naught, but a bit o' red come into her face as were white of a regular thing. Says Jesse, tryin' his best to be civil, 'Nay, lad, it's like this. You've getten to choose which way it's goin' to be. I'll ha' nobody across ma doorstep as goes a-drinkin', an' borrows my lass's money to spend i' their drink. Ho'd tha tongue, 'Liza,' sez he, when she wanted to put in a word 'at I were welcome to th' brass, and she were none afraid that I wouldn't pay it back. Then the Reverend cuts in, seein' as Jesse were losin' his temper, an' they fair beat me among them. But it were 'Liza, as looked an' said naught, as did more than either o' their tongues, an' soa I concluded to get converted."

"Fwhat?" shouted Mulvaney. Then, checking himself, he said softly, "Let be! Let be! Sure the Blessed Virgin is the mother of all religion an' most women; an' there's a dale av piety in a girl if the men would only let ut stay there. I'd ha' been converted myself under the circumstances."

"Nay, but," pursued Learoyd with a blush, "I meaned it."

Ortheris laughed as loudly as he dared, having regard to his business at the time.

"Ay, Ortheris, you may laugh, but you didn't know yon preacher Barraclough—a little white-faced chap, wi' a voice as 'ud wile a bird off an a bush, and a way o' layin' hold of folks as made them think they'd never had a live man for a friend before. You never saw him, an'—an'—you never seed 'Liza Roantree—never seed 'Liza Roantree. . . . Happen it was as much 'Liza as th' preacher and her father, but anyways they all meaned it, an' I was fair shamed o' mysen, an' so I become what they called a changed character. And when I think on, it's hard to believe as yon chap going to prayermeetin's, chapel, and class-meetin's were me. But I nevet had naught to say for mysen, though there was a deal o' shoutin', and old Sammy Strother, as were almost clemmed to death and doubled up with the rheumatics, would sing out, 'Joyful! Joyful!' and 'at it were better to go up to heaven in a coal-basket than down to hell i' a coach an' six. And he would put his poor old claw on my shoulder, sayin', 'Doesn't tha feel it, tha great lump? Doesn't tha feel it?' An' sometimes I thought I did, and then again I thought I didn't, an' how was that?"

"The iverlastin' nature av mankind," said Mulvaney. "An', furthermore, I misdoubt you were built for the Primitive Methodians. They're new corps anyways. I hold by the Ould Church, for she's the mother of them all—ay, an' the father, too. I like her bekase she's most remarkable regimental in her fittings. I may die in Honolulu, Nova Zambra, or Cape Cayenne, but wherever I die, me bein' fwhat I am, an' a priest handy, I go under the same orders an' the same words an' the same unction as tho' the Pope himself come down from the roof av St. Peter's to see me off. There's neither high nor low, nor broad nor deep, nor betwixt nor between wid her, an' that's what I like. But mark you, she's no manner av Church for a wake man, bekaze she takes the body and the soul av him, onless he has his proper work to do. I remember when my father died that was three months comin' to his grave; begad he'd ha' sold the she-been above our heads for ten minutes' quittance of purgathory. An' he did all he could. That's why I say ut takes a strong man to deal with the Ould Church, an' for that reason you'll find so many women go there. An' that same's a conundrum."

"Wot's the use o' worritin' 'bout these things?" said Ortheris. "You're bound to find all out quicker nor you want to, any'ow." He jerked the cartridge out of the breech-lock into the palm of his hand. "Ere's my chaplain," he said, and made the venomous black-headed bullet bow like a marionette. " 'E's goin' to teach a man all about which is which, an' wot's true, after all, before sundown. But wot 'appened after that, Jock?"

"There was one thing they boggled at, and almost shut th' gate i' my face for, and that were my dog Blast, th' only one saved out o' a litter o' pups as was blowed up when a keg o' minin' powder loosed off in th' store-keeper's hut. They liked his name no better than his business, which were fightin' every dog he comed across; a rare good dog, wi' spots o' black and pink on his face, one ear gone, and lame o' one side wi' being driven in a basket through an iron roof, a matter of half a mile.

"They said I mum give him up 'cause he were worldly and low; and would I let mysen be shut out of heaven for the sake on a dog? 'Nay,' says I, 'if th' door isn't wide enough for th' pair on us, we'll stop outside, for we'll none be parted.' And th' preacher spoke up for Blast, as had a likin' for him from th' first—I reckon that was why I come to like th' preacher—and wouldn't hear o' changin' his name to Bless, as some o' them wanted. So th' pair on us became reg'lar chapel-members. But it's hard for a young chap o' my build to cut traces from the world, th' flesh, an' the devil all uv a heap. Yet I stuck to it for a long time, while th' lads as used to stand about th' town-end an' lean ower th' bridge, spittin' into th' beck o' a Sunday, would call after, 'Sitha, Learoyd, when's to bean to preach, 'cause we're comin' to hear tha.'—'Ho'd that jaw. He hasn't getten th' white choaker on ta morn,' another lad would say, and I had to double my fists hard i' th' bottom of my Sunday coat, and say to mysen, 'If 'twere Monday and I warn't a member o' the Primitive Methodists, I'd leather all th' lot of yond'.' That was th' hardest of all—to know that I could fight and I mustn't fight."

Sympathetic grunts from Mulvaney.

"So what wi' singin', practicin', and class-meetin's, and th' big fiddle, as he made me take between my knees, I spent a deal o' time i' Jesse Roantree's house-place. But often as I was there, th' preacher fared to me to go oftener, and both th' old man an' th' young woman were pleased to have him. He lived i' Pately Brig, as were a goodish step off, but he come. He come all the same. I liked him as well or better as any man I'd ever seen i' one way, and yet I hated him wi' all my heart i' t'other, and we watched each other like cat and mouse, but civil as you please, for I was on my best behavior, and he was that fair and open that I was bound to be fair with him. Rare good company he was, if I hadn't wanted to wring his cliver little neck half of the time. Often and often when he was goin' from Jesse's I'd set him a bit on the road."

"See 'im 'ome, you mean?" said Ortheris.

"Ay. It's a way we have i' Yorkshire o' seein' friends off. You was a friend as I didn't want to come back, and he didn't want me to come back neither, and so we'd walk together toward Pately, and then he'd set me back again, and there we'd be wal two o'clock i' the mornin' settin' each other to an' fro like a blasted pair o' pendulums twixt hill and valley, long after th' light had gone out i' 'Liza's window, as both on us had been look-ing at, pretending to watch the moon."

"Ah!" broke in Mulvaney, "ye'd no chanst against the maraudin' psalm-singers. They'll take the airs an' the graces instid av the man nine times out av ten, an' they only find the blunder later—the wimmen."

"That's just where yo're wrong," said Learoyd, reddening under the freckled tan of his cheeks. "I was th' first wi' 'Liza, an' you'd think that were enough. But th' parson were a steady-gaited sort o' chap, and Jesse were strong o' his side, and all th' women i' the congregation dinned it to 'Liza 'at she were fair fond to take up wi' a wastrel ne'er-do-weel like me, as was scarcelins respectable an' a fighting dog at his heels. It was all very well for her to be doing me good and saving my soul, but she must mind as she didn't do herself harm. They talk o' rich folk bein' stuck up an' genteel, but for cast-iron pride o' respectability there's naught like poor chapel folk. It's as cold as th' wind o' Greenhow Hill—ay, and colder for 'twill never change. And now I come to think on it, one at strangest things I know is 'at they couldn't abide th' thought o' soldiering. There's a vast o' fightin' i' th' Bible, and there's a deal of Methodists i' th' army; but to hear chapel folk talk you'd think that soldierin' were next door, an' t'other side, to hangin'. I' their meetin's all their talk is o' fightin'. When Sammy Strother were stuck for summat to say in his prayers, he'd sing out, 'Th' sword o' th' Lord and o' Gideon.' They were allus at it about puttin' on th' whole armor o' right-eousness, an' fightin' the good fight o' faith. And then, atop o' 't all, they held a prayer-meetin' ower a young chap as wanted to 'list, and nearly deaf-ened him till he picked up his hat and fair ran away. And they'd tell tales in th' Sunday-school o' bad lads as had been thumped and brayed for bird-nesting o' Sundays and playin' truant o' week days, and how they took to wrestlin', dog-fightin', rabbit-runnin', and drinkin', till at last, as if 'twere a hepitaph on a gravestone, they damned him across th' moors wi', 'an' then he went and 'listed for a soldier,' an' they'd all fetch a deep breath, and throw up their eyes like a hen drinkin'."

"Fwhy is ut?" said Mulvaney, bringing down his hand on his thigh with a crack. "In the name av God, fwhy is ut? I've seen ut, tu. They cheat an' they swindle, an' they lie an' they slander, an' fifty things fifty times worse; but the last an' the worst by their reckonin' is to serve the Widdy honest. It's like the talk av childer—seein' things all round."

"Plucky lot of fightin' good fights of whatsername they'd do if we didn't see they had a quiet place to fight in. And such fightin' as theirs is! Cats on the tiles. T'other callin' to which to come on. I'd give a month's pay to get some o' them broad-backed beggars in London sweatin' through a day's road-makin' an' a night's rain. They'd carry on a deal afterward—same as we're supposed to carry on. I've bin turned out of a measly arf-license pub down Lambeth way, full o' greasy kebmen, 'fore now," said Ortheris with an oath.

"Maybe you were dhrunk," said Mulvaney, soothingly.

"Worse nor that. The Forders were drunk. I was wearin' the Queen's uniform."

"I'd no particular thought to be a soldier i' them days," said Learoyd, still keeping his eye on the bare hill opposite, "but this sort o' talk put it i' my head. They was so good, th' chapel folk, that they tumbled ower t'other side. But I stuck to it for 'Liza's sake, specially as she was learning me to sing the bass part in a horotorio as Jesse were gettin' up. She sung like a throstle hersen, and we had practicin's night after night for a matter of three months."

"I know what a horotorio is," said Ortheris, pertly. "It's a sort of chaplain's sing-song—words all out of the Bible, and hullabalooiah choruses."

"Most Greenhow Hill Folks played some instrument or t'other, an' they all sung so you might have heard them miles away, and they were so pleased wi' the noise they made they didn't fair to want onybody to listen. The preacher sung high seconds when he wasn't playin' the flute, an' they set me, as hadn't got far with big fiddle, again Willie Satterthwaite, to jog his elbow when he had to get a' gate playin'. Old Jesse was happy if ever a man was, for he were th' conductor an' th' first fiddle an' th' leadin' singer, beatin' time wi' his fiddle-stick, till at times he'd rap with it on the table, and cry out, 'Now, you mun all stop; it's my turn.' And he'd face round to his front, fair sweating wi' pride, to sing th' tenor solos. But he were grandest i' th' choruses, waggin' his head, flinging his arms round like a windmill, and singin' hisself black in the face. A rare singer were Jesse.

"Yo' see, I was not o' much account wi' 'em all exceptin' to 'Liza Roantree, and I had a deal o' time settin' quiet at meetings and horotorio practices to hearken their talk, and if it were strange to me at beginnin', it got stranger still at after, when I was shut on it, and could study what it meaned.

"Just after th' horotorios come off, 'Liza, as had allus been weakly like, was took very bad. I walked Dr. Warbottom's horse up and down a deal of times while he were inside, where they wouldn't let me go, though I fair ached to see her.

" 'She'll be better i' noo, lad—better i' noo,' he used to say. 'Tha maun ha' patience.' Then they said if I was quiet I might go in, and th' Reverend Amos Barraclough used to read to her lyin' propped up among th' pillows. Then she began to mend a bit, and they let me carry her on to th' settle, and when it got warm again she went about same as afore. Th' preacher and me and Blast was a deal together i' them days, and i' one way we was rare good comrades. But I could ha' stretched him time and again with a good will. I mind one day he said he would like to go down into th' bowels o' th' earth, and see how th' Lord had builded th' framework o' th' everlastin' hills. He were one of them chaps as had a gift o' sayin' things. They rolled off the tip of his clever tongue, same as Mulvaney here, as would ha' made a rare good preacher if he had nobbut given his mind to it. I lent him a suit o' miner's kit as almost buried th' little man, and his white face down i' th' coat-collar and hatflap looked like the face of a boggart, and he cowered down i' th' bottom o' the waggon. I was drivin' a tram as led up a bit of an incline up to th' cave where the engine was pumpin', and where th' ore was brought up and put into th' waggons as went down o' themselves, me puttin' th' brake on and th' horses a-trottin' after. Long as it was daylight we were good friends, but when we got fair into th' dark, and could nobbut see th' day shinin' at the hole like a lamp at a street-end, I feeled downright wicked. Ma religion dropped all away from me when I looked back at him as were always comin' between me and 'Liza. The talk was 'at they were to be wed when she got better, an' I couldn't get her to say yes or nay to it. He began to sing a hymn in his thin voice, and I came out wi' a chorus that was all cussin' an' swearin' at my horses, an' I began to know how I hated him. He were such a little chap, too. I could drop him wi' one hand down Garstang's Copper-hole—a place where th' beck slithered ower th' edge on a rock, and fell wi' a bit of a whisper into a pit as no rope i' Greenhow could plump."

Again Learoyd rooted up the innocent violets. "Ay, he should see th' bowels o' th' earth an' never naught else. I could take him a mile or two along th' drift, and leave him wi' his candle doused to cry hallelujah, wi' none to hear him and say amen. I was to lead him down th' ladder-way to th' drift where Jesse Roantree was workin', and why shouldn't he slip on th' ladder, wi' my feet on his fingers till they loosed grip, and I put him down wi' my heel? If I went fust down th' ladder I could click hold on him and chuck him over my head, so as he should go squshin' down the shaft, breakin' his bones at ev'ry timberin' as Bill Appleton did when he was fresh, and hadn't a bone left when he wrought to th' bottom. Niver a blasted leg to walk from Pately. Niver an arm to put round 'Liza Roantree's waist. Niver no more—niver no more."

The thick lips curled back over the yellow teeth, and that flushed face was not pretty to look upon. Mulvaney nodded sympathy, and Ortheris, moved by his comrade's passion, brought up the rifle to his shoulder, and searched the hillside for his quarry, muttering ribaldry about a sparrow, a spout, and a thunderstorm. The voice of the watercourse supplied the necessary small talk till Learoyd picked up his story.

"But it's none so easy to kill a man like yon. When I'd given up my horses to th' lad as took my place and I was showin' th' preacher th' workin's, shoutin' into his ear across th' clang o' th' pumpin' engines, I saw he were afraid o' naught; and when the lamplight showed his black eyes, I could feel as he was masterin' me again. I were no better nor Blast chained up short and growlin' i' the depths of him while a strange dog went safe past.

" 'Th'art a coward and a fool,' I said to mysen; an' I wrestled i' my mind again' him till, when we come to Garstang's Copper-hole, I laid hold o' the preacher and lifted him up over my head and held him into the darkest on it. 'Now, lad,' I says, 'it's to be one or t'other on us—thee or me—for 'Liza Roantree. Why, isn't thee afraid for thysen?' I says, for he were still i' my arms as a sack. 'Nay; I'm but afraid for thee, my poor lad, as knows naught,' says he. I set him down on th' edge, an' th' beck run stiller, an' there was no more buzzin' in my head like when th' bee come through th' window o' Jesse's house. 'What dost tha mean?' says I.

" 'I've often thought as thou ought to know,' says he, 'but 'twas hard to tell thee. 'Liza Roantree's for neither on us, nor for nobody o' this earth.

Dr. Warbottom says—and he knows her, and her mother before her—that she is in a decline, and she cannot live six months longer. He's known it for many a day. Steady, John! Steady!' says he. And that weak little man pulled me further back and set me again' him, and talked it all over quiet and still, me turnin' a bunch o' candles in my hand, and counting them ower and ower again as I listened. A deal on it were th' regular preachin' talk, but there were a vast lot as made me begin to think as he were more of a man than I'd ever given him credit for, till I were cut as deep for him as I were for mysen.

"Six candles we had, and we crawled and climbed all that day while they lasted, and I said to mysen, ' 'Liza Roantree hasn't six months to live.' And when we came into th' daylight again we were like dead men to look at, an' Blast came behind us without so much as waggin' his tail. When I saw 'Liza again she looked at me a minute and says, 'Who's telled tha? For I see tha knows.' And she tried to smile as she kissed me, and I fair broke down.

"Yo' see, I was a young chap i' them days, and had seen naught o' life, let alone death, as is allus a-waitin'. She told me as Dr. Warbottom said as Greenhow air was too keen, and they were goin' to Bradford, to Jesse's brother David, as worked i' a mill, and I mun hold up like a man and a Christian, and she'd pray for me. Well, and they went away, and the preacher that same back end o' th' year were appointed to another circuit, as they call it, and I were left alone on Greenhow Hill.

"I tried, and I tried hard, to stick to th' chapel, but 'tweren't th' same thing at after. I hadn't 'Eliza's voice to follow i' th' singin', nor her eyes a-shinin' acrost their heads. And i' th' class-meetings they said as I mun have some experiences to tell, and I hadn't a word to say for mysen.

"Blast and me moped a good deal, and happen we didn't behave ourselves over well, for they dropped us and wondered however they'd come to take us up. I can't tell how we got through th' time, while i' th' winter I gave up my job and went to Bradford. Old Jesse were at th' door o' th' house, in a long street o' little houses. He'd been sendin' th' children 'way as were clatterin' their clogs in the causeway, for she were asleep.

" 'Is it thee?' he says; 'but you're not to see her. I'll none have her wakened for a nowt like thee. She's goin' fast, and she mun go in peace. Thou'lt never be good for naught i' th' world, and as long as thou lives thou'll never play the big fiddle. Get away, lad, get away!' So he shut the door softly i' my face.

"Nobody never made Jesse my master, but it seemed to me he was about right, and I went away into the town and knocked up against a recruiting sergeant. The old tales o' th' chapel folk came buzzin' into my head. I was to get away, and this were th' regular road for the likes o' me. I 'listed there and then, took th' Widow's shillin', and had a bunch o' ribbons pinned i' my hat.

"But next day I found my way to David Roantree's door, and Jesse came to open it. Says he, 'Thou's come back again wi' th' devil's colors flyin''—thy true colors, as I always told thee.'

"But I begged and prayed of him to let me see her nobbut to say good-bye, till a woman calls down th' stairway, 'She says John Learoyd's to come up.' Th' old man shifts aside in a flash, and lays his hand on my arm, quite gentle like. 'But thou'lt be quiet, John,' says he, 'for she's rare and weak. Thou was allus a good lad.'

"Her eyes were all alive wi' light, and her hair was thick on the pillow round her, but her cheeks were thin—thin to frighten a man that's strong. 'Nay, father, yo mayn't say th' devil's colors. Them ribbons is pretty.' An' she held out her hands for th' hat, an' she put all straight as a woman will wi' ribbons. 'Nay, but what they're pretty,' she says. 'Eh, but I'd ha' liked to see thee i' thy red coat, John, for thou was allus my own lad—my very own lad, and none else.'

"She lifted up her arms, and they come round my neck i' a gentle grip, and they slacked away, and she seemed fainting. 'Now yo' mun get away, lad,' says Jesse, and I picked up my hat and I came downstairs.

"Th' recruiting sergeant were waitin' for me at th' corner public-house. 'You've seen your sweetheart?' says he. 'Yes, I've seen her,' says I. 'Well, we'll have a quart now, and you'll do your best to forget her,' says he, bein' one o' them smart, bustlin' chaps. 'Ay, sergeant,' says I. 'Forget her.' And I've been forgettin' her ever since."

He threw away the wilted clump of white violets as he spoke. Ortheris suddenly rose to his knees, his rifle at his shoulder, and peered across the valley in the clear afternoon light. His chin cuddled the stock, and there was a twitching of the muscles of the right cheek as he sighted; Private Stanley Ortheris was engaged on his business. A speck of white crawled up the water-course.

"See that beggar? . . . Got 'im."

Seven hundred yards away, and a full two hundred down the hillside, the deserter of the Aurangabadis pitched forward, rolled down a red rock, and lay very still, with his face in a clump of blue gentians, while a big raven flapped out of the pine wood to make investigation.

"That's a clean shot, little man," said Mulvaney.

Learoyd thoughtfully watched the smoke clear away. "Happen there was a lass tewed up wi' him, too," said he.

Ortheris did not reply. He was staring across the valley, with the smile of the artist who looks on the completed work.

COMMENTARY

Some writers are referred to as "great story tellers." They are usually men of pronounced talent whose artistic intelligence and conscience function intermittently. They resemble the little girl with the curl in the middle of

her forehead. When they are good they are very, very good, but their performances are apt to be uneven. Some critics hold that this is because they
are more interested in the *story* they are telling than in the *way* in which they
tell it. As a matter of fact, they reverse Aristotle's formula, according to which
characters and incidents are included in a play for the sake of the main
action, since "the end is everything"; they fail because they have not thought
enough about the story they are telling.

Rudyard Kipling is such a writer. When he is at his best he is superb,
but many of his stories have an anecdotal quality and he is, on the whole,
more concerned with character and incidents than with the main action.

"On Greenhow Hill," like all of the *Soldiers Three* stories, is told by
a First Person Narrator (see Appendix A, p. 624). Henry James called this
method, with which he scored one of his most notable successes in *The Turn
of the Screw,* the "most barbarous of devices." It poses at the start a difficult
technical problem: to what extent does the narrator participate in the action?

Kipling's narrator, a war correspondent, does not participate except
through his curiosity—the passionate, insatiable curiosity of the artist—and
his willingness to listen. But the play of his intelligence brings events into a
sharp focus and it is his urbane, humorous style which gives the stories
their remarkable tonal unity.

"On Greenhow Hill" is told in the same casual, authoritative accents
we have heard so often, but the narrator himself is puzzlingly absent from
the scene. He does not contribute so much as a question to help the action
along. We can only conclude that Kipling had grown so accustomed to
using him as a mouth-piece that he did not feel the necessity of indicating
his physical presence.

"On Greenhow Hill" is, thus, a story within a story. Mulvaney, for
once, is in the background, but he sheds, as it were, an effulgence over the
scene. It is because we have admired him so often and so heartily that we
are glad to see Ortheris take the spotlight with his marksmanship and it is
partly because we have listened so long and so raptly to Mulvaney that we
bend a willing ear to Learoyd's story of how he—and as reflection shows—
many another man came "to take the Queen's shilling." But the action lags
at the very moment when Learoyd begins his story. Ortheris tells him to
"Discourse, Don Juan," but the remark is patently a feed line. Our attention
wanders for the moment and though we are later much moved by what
Learoyd tells us we never quite lose ourselves in the story. The veils of his
memory and perceptions are between us and the event. The dramatic effect
of the whole action is somewhat impaired by the awkward transition,
which Kipling could have made with ease if he had thought it necessary to
put his mind on such matters.

The story has an unusually long Complication (see Appendix A, p. 630).
Ortheris's efforts to shoot the deserter and Learoyd's story of his past life
occupy our attention antiphonally until the moment of Resolution when
the deserter pitches forward and lies with his face in a clump of blue gen-

tians, and we realize from Learoyd's "Happen there was a lass tewed up wi'
him, too," that he has all along been identifying himself with the deserter.
Ortheris's smile as he stares across the valley, "the smile of the artist who
looks at the completed work," may be taken as the army's answer to the
challenge contained in Learoyd's remark, although it is perfectly in keeping
with Ortheris's character as we know it. "On Greenhow Hill" is more complicated in structure than most of Kipling's stories. The glimpse of the men
against their former backgrounds—the fact that there have been few women
in Ortheris's life tells us as much about his life as Learoyd's love for Liza
Roantree tells us about his—gives them even more of the substance of real
life than they have had hitherto. The action, therefore, taking place on a
larger stage than most of the barracks room stories, gains in significance.

Kipling did not plumb the depths of the human heart, but he registered
with precision the rhythm of its beats. He makes even the routine of a
soldier's life interesting:

> "Wot a 'evinly clear drop for a bullet acrost! How much d'you
> make it, Mulvaney?"
> "Seven hunder. Maybe a trifle less, becaze the air's so thin."

It is no wonder that at the height of his fame people all over the
English-speaking world were talking about "bhistis" and "dhoolis" and
"kitmagars" and other objects they had never set eye on. He made his
readers see them.

The fact that he is writing about an alien land does not seem to offer
him any difficulties. He conveys the differences between the British Tommies,
for instance, and the men of the native corps, in action, either by an account
of what the men said or did, or by one of the narrator's reflections, so placed
and timed that it contributes directly to the action. Mulvaney, Ortheris, and
Learoyd pass the Aurangabadis at their road making and Ortheris tells them
that he is out to "pot" the deserter from the regiment. The slightly stilted,
slightly formal cadences of the Aurangabadi private's reply shows that he is
speaking a language not native to him:

> "The pig went away mocking us . . . I had one shot at him . . .
> He's my cousin, and I ought to have cleared our dishonour. But good
> luck to you."

Kipling seemed able to invest any incident he touched with the air of
reality and was, perhaps, betrayed by this virtuosity. The structure of his
stories is rarely as good as the individual incidents. "The Brushwood Boy"
is an example of this chink in his armor. The story, like James's *The Turn
of the Screw* or Lawrence's "The Rocking Horse Winner," hinges on the
supernatural, but Kipling apparently has not faced the fact that he must
convince us that what he is relating actually happened. We follow the Brushwood Boy through school, out to India and, back in England, seem to feel
the turf give under our own feet as we walk beside him to the river bank

where a four-pounder will rise to his lure. But when we come to the Resolution of the story—which is properly no Resolution, merely a climax—we balk. We cannot believe that he and Celia Allardyce have dreamed the same dreams since childhood; Kipling takes no steps to make us believe it and we leave the story with a feeling of dissatisfaction.

James Joyce

THE DEAD

LILY, the caretaker's daughter, was literally run off her feet. Hardly had she brought one gentleman into the little pantry behind the office on the ground floor and helped him off with his overcoat than the wheezy hall-door bell clanged again and she had to scamper along the bare hallway to let in another guest. It was well for her she had not to attend to the ladies also. But Miss Kate and Miss Julia had thought of that and had converted the bathroom upstairs into a ladies' dressing-room. Miss Kate and Miss Julia were there, gossiping and laughing and fussing, walking after each other to the head of the stairs, peering down over the banisters and calling down to Lily to ask her who had come.

It was always a great affair, the Misses Morkan's annual dance. Everybody who knew them came to it, members of the family, old friends of the family, the members of Julia's choir, any of Kate's pupils that were grown up enough, and even some of Mary Jane's pupils too. Never once had it fallen flat. For years and years it had gone off in splendid style, as long as anyone could remember; ever since Kate and Julia, after the death of their brother Pat, had left the house in Stoney Batter and taken Mary Jane, their only niece, to live with them in the dark, gaunt house on Usher's Island, the upper part of which they had rented from Mr. Fulham, the corn-factor on the ground floor. That was a good thirty years ago if it was a day. Mary Jane, who was then a little girl in short clothes, was now the main prop of the household, for she had the organ in Haddington Road. She had been through the Academy and gave a pupils' concert every year in the upper room of the Antient Concert Rooms. Many of her pupils belonged to the better-class families on the Kingstown and Dalkey line. Old as they were, her aunts also did their share. Julia, though she was quite grey, was still the leading soprano in Adam and Eve's, and Kate, being too feeble to go about much, gave music lessons to beginners on the old square piano in the back room. Lily, the caretaker's daughter, did housemaid's work for them. Though their life was modest, they believed in eating well; the best of everything: diamond-bone sirloins, three-shilling tea and the best bottled stout. But Lily seldom made a mistake in the orders, so that she got on well with her three mistresses. They were fussy, that was all. But the only thing they would not stand was back answers.

Of course, they had good reason to be fussy on such a night. And then it was long after ten o'clock and yet there was no sign of Gabriel and his wife. Besides they were dreadfully afraid that Freddy Malins might turn up screwed. They would not wish for worlds that any of Mary Jane's pupils should see him under the influence; and when he was like that it was sometimes very hard to manage him. Freddy Malins always came late, but they wondered what could be keeping Gabriel: and that was what brought them every two minutes to the banisters to ask Lily had Gabriel or Freddy come.

"O, Mr. Conroy," said Lily to Gabriel when she opened the door for him, "Miss Kate and Miss Julia thought you were never coming. Goodnight, Mrs. Conroy."

"I'll engage they did," said Gabriel, "but they forget that my wife here takes three mortal hours to dress herself."

He stood on the mat, scraping the snow from his goloshes, while Lily led his wife to the foot of the stairs and called out:

"Miss Kate, here's Mrs. Conroy."

Kate and Julia came toddling down the dark stairs at once. Both of them kissed Gabriel's wife, said she must be perished alive, and asked was Gabriel with her.

"Here I am as right as the mail, Aunt Kate! Go on up. I'll follow," called out Gabriel from the dark.

He continued scraping his feet vigorously while the three women went upstairs, laughing, to the ladies' dressing-room. A light fringe of snow lay like a cape on the shoulders of his overcoat and like toecaps on the toes of his goloshes; and, as the buttons of his overcoat slipped with a squeaking noise through the snow-stiffened frieze, a cold, fragrant air from out-of-doors escaped from crevices and folds.

"Is it snowing again, Mr. Conroy?" asked Lily.

She had preceded him into the pantry to help him off with his overcoat. Gabriel smiled at the three syllables she had given his surname and glanced at her. She was a slim, growing girl, pale in complexion and with hay-coloured hair. The gas in the pantry made her look still paler. Gabriel had known her when she was a child and used to sit on the lowest step nursing a rag doll.

"Yes, Lily," he answered, "and I think we're in for a night of it."

He looked up at the pantry ceiling, which was shaking with the stamping and shuffling of feet on the floor above, listened for a moment to the piano and then glanced at the girl, who was folding his overcoat carefully at the end of a shelf.

"Tell me, Lily," he said in a friendly tone, "do you still go to school?"

"O no, sir," she answered. "I'm done schooling this year and more."

"O, then," said Gabriel gaily, "I suppose we'll be going to your wedding one of these fine days with your young man, eh?"

The girl glanced back at him over her shoulder and said with great bitterness:

"The men that is now is only all palaver and what they can get out of you."

Gabriel coloured, as if he felt he had made a mistake and, without looking at her, kicked off his goloshes and flicked actively with his muffler at his patent-leather shoes.

He was a stout, tallish young man. The high colour of his cheeks pushed upwards even to his forehead, where it scattered itself in a few formless patches of pale red; and on his hairless face there scintillated restlessly the polished lenses and the bright gilt rims of the glasses which screened his delicate and restless eyes. His glossy black hair was parted in the middle and brushed in a long curve behind his ears where it curled slightly beneath the groove left by his hat.

When he had flicked lustre into his shoes he stood up and pulled his waistcoat down more tightly on his plump body. Then he took a coin rapidly from his pocket.

"O Lily," he said, thrusting it into her hands, "it's Christmas-time, isn't it? Just . . . here's a little. . . ."

He walked rapidly towards the door.

"O no, sir!" cried the girl, following him. "Really, sir, I wouldn't take it."

"Christmas-time! Christmas-time!" said Gabriel, almost trotting to the stairs and waving his hand to her in deprecation.

The girl, seeing that he had gained the stairs, called out after him:

"Well, thank you, sir."

He waited outside the drawing-room door until the waltz should finish, listening to the skirts that swept against it and to the shuffling of feet. He was still discomposed by the girl's bitter and sudden retort. It had cast a gloom over him which he tried to dispel by arranging his cuffs and the bows of his tie. He then took from his waistcoat pocket a little paper and glanced at the headings he had made for his speech. He was undecided about the lines from Robert Browning, for he feared they would be above the heads of his hearers. Some quotation that they would recognise from Shakespeare or from the Melodies would be better. The indelicate clacking of the men's heels and the shuffling of their soles reminded him that their grade of culture differed from his. He would only make himself ridiculous by quoting poetry to them which they could not understand. They would think that he was airing his superior education. He would fail with them just as he had failed with the girl in the pantry. He had taken up a wrong tone. His whole speech was a mistake from first to last, an utter failure.

Just then his aunts and his wife came out of the ladies' dressing-room. His aunts were two small, plainly dressed old women. Aunt Julia was an inch or so the taller. Her hair, drawn low over the tops of her ears, was grey; and grey also, with darker shadows, was her large flaccid face. Though she was stout in build and stood erect, her slow eyes and parted lips gave her the appearance of a woman who did not know where she was or where she was going. Aunt Kate was more vivacious. Her face, healthier than her sister's, was all puckers and creases, like a shrivelled red apple, and her hair, braided in the same old-fashioned way, had not lost its ripe nut colour.

They both kissed Gabriel frankly. He was their favourite nephew, the son of their dead elder sister, Ellen, who had married T. J. Conroy of the Port and Docks.

"Gretta tells me you're not going to take a cab back to Monkstown tonight, Gabriel," said Aunt Kate.

"No," said Gabriel, turning to his wife, "we had quite enough of that last year, hadn't we? Don't you remember, Aunt Kate, what a cold Gretta got out of it? Cab windows rattling all the way, and the east wind blowing in after we passed Merrion. Very jolly it was. Gretta caught a dreadful cold."

Aunt Kate frowned severely and nodded her head at every word.

"Quite right, Gabriel, quite right," she said. "You can't be too careful."

"But as for Gretta there," said Gabriel, "she'd walk home in the snow if she were let."

Mrs. Conroy laughed.

"Don't mind him, Aunt Kate," she said. "He's really an awful bother, what with green shades for Tom's eyes at night and making him do the dumb-bells, and forcing Eva to eat the stirabout. The poor child! And she simply hates the sight of it! . . . O, but you'll never guess what he makes me wear now!"

She broke out into a peal of laughter and glanced at her husband, whose admiring and happy eyes had been wandering from her dress to her face and hair. The two aunts laughed heartily, too, for Gabriel's solicitude was a standing joke with them.

"Goloshes!" said Mrs. Conroy. "That's the latest. Whenever it's wet underfoot I must put on my goloshes. Tonight even, he wanted me to put them on, but I wouldn't. The next thing he'll buy me will be a diving suit."

Gabriel laughed nervously and patted his tie reassuringly, while Aunt Kate nearly doubled herself, so heartily did she enjoy the joke. The smile soon faded from Aunt Julia's face and her mirthless eyes were directed towards her nephew's face. After a pause she asked:

"And what are goloshes, Gabriel?"

"Goloshes, Julia!" exclaimed her sister. "Goodness me, don't you know what goloshes are? You wear them over your . . . over your boots, Gretta, isn't it?"

"Yes," said Mrs. Conroy. "Guttapercha things. We both have a pair now. Gabriel says everyone wears them on the Continent."

"O, on the Continent," murmured Aunt Julia, nodding her head slowly.

Gabriel knitted his brows and said, as if he were slightly angered:

"It's nothing very wonderful, but Gretta thinks it very funny because she says the word reminds her of Christy Minstrels."

"But tell me, Gabriel," said Aunt Kate, with brisk tact. "Of course, you've seen about the room. Gretta was saying . . ."

"O, the room is all right," replied Gabriel. "I've taken one in the Gresham."

"To be sure," said Aunt Kate, "by far the best thing to do. And the children, Gretta, you're not anxious about them?"

"O, for one night," said Mrs. Conroy. "Besides, Bessie will look after them."

"To be sure," said Aunt Kate again. "What a comfort it is to have a girl like that, one you can depend on! There's that Lily, I'm sure I don't know what has come over her lately. She's not the girl she was at all."

Gabriel was about to ask his aunt some questions on this point, but she broke off suddenly to gaze after her sister, who had wandered down the stairs and was craning her neck over the banisters.

"Now, I ask you," she said almost testily, "where is Julia going? Julia! Julia! Where are you going?"

Julia, who had gone half way down one flight, came back and announced blandly: "Here's Freddy."

At the same moment a clapping of hands and a final flourish of the pianist told that the waltz had ended. The drawing-room door was opened from within and some couples came out. Aunt Kate drew Gabriel aside hurriedly and whispered into his ear:

"Slip down, Gabriel, like a good fellow and see if he's all right, and don't let him up if he's screwed. I'm sure he's screwed. I'm sure he is."

Gabriel went to the stairs and listened over the banisters. He could hear two persons talking in the pantry. Then he recognised Freddy Malins' laugh. He went down the stairs noisily.

"It's such a relief," said Aunt Kate to Mrs. Conroy, "that Gabriel is here. I always feel easier in my mind when he's here. . . . Julia, there's Miss Daly and Miss Power will take some refreshment. Thanks for your beautiful waltz, Miss Daly. It made lovely time."

A tall wizen-faced man, with a stiff grizzled moustache and swarthy skin, who was passing out with his partner, said:

"And may we have some refreshment, too, Miss Morkan?"

"Julia," said Aunt Kate summarily, "and here's Mr. Browne and Miss Furlong. Take them in, Julia, with Miss Daly and Miss Power."

"I'm the man for the ladies," said Mr. Browne, pursing his lips until his moustache bristled and smiling in all his wrinkles. "You know, Miss Morkan, the reason they are so fond of me is——"

He did not finish his sentence, but, seeing that Aunt Kate was out of earshot, at once led the three young ladies into the back room. The middle of the room was occupied by two square tables placed end to end, and on these Aunt Julia and the caretaker were straightening and smoothing a large cloth. On the sideboard were arrayed dishes and plates, and glasses and bundles of knives and forks and spoons. The top of the closed square piano served also as a sideboard for viands and sweets. At a smaller sideboard in one corner two young men were standing, drinking hop-bitters.

Mr. Browne led his charges thither and invited them all, in jest, to some ladies' punch, hot, strong and sweet. As they said they never took anything strong, he opened three bottles of lemonade for them. Then he asked one of the young men to move aside, and, taking hold of the decanter, filled out for himself a goodly measure of whisky. The young men eyed him respectfully while he took a trial sip.

"God help me," he said, smiling, "it's the doctor's orders."

His wizened face broke into a broader smile, and the three young ladies laughed in musical echo to his pleasantry, swaying their bodies to and fro, with nervous jerks of their shoulders. The boldest said:

"O, now, Mr. Browne, I'm sure the doctor never ordered anything of the kind."

Mr. Browne took another sip of his whisky and said, with sidling mimicry:

"Well, you see, I'm like the famous Mrs. Cassidy, who is reported to have said: 'Now, Mary Grimes, if I don't take it, make me take it, for I feel I want it.' "

His hot face had leaned forward a little too confidentially and he had assumed a very low Dublin accent so that the young ladies, with one instinct, received his speech in silence. Miss Furlong, who was one of Mary Jane's pupils, asked Miss Daly what was the name of the pretty waltz she had played; and Mr. Browne, seeing that he was ignored, turned promptly to the two young men who were more appreciative.

A red-faced young woman, dressed in pansy, came into the room, excitedly clapping her hands and crying:

"Quadrilles! Quadrilles!"

Close on her heels came Aunt Kate, crying:

"Two gentlemen and three ladies, Mary Jane!"

"O, here's Mr. Bergin and Mr. Kerrigan," said Mary Jane. "Mr. Kerrigan, will you take Miss Power? Miss Furlong, may I get you a partner, Mr. Bergin. O, that'll just do now."

"Three ladies, Mary Jane," said Aunt Kate.

The two young gentlemen asked the ladies if they might have the pleasure, and Mary Jane turned to Miss Daly.

"O, Miss Daly, you're really awfully good, after playing for the last two dances, but really we're so short of ladies tonight."

"I don't mind in the least, Miss Morkan."

"But I've a nice partner for you, Mr. Bartell D'Arcy, the tenor. I'll get him to sing later on. All Dublin is raving about him."

"Lovely voice, lovely voice!" said Aunt Kate.

As the piano had twice begun the prelude to the first figure Mary Jane led her recruits quickly from the room. They had hardly gone when Aunt Julia wandered slowly into the room, looking behind her at something.

"What is the matter, Julia?" asked Aunt Kate anxiously. "Who is it?"

Julia, who was carrying in a column of table-napkins, turned to her sister and said, simply, as if the question had surprised her:

"It's only Freddy, Kate, and Gabriel with him."

In fact right behind her Gabriel could be seen piloting Freddy Malins across the landing. The latter, a young man of about forty, was of Gabriel's size and build, with very round shoulders. His face was fleshy and pallid, touched with colour only at the thick hanging lobes of his ears and at the wide wings of his nose. He had coarse features, a blunt nose, a convex and receding brow, tumid and protruded lips. His heavy-lidded eyes and the disorder of his scanty hair made him look sleepy. He was laughing heartily in a high key at a story which he had been telling Gabriel on the stairs and at the same time rubbing the knuckles of his left fist backwards and forwards into his left eye.

"Good evening, Freddy," said Aunt Julia.

Freddy Malins bade the Misses Morkan good-evening in what seemed an offhand fashion by reason of the habitual catch in his voice and then, seeing that Mr. Browne was grinning at him from the sideboard, crossed the room on rather shaky legs and began to repeat in an undertone the story he had just told to Gabriel.

"He's not so bad, is he?" said Aunt Kate to Gabriel.

Gabriel's brows were dark but he raised them quickly and answered:

"O, no, hardly noticeable."

"Now, isn't he a terrible fellow!" she said. "And his poor mother made him take the pledge on New Year's Eve. But come on, Gabriel, into the drawing-room."

Before leaving the room with Gabriel she signalled to Mr. Browne by frowning and shaking her forefinger in warning to and fro. Mr. Browne nodded in answer and, when she had gone, said to Freddy Malins:

"Now, then, Teddy, I'm going to fill you out a good glass of lemonade just to buck you up."

Freddy Malins, who was nearing the climax of his story, waved the offer aside impatiently but Mr. Browne, having first called Freddy Malins' attention to a disarray in his dress, filled out and handed him a full glass of lemonade. Freddy Malins' left hand accepted the glass mechanically, his right hand being engaged in the mechanical readjustment of his dress. Mr. Browne, whose face was once more wrinkling with mirth, poured out for himself a glass of whisky while Freddy Malins exploded, before he had well reached the climax of his story, in a kink of high-pitched bronchitic laughter and, setting down his untasted and overflowing glass, began to rub the knuckles of his left fist backwards and forwards into his left eye, repeating words of his last phrase as well as his fit of laughter would allow him.

.   .   .   .

Gabriel could not listen while Mary Jane was playing her Academy piece, full of runs and difficult passages, to the hushed drawing-room. He liked music but the piece she was playing had no melody for him and he doubted whether it had any melody for the other listeners, though they had begged Mary Jane to play something. Four young men, who had come from the refreshment-room to stand in the doorway at the sound of the piano, had gone away quietly in couples after a few minutes. The only persons who seemed to follow the music were Mary Jane herself, her hands racing along the key-board or lifted from it at the pauses like those of a priestess in momentary imprecation, and Aunt Kate standing at her elbow to turn the page.

Gabriel's eyes, irritated by the floor, which glittered with beeswax under the heavy chandelier, wandered to the wall above the piano. A picture of the balcony scene in *Romeo and Juliet* hung there and beside it was a picture of the two murdered princes in the Tower which Aunt Julia had worked in red, blue and brown wools when she was a girl. Probably in the school they had gone to as girls that kind of work had been taught for one year. His mother had worked for him as a birthday present a waistcoat of purple tabinet, with little foxes' heads upon it, lined with brown satin and having round mulberry buttons. It was strange that his mother had had no musical talent though Aunt Kate used to call her the brains carrier of the Morkan family. Both she and Julia had always seemed a little proud of their serious and matronly sister. Her photograph stood before the pierglass. She held an open book on her knees and was pointing out something in it to Constantine who, dressed in a man-o'-war suit, lay at her feet. It was she who had chosen the names of her sons for she was very sensible of the dignity of family life. Thanks to her, Constantine was now senior curate in Balbriggan and, thanks to her, Gabriel himself had taken his degree in the Royal University. A shadow passed over his face as he remembered her sullen opposition to his marriage. Some slighting phrases she had used still rankled in his memory; she had once spoken of Gretta as being country cute and that was not true of Gretta at all. It was Gretta who had nursed her during all her last long illness in their house at Monkstown.

He knew that Mary Jane must be near the end of her piece for she was playing again the opening melody with runs of scales after every bar and while he waited for the end the resentment died down in his heart. The piece ended with a trill of octaves in the treble and a final deep octave in the bass. Great applause greeted Mary Jane as, blushing and rolling up her music nervously, she escaped from the room. The most vigorous clapping came from the four young men in the doorway who had gone away to the refreshment-room at the beginning of the piece but had come back when the piano had stopped.

Lancers were arranged. Gabriel found himself partnered with Miss Ivors. She was a frank-mannered talkative young lady, with a freckled face and prominent brown eyes. She did not wear a low-cut bodice and the large brooch which was fixed in the front of her collar bore on it an Irish device and motto.

When they had taken their places she said abruptly:

"I have a crow to pluck with you."

"With me?" said Gabriel.

She nodded her head gravely.

"What is it?" asked Gabriel, smiling at her solemn manner.

"Who is G. C.?" answered Miss Ivors, turning her eyes upon him.

Gabriel coloured and was about to knit his brows, as if he did not understand, when she said bluntly:

"O, innocent Amy! I have found out that you write for *The Daily Express.* Now, aren't you ashamed of yourself?"

"Why should I be ashamed of myself?" asked Gabriel, blinking his eyes and trying to smile.

"Well, I'm ashamed of you," said Miss Ivors frankly. "To say you'd write for a paper like that. I didn't think you were a West Briton."

A look of perplexity appeared on Gabriel's face. It was true that he wrote a literary column every Wednesday in *The Daily Express,* for which he was paid fifteen shillings. But that did not make him a West Briton surely. The books he received for review were almost more welcome than the paltry cheque. He loved to feel the covers and turn over the pages of newly printed books. Nearly every day when his teaching in the college was ended he used to wander down the quays to the second-hand booksellers, to Hickey's on Bachelor's Walk, to Webb's or Massey's on Aston's Quay, or to O'Clohissey's in the by-street. He did not know how to meet her charge. He wanted to say that literature was above politics. But they were friends of many years' standing and their careers had been parallel, first at the University and then as teachers: he could not risk a grandiose phrase with her. He continued blinking his eyes and trying to smile and murmured lamely that he saw nothing political in writing reviews of books.

When their turn to cross had come he was still perplexed and inattentive. Miss Ivors promptly took his hand in a warm grasp and said in a soft friendly tone:

"Of course, I was only joking. Come, we cross now."

When they were together again she spoke of the University question and Gabriel felt more at ease. A friend of hers had shown her his review of Browning's poems. That was how she had found out the secret: but she liked the review immensely. Then she said suddenly:

"O, Mr. Conroy, will you come for an excursion to the Aran Isles this summer? We're going to stay there a whole month. It will be splendid out in the Atlantic. You ought to come. Mr. Clancy is coming, and Mr. Kilkelly and Kathleen Kearney. It would be splendid for Gretta too if she'd come. She's from Connacht, isn't she?"

"Her people are," said Gabriel shortly.

"But you will come, won't you?" said Miss Ivors, laying her warm hand eagerly on his arm.

"The fact is," said Gabriel, "I have just arranged to go——"

"Go where?" asked Miss Ivors.

"Well, you know, every year I go for a cycling tour with some fellows and so——"

"But where?" asked Miss Ivors.

"Well, we usually go to France or Belgium or perhaps Germany," said Gabriel awkwardly.

"And why do you go to France and Belgium," said Miss Ivors, "instead of visiting your own land?"

"Well," said Gabriel, "it's partly to keep in touch with the languages and partly for a change."

"And haven't you your own language to keep in touch with—Irish?" asked Miss Ivors.

"Well," said Gabriel, "if it comes to that, you know, Irish is not my language."

Their neighbours had turned to listen to the cross-examination. Gabriel glanced right and left nervously and tried to keep his good humour under the ordeal which was making a blush invade his forehead.

"And haven't you your own land to visit," continued Miss Ivors, "that you know nothing of, your own people, and your own country?"

"O, to tell you the truth," retorted Gabriel suddenly, "I'm sick of my own country, sick of it!"

"Why?" asked Miss Ivors.

Gabriel did not answer for his retort had heated him.

"Why?" repeated Miss Ivors.

They had to go visiting together and, as he had not answered her, Miss Ivors said warmly:

"Of course, you've no answer."

Gabriel tried to cover his agitation by taking part in the dance with great energy. He avoided her eyes for he had seen a sour expression on her face. But when they met in the long chain he was surprised to feel his hand firmly pressed. She looked at him from under her brows for a moment quizzically until he smiled. Then, just as the chain was about to start again, she stood on tiptoe and whispered into his ear:

"West Briton!"

When the lancers were over Gabriel went away to a remote corner of the room where Freddy Malins' mother was sitting. She was a stout feeble old woman with white hair. Her voice had a catch in it like her son's and she stuttered slightly. She had been told that Freddy had come and that he was nearly all right. Gabriel asked her whether she had had a good crossing. She lived with her married daughter in Glasgow and came to Dublin on a visit once a year. She answered placidly that she had had a beautiful crossing and that the captain had been most attentive to her. She spoke also of the beautiful house her daughter kept in Glasgow, and of all the friends they had there. While her tongue rambled on Gabriel tried to banish from his mind all memory of the unpleasant incident with Miss Ivors. Of course the

girl or woman, or whatever she was, was an enthusiast but there was a time
for all things. Perhaps he ought not to have answered her like that. But she
had no right to call him a West Briton before people, even in joke. She had
tried to make him ridiculous before people, heckling him and staring at him
with her rabbit's eyes.

He saw his wife making her way towards him through the waltzing
couples. When she reached him she said into his ear:

"Gabriel, Aunt Kate wants to know won't you carve the goose as usual.
Miss Daly will carve the ham and I'll do the pudding."

"All right," said Gabriel.

"She's sending in the younger ones first as soon as this waltz is over so
that we'll have the table to ourselves."

"Were you dancing?" asked Gabriel.

"Of course I was. Didn't you see me? What row had you with Molly
Ivors?"

"No row. Why? Did she say so?"

"Something like that. I'm trying to get that Mr. D'Arcy to sing. He's
full of conceit, I think."

"There was no row," said Gabriel moodily, "only she wanted me to go
for a trip to the west of Ireland and I said I wouldn't."

His wife clasped her hands excitedly and gave a little jump.

"O, do go, Gabriel," she cried. "I'd love to see Galway again."

"You can go if you like," said Gabriel coldly.

She looked at him for a moment, then turned to Mrs. Malins and said:
"There's a nice husband for you, Mrs. Malins."

While she was threading her way back across the room Mrs. Malins,
without adverting to the interruption, went on to tell Gabriel what beautiful
places there were in Scotland and beautiful scenery. Her son-in-law brought
them every year to the lakes and they used to go fishing. Her son-in-law
was a splendid fisher. One day he caught a beautiful big fish and the man
in the hotel cooked it for their dinner.

Gabriel hardly heard what she said. Now that supper was coming near
he began to think again about his speech and about the quotation. When he
saw Freddy Malins coming across the room to visit his mother Gabriel left
the chair free for him and retired into the embrasure of the window. The
room had already cleared and from the back room came the clatter of plates
and knives. Those who still remained in the drawing-room seemed tired of
dancing and were conversing quietly in little groups. Gabriel's warm trembling fingers tapped the cold pane of the window. How cool it must be outside! How pleasant it would be to walk out alone, first along by the river
and then through the park! The snow would be lying on the branches of
the trees and forming a bright cap on the top of the Wellington Monument.
How much more pleasant it would be there than at the supper-table!

He ran over the headings of his speech: Irish hospitality, sad memories,
the Three Graces, Paris, the quotation from Browning. He repeated to him-

self a phrase he had written in his review: "One feels that one is listening to a thought-tormented music." Mss Ivors had praised the review. Was she sincere? Had she really any life of her own behind all her propagandism? There had never been any ill-feeling between them until that night. It unnerved him to think that she would be at the supper-table, looking up at him while he spoke with her critical quizzing eyes. Perhaps she would not be sorry to see him fail in his speech. An idea came into his mind and gave him courage. He would say, alluding to Aunt Kate and Aunt Julia: "Ladies and Gentlemen, the generation which is now on the wane among us may have had its faults but for my part I think it had certain qualities of hospitality, of humour, of humanity, which the new and very serious and hypereducated generation that is growing up around us seems to me to lack." Very good: that was one for Miss Ivors. What did he care that his aunts were only two ignorant old women?

A murmur in the room attracted his attention. Mr. Browne was advancing from the door, gallantly escorting Aunt Julia, who leaned upon his arm, smiling and hanging her head. An irregular musketry of applause escorted her also as far as the piano and then, as Mary Jane seated herself on the stool, and Aunt Julia, no longer smiling, half turned so as to pitch her voice fairly into the room, gradually ceased. Gabriel recognised the prelude. It was that of an old song of Aunt Julia's—*Arrayed for the Bridal*. Her voice, strong and clear in tone, attacked with great spirit the runs which embellish the air and though she sang very rapidly she did not miss even the smallest of the grace notes. To follow the voice, without looking at the singer's face, was to feel and share the excitement of swift and secure flight. Gabriel applauded loudly with all the others at the close of the song and loud applause was borne in from the invisible supper-table. It sounded so genuine that a little colour struggled into Aunt Julia's face as she bent to replace in the music-stand the old leather-bound song-book that had her initials on the cover. Freddy Malins, who had listened with his head perched sideways to hear her better, was still applauding when everyone else had ceased and talking animatedly to his mother who nodded her head gravely and slowly in acquiescence. At last, when he could clap no more, he stood up suddenly and hurried across the room to Aunt Julia whose hand he seized and held in both his hands, shaking it when words failed him or the catch in his voice proved too much for him.

"I was just telling my mother," he said, "I never heard you sing so well, never. No, I never heard your voice so good as it is tonight. Now! Would you believe that now? That's the truth. Upon my word and honour that's the truth. I never heard your voice sound so fresh and so . . . so clear and fresh, never."

Aunt Julia smiled broadly and murmured something about compliments as she released her hand from his grasp. Mr. Browne extended his open hand towards her and said to those who were near him in the manner of a showman introducing a prodigy to an audience:

"Miss Julia Morkan, my latest discovery!"

He was laughing very heartily at this himself when Freddy Malins turned to him and said:

"Well, Browne, if you're serious you might make a worse discovery. All I can say is I never heard her sing half so well as long as I am coming here. And that's the honest truth."

"Neither did I," said Mr. Browne. "I think her voice has greatly improved."

Aunt Julia shrugged her shoulders and said with meek pride:

"Thirty years ago I hadn't a bad voice as voices go."

"I often told Julia," said Aunt Kate emphatically, "that she was simply thrown away in that choir. But she never would be said by me."

She turned as if to appeal to the good sense of the others against a refractory child while Aunt Julia gazed in front of her, a vague smile of reminiscence playing on her face.

"No," continued Aunt Kate, "she wouldn't be said or led by anyone, slaving there in that choir night and day, night and day. Six o'clock on Christmas morning! And all for what?"

"Well, isn't it for the honour of God, Aunt Kate?" asked Mary Jane, twisting round on the piano-stool and smiling.

Aunt Kate turned fiercely on her niece and said:

"I know all about the honour of God, Mary Jane, but I think it's not at all honourable for the pope to turn out the women out of the choirs that have slaved there all their lives and put little whipper-snappers of boys over their heads. I suppose it is for the good of the Church if the pope does it. But it's not just, Mary Jane, and it's not right."

She had worked herself into a passion and would have continued in defence of her sister for it was a sore subject with her but Mary Jane, seeing that all the dancers had come back, intervened pacifically:

"Now, Aunt Kate, you're giving scandal to Mr. Browne who is of the other persuasion."

Aunt Kate turned to Mr. Browne, who was grinning at this allusion to his religion, and said hastily:

"O, I don't question the pope's being right. I'm only a stupid old woman and I wouldn't presume to do such a thing. But there's such a thing as common everyday politeness and gratitude. And if I were in Julia's place I'd tell that Father Healey straight up to his face . . ."

"And besides, Aunt Kate," said Mary Jane, "we really are all hungry and when we are hungry we are all very quarrelsome."

"And when we are thirsty we are also quarrelsome," added Mr. Browne.

"So that we had better go to supper," said Mary Jane, "and finish the discussion afterwards."

On the landing outside the drawing-room Gabriel found his wife and Mary Jane trying to persuade Miss Ivors to stay for supper. But Miss Ivors, who had put on her hat and was buttoning her cloak, would not stay.

She did not feel in the least hungry and she had already overstayed her time.

"But only for ten minutes, Molly," said Mrs. Conroy. "That won't delay you."

"To take a pick itself," said Mary Jane, "after all your dancing."

"I really couldn't," said Miss Ivors.

"I am afraid you didn't enjoy yourself at all," said Mary Jane hopelessly.

"Ever so much, I assure you," said Miss Ivors, "but you really must let me run off now."

"But how can you get home?" asked Mrs. Conroy.

"O, it's only two steps up the quay."

Gabriel hesitated a moment and said:

"If you will allow me, Miss Ivors, I'll see you home if you are really obliged to go."

But Miss Ivors broke away from them.

"I won't hear of it," she cried. "For goodness' sake go in to your suppers and don't mind me. I'm quite well able to take care of myself."

"Well, you're the comical girl, Molly," said Mrs. Conroy frankly.

"Beannacht libh," cried Miss Ivors, with a laugh, as she ran down the staircase.

Mary Jane gazed after her, a moody puzzled expression on her face, while Mrs. Conroy leaned over the banisters to listen for the hall-door. Gabriel asked himself was he the cause of her abrupt departure. But she did not seem to be in ill humour: she had gone away laughing. He stared blankly down the staircase.

At the moment Aunt Kate came toddling out of the supper-room, almost wringing her hands in despair.

"Where is Gabriel?" she cried. "Where on earth is Gabriel? There's everyone waiting in there, stage to let, and nobody to carve the goose!"

"Here I am, Aunt Kate!" cried Gabriel, with sudden animation, "ready to carve a flock of geese, if necessary."

A fat brown goose lay at one end of the table and at the other end, on a bed of creased paper strewn with sprigs of parsley, lay a great ham, stripped of its outer skin and peppered over with crust crumbs, a neat paper frill round its shin and beside this was a round of spiced beef. Between these rival ends ran parallel lines of side-dishes: two little minsters of jelly, red and yellow; a shallow dish full of blocks of blancmange and red jam, a large green leaf-shaped dish with a stalk-shaped handle, on which lay bunches of purple raisins and peeled almonds, a companion dish on which lay a solid rectangle of Smyrna figs, a dish of custard topped with grated nutmeg, a small bowl full of chocolates and sweets wrapped in gold and silver papers and a glass vase in which stood some tall celery stalks. In the centre of the table there stood, as sentries to a fruit-stand which upheld a pyramid of oranges and American apples, two squat old-fashioned decanters of cut glass, one containing port and the other dark sherry. On the closed square piano a pudding in a huge yellow dish lay in waiting and behind it were three squads of bottles of stout and ale and minerals, drawn up according to the colours of their uniforms, the first two black, with brown and red labels, the third and smallest squad white, with transverse green sashes.

Gabriel took his seat boldly at the head of the table and, having looked to the edge of the carver, plunged his fork firmly into the goose. He felt quite at ease now for he was an expert carver and liked nothing better than to find himself at the head of a well-laden table.

"Miss Furlong, what shall I send you?" he asked. "A wing or a slice of the breast?"

"Just a small slice of the breast."

"Miss Higgins, what for you?"

"O, anything at all, Mr. Conroy."

While Gabriel and Miss Daly exchanged plates of goose and plates of ham and spiced beef Lily went from guest to guest with a dish of hot floury potatoes wrapped in a white napkin. This was Mary Jane's idea and she had also suggested apple sauce for the goose but Aunt Kate had said that plain roast goose without any apple sauce had always been good enough for her and she hoped she might never eat worse. Mary Jane waited on her pupils and saw that they got the best slices and Aunt Kate and Aunt Julia opened and carried across from the piano bottles of stout and ale for the gentlemen and bottles of minerals for the ladies. There was a great deal of confusion and laughter and noise, the noise of orders and counter-orders, of knives and forks, of corks and glass-stoppers. Gabriel began to carve second helpings as soon as he had finshed the first round without serving himself. Everyone protested loudly so that he compromised by taking a long draught of stout for he had found the carving hot work. Mary Jane settled down quietly to her supper but Aunt Kate and Aunt Julia were still toddling round the table, walking on each other's heels, getting in each other's way and giving each other unheeded orders. Mr. Browne begged of them to sit down and eat their suppers and so did Gabriel but they said there was time enough, so that, at last, Freddy Malins stood up and, capturing Aunt Kate, plumped her down on her chair amid general laughter.

When everyone had been well served Gabriel said, smiling:

"Now, if anyone wants a little more of what vulgar people call stuffing let him or her speak."

A chorus of voices invited him to begin his own supper and Lily came forward with three potatoes which she had reserved for him.

"Very well," said Gabriel amiably, as he took another preparatory draught, "kindly forget my existence, ladies and gentlemen, for a few minutes."

He set to his supper and took no part in the conversation with which the table covered Lily's removal of the plates. The subject of talk was the opera company which was then at the Theatre Royal. Mr. Bartell D'Arcy, the tenor, a dark-complexioned young man with a smart moustache, praised very highly the leading contralto of the company but Miss Furlong thought she had a rather vulgar style of production. Freddy Malins said there was a Negro chieftain singing in the second part of the Gaiety pantomime who had one of the finest tenor voices he had ever heard.

"Have you heard him?" he asked Mr. Bartell D'Arcy across the table.

"No," answered Mr. Bartell D'Arcy carelessly.

"Because," Freddy Malins explained, "now I'd be curious to hear your opinion of him. I think he has a grand voice."

"It takes Teddy to find out the really good things," said Mr. Browne familiarly to the table.

"And why couldn't he have a voice too?" asked Freddy Malins sharply. "Is it because he's only a black?"

Nobody answered this question and Mary Jane led the table back to the legitimate opera. One of her pupils had given her a pass for *Mignon*. Of course it was very fine, she said, but it made her think of poor Georgina Burns. Mr. Browne could go back farther still, to the old Italian companies that used to come to Dublin—Tietjens, Ilma de Murzka, Campanini, the great Trebelli, Giuglini, Ravelli, Aramburo. Those were the days, he said, when there was something like singing to be heard in Dublin. He told too of how the top gallery of the old Royal used to be packed night after night, of how one night an Italian tenor had sung five encores to *Let me like a Soldier fall,* introducing a high C every time, and of how the gallery boys would sometimes in their enthusiasm unyoke the horses from the carriage of some great *prima donna* and pull her themselves through the streets to her hotel. Why did they never play the grand old operas now, he asked, *Dinorah, Lucrezia Borgia?* Because they could not get the voices to sing them: that was why.

"O, well," said Mr. Bartell D'Arcy, "I presume there are as good singers today as there were then."

"Where are they?" asked Mr. Browne defiantly.

"In London, Paris, Milan," said Mr. Bartell D'Arcy warmly. "I suppose Caruso, for example, is quite as good, if not better than any of the men you have mentioned."

"Maybe so," said Mr. Browne. "But I may tell you I doubt it strongly."

"O, I'd give anything to hear Caruso sing," said Mary Jane.

"For me," said Aunt Kate, who had been picking a bone, "there was only one tenor. To please me, I mean. But I suppose none of you ever heard of him."

"Who was he, Miss Morkan?" asked Mr. Bartell D'Arcy politely.

"His name," said Aunt Kate, "was Parkinson. I heard him when he was in his prime and I think he had then the purest tenor voice that was ever put into a man's throat."

"Strange," said Mr. Bartell D'Arcy. "I never even heard of him."

"Yes, yes, Miss Morkan is right," said Mr. Browne. "I remember hearing of old Parkinson but he's too far back for me."

"A beautiful, pure, sweet, mellow English tenor," said Aunt Kate with enthusiasm.

Gabriel having finished, the huge pudding was transferred to the table. The clatter of forks and spoons began again. Gabriel's wife served out spoonfuls of the pudding and passed the plates down the table. Midway down they were held up by Mary Jane, who replenished them with raspberry or orange jelly or with blancmange and jam. The pudding was of Aunt Julia's making and she received praises for it from all quarters. She herself said that it was not quite brown enough.

"Well, I hope, Miss Morkan," said Mr. Browne, "that I'm brown enough for you because, you know, I'm all brown."

All the gentlemen, except Gabriel, ate some of the pudding out of compliment to Aunt Julia. As Gabriel never ate sweets the celery had been left for him. Freddy Malins also took a stalk of celery and ate it with his pudding. He had been told that celery was a capital thing for the blood and he was just then under doctor's care. Mrs. Malins, who had been silent all through the supper, said that her son was going down to Mount Melleray in a week or so. The table then spoke of Mount Melleray, how bracing the air was down there, how hospitable the monks were and how they never asked for a penny-piece from their guests.

"And do you mean to say," asked Mr. Browne incredulously, "that a chap can go down there and put up there as if it were a hotel and live on the fat of the land and then come away without paying anything?"

"O, most people give some donation to the monastery when they leave," said Mary Jane.

"I wish we had an institution like that in our Church," said Mr. Browne candidly.

He was astonished to hear that the monks never spoke, got up at two in the morning and slept in their coffins. He asked what they did it for.

"That's the rule of the order," said Aunt Kate firmly.

"Yes, but why?" asked Mr. Browne.

Aunt Kate repeated that it was the rule, that was all. Mr. Browne still seemed not to understand. Freddy Malins explained to him, as best he could, that the monks were trying to make up for the sins committed by all the sinners in the outside world. The explanation was not very clear for Mr. Browne grinned and said:

"I like that idea very much but wouldn't a comfortable spring bed do them as well as a coffin?"

"The coffin," said Mary Jane, "is to remind them of their last end."

As the subject had grown lugubrious it was buried in a silence of the table during which Mrs. Malins could be heard saying to her neighbour in an indistinct undertone:

"They are very good men, the monks, very pious men."

The raisins and almonds and figs and apples and oranges and chocolates and sweets were now passed about the table and Aunt Julia invited all the guests to have either port or sherry. At first Mr. Bartell D'Arcy refused to take either but one of his neighbours nudged him and whispered something to him upon which he allowed his glass to be filled. Gradually as the last glasses were being filled the conversation ceased. A pause followed, broken only by the noise of the wine and by unsettlings of chairs. The Misses Morkan, all three, looked down at the tablecloth. Someone coughed once or twice and then a few gentlemen patted the table gently as a signal for silence. The silence came and Gabriel pushed back his chair and stood up.

The patting at once grew louder in encouragement and then ceased altogether. Gabriel leaned his ten trembling fingers on the tablecloth and smiled nervously at the company. Meeting a row of upturned faces he raised his eyes to the chandelier. The piano was playing a waltz tune and he could hear the skirts sweeping against the drawing-room door. People, perhaps, were standing in the snow on the quay outside, gazing up at the lighted windows and listening to the waltz music. The air was pure there. In the distance lay the park where the trees were weighted with snow. The Wellington Monument wore a gleaming cap of snow that flashed westward over the white field of Fifteen Acres.

He began:

"Ladies and Gentlemen,

"It has fallen to my lot this evening, as in years past, to perform a very pleasing task but a task for which I am afraid my poor powers as a speaker are all too inadequate."

"No, no!" said Mr. Browne.

"But, however that may be, I can only ask you tonight to take the will for the deed and to lend me your attention for a few moments while I endeavour to express to you in words what my feelings are on this occasion.

"Ladies and Gentlemen, it is not the first time that we have gathered together under this hospitable roof, around this hospitable board. It is not the first time that we have been the recipients—or perhaps, I had better say, the victims—of the hospitality of certain good ladies."

He made a circle in the air with his arm and paused. Everyone laughed or smiled at Aunt Kate and Aunt Julia and Mary Jane who all turned crimson with pleasure. Gabriel went on more boldly:

"I feel more strongly with every recurring year that our country has no tradition which does it so much honour and which it should guard so jealously as that of its hospitality. It is a tradition that is unique as far as my experience goes (and I have visited not a few places abroad) among the modern nations. Some would say, perhaps, that with us it is rather a failing than anything to be boasted of. But granted even that, it is, to my mind, a princely failing, and one that I trust will long be cultivated among us. Of one thing, at least, I am sure. As long as this one roof shelters the good ladies aforesaid—and I wish from my heart it may do so for many and many

a long year to come—the tradition of genuine warm-hearted courteous Irish
hospitality, which our forefathers have handed down to us and which we in
turn must hand down to our descendants, is still alive among us."

A hearty murmur of assent ran round the table. It shot through Gabriel's
mind that Miss Ivors was not there and that she had gone away discourteously: and he said with confidence in himself:

"Ladies and Gentlemen,

"A new generation is growing up in our midst, a generation actuated
by new ideas and new principles. It is serious and enthusiastic for these new
ideas and its enthusiasm, even when it is misdirected, is, I believe, in the
main sincere. But we are living in a sceptical and, if I may use the phrase,
a thought-tormented age: and sometimes I fear that this new generation,
educated or hypereducated as it is, will lack those qualities of humanity, of
hospitality, of kindly humour which belonged to an older day. Listening
tonight to the names of all those great singers of the past it seemed to me, I
must confess, that we were living in a less spacious age. Those days might,
without exaggeration, be called spacious days: and if they are gone beyond
recall let us hope, at least, that in gatherings such as this we shall still speak
of them with pride and affection, still cherish in our hearts the memory of
those dead and gone great ones whose fame the world will not willingly
let die."

"Hear, hear!" said Mr. Browne loudly.

"But yet," continued Gabriel, his voice falling into a softer inflection,
"there are always in gatherings such as this sadder thoughts that will recur
to our minds: thoughts of the past, of youth, of changes, of absent faces that
we miss here tonight. Our path through life is strewn with many such sad
memories: and were we to brood upon them always we could not find the
heart to go on bravely with our work among the living. We have all of us
living duties and living affections which claim, and rightly claim, our
strenuous endeavours.

"Therefore, I will not linger on the past. I will not let any gloomy
moralising intrude upon us here tonight. Here we are gathered together for
a brief moment from the bustle and rush of our everyday routine. We are
met here as friends, in the spirit of good-fellowship, as colleagues, also to a
certain extent, in the true spirit of *camaraderie,* and as the guests of—what
shall I call them?—the Three Graces of the Dublin musical world."

The table burst into applanse and laughter at this allusion. Aunt Julia
vainly asked each of her neighbours in turn to tell her what Gabriel had said.

"He says we are the Three Graces, Aunt Julia," said Mary Jane.

Aunt Julia did not understand but she looked up, smiling, at Gabriel,
who continued in the same vein:

"Ladies and Gentlemen,

"I will not attempt to play tonight the part that Paris played on another
occasion. I will not attempt to choose between them. The task would be an
invidious one and one beyond my poor powers. For when I view them in

turn, whether it be our chief hostess herself, whose good heart, whose too good heart, has become a byword with all who know her, or her sister, who seems to be gifted with perennial youth and whose singing must have been a surprise and a revelation to us all tonight, or, last but not least, when I consider our youngest hostess, talented, cheerful, hard-working and the best of nieces, I confess, Ladies and Gentlemen, that I do not know to which of them I should award the prize."

Gabriel glanced down at his aunts and, seeing the large smile on Aunt Julia's face and the tears which had risen to Aunt Kate's eyes, hastened to his close. He raised his glass of port gallantly, while every member of the company fingered a glass expectantly, and said loudly:

"Let us toast them all three together. Let us drink to their health, wealth, long life, happiness and prosperity and may they long continue to hold the proud and self-won position which they hold in their profession and the position of honour and affection which they hold in our hearts."

All the guests stood up, glass in hand, and turning towards the three seated ladies, sang in unison, with Mr. Browne as leader:

> *For they are jolly gay fellows,*
> *For they are jolly gay fellows,*
> *For they are jolly gay fellows,*
> *Which nobody can deny.*

Aunt Kate was making frank use of her handkerchief and even Aunt Julia seemed moved. Freddy Malins beat time with his pudding-fork and the singers turned towards one another, as if in melodious conference, while they sang with emphasis:

> *Unless he tells a lie,*
> *Unless he tells a lie,*

Then, turning once more towards their hostesses, they sang:

> *For they are jolly gay fellows,*
> *For they are jolly gay fellows,*
> *For they are jolly gay fellows,*
> *Which nobody can deny.*

The acclamation which followed was taken up beyond the door of the supper-room by many of the other guests and renewed time after time, Freddy Malins acting as officer with his fork on high.

.   .   .   .

The piercing morning air came into the hall where they were standing so that Aunt Kate said:

"Close the door, somebody. Mrs. Malins will get her death of cold."

"Browne is out there, Aunt Kate," said Mary Jane.

"Browne is everywhere," said Aunt Kate, lowering her voice.

Mary Jane laughed at her tone.

"Really," she said archly, "he is very attentive."

"He has been laid on here like the gas," said Aunt Kate in the same tone, "all during the Christmas."

She laughed herself this time good-humouredly and then added quickly:

"But tell him to come in, Mary Jane, and close the door. I hope to goodness he didn't hear me."

At that moment the hall-door was opened and Mr. Browne came in from the doorstep, laughing as if his heart would break. He was dressed in a long green overcoat with mock astrakhan cuffs and collar and wore on his head an oval fur cap. He pointed down the snow-covered quay from where the sound of shrill prolonged whistling was borne in.

"Teddy will have all the cabs in Dublin out," he said.

Gabriel advanced from the little pantry behind the office, struggling into his overcoat and, looking round the hall, said:

"Gretta not down yet?"

"She's getting on her things, Gabriel," said Aunt Kate.

"Who's playing up there?" asked Gabriel.

"Nobody. They're all gone."

"O no, Aunt Kate," said Mary Jane. "Bartell D'Arcy and Miss O'Callaghan aren't gone yet."

"Someone is fooling at the piano anyhow," said Gabriel.

Mary Jane glanced at Gabriel and Mr. Browne and said with a shiver:

"It makes me feel cold to look at you two gentlemen muffled up like that. I wouldn't like to face your journey home at this hour."

"I'd like nothing better this minute," said Mr. Browne stoutly, "than a rattling fine walk in the country or a fast drive with a good spanking goer between the shafts."

"We used to have a very good horse and trap at home," said Aunt Julia sadly.

"The never-to-be-forgotten Johnny," said Mary Jane, laughing.

Aunt Kate and Gabriel laughed too.

"Why, what was wonderful about Johnny?" asked Mr. Browne.

"The late lamented Patrick Morkan, our grandfather, that is," explained Gabriel, "commonly known in his later years as the old gentleman, was a glue-boiler."

"O, now, Gabriel," said Aunt Kate, laughing, "he had a starch mill."

"Well, glue or starch," said Gabriel, "the old gentleman had a horse by the name of Johnny. And Johnny used to work in the old gentleman's mill, walking round and round in order to drive the mill. That was all very well; but now comes the tragic part about Johnny. One fine day the old gentleman thought he'd like to drive out with the quality to a military review in the park."

"The Lord have mercy on his soul," said Aunt Kate compassionately.

"Amen," said Gabriel. "So the old gentleman, as I said, harnessed Johnny and put on his very best tall hat and his very best stock collar and drove out in grand style from his ancestral mansion somewhere near Back Lane, I think."

Everyone laughed, even Mrs. Malins, at Gabriel's manner and Aunt Kate said:

"O, now, Gabriel, he didn't live in Back Lane, really. Only the mill was there."

"Out from the mansion of his forefathers," continued Gabriel, "he drove with Johnny. And everything went on beautifully until Johnny came in sight of King Billy's statue: and whether he fell in love with the horse King Billy sits on or whether he thought he was back again in the mill, anyhow he began to walk round the statue."

Gabriel paced in a circle round the hall in his goloshes amid the laughter of the others.

"Round and round he went," said Gabriel, "and the old gentleman, who was a very pompous old gentleman, was highly indignant. 'Go on, sir! What do you mean, sir? Johnny! Johnny! Most extraordinary conduct! Can't understand the horse!'"

The peal of laughter which followed Gabriel's imitation of the incident was interrupted by a resounding knock at the hall door. Mary Jane ran to open it and let in Freddy Malins. Freddy Malins, with his hat well back on his head and his shoulders humped with cold, was puffing and steaming after his exertions.

"I could only get one cab," he said.

"O, we'll find another along the quay," said Gabriel.

"Yes," said Aunt Kate. "Better not keep Mrs. Malins standing in the draught."

Mrs. Malins was helped down the front steps by her son and Mr. Browne and, after many manœuvres, hoisted into the cab. Freddy Malins clambered in after her and spent a long time settling her on the seat, Mr. Browne help-ing him with advice. At last she was settled comfortably and Freddy Malins invited Mr. Browne into the cab. There was a good deal of confused talk, and then Mr. Browne got into the cab. The cabman settled his rug over his knees, and bent down for the address. The confusion grew greater and the cabman was directed differently by Freddy Malins and Mr. Browne, each of whom had his head out through a window of the cab. The difficulty was to know where to drop Mr. Browne along the route, and Aunt Kate, Aunt Julia and Mary Jane helped the discussion from the doorstep with cross-directions and contradictions and abundance of laughter. As for Freddy Malins he was speechless with laughter. He popped his head in and out of the window every moment to the great danger of his hat, and told his mother how the discussion was progressing, till at last Mr. Browne shouted to the bewildered cabman above the din of everybody's laughter:

"Do you know Trinity College?"

"Yes, sir," said the cabman.

"Well, drive bang up against Trinity College gates," said Mr. Browne, "and then we'll tell you where to go. You understand now?"

"Yes, sir," said the cabman.

"Make like a bird for Trinity College."

"Right, sir," said the cabman.

The horse was whipped up and the cab rattled off along the quay amid a chorus of laughter and adieus.

Gabriel had not gone to the door with the others. He was in a dark part of the hall gazing up the staircase. A woman was standing near the top of the first flight, in the shadow also. He could not see her face but he could see the terra-cotta and salmon-pink panels of her skirt which the shadow made appear black and white. It was his wife. She was leaning on the banisters, listening to something. Gabriel was surprised at her stillness and strained his ear to listen also. But he could hear little save the noise of laughter and dispute on the front steps, a few chords struck on the piano and a few notes of a man's voice singing.

He stood still in the gloom of the hall, trying to catch the air that the voice was singing and gazing up at his wife. There was grace and mystery in her attitude as if she were a symbol of something. He asked himself what is a woman standing on the stairs in the shadow, listening to distant music, a symbol of. If he were a painter he would paint her in that attitude. Her blue felt hat would show off the bronze of her hair against the darkness and the dark panels of her skirt would show off the light ones. *Distant Music* he would call the picture if he were a painter.

The hall-door was closed; and Aunt Kate, Aunt Julia and Mary Jane came down the hall, still laughing.

"Well, isn't Freddy terrible?" said Mary Jane. "He's really terrible."

Gabriel said nothing but pointed up the stairs towards where his wife was standing. Now that the hall-door was closed the voice and the piano could be heard more clearly. Gabriel held up his hand for them to be silent. The song seemed to be in the old Irish tonality and the singer seemed uncertain both of his words and of his voice. The voice, made plaintive by distance and by the singer's hoarseness, faintly illuminated the cadence of the air with words expressing grief:

> *O, the rain falls on my heavy locks*
> *And the dew wets my skin,*
> *My babe lies cold . . .*

"O," exclaimed Mary Jane. "It's Bartell D'Arcy singing and he wouldn't sing all the night. O, I'll get him to sing a song before he goes."

"O, do, Mary Jane," said Aunt Kate.

Mary Jane brushed past the others and ran to the staircase, but before she reached it the singing stopped and the piano was closed abruptly.

"O, what a pity!" she cried. "Is he coming down, Gretta?"

Gabriel heard his wife answer yes and saw her come down towards them. A few steps behind her were Mr. Bartell D'Arcy and Miss O'Callaghan.

"O, Mr. D'Arcy," cried Mary Jane, "it's downright mean of you to break off like that when we were all in raptures listening to you."

"I have been at him all the evening," said Miss O'Callaghan, "and Mrs. Conroy, too, and he told us he had a dreadful cold and couldn't sing."

"O, Mr. D'Arcy," said Aunt Kate, "now that was a great fib to tell."

"Can't you see that I'm as hoarse as a crow?" said Mr. D'Arcy roughly.

He went into the pantry hastily and put on his overcoat. The others, taken aback by his rude speech, could find nothing to say. Aunt Kate wrinkled her brows and made signs to the others to drop the subject. Mr. D'Arcy stood swathing his neck carefully and frowning.

"It's the weather," said Aunt Julia, after a pause.

"Yes, everybody has colds," said Aunt Kate readily, "everybody."

"They say," said Mary Jane, "we haven't had snow like it for thirty years; and I read this morning in the newspapers that the snow is general all over Ireland."

"I love the look of snow," said Aunt Julia sadly.

"So do I," said Miss O'Callaghan. "I think Christmas is never really Christmas unless we have the snow on the ground."

"But poor Mr. D'Arcy doesn't like the snow," said Aunt Kate, smiling.

Mr. D'Arcy came from the pantry, fully swathed and buttoned, and in a repentant tone told them the history of his cold. Everyone gave him advice and said it was a great pity and urged him to be very careful of his throat in the night air. Gabriel watched his wife, who did not join in the conversation. She was standing right under the dusty fanlight and the flame of the gas lit up the rich bronze of her hair, which he had seen her drying at the fire a few days before. She was in the same attitude and seemed unaware of the talk about her. At last she turned towards them and Gabriel saw that there was colour on her cheeks and that her eyes were shining. A sudden tide of joy went leaping out of his heart.

"Mr. D'Arcy," she said, "what is the name of that song you were singing?"

"It's called *The Lass of Aughrim*," said Mr. D'Arcy, "but I couldn't remember it properly. Why? Do you know it?"

"*The Lass of Aughrim*," she repeated. "I couldn't think of the name."

"It's a very nice air," said Mary Jane. "I'm sorry you were not in voice tonight."

"Now, Mary Jane," said Aunt Kate, "don't annoy Mr. D'Arcy. I won't have him annoyed."

Seeing that all were ready to start she shepherded them to the door, where good-night was said:

"Well, good-night, Aunt Kate, and thanks for the pleasant evening."

"Good-night, Gabriel. Good-night, Gretta!"

"Good-night, Aunt Kate, and thanks ever so much. Good-night, Aunt Julia."

"O, good-night, Gretta. I didn't see you."

"Good-night, Mr. D'Arcy. Good-night, Miss O'Callaghan."

"Good-night, Miss Morkan."

"Good-night, again."

"Good-night, all. Safe home."

"Good-night. Good night."

The morning was still dark. A dull, yellow light brooded over the houses and the river; and the sky seemed to be descending. It was slushy underfoot; and only streaks and patches of snow lay on the roofs, on the parapets of the quay and on the area railings. The lamps were still burning redly in the murky air and, across the river, the palace of the Four Courts stood out menacingly against the heavy sky.

She was walking on before him with Mr. Bartell D'Arcy, her shoes in a brown parcel tucked under one arm and her hands holding her skirt up from the slush. She had no longer any grace of attitude, but Gabriel's eyes were still bright with happiness. The blood went bounding along his veins; and the thoughts went rioting through his brain, proud, joyful, tender, valorous.

She was walking on before him so lightly and so erect that he longed to run after her noiselessly, catch her by the shoulders and say something foolish and affectionate into her ear. She seemed to him so frail that he longed to defend her against something and then to be alone with her. Moments of their secret life together like stars upon his memory. A heliotrope envelope was lying beside his breakfast cup and he was caressing it with his hand. Birds were twittering in the ivy and the sunny web of the curtain was shimmering along the floor: he could not eat for happiness. They were standing on the crowded platform and he was placing a ticket inside the warm palm of her glove. He was standing with her in the cold, looking in through a grated window at a man making bottles in a roaring furnace. It was very cold. Her face, fragrant in the cold air, was quite close to his; and suddenly he called out to the man at the furnace:

"Is the fire hot, sir?"

But the man could not hear with the noise of the furnace. It was just as well. He might have answered rudely.

A wave of yet more tender joy escaped from his heart and went coursing in warm flood along his arteries. Like the tender fire of stars moments of their life together, that no one knew of or would ever know of, broke upon and illumined his memory. He longed to recall to her those moments, to make her forget the years of their dull existence together and remember only their moments of ecstasy. For the years, he felt, had not quenched his soul or hers. Their children, his writing, her household cares had not quenched all their souls' tender fire. In one letter that he had written to her then he had said:

"Why is it that words like these seem to me so dull and cold? Is it because there is no word tender enough to be your name?"

Like distant music these words that he had written years before were borne towards him from the past. He longed to be alone with her. When the others had gone away, when he and she were in the room in the hotel, then they would be alone together. He would call her softly:

"Gretta!"

Perhaps she would not hear at once: she would be undressing. Then something in his voice would strike her. She would turn and look at him. . . .

At the corner of Winetavern Street they met a cab. He was glad of its rattling noise as it saved him from conversation. She was looking out of the window and seemed tired. The others spoke only a few words, pointing out some building or street. The horse galloped along wearily under the murky morning sky, dragging his old rattling box after his heels, and Gabriel was again in a cab with her, galloping to catch the boat, galloping to their honeymoon.

As the cab drove across O'Connell Bridge Miss O'Callaghan said:

"They say you never cross O'Connell Bridge without seeing a white horse."

"I see a white man this time," said Gabriel.

"Where?" asked Mr. Bartell D'Arcy.

Gabriel pointed to the statue, on which lay patches of snow. Then he nodded familiarly to it and waved his hand.

"Good-night, Dan," he said gaily.

When the cab drew up before the hotel, Gabriel jumped out and, in spite of Mr. Bartell D'Arcy's protest, paid the driver. He gave the man a shilling over his fare. The man saluted and said:

"A prosperous New Year to you, sir."

"The same to you," said Gabriel cordially.

She leaned for a moment on his arm in getting out of the cab and while standing at the curbstone, bidding the others good-night. She leaned lightly on his arm, as lightly as when she had danced with him a few hours before. He had felt proud and happy then, happy that she was his, proud of her grace and wifely carriage. But now, after the kindling again of so many memories, the first touch of her body, musical and strange and perfumed, sent through him a keen pang of lust. Under cover of her silence he pressed her arm closely to his side; and, as they stood at the hotel door, he felt that they had escaped from their lives and duties, escaped from home and friends and run away together with wild and radiant hearts to a new adventure.

An old man was dozing in a great hooded chair in the hall. He lit a candle in the office and went before them to the stairs. They followed him in silence, their feet falling in soft thuds on the thickly carpeted stairs. She mounted the stairs behind the porter, her head bowed in the ascent, her frail shoulders curved as with a burden, her skirt girt tightly about her. He could have flung his arms about her hips and held her still, for his arms were trembling with desire to seize her and only the stress of his nails against the palms of his hands held the wild impulse of his body in check. The porter halted on the stairs to settle his guttering candle. They halted, too, on the steps below him. In the silence Gabriel could hear the falling of the molten wax into the tray and the thumping of his own heart against his ribs.

The porter led them along a corridor and opened a door. Then he set his unstable candle down on a toilet-table and asked at what hour they were to be called in the morning.

"Eight," said Gabriel.

The porter pointed to the tap of the electric-light and began a muttered apology, but Gabriel cut him short.

"We don't want any light. We have light enough from the street. And I say," he added, pointing to the candle, "you might remove that handsome article, like a good man."

The porter took up his candle again, but slowly, for he was surprised by such a novel idea. Then he mumbled good-night and went out. Gabriel shot the lock to.

A ghastly light from the street lamp lay in a long shaft from one window to the door. Gabriel threw his overcoat and hat on a couch and crossed the room towards the window. He looked down into the street in order that his emotion might calm a little. Then he turned and leaned against a chest of drawers with his back to the light. She had taken off her hat and cloak and was standing before a large swinging mirror, unhooking her waist. Gabriel paused for a few moments, watching her, and then said:

"Gretta!"

She turned away from the mirror slowly and walked along the shaft of light towards him. Her face looked so serious and weary that the words would not pass Gabriel's lips. No, it was not the moment yet.

"You look tired," he said.

"I am a little," she answered.

"You don't feel ill or weak?"

"No, tired: that's all."

She went on to the window and stood there, looking out. Gabriel waited again and then, fearing that diffidence was about to conquer him, he said abruptly:

"By the way, Gretta!"

"What is it?"

"You know that poor fellow Malins?" he said quickly.

"Yes. What about him?"

"Well, poor fellow, he's a decent sort of chap, after all," continued Gabriel in a false voice. "He gave me back that sovereign I lent him, and I didn't expect it, really. It's a pity he wouldn't keep away from that Browne, because he's not a bad fellow, really."

He was trembling now with annoyance. Why did she seem so abstracted? He did not know how he could begin. Was she annoyed, too, about something? If she would only turn to him or come to him of her own accord! To take her as she was would be brutal. No, he must see some ardour in her eyes first. He longed to be master of her strange mood.

"When did you lend him the pound?" she asked, after a pause.

Gabriel strove to restrain himself from breaking out into brutal language about the sottish Malins and his pound. He longed to cry to her from his soul, to crush her body against his, to overmaster her. But he said:

"O, at Christmas, when he opened that little Christmas-card shop in Henry Street."

He was in such a fever of rage and desire that he did not hear her come from the window. She stood before him for an instant, looking at him strangely. Then, suddenly raising herself on tiptoe and resting her hands lightly on his shoulders, she kissed him.

"You are a very generous person, Gabriel," she said.

Gabriel, trembling with delight at her sudden kiss and at the quaintness of her phrase, put his hands on her hair and began smoothing it back, scarcely touching it with his fingers. The washing had made it fine and brilliant. His heart was brimming over with happiness. Just when he was wishing for it she had come to him of her own accord. Perhaps her thoughts had been running with his. Perhaps she had felt the impetuous desire that was in him, and then the yielding mood had come upon her. Now that she had fallen to him so easily, he wondered why he had been so diffident.

He stood, holding her head between his hands. Then, slipping one arm swiftly about her body and drawing her towards him, he said softly:

"Gretta, dear, what are you thinking about?"

She did not answer nor yield wholly to his arm. He said again, softly:

"Tell me what it is, Gretta. I think I know what is the matter. Do I know?"

She did not answer at once. Then she said in an outburst of tears:

"O, I am thinking about that song, *The Lass of Aughrim*."

She broke loose from him and ran to the bed and, throwing her arms across the bed-rail, hid her face. Gabriel stood stock-still for a moment in astonishment and then followed her. As he passed in the way of the cheval-glass he caught sight of himself in full length, his broad, well-filled shirt-front, the face whose expression always puzzled him when he saw it in a mirror, and his glimmering gilt-rimmed eyeglasses. He halted a few paces from her and said:

"What about the song? Why does that make you cry?"

She raised her head from her arms and dried her eyes with the back of her hand like a child. A kinder note than he had intended went into his voice.

"Why, Gretta?" he asked.

"I am thinking about a person long ago who used to sing that song."

"And who was the person long ago?" asked Gabriel, smiling.

"It was a person I used to know in Galway when I was living with my grandmother," she said.

The smile passed away from Gabriel's face. A dull anger began to gather again at the back of his mind and the dull fires of his lust began to glow angrily in his veins.

"Someone you were in love with?" he asked ironically.

"It was a young boy I used to know," she answered, "named Michael Furey. He used to sing that song, *The Lass of Aughrim*. He was very delicate."

Gabriel was silent. He did not wish her to think that he was interested in this delicate boy.

"I can see him so plainly," she said, after a moment. "Such eyes as he had: big, dark eyes! And such an expression in them—an expression!"

"O, then, you are in love with him?" said Gabriel.

"I used to go out walking with him," she said, "when I was in Galway."

A thought flew across Gabriel's mind.

"Perhaps that was why you wanted to go to Galway with that Ivors girl?" he said coldly.

She looked at him and asked in surprise:

"What for?"

Her eyes made Gabriel feel awkward. He shrugged his shoulders and said:

"How do I know? To see him, perhaps."

She looked away from him along the shaft of light towards the window in silence.

"He is dead," she said at length. "He died when he was only seventeen. Isn't it a terrible thing to die so young as that?"

"What was he?" asked Gabriel, still ironically.

"He was in the gasworks," she said.

Gabriel felt humiliated by the failure of his irony and by the evocation of this figure from the dead, a boy in the gasworks. While he had been full of memories of their secret life together, full of tenderness and joy and desire, she had been comparing him in her mind with another. A shameful consciousness of his own person assailed him. He saw himself as a ludicrous figure, acting as a pennyboy for his aunts, a nervous, well-meaning sentimentalist, orating to vulgarians and idealising his own clownish lusts, the pitiable fatuous fellow he had caught a glimpse of in the mirror. Instinctively he turned his back more to the light lest she might see the shame that burned upon his forehead.

He tried to keep up his tone of cold interrogation, but his voice when he spoke was humble and indifferent.

"I suppose you were in love with this Michael Furey, Gretta," he said.

"I was great with him at that time," she said.

Her voice was veiled and sad. Gabriel, feeling now how vain it would be to try to lead her whither he had purposed, caressed one of her hands and said, also sadly:

"And what did he die of so young, Gretta? Consumption, was it?"

"I think he died for me," she answered.

A vague terror seized Gabriel at this answer, as if, at that hour when he had hoped to triumph, some impalpable and vindictive being was coming against him, gathering forces against him in its vague world. But he shook himself free of it with an effort of reason and continued to caress her hand. He did not question her again, for he felt that she would tell him of herself. Her hand was warm and moist: it did not respond to his touch, but he continued to caress it just as he had caressed her first letter to him that spring morning.

"It was in the winter," she said, "about the beginning of the winter when I was going to leave my grandmother's and come up here to the convent. And he was ill at the time in his lodgings in Galway and wouldn't be let out, and his people in Oughterard were written to. He was in decline, they said, or something like that. I never knew rightly."

She paused for a moment and sighed.

"Poor fellow," she said. "He was very fond of me and he was such a gentle boy. We used to go out together, walking, you know, Gabriel, like the way they do in the country. He was going to study singing only for his health. He had a very good voice, poor Michael Furey."

"Well; and then?" asked Gabriel.

"And then when it came to the time for me to leave Galway and come up to the convent he was much worse and I wouldn't be let see him so I wrote him a letter saying I was going up to Dublin and would be back in the summer, and hoping he would be better then."

She paused for a moment to get her voice under control, and then went on:

"Then the night before I left, I was in my grandmother's house in Nuns' Island, packing up, and I heard gravel thrown up against the window. The window was so wet I couldn't see, so I ran downstairs as I was and slipped out the back into the garden and there was the poor fellow at the end of the garden, shivering."

"And did you not tell him to go back?" asked Gabriel.

"I implored of him to go home at once and told him he would get his death in the rain. But he said he did not want to live. I can see his eyes as well as well! He was standing at the end of the wall where there was a tree."

"And did he go home?" asked Gabriel.

"Yes, he went home. And when I was only a week in the convent he died and he was buried in Oughterard, where his people came from. O, the day I heard that, that he was dead!"

She stopped, choking with sobs, and, overcome by emotion, flung herself face downward on the bed, sobbing in the quilt. Gabriel held her hand for a moment longer, irresolutely, and then, shy of intruding on her grief, let it fall gently and walked quietly to the window.

She was fast asleep.

Gabriel, leaning on his elbow, looked for a few moments unresentfully on her tangled hair and half-open mouth, listening to her deep-drawn breath. So she had had that romance in her life: a man had died for her sake. It hardly pained him now to think how poor a part he, her husband, had played in her life. He watched her while she slept, as though he and she had never lived together as man and wife. His curious eyes rested long upon her face and on her hair: and, as he thought of what she must have been then, in that time of her first girlish beauty, a strange, friendly pity for her entered his soul. He did not like to say even to himself that her face was no longer beautiful, but he knew that it was no longer the face for which Michael Furey had braved death.

Perhaps she had not told him all the story. His eyes moved to the chair over which she had thrown some of her clothes. A petticoat string dangled to the floor. One boot stood upright, its limp upper fallen down: the fellow of it lay upon its side. He wondered at his riot of emotions of an hour before. From what had it proceeded? From his aunt's supper, from his own foolish speech, from the wine and dancing, the merry-making when saying good-night in the hall, the pleasure of the walk along the river in the snow. Poor Aunt Julia! She, too, would soon be a shade with the shade of Patrick Morkan and his horse. He had caught that haggard look upon her face for a moment when she was singing *Arrayed for the Bridal*. Soon, perhaps, he would be sitting in that same drawing-room, dressed in black, his silk hat on his knees. The blinds would be drawn down and Aunt Kate would be sitting beside him, crying and blowing her nose and telling him how Julia had died. He would cast about in his mind for some words that might console her, and would find only lame and useless ones. Yes, yes: that would happen very soon.

The air of the room chilled his shoulders. He stretched himself cautiously along under the sheets and lay down beside his wife. One by one, they were all becoming shades. Better pass boldly into that other world, in the full glory of some passion, than fade and wither dismally with age. He thought of how she who lay beside him had locked in her heart for so many years that image of her lover's eyes when he had told her that he did not wish to live.

Generous tears filled Gabriel's eyes. He had never felt like that himself towards any woman, but he knew that such a feeling must be love. The tears gathered more thickly in his eyes and in the partial darkness he imagined he saw the form of a young man standing under a dripping tree. Other forms were near. His soul had approached that region where dwell the vast hosts of the dead. He was conscious of, but could not apprehend, their wayward and flickering existence. His own identity was fading out into a grey impalpable world: the solid world itself, which these dead had one time reared and lived in, was dissolving and dwindling.

A few light taps upon the pane made him turn to the window. It had begun to snow again. He watched sleepily the flakes, silver and dark, falling obliquely against the lamplight. The time had come for him to set out on his journey westward. Yes, the newspapers were right: snow was general all over Ireland. It was falling on every part of the dark central plain, on the treeless hills, falling softly upon the Bog of Allen and, farther westward, softly falling into the dark mutinous Shannon waves. It was falling, too, upon every part of the lonely churchyard on the hill where Michael Furey lay buried. It lay thickly drifted on the crooked crosses and headstones, on the spears of the little gate, on the barren thorns. His soul swooned slowly as he heard the snow falling faintly through the universe and faintly falling, like the descent of their last end, upon all the living and the dead.

COMMENTARY

In "The Dead" James Joyce brings to the highest pitch of perfection in English the naturalism of Flaubert; it may be questioned whether his great predecessor and master was able so completely to lift the objective detail of his material up to the symbolic level (see Appendix A, p. 633), as Joyce does in this great story. If the art of naturalism consists mainly in making *active* those elements which had hitherto in fiction remained *inert,* that is, description and expository summary, the further push given the method by Joyce consists in manipulating what at first sight seems to be mere physical detail into dramatic symbolism. As Gabriel Conroy, the "hero" of "The Dead," enters the house of his aunts, he scrapes snow from his galoshes on the door mat; by the time the story ends the snow has filled all the visible earth, and stands as the symbol of the revelation of Gabriel's inner life.

Joyce's method here is that of the Roving Narrator (see Appendix A, p. 626); that is to say, the author suppresses himself but does not allow the hero to tell his own story, for the reason that "psychic distance" is necessary to the end in view. This end is the *sudden* revelation to Gabriel of his egoistic relation to his wife and, through that revelation, of his inadequate response to his entire experience. Thus Joyce must establish his Central Intelligence (see Appendix A, p. 626) through Gabriel's eyes, but a little above and outside him at the same time, so that we shall know him at a given moment only through what he sees and feels in terms of that moment.

The story opens with the maid, Lily, who all day has been helping her mistresses, the Misses Morkan, Gabriel's aunts, prepare for their annual party. Here, as in the opening paragraph of Joyce's other masterpiece in *Dubliners,* "Araby," we open with a neutral or suspended point of view; just as Crane begins "The Open Boat" with: "None of them knew the color of the sky." Lily is "planted" because, when Gabriel arrives, he must enter the scene dramatically, and not merely be *reported* as entering; if his eye is to *see* the story, the eye must be established actively, and it is so established in the little incident with Lily. If he is to see the action for us, he must come authoritatively out of the scene, not throw himself out at us. After he flicks the snow, he sounds his special note; it is a false note indicating his inadequate response to people and even his lack of respect for them. He refers patronizingly to Lily's personal life; when she cries out in protest, he makes it worse by offering her money. From that moment we know Gabriel Conroy, but we have not been *told* what he is: we have had him *rendered*.

In fact, from the beginning to the end of the story we are never told anything; we are shown everything. We are not told, for example, that the *milieu* of the story is the provincial, middle-class, "cultivated" society of Dublin at the turn of the century; we are not told that Gabriel represents its emotional sterility (as contrasted with the "peasant" richness of his wife Gretta), its complacency, its devotion to genteel culture, its sentimental evasion of "reality." All this we see dramatized; it is all made active. Nothing is given us from the externally omniscient point of view (see Appendix A, p. 623). At the moment Gabriel enters the house the eye shifts from Lily to Gabriel. It is necessary, of course, at this first appearance that *we* should see him: there is a brief description; but it is not Joyce's description; we see him as Lily sees him—or might see him if she had Joyce's superior command of the whole situation. This, in fact, is the method of "The Dead." From this point on we are never far from Gabriel's physical sight; yet we are constantly looking through his physical eyes at values and insights of which he is incapable. The significance of the *milieu,* the complacency of Gabriel's feeling for his wife, her romantic image of her lover Michael Furey, what Miss Ivors means in that particular society, would have been put before us, in the pre-James era, as exposition and commentary through the direct intercession of the author; and it would have remained inert.

Take Miss Ivors: she is a flat character, she disappears the moment Joyce is through with her, when she has served his purpose. She is there to elicit from Gabriel a certain quality, his relation to his culture at the intellectual and social level; but she is not in herself a *necessary* character. To this sort of character, whose mechanical use must be given the look of reality, James applied the term *ficelle*. She makes it possible for Joyce to charge with imaginative activity an important phase of Gabriel's life which he would otherwise have been compelled to give us as mere information. Note also that this particular *ficelle* is a woman: she stands for the rich and complex life of the Irish people out of which Gabriel's wife has come, and we are thus given a subtle dramatic presentation of a spiritual limitation which focusses symbolically, at the end of the story, upon his relation to his wife.

The examples of naturalistic detail which operate also at the symbolic level will sufficiently indicate to the reader the close texture of "The Dead." We should say, conversely, that the symbolism itself derives its validity from its being, in the first place, a visible and experienced moment in the consciousness of a character.

Take the incident when Gabriel looks into the mirror. It serves two purposes. First, we need to *see* Gabriel again and more closely than we saw him when he entered the house; we know him better morally and we must see him more clearly physically. At the same time, he looks into the mirror because he is not, and has never been, concerned with an objective situation; he is wrapped in himself. The mirror is an old and worn symbol of Narcissism, but here it is effective because its first impact is through the action; it is not laid on the action from the outside.

As the party breaks up, we see Gabriel downstairs; upstairs Mr. Bartell D'Arcy is singing (hoarsely and against his will) "The Lass of Aughrim." Gabriel looks up the stairs:

> A woman was standing near the top of the first flight, in the shadow also. He could not see her face but he could see the terra-cotta and salmon-pink panels of her skirt which the shadow made appear black and white. It was his wife. Gabriel was surprised at her stillness . . .

She is listening to the song. As she stands, one hand on the banister, listening, Gabriel has an access of romantic feeling. *"Distant Music* he would call the picture if he were a painter." At this moment Gabriel's whole situation in life begins to be reversed, and because he will not be aware until the end of the significance of the reversal, its impact upon the reader from here on is an irony of increasing power. As he feels drawn to his wife, he sees her romantically, with unconscious irony, as "Distant Music," little suspecting how distant she is. He sees only the "lower" part of her figure; the "upper" is involved with the song, the meaning of which, for her, we do not yet know. The concealment of the "upper" and the visibility, to Gabriel, of the "lower," constitute a symbol, dramatically and naturalistically *active,* of Gabriel's relation to his wife: he has never acknowledged her spirit, her identity as a person; he knows only her body. And at the end, when he tries to possess her physically, she reveals with crushing force her full being, her own separate life, in the story of Michael Furey, whose image has been brought back to her by the singing of Mr. Bartell D'Arcy.

The image of Michael provides our third example. The incident is one of great technical difficulty, for no preparation, in its own terms, was possible. How, we might ask ourselves, was Joyce to convey to us (and to Gabriel) the reality of Gretta's boy lover (see Appendix A, p. 621)? Could he let Gretta say that a boy named Michael Furey was in love with her, that he died young, that she had never forgotten him because, it seemed to her, he must have died for love of her? This would be mere statement, mere reporting. Let us see how Joyce does it.

> "Some one you were in love with?" he asked ironically.
> "It was a young boy I used to know," she answered, "named Michael Furey. He used to sing that song, *The Lass of Aughrim.* He was very delicate."

Having established in the immediate dramatic context, in relation to Gabriel, her emotion for Michael, who had created for her a complete and inviolable moment, she is able to proceed to details which are living details because they have been acted upon by her memory: his big, dark eyes; his job at the gasworks; his death at seventeen. But these are not enough to create space around him, not enough to present his image.

> ". . . I heard gravel thrown up against the window. The window was so wet I couldn't see, so I ran downstairs as I was and slipped out the back into the garden and there was the poor fellow at the end of the garden, shivering."

Up to this passage, we have been *told* about Michael; we now begin to *see* him. And we see him in the following passage:

> "I implored him to go home at once and told him he would get his death in the rain. But he said he did not want to live. I can see his eyes as well as well! He was standing at the end of the wall where was a tree."

Without the wall and the tree to give him space he would not exist; these details cut him loose from Gretta's story and present him in the round.

The overall symbol, the snow, which we first see as a scenic detail on the toe of Gabriel's galoshes, gradually expands until at the end it gathers up the entire action. The snow is the story. It is not necessary to separate its development from the dramatic structure or to point out in detail how at every moment, including the splendid climax, it reaches us through the eye as a naturalistic feature of the background. Its symbolic operation is of greater importance. At the beginning, the snow is the cold and even hostile force of nature, humanly indifferent, enclosing the warm conviviality of the Misses Morkan's party. But just as the human action in which Gabriel is involved develops in the pattern of the plot of Reversal, his situation at the end being the opposite of its beginning, so the snow reverses its meaning, in a kind of rhetorical dialectic: from naturalistic *coldness* it develops into a symbol of warmth, of expanded consciousness; it stands for Gabriel's escape from his own ego into the larger world of humanity, including "all the living and the dead."

Franz Kafka

THE HUNTER GRACCHUS

TWO BOYS were sitting on the harbour wall playing with dice. A man was reading a newspaper on the steps of the monument, resting in the shadow of a hero who was flourishing his sword on high. A girl was filling her bucket at the fountain. A fruit-seller was lying beside his scales, staring out to sea. Through the vacant window and door openings of a café one could see two men quite at the back drinking their wine. The proprietor was sitting at a table in front and dozing. A bark was silently making for the little harbour, as if borne by invisible means over the water. A man in a blue blouse climbed ashore and drew the rope through a ring. Behind the boatman two other men in dark coats with silver buttons carried a bier, on which, beneath a great flower-patterned tasselled silk cloth, a man was apparently lying.

Nobody on the quay troubled about the newcomers; even when they lowered the bier to wait for the boatman, who was still occupied with his rope, nobody went nearer, nobody asked them a question, nobody accorded them an inquisitive glance.

The pilot was still further detained by a woman who, a child at her breast, now appeared with loosened hair on the deck of the boat. Then he advanced and indicated a yellowish two-storeyed house that rose abruptly on the left beside the sea; the bearers took up their burden and bore it to the low but gracefully pillared door. A little boy opened a window just in time to see the party vanishing into the house, then hastily shut the window again. The door too was now shut; it was of black oak, and very strongly made. A flock of doves which had been flying round the belfry alighted in the street before the house. As if their food were stored within, they assembled in front of the door. One of them flew up to the first storey and pecked at the window-pane. They were bright-hued, well-tended, beautiful birds. The woman on the boat flung grain to them in a wide sweep; they ate it up and flew across to the woman.

A man in a top hat tied with a band of crêpe now descended one of the narrow and very steep lanes that led to the harbour. He glanced round vigilantly, everything seemed to displease him, his mouth twisted at the sight of some offal in a corner. Fruit skins were lying on the steps of the monument; he swept them off in passing with his stick. He rapped at the house door, at the same time taking his top hat from his head with his black-gloved

hand. The door was opened at once, and some fifty little boys appeared in
two rows in the long entry-hall, and bowed to him.

The boatman descended the stairs, greeted the gentlemen in black, conducted him up to the first storey, led him round the bright and elegant loggia
which encircled the courtyard, and both of them entered, while the boys
pressed after them at a respectful distance, a cool spacious room looking
towards the back, from whose window no habitation, but only a bare,
blackish grey rocky wall was to be seen. The bearers were busied in setting
up and lighting several long candles at the head of the bier, yet these did not
give light, but only scared away the shadows which had been immobile till
then, and made them flicker over the walls. The cloth covering the bier had
been thrown back. Lying on it was a man with wildly matted hair, who
looked somewhat like a hunter. He lay without motion and, it seemed,
without breathing, his eyes closed; yet only his trappings indicated that this
man was probably dead.

The gentleman stepped up to the bier, laid his hand on the brow of the
man lying upon it, then kneeled down and prayed. The boatman made a
sign to the bearers to leave the room; they went out, drove away the boys
who had gathered outside, and shut the door. But even that did not seem to
satisfy the gentleman, he glanced at the boatman; the boatman understood,
and vanished through a side door into the next room. At once the man on the
bier opened his eyes, turned his face painfully towards the gentleman, and
said: "Who are you?" Without any mark of surprise the gentleman rose
from his kneeling posture and answered: "The Burgomaster of Riva."

The man on the bier nodded, indicated a chair with a feeble movement
of his arm, and said, after the Burgomaster had accepted his invitation: "I
knew that, of course, Burgomaster, but in the first moments of returning
consciousness I always forget, everything goes round before my eyes, and it is
best to ask about anything even if I know. You too probably know that I
am the hunter Gracchus."

"Certainly," said the Burgomaster. "Your arrival was announced to me
during the night. We had been asleep for a good while. Then towards
midnight my wife cried: 'Salvatore'—that's my name—'look at that dove at
the window.' It was really a dove, but as big as a cock. It flew over me and
said in my ear: 'To-morrow the dead hunter Gracchus is coming; receive
him in the name of the city.'"

The hunter nodded and licked his lips with the tip of his tongue: "Yes,
the doves flew here before me. But do you believe, Burgomaster, that I shall
remain in Riva?"

"I cannot say that yet," replied the Burgomaster. "Are you dead?"

"Yes," said the hunter, "as you see. Many years ago, yes, it must be a
great many years ago, I fell from a precipice in the Black Forest—that is in
Germany—when I was hunting a chamois. Since then I have been dead."

"But you are alive too," said the Burgomaster.

"In a certain sense," said the hunter, "in a certain sense I am alive too.

My death ship lost its way; a wrong turn of the wheel, a moment's absence of mind on the pilot's part, a longing to turn aside towards my lovely native country, I cannot tell what it was; I only know this, that I remained on earth and that ever since my ship has sailed earthly waters. So I, who asked for nothing better than to live among my mountains, travel after my death through all the lands of the earth."

"And you have no part in the other world?" asked the Burgomaster, knitting his brow.

"I am for ever," replied the hunter, "on the great stair that leads up to it. On that infinitely wide and spacious stair I clamber about, sometimes up, sometimes down, sometimes on the right, sometimes on the left, always in motion. The hunter has been turned into a butterfly. Do not laugh."

"I am not laughing," said the Burgomaster in self-defence.

"That is very good of you," said the hunter. "I am always in motion. But when I make a supreme flight and see the gate actually shining before me I awaken presently on my old ship, still stranded forlornly in some earthly sea or other. The fundamental error of my one-time death grins at me as I lie in my cabin. Julia, the wife of the pilot, knocks at the door and brings me on my bier the morning drink of the land whose coasts we chance to be passing. I lie on a wooden pallet, I wear—it cannot be a pleasure to look at me —a filthy winding sheet, my hair and beard, black tinged with grey, have grown together inextricably, my limbs are covered with a great flower-patterned woman's shawl with long fringes. A sacramental candle stands at my head and lights me. On the wall opposite me is a little picture, evidently of a Bushman who is aiming his spear at me and taking cover as best he can behind a beautifully painted shield. On shipboard one is often a prey to stupid imaginations, but that is the stupidest of them all. Otherwise my wooden case is quite empty. Through a hole in the side wall come in the warm airs of the southern night, and I hear the water slapping against the old boat.

"I have lain here ever since the time when, as the hunter Gracchus living in the Black Forest, I followed a chamois and fell from a precipice. Everything happened in good order. I pursued, I fell, bled to death in a ravine, died, and this ship should have conveyed me to the next world. I can still remember how gladly I stretched myself out on this pallet for the first time. Never did the mountains listen to such songs from me as these shadowy walls did then.

"I had been glad to live and I was glad to die. Before I stepped aboard, I joyfully flung away my wretched load of ammunition, my knapsack, my hunting rifle that I had always been proud to carry, and I slipped into my winding sheet like a girl into her marriage dress. I lay and waited. Then came the mishap."

"A terrible fate," said the Burgomaster, raising his hand defensively. "And you bear no blame for it?"

"None," said the hunter. "I was a hunter; was there any sin in that? I followed my calling as a hunter in the Black Forest, where there were still wolves in those days. I lay in ambush, shot, hit my mark, flayed the skins from my victims: was there any sin in that? My labours were blessed. 'The great hunter of the Black Forest' was the name I was given. Was there any sin in that?"

"I am not called upon to decide that," said the Burgomaster, "but to me also there seems to be no sin in such things. But, then whose is the guilt?"

"The boatman's," said the hunter. "Nobody will read what I say here, no one will come to help me; even if all the people were commanded to help me, every door and window would remain shut, everybody would take to bed and draw the bedclothes over his head, the whole earth would become an inn for the night. And there is sense in that, for nobody knows of me, and if anyone knew he would not know where I could be found, and if he knew where I could be found, he would not know how to deal with me, he would not know how to help me. The thought of helping me is an illness that has to be cured by taking to one's bed.

"I know that, and so I do not shout to summon help, even though at moments—when I lose control over myself, as I have done just now, for instance—I think seriously of it. But to drive out such thoughts I need only look round me and verify where I am, and—I can safely assert—have been for hundreds of years."

"Extraordinary," said the Burgomaster, "extraordinary.—And now do you think of staying here in Riva with us?"

"I think not," said the hunter with a smile, and, to excuse himself, he laid his hand on the Burgomaster's knee. "I am here, more than that I do not know, further than that I cannot go. My ship has no rudder, and it is driven by the wind that blows in the undermost regions of death."

COMMENTARY

Franz Kafka occupies somewhat the same position in the literary world of today that Ernest Hemingway occupied before the Second World War. The two writers have one thing in common: they are both masters of naturalism. But our age, as Edmund Wilson has shown in his *Axel's Castle,* has two trends, Naturalism and Symbolism, or Symbolism based upon Naturalism (see Appendix A, p. 633). The symbolism which operates in Hemingway's stories refers to a narrow range of experience and seems inadequate today. The world appears to have shifted under our feet. We have seen whole countries ravaged, whole populations decimated. We can hardly believe any longer in the Divinity of Man. We are more concerned today with Man's relation to God.

Hemingway, giving expression to the doubts, the anguish, the soul searchings of the men and women of the twenties, is voicing—and perhaps unconsciously beginning to question—the belief in the Divinity of Man which has so long been held as an article of faith by the civilized world. "Today is Friday," a short and little known piece (it is really a little play), is the only one of his stories which attempts to treat overtly the relation of Man to God. Three Roman soldiers are talking in a drinking place after the Crucifixion:

> 1st Roman Soldier—You see his girl?
> 2nd Soldier—Wasn't I standing right by her?
> 1st Soldier—She's a nice looker.
> 2nd Soldier—I knew her before he did. (He winks at the wine-seller.)
> 1st Soldier—I used to see her around the town.
> 2nd Soldier—She used to have a lot of stuff. He never brought *her* no luck.
> 1st Soldier—Oh, he ain't lucky. But he looked pretty good to me in there today.
> 2nd Soldier—What became of his gang?
> 1st Soldier—Oh, they faded out. Just the women stuck by him.
> 2nd Soldier—They were a pretty yellow crowd. When they seen him go up they didn't want any of it.
> 1st Soldier—The women stuck all right.
> 2nd Soldier—Sure, they stuck all right.
> 1st Soldier—You see me slip the old spear into him?
> 2nd Soldier—You'll get into trouble doing that some day.
> 1st Soldier—It was the least I could do for him. I tell you he looked pretty good to me in there today.

Christ's Divinity is hinted at. There is even the possibility of conversion, for the Second Soldier says later: "Any time you show me one that doesn't want to get down off the cross when the time comes—when the time comes, I mean—I'll climb up with him." But the beautifully rendered, expertly timed dialogue (which may well serve the student as a model) proceeds by means of bashful understatements. Christ, suffering on the Cross for the sins of Mankind, does not elicit any more eloquence from the writer than a courageous but unlucky prize fighter could have called forth. At the end of the story, the Second Soldier makes a comment familiar to Hemingway's readers: "You been out here too long. That's all." Man, remaining just as he is, undergoing, that is to say, no spiritual change, may yet solve his problems by going on—or going back—to a country where everything will be "fine."

Hemingway's early heroes are rarely middle-aged persons. They are returned soldiers, or adolescents, or Spaniards, like the bull-fighter Manuel Garcia, or expatriates, like Jake Barnes, seeking the answer to the question they are forever asking by returning to lost innocence or taking up their abode in some foreign land.

Kafka presents a surface which is as strictly naturalistic as Hemingway's in details, but he is dealing with a problem more complicated than Hemingway's: the relation of Man to God.

There have been fiction writers before him who concerned themselves with the same problem, in this country, notably Hawthorne. Too often, with him, myth turns into allegory. Kafka's stories are more dramatic, consisting on the surface of action presented in convincing detail. His meaning, which constitutes another level of action, is cryptic, and must be sought for in his symbols.

"The Hunter Gracchus," which, though short, exhibits his fictional gifts in perfection, is the story of a Christ who has been crucified but has never been able to ascend into Heaven.

The viewpoint is that of the omniscient narrator (see Appendix A, p. 623). The scenes are pictorial throughout. The opening scene shows the world of men at their various occupations. Boys are shooting dice, a man is reading a newspaper, a girl is filling her bucket at a fountain, two men are drinking wine in a café while the proprietor dozes at a table outside. The architecture of this setting reminds one of allegorical paintings of the fourteenth century. In such paintings a window or a vista often opens on what artists call "infinite space." In Kafka's scene spatial perspective is symbolic and also prepares for the Complication of the action (see Appendix A, p. 630): the man is reading the newspaper in the shadow of a hero who is flourishing a sword on high, a fruit seller is lying beside his scales, staring out to sea, where a bark is "silently making for the little harbour as if drawn by invisible means over the water."

The Complication is the arrival of the dead hunter, Gracchus (Christ), in any harbour (any community). Kafka evidently thinks of Christ's passion as being continuously enacted. The boatman (the Church) transfers the bier to the shore. Doves light on the bier, as the Holy Spirit, in the form of a dove, once alighted on the head of Christ, but "nobody on the quay troubled about the newcomers . . . nobody asked them a question, nobody accorded them even an inquisitive glance."

The action proper begins when the burgomaster of the town, whose name is significantly "Salvatore," goes into the room where the body of the dead hunter lies on its bier, goes, that is, to church. He gives the boatman a glance and the boatman vanishes through a side door into another room. (Since the soul is seeking salvation in terms of a Protestant theology it dispenses with the Roman Catholic sacrament of Confession.)

Salvatore (the soul) then communes with the hunter (Christ), who deplores his condition: "It cannot be a pleasure to look at me," and then relates the story of his Incarnation and Crucifixion. Pursuing his calling (the saving of souls) he fell down a precipice (became Incarnate), bled to death in a ravine (was crucified), died, but did not ascend into Heaven; his death ship "lost its way."

Salvatore expresses his attitude towards the Doctrine of Original Sin when he asks whose was the guilt. The Hunter replies that it is the boatman's (the Church's) but he does not feel that the boatman has been guilty of anything more than "a wrong turn of the wheel," "a moment's absence of mind." The result of this mischance is the Resolution (see Appendix A,

p. 630) of the action: Christ has not been able to become Christ, but remains "forever on the great stair that leads to Heaven, sometimes up, sometimes down . . . always in motion." The Hunter (of souls) has been turned into a butterfly, an ancient symbol for the soul.

The artist, as such, does not defend or criticize the myth of his age, he merely portrays it. Kafka's subject-matter is the Scheme of Redemption, as set forth in Neo-Calvinist theology and the philosophy of "Crisis," and his allegorical symbolism is as exact, if not as full as Dante's, but his participation in the faith is not as complete. His skepticism shows itself occasionally in wry ambiguities. The dove which warns Salvatore of Gracchus's arrival is as big as a cock and it evokes the image of the cock which crowed to herald the betrayal of Christ. The pessimism of our age finds expression in the crowning sentence of this remarkable story: "My ship has no rudder, and it is driven by a wind that blows in the undermost regions of death."

Stephen Crane

THE OPEN BOAT

A Tale Intended to be After the Fact. Being the Experience of Four
Men From the Sunk Steamer "Commodore."

i

NONE of them knew the color of the sky. Their eyes glanced level, and were fastened upon the waves that swept toward them. These waves were of the hue of slate, save for the tops, which were of foaming white, and all of the men knew the colors of the sea. The horizon narrowed and widened, and dipped and rose, and at all times its edge was jagged with waves that seemed thrust up in points like rocks. Many a man ought to have a bath-tub larger than the boat which here rode upon the sea. These waves were most wrongfully and barbarously abrupt and tall, and each froth-top was a problem in small-boat navigation.

The cook squatted in the bottom and looked with both eyes at the six inches of gunwale which separated him from the ocean. His sleeves were rolled over his fat forearms, and the two flaps of his unbuttoned vest dangled as he bent to bail out the boat. Often he said: "Gawd! That was a narrow clip." As he remarked it he invariably gazed eastward over the broken sea.

The oiler, steering with one of the two oars in the boat, sometimes raised himself suddenly to keep clear of water that swirled in over the stern. It was a thin little oar and it seemed often ready to snap.

The correspondent, pulling at the other oar, watched the waves and wondered why he was there.

The injured captain, lying in the bow, was at this time buried in that profound dejection and indifference which comes, temporarily at least, to even the bravest and most enduring when, willy nilly, the firm fails, the army loses, the ship goes down. The mind of the master of a vessel is rooted deep in the timbers of her, though he commands for a day or a decade, and this captain had on him the stern impression of a scene in the greys of dawn of seven turned faces, and later a stump of a top-mast with a white ball on it that slashed to and fro at the waves, went low and lower, and down. Thereafter there was something strange in his voice. Although steady, it was deep with mourning, and of a quality beyond oration or tears.

"Keep 'er a little more south, Billie," said he.

" 'A little more south,' sir," said the oiler in the stern.

A seat in this boat was not unlike a seat upon a bucking broncho, and by the same token, a broncho is not much smaller. The craft pranced and reared, and plunged like an animal. As each wave came, and she rose for it, she seemed like a horse making at a fence outrageously high. The manner of her scramble over these walls of water is a mystic thing, and, moreover, at the top of them were ordinarily these problems in white water, the foam racing down from the summit of each wave, requiring a new leap, and a leap from the air. Then, after scornfully bumping a crest, she would slide, and race, and splash down a long incline, and arrive bobbing and nodding in front of the next menace.

A singular disadvantage of the sea lies in the fact that after successfully surmounting one wave you discover that there is another behind it just as important and just as nervously anxious to do something effective in the way of swamping boats. In a ten-foot dingey one can get an idea of the resources of the sea in the line of waves that is not probable to the average experience which is never at sea in a dingey. As each slatey wall of water approached, it shut all else from the view of the men in the boat, and it was not difficult to imagine that this particular wave was the final outburst of the ocean, the last effort of the grim water. There was a terrible grace in the move of the waves, and they came in silence, save for the snarling of the crests.

In the wan light, the faces of the men must have been grey. Their eyes must have glinted in strange ways as they gazed steadily astern. Viewed from a balcony, the whole thing would doubtless have been weirdly picturesque. But the men in the boat had no time to see it, and if they had had leisure there were other things to occupy their minds. The sun swung steadily up the sky, and they knew it was broad day because the color of the sea changed from slate to emerald-green, streaked with amber lights, and the foam was like tumbling snow. The process of the breaking day was unknown to them. They were aware only of this effect upon the color of the waves that rolled toward them.

In disjointed sentences the cook and the correspondent argued as to the difference between a life-saving station and a house of refuge. The cook had said: "There's a house of refuge just north of the Mosquito Inlet Light, and as soon as they see us, they'll come off in their boat and pick us up."

"As soon as who see us?" said the correspondent.

"The crew," said the cook.

"Houses of refuge don't have crews," said the correspondent. "As I understand them, they are only places where clothes and grub are stored for the benefit of shipwrecked people. They don't carry crews."

"Oh, yes, they do," said the cook.

"No, they don't," said the correspondent.

"Well, we're not there yet, anyhow," said the oiler, in the stern.

"Well," said the cook, "perhaps it's not a house of refuge that I'm think-

ing of as being near Mosquito Inlet Light. Perhaps it's a life-saving station."

"We're not there yet," said the oiler, in the stern.

ii

As the boat bounced from the top of each wave, the wind tore through
the hair of the hatless men, and as the craft plopped her stern down again
the spray splashed past them. The crest of each of these waves was a hill,
from the top of which the men surveyed, for a moment, a broad tumultuous
expanse, shining and wind-riven. It was probably splendid. It was probably
glorious, this play of the free sea, wild with lights of emerald and white and
amber.

"Bully good thing it's an on-shore wind," said the cook. "If not, where
would we be? Wouldn't have a show."

"That's right," said the correspondent.

The busy oiler nodded his assent.

Then the captain, in the bow, chuckled in a way that expressed humor,
contempt, tragedy, all in one. "Do you think we've got much of a show now,
boys?" said he.

Whereupon the three were silent, save for a trifle of hemming and haw-
ing. To express any particular optimism at this time they felt to be childish
and stupid, but they all doubtless possessed this sense of the situation in their
mind. A young man thinks doggedly at such times. On the other hand, the
ethics of their condition was decidedly against any open suggestion of hopelessness. So they were silent.

"Oh, well," said the captain, soothing his children, "we'll get ashore
all right."

But there was that in his tone which made them think, so the oiler
quoth: "Yes! If this wind holds!"

The cook was bailing: "Yes! If we don't catch hell in the surf."

Canton flannel gulls flew near and far. Sometimes they sat down on the
sea, near patches of brown seaweed that rolled on the waves with a movement like carpets on a line in a gale. The birds sat comfortably in groups,
and they were envied by some in the dingey, for the wrath of the sea was
no more to them than it was to a covey of prairie chickens a thousand miles
inland. Often they came very close and stared at the men with black bead-
like eyes. At these times they were uncanny and sinister in their unblinking
scrutiny, and the men hooted angrily at them, telling them to be gone. One
came, and evidently decided to alight on the top of the captain's head. The
bird flew parallel to the boat and did not circle, but made short sidelong
jumps in the air in chicken-fashion. His black eyes were wistfully fixed upon
the captain's head. "Ugly brute," said the oiler to the bird. "You look as if
you were made with a jack-knife." The cook and the correspondent swore
darkly at the creature. The captain naturally wished to knock it away with

the end of the heavy painter; but he did not dare do it, because anything resembling an emphatic gesture would have capsized this freighted boat, and so with his open hand, the captain gently and carefully waved the gull away. After it had been discouraged from the pursuit the captain breathed easier on account of his hair, and others breathed easier because the bird struck their minds at this time as being somehow grewsome and ominous.

In the meantime the oiler and the correspondent rowed. And also they rowed.

They sat together in the same seat, and each rowed an oar. Then the oiler took both oars; then the correspondent took both oars; then the oiler; then the correspondent. They rowed and they rowed. The very ticklish part of the business was when the time came for the reclining one in the stern to take his turn at the oars. By the very last star of truth, it is easier to steal eggs from under a hen than it was to change seats in the dingey. First the man in the stern slid his hand along the thwart and moved with care, as if he were of Sèvres. Then the man in the rowing seat slid his hand along the other thwart. It was all done with the most extraordinary care. As the two sidled past each other, the whole party kept watchful eyes on the coming wave, and the captain cried: "Look out now! Steady there!"

The brown mats of seaweed that appeared from time to time were like islands, bits of earth. They were traveling, apparently, neither one way nor the other. They were, to all intents, stationary. They informed the men in the boat that it was making progress slowly toward the land.

The captain, rearing cautiously in the bow, after the dingey soared on a great swell, said that he had seen the lighthouse at Mosquito Inlet. Presently the cook remarked that he had seen it. The correspondent was at the oars then, and for some reason he too wished to look at the lighthouse, but his back was toward the far shore and the waves were important, and for some time he could not seize an opportunity to turn his head. But at last there came a wave more gentle than the others, and when at the crest of it he swiftly scoured the western horizon.

"See it?" said the captain.

"No," said the correspondent slowly, "I didn't see anything."

"Look again," said the captain. He pointed. "It's exactly in that direction."

At the top of another wave, the correspondent did as he was bid, and this time his eyes chanced on a small still thing on the edge of the swaying horizon. It was precisely like the point of a pin. It took an anxious eye to find a lighthouse so tiny.

"Think we'll make it, captain?"

"If this wind holds and the boat don't swamp, we can't do much else," said the captain.

The little boat, lifted by each towering sea, and splashed viciously by the crests, made progress that in the absence of seaweed was not apparent to those in her. She seemed just a wee thing wallowing, miraculously top-up, at the mercy of five oceans. Occasionally, a great spread of water, like white flames, swarmed into her.

"Bail her, cook," said the captain serenely.

"All right, captain," said the cheerful cook.

iii

It would be difficult to describe the subtle brotherhood of men that was here established on the seas. No one said that it was so. No one mentioned it. But it dwelt in the boat, and each man felt it warm him. They were a captain, an oiler, a cook, and a correspondent, and they were friends, friends in a more curiously iron-bound degree than may be common. The hurt captain, lying against the water-jar in the bow, spoke always in a low voice and calmly, but he could never command a more ready and swiftly obedient crew than the motley three of the dingey. It was more than a mere recognition of what was best for the common safety. There was surely in it a quality that was personal and heartfelt. And after this devotion to the commander of the boat there was this comradeship that the correspondent, for instance, who had been taught to be cynical of men, knew even at the time was the best experience of his life. But no one said that it was so. No one mentioned it.

"I wish we had a sail," remarked the captain. "We might try my overcoat on the end of an oar and give you two boys a chance to rest." So the cook and the correspondent held the mast and spread wide the overcoat. The oiler steered, and the little boat made good way with her new rig. Sometimes the oiler had to scull sharply to keep a sea from breaking into the boat, but otherwise sailing was a success.

Meanwhile the lighthouse had been growing slowly larger. It had now almost assumed color, and appeared like a little grey shadow on the sky. The man at the oars could not be prevented from turning his head rather often to try for a glimpse of this little grey shadow.

At last, from the top of each wave the men in the tossing boat could see land. Even as the lighthouse was an upright shadow on the sky, this land seemed but a long black shadow on the sea. It certainly was thinner than paper. "We must be about opposite New Smyrna," said the cook, who had coasted this shore often in schooners. "Captain, by the way, I believe they abandoned that life-saving station there about a year ago."

"Did they?" said the captain.

The wind slowly died away. The cook and the correspondent were not now obliged to slave in order to hold high the oar. But the waves continued their old impetuous swooping at the dingey, and the little craft, no longer under way, struggled woundily over them. The oiler or the correspondent took the oars again.

Shipwrecks are à propos of nothing. If men could only train for them and have them occur when the men had reached pink condition, there would be less drowning at sea. Of the four in the dingey none had slept any time worth mentioning for two days and two nights previous to embarking in the dingey, and in the excitement of clambering about the deck of a foundering ship they had also forgotten to eat heartily.

For these reasons, and for others, neither the oiler nor the correspondent was fond of rowing at this time. The correspondent wondered ingenuously how in the name of all that was sane could there be people who thought it amusing to row a boat. It was not an amusement; it was a diabolical punishment, and even a genius of mental aberrations could never conclude that it was anything but a horror to the muscles and a crime against the back. He mentioned to the boat in general how the amusement of rowing struck him, and the weary-faced oiler smiled in full sympathy. Previously to the foundering, by the way, the oiler had worked double-watch in the engine-room of the ship.

"Take her easy, now, boys," said the captain. "Don't spend yourselves. If we have to run a surf you'll need all your strength, because we'll sure have to swim for it. Take your time."

Slowly the land arose from the sea. From a black line it became a line of black and a line of white, trees and sand. Finally, the captain said that he could make out a house on the shore. "That's the house of refuge, sure," said the cook. "They'll see us before long, and come out after us."

The distant lighthouse reared high. "The keeper ought to be able to make us out now, if he's looking through a glass," said the captain. "He'll notify the life-saving people."

"None of those other boats could have got ashore to give word of the wreck," said the oiler, in a low voice. "Else the lifeboat would be out hunting us."

Slowly and beautifully the land loomed out of the sea. The wind came again. It had veered from the north-east to the south-east. Finally, a new sound struck the ears of the men in the boat. It was the low thunder of the surf on the shore. "We'll never be able to make the lighthouse now," said the captain. "Swing her head a little more north, Billie," said he.

" 'A little more north,' sir," said the oiler.

Whereupon the little boat turned her nose once more down the wind, and all but the oarsman watched the shore grow. Under the influence of this expansion doubt and direful apprehension was leaving the minds of the men. The management of the boat was still most absorbing, but it could not prevent a quiet cheerfulness. In an hour, perhaps, they would be ashore.

Their backbones had become thoroughly used to balancing in the boat, and they now rode this wild colt of a dingey like circus men. The correspondent thought that he had been drenched to the skin, but happening to feel in the top pocket of his coat, he found therein eight cigars. Four of them were soaked with sea-water; four were perfectly scathless. After a search, somebody produced three dry matches, and thereupon the four waifs rode impudently in their little boat, and with an assurance of an impending rescue shining in their eyes, puffed at the big cigars and judged well and ill of all men. Everybody took a drink of water.

iv

"Cook," remarked the captain, "there don't seem to be any signs of life about your house of refuge."

"No," replied the cook. "Funny they don't see us!"

A broad stretch of lowly coast lay before the eyes of the men. It was of dunes topped with dark vegetation. The roar of the surf was plain, and sometimes they could see the white lip of a wave as it spun up the beach. A tiny house was blocked out black upon the sky. Southward, the slim light-house lifted its little grey length.

Tide, wind, and waves were swinging the dingey northward. "Funny they don't see us," said the men.

The surf's roar was here dulled, but its tone was, nevertheless, thunderous and mighty. As the boat swam over the great rollers, the men sat listening to this roar. "We'll swamp sure," said everybody.

It is fair to say here that there was not a life-saving station within twenty miles in either direction, but the men did not know this fact, and in consequence they made dark and opprobrious remarks concerning the eyesight of the nation's life-savers. Four scowling men sat in the dingey and surpassed records in the invention of epithets.

"Funny they don't see us."

The lightheartedness of a former time had completely faded. To their sharpened minds it was easy to conjure pictures of all kinds of incompetency and blindness and, indeed, cowardice. There was the shore of the populous land, and it was bitter and bitter to them that from it came no sign.

"Well," said the captain, ultimately, "I suppose we'll have to make a try for ourselves. If we stay out here too long, we'll none of us have strength left to swim after the boat swamps."

And so the oiler, who was at the oars, turned the boat straight for the shore. There was a sudden tightening of muscle. There was some thinking.

"If we don't all get ashore—" said the captain. "If we don't all get ashore, I suppose you fellows know where to send news of my finish?"

They then briefly exchanged some addresses and admonitions. As for the reflections of the men, there was a great deal of rage in them. Perchance they might be formulated thus: "If I am going to be drowned—if I am going to be drowned—if I am going to be drowned, why in the name of the seven mad gods who rule the sea, was I allowed to come thus far and contemplate sand and trees? Was I brought here merely to have my nose dragged away as I was about to nibble the sacred cheese of life? It is preposterous. If this old ninny-woman, Fate, cannot do better than this, she should be deprived of the management of men's fortunes. She is an old hen who knows not her intention. If she has decided to drown me, why did she not do it in the beginning and save me all this trouble? The whole affair is absurd. . . . But no, she cannot mean to drown me. She dare not drown me. She cannot drown me. Not after all this work." Afterward the man might have had an impulse to shake his fist at the clouds: "Just you drown me, now, and then hear what I call you!"

The billows that came at this time were more formidable. They seemed always just about to break and roll over the little boat in a turmoil of foam. There was a preparatory and long growl in the speech of them. No mind unused to the sea would have concluded that the dingey could ascend these sheer heights in time. The shore was still afar. The oiler was a wily surfman. "Boys," he said swiftly, "she won't live three minutes more, and we're too far out to swim. Shall I take her to sea again, captain?"

"Yes! Go ahead!" said the captain.

This oiler, by a series of quick miracles, and fast and steady oarsmanship, turned the boat in the middle of the surf and took her safely to sea again.

There was a considerable silence as the boat bumped over the furrowed sea to deeper water. Then somebody in gloom spoke. "Well, anyhow, they must have seen us from the shore by now."

The gulls went in slanting flight up the wind toward the grey desolate east. A squall, marked by dingy clouds, and clouds brick-red, like smoke from a burning building, appeared from the south-east.

"What do you think of those life-saving people? Ain't they peaches?"

"Funny they haven't seen us."

"Maybe they think we're out here for sport! Maybe they think we're fishin'. Maybe they think we're damned fools."

It was a long afternoon. A changed tide tried to force them southward, but the wind and wave said northward. Far ahead, where coast-line, sea, and sky formed their mighty angle, there were little dots which seemed to indicate a city on the shore.

"St. Augustine?"

The captain shook his head. "Too near Mosquito Inlet."

And the oiler rowed, and then the correspondent rowed. Then the oiler rowed. It was a weary business. The human back can become the seat of more aches and pains than are registered in books for the composite anatomy of a regiment. It is a limited area, but it can become the theatre of innumerable muscular conflicts, tangles, wrenches, knots, and other comforts.

"Did you ever like to row, Billie?" asked the correspondent.

"No," said the oiler. "Hang it!"

When one exchanged the rowing-seat for a place in the bottom of the boat, he suffered a bodily depression that caused him to be careless of everything save an obligation to wiggle one finger. There was cold sea-water swashing to and fro in the boat, and he lay in it. His head, pillowed on a thwart, was within an inch of the swirl of a wave crest, and sometimes a particularly obstreperous sea came in-board and drenched him once more. But these matters did not annoy him. It is almost certain that if the boat had capsized he would have tumbled comfortably out upon the ocean as if he felt sure that it was a great soft mattress.

"Look! There's a man on the shore!"

"Where?"

"There! See 'im? See 'im?"

"Yes, sure! He's walking along."

"Now he's stopped. Look! He's facing us!"

"He's waving at us!"

"So he is! By thunder!"

"Ah, now we're all right! Now we're all right! There'll be a boat out here for us in half-an-hour."

"He's going on. He's running. He's going up to that house there."

The remote beach seemed lower than the sea, and it required a searching glance to discern the little black figure. The captain saw a floating stick and they rowed to it. A bath-towel was by some weird chance in the boat, and, tying this on the stick, the captain waved it. The oarsman did not dare turn his head, so he was obliged to ask questions.

"What's he doing now?"

"He's standing still again. He's looking, I think. . . . There he goes again. Toward the house. . . . Now he's stopped again."

"Is he waving at us?"

"No, not now! He was, though."

"Look! There comes another man!"

"He's running."

"Look at him go, would you."

"Why, he's on a bicycle. Now he's met the other man. They're both waving at us. Look!"

"There comes something up the beach."

"What the devil is that thing?"

"Why it looks like a boat."

"Why, certainly it's a boat."

"No, it's on wheels."

"Yes, so it is. Well, that must be the life-boat. They drag them along shore on a wagon."

"That's the life-boat, sure."

"No, by ——, it's—it's an omnibus."

"I tell you it's a life-boat."

"It is not! It's an omnibus. I can see it plain. See? One of these big hotel omnibuses."

"By thunder, you're right. It's an omnibus, sure as fate. What do you suppose they are doing with an omnibus? Maybe they are going around collecting the life-crew, hey?"

"That's it, likely. Look! There's a fellow waving a little black flag. He's standing on the steps of the omnibus. There come those other two fellows.

Now they're all talking together. Look at the fellow with the flag. Maybe he ain't waving it."

"That ain't a flag, is it? That's his coat. Why, certainly, that's his coat."

"So it is. It's his coat. He's taken it off and is waving it around his head. But would you look at him swing it."

"Oh, say, there isn't any life-saving station there. That's just a winter resort hotel omnibus that has brought over some of the boarders to see us drown."

"What's that idiot with the coat mean? What's he signaling, anyhow?"

"It looks as if he were trying to tell us to go north. There must be a life-saving station up there."

"No! He thinks we're fishing. Just giving us a merry hand. See? Ah, there, Willie!"

"Well, I wish I could make something out of those signals. What do you suppose he means?"

"He don't mean anything. He's just playing."

"Well, if he'd just signal us to try the surf again, or to go to sea and wait, or go north, or go south, or go to hell—there would be some reason in it. But look at him. He just stands there and keeps his coat revolving like a wheel. The ass!"

"There come more people."

"Now there's quite a mob. Look! Isn't that a boat?"

"Where? Oh, I see where you mean. No, that's no boat."

"That fellow is still waving his coat."

"He must think we like to see him do that. Why don't he quit it? It don't mean anything."

"I don't know. I think he is trying to make us go north. It must be that there's a life-saving station there somewhere."

"Say, he ain't tired yet. Look at 'im wave."

"Wonder how long he can keep that up. He's been revolving his coat ever since he caught sight of us. He's an idiot. Why aren't they getting men to bring a boat out? A fishing boat—one of those big yawls—could come out here all right. Why don't he do something?"

"Oh, it's all right, now."

"They'll have a boat out here for us in less than no time, now that they've seen us."

A faint yellow tone came into the sky over the low land. The shadows on the sea slowly deepened. The wind bore coldness with it, and the men began to shiver.

"Holy smoke!" said one, allowing his voice to express his impious mood, "if we keep on monkeying out here! If we've got to flounder out here all night!"

"Oh, we'll never have to stay here all night! Don't you worry. They've seen us now, and it won't be long before they'll come chasing out after us."

The shore grew dusky. The man waving a coat blended gradually into this gloom, and it swallowed in the same manner the omnibus and the group of people. The spray, when it dashed uproariously over the side, made the voyagers shrink and swear like men who were being branded.

"I'd like to catch the chump who waved the coat. I feel like soaking him one, just for luck."

"Why? What did he do?"

"Oh, nothing, but then he seemed so damned cheerful."

In the meantime the oiler rowed, and then the correspondent rowed, and then the oiler rowed. Grey-faced and bowed forward, they mechanically, turn by turn, plied the leaden oars. The form of the lighthouse had vanished from the southern horizon, but finally a pale star appeared, just lifting from the sea. The streaked saffron in the west passed before the all-merging darkness, and the sea to the east was black. The land had vanished, and was expressed only by the low and drear thunder of the surf.

"If I am going to be drowned—if I am going to be drowned—if I am going to be drowned, why, in the name of the seven mad gods who rule the sea, was I allowed to come thus far and contemplate sand and trees? Was I brought here merely to have my nose dragged away as I was about to nibble the sacred cheese of life?"

The patient captain, drooped over the water-jar, was sometimes obliged to speak to the oarsman.

"Keep her head up! Keep her head up!"

" 'Keep her head up,' sir." The voices were weary and low.

This was surely a quiet evening. All save the oarsman lay heavily and listlessly in the boat's bottom. As for him, his eyes were just capable of noting the tall black waves that swept forward in a most sinister silence, save for an occasional subdued growl of a crest.

The cook's head was on a thwart, and he looked without interest at the water under his nose. He was deep in other scenes. Finally he spoke. "Billie," he murmured, dreamfully, "what kind of pie do you like best?"

V

"Pie," said the oiler and the correspondent, agitatedly. "Don't talk about those things, blast you!"

"Well," said the cook, "I was just thinking about ham sandwiches and—"

A night on the sea in an open boat is a long night. As darkness settled finally, the shine of the light, lifting from the sea in the south, changed to full gold. On the northern horizon a new light appeared, a small bluish gleam on the edge of the waters. These two lights were the furniture of the world. Otherwise there was nothing but waves.

Two men huddled in the stern, and distances were so magnificent in the dingey that the rower was enabled to keep his feet partly warmed by thrusting them under his companions. Their legs indeed extended far under the rowing-seat until they touched the feet of the captain forward. Sometimes, despite the efforts of the tired oarsman, a wave came piling into the boat, an icy wave of the night, and the chilling water soaked them anew. They would twist their bodies for a moment and groan, and sleep the dead sleep once more, while the water in the boat gurgled about them as the craft rocked.

The plan of the oiler and the correspondent was for one to row until he lost the ability, and then arouse the other from his sea-water couch in the bottom of the boat.

The oiler plied the oars until his head drooped forward, and the over-powering sleep blinded him. And he rowed yet afterward. Then he touched a man in the bottom of the boat, and called his name. "Will you spell me for a little while?" he said, meekly.

"Sure, Billie," said the correspondent, awakening and dragging himself to a sitting position. They exchanged places carefully, and the oiler, cuddling down in the sea-water at the cook's side, seemed to go to sleep instantly.

The particular violence of the sea had ceased. The waves came without snarling. The obligation of the man at the oars was to keep the boat headed so that the tilt of the rollers would not capsize her, and to preserve her from filling when the crests rushed past. The black waves were silent and hard to be seen in the darkness. Often one was almost upon the boat before the oarsman was aware.

In a low voice the correspondent addressed the captain. He was not sure that the captain was awake, although this iron man seemed to be always awake. "Captain, shall I keep her making for that light north, sir?"

The same steady voice answered him. "Yes. Keep it about two points off the port bow."

The cook had tied a life-belt around himself in order to get even the warmth which this clumsy cork contrivance could donate, and he seemed almost stove-like when a rower, whose teeth invariably chattered wildly as soon as he ceased his labor, dropped down to sleep.

The correspondent, as he rowed, looked down at the two men sleeping under-foot. The cook's arm was around the oiler's shoulders, and, with their fragmentary clothing and haggard faces, they were the babes of the sea, a grotesque rendering of the old babes in the wood.

Later he must have grown stupid at his work, for suddenly there was a growling of water, and a crest came with a roar and a swash into the boat, and it was a wonder that it did not set the cook afloat in his life-belt. The cook continued to sleep, but the oiler sat up, blinking his eyes and shaking with the new cold.

"Oh, I'm awful sorry, Billie," said the correspondent contritely.

"That's all right, old boy," said the oiler, and lay down again and was asleep.

Presently it seemed that even the captain dozed, and the correspondent thought that he was the one man afloat on all the oceans. The wind had a voice as it came over the waves, and it was sadder than the end.

There was a long, loud swishing astern of the boat, and a gleaming trail of phosphorescence, like blue flame, was furrowed on the black waters. It might have been made by a monstrous knife.

Then there came a stillness, while the correspondent breathed with the open mouth and looked at the sea.

Suddenly there was another swish and another long flash of bluish light, and this time it was alongside the boat, and might almost have been reached with an oar. The correspondent saw an enormous fin speed like a shadow through the water, hurling the crystalline spray and leaving the long glowing trail.

The correspondent looked over his shoulder at the captain. His face was hidden, and he seemed to be asleep. He looked at the babes of the sea. They certainly were asleep. So, being bereft of sympathy, he leaned a little way to one side and swore softly into the sea.

But the thing did not then leave the vicinity of the boat. Ahead or astern, on one side or the other, at intervals long or short, fled the long sparkling streak, and there was to be heard the whirroo of the dark fin. The speed and power of the thing was greatly to be admired. It cut the water like a gigantic and keen projectile.

The presence of this biding thing did not affect the man with the same horror that it would if he had been a picnicker. He simply looked at the sea dully and swore in an undertone.

Nevertheless, it is true that he did not wish to be alone. He wished one of his companions to awaken by chance and keep him company with it. But the captain hung motionless over the water-jar, and the oiler and the cook in the bottom of the boat were plunged in slumber.

vi

"If I am going to be drowned—if I am going to be drowned—if I am going to be drowned, why, in the name of the seven mad gods who rule the sea, was I allowed to come thus far and contemplate sand and trees?"

During this dismal night, it may be remarked that a man would conclude that it was really the intention of the seven mad gods to drown him, despite the abominable injustice of it. For it was certainly an abominable injustice to drown a man who had worked so hard, so hard. The man felt it would be a crime most unnatural. Other people had drowned at sea since galleys swarmed with painted sails, but still—

When it occurs to a man that nature does not regard him as important, and that she feels she would not maim the universe by disposing of him, he at first wishes to throw bricks at the temple, and he hates deeply the fact that there are no bricks and no temples. Any visible expression of nature would surely be pelleted with his jeers.

Then, if there be no tangible thing to hoot he feels, perhaps, the desire to confront a personification and indulge in pleas, bowed to one knee, and with hands supplicant, saying: "Yes, but I love myself."

A high cold star on a winter's night is the word he feels that she says to him. Thereafter he knows the pathos of his situation.

The men in the dingey had not discussed these matters, but each had, no doubt, reflected upon them in silence and according to his mind. There was seldom any expression upon their faces save the general one of complete weariness. Speech was devoted to the business of the boat.

To chime the notes of his emotion, a verse mysteriously entered the correspondent's head. He had even forgotten that he had forgotten this verse, but it suddenly was in his mind.

"A soldier of the Legion lay dying in Algiers,
 There was a lack of woman's nursing, there was dearth of woman's tears;
 But a comrade stood beside him, and he took that comrade's hand,
 And he said: 'I shall never see my own, my native land.'"

In his childhood, the correspondent had been made acquainted with the fact that a soldier of the Legion lay dying in Algiers, but he had never regarded the fact as important. Myriads of his school-fellows had informed him of the soldier's plight, but the dinning had naturally ended by making him perfectly indifferent. He had never considered it his affair that a soldier of the Legion lay dying in Algiers, nor had it appeared to him as a matter for sorrow. It was less to him than the breaking of a pencil's point.

Now, however, it quaintly came to him as a human, living thing. It was no longer merely a picture of a few throes in the breast of a poet, meanwhile drinking tea and warming his feet at the grate; it was an actuality—stern, mournful, and fine.

The correspondent plainly saw the soldier. He lay on the sand with his feet out straight and still. While his pale left hand was upon his chest in an attempt to thwart the going of his life, the blood came between his fingers. In the far Algerian distance, a city of low square forms was set against a sky that was faint with the last sunset hues. The correspondent, plying the oars and dreaming of the slow and slower movements of the lips of the soldier, was moved by a profound and perfectly impersonal comprehension. He was sorry for the soldier of the Legion who lay dying in Algiers.

The thing which had followed the boat and waited had evidently grown bored at the delay. There was no longer to be heard the slash of the cut-water, and there was no longer the flame of the long trail. The light in the north still glimmered, but it was apparently no nearer to the boat. Sometimes the boom of the surf rang in the correspondent's ears, and he turned the craft seaward then and rowed harder. Southward, some one had evidently built a watch-fire on the beach. It was too low and too far to be seen, but it made a shimmering, roseate reflection upon the bluff back of it, and this could be discerned from the boat. The wind came stronger, and sometimes a wave suddenly raged out like a mountain-cat, and there was to be seen the sheen and sparkle of a broken crest.

The captain, in the bow, moved on his water-jar and sat erect. "Pretty long night," he observed to the correspondent. He looked at the shore. "Those life-saving people take their time."

"Did you see that shark playing around?"

"Yes, I saw him. He was a big fellow, all right."

"Wish I had known you were awake."

Later the correspondent spoke into the bottom of the boat.

"Billie!" There was a slow and gradual disentanglement. "Billie, will you spell me?" "Sure," said the oiler.

As soon as the correspondent touched the cold comfortable sea-water in the bottom of the boat, and had huddled close to the cook's life-belt he was deep in sleep, despite the fact that his teeth played all the popular airs. This sleep was so good to him that it was but a moment before he heard a voice call his name in a tone that demonstrated the last stages of exhaustion. "Will you spell me?"

"Sure, Billie."

The light in the north had mysteriously vanished, but the correspondent took his course from the wide-awake captain.

Later in the night they took the boat farther out to sea, and the captain directed the cook to take one oar at the stern and keep the boat facing the seas. He was to call out if he should hear the thunder of the surf. This plan enabled the oiler and the correspondent to get respite together. "We'll give those boys a chance to get into shape again," said the captain. They curled down and, after a few preliminary chatterings and trembles, slept once more the dead sleep. Neither knew they had bequeathed to the cook the company of another shark, or perhaps the same shark.

As the boat caroused on the waves, spray occasionally bumped over the side and gave them a fresh soaking, but this had no power to break their repose. The ominous slash of the wind and the water affected them as it would have affected mummies.

"Boys," said the cook, with the notes of every reluctance in his voice, "she's drifted in pretty close. I guess one of you had better take her to sea again." The correspondent, aroused, heard the crash of the toppled crests.

As he was rowing, the captain gave him some whisky-and-water, and this steadied the chills out of him. "If I ever get ashore and anybody shows me even a photograph of an oar—"

At last there was a short conversation.

"Billie. . . . Billie, will you spell me?"

"Sure," said the oiler.

vii

When the correspondent again opened his eyes, the sea and the sky were each of the grey hue of the dawning. Later, carmine and gold was painted upon the waters. The morning appeared finally, in its splendor, with a sky of pure blue, and the sunlight flamed on the tips of the waves.

On the distant dunes were set many little black cottages, and a tall white windmill reared above them. No man, nor dog, nor bicycle appeared on the beach. The cottages might have formed a deserted village.

The voyagers scanned the shore. A conference was held in the boat. "Well," said the captain, "if no help is coming we might better try a run through the surf right away. If we stay out here much longer we will be too weak to do anything for ourselves at all." The others silently acquiesced in this reasoning. The boat was headed for the beach. The correspondent wondered if none ever ascended the tall wind-tower, and if then they never looked seaward. This tower was a giant, standing with its back to the plight of the ants. It represented in a degree, to the correspondent, the serenity of nature amid the struggles of the individual—nature in the wind, and nature in the vision of men. She did not seem cruel to him then, nor beneficent, nor treacherous, nor wise. But she was indifferent, flatly indifferent. It is, perhaps, plausible that a man in this situation, impressed with the unconcern of the universe, should see the innumerable flaws of his life, and have them taste wickedly in his mind and wish for another chance. A distinction between right and wrong seems absurdly clear to him, then, in this new ignorance of the grave-edge, and he understands that if he were given another opportunity he would mend his conduct and his words, and be better and brighter during an introduction or at a tea.

"Now, boys," said the captain, "she is going to swamp, sure. All we can do is to work her in as far as possible, and then when she swamps, pile out and scramble for the beach. Keep cool now, and don't jump until she swamps sure."

The oiler took the oars. Over his shoulders he scanned the surf. "Captain," he said, "I think I'd better bring her about, and keep her head-on to the seas and back her in."

"All right, Billie," said the captain. "Back her in." The oiler swung the boat then and, seated in the stern, the cook and the correspondent were obliged to look over their shoulders to contemplate the lonely and indifferent shore.

The monstrous in-shore rollers heaved the boat high until the men were again enabled to see the white sheets of water scudding up the slanted beach. "We won't get in very close," said the captain. Each time a man could wrest his attention from the rollers, he turned his glance toward the shore, and in the expression of the eyes during this contemplation there was a singular quality. The correspondent, observing the others, knew that they were not afraid, but the full meaning of their glances was shrouded.

As for himself, he was too tired to grapple fundamentally with the fact. He tried to coerce his mind into thinking of it, but the mind was dominated at this time by the muscles, and the muscles said they did not care. It merely occurred to him that if he should drown it would be a shame.

There were no hurried words, no pallor, no plain agitation. The men simply looked at the shore. "Now, remember to get well clear of the boat when you jump," said the captain.

Seaward the crest of a roller suddenly fell with a thunderous crash, and the long white comber came roaring down upon the boat.

"Steady now," said the captain. The men were silent. They turned their eyes from the shore to the comber and waited. The boat slid up the incline, leaped at the furious top, bounced over it, and swung down the long back of the wave. Some water had been shipped and the cook bailed it out.

But the next crest crashed also. The tumbling, boiling flood of white water caught the boat and whirled it almost perpendicular. Water swarmed in from all sides. The correspondent had his hands on the gunwale at this time, and when the water entered at that place he swiftly withdrew his fingers, as if he objected to wetting them.

The little boat, drunken with this weight of water, reeled and snuggled deeper into the sea.

"Bail her out, cook! Bail her out," said the captain.

"All right, captain," said the cook.

"Now, boys, the next one will do for us, sure," said the oiler. "Mind to jump clear of the boat."

The third wave moved forward, huge, furious, implacable. It fairly swallowed the dingey, and almost simultaneously the men tumbled into the sea. A piece of lifebelt had lain in the bottom of the boat, and as the correspondent went overboard he held this to his chest with his left hand.

The January water was icy, and he reflected immediately that it was colder than he had expected to find it on the coast of Florida. This appeared to his dazed mind as a fact important enough to be noted at the time. The coldness of the water was sad; it was tragic. This fact was somehow so mixed and confused with his opinion of his own situation that it seemed almost a proper reason for tears. The water was cold.

When he came to the surface he was conscious of little but the noisy water. Afterward he saw his companions in the sea. The oiler was ahead in the race. He was swimming strongly and rapidly. Off to the correspondent's left, the cook's great white and corked back bulged out of the water, and in the rear the captain was hanging with his one good hand to the keel of the overturned dingey.

There is a certain immovable quality to a shore, and the correspondent wondered at it amid the confusion of the sea.

It seemed also very attractive, but the correspondent knew that it was a long journey, and he paddled leisurely. The piece of life-preserver lay under him, and sometimes he whirled down the incline of a wave as if he were on a hand-sled.

But finally he arrived at a place in the sea where travel was beset with difficulty. He did not pause swimming to inquire what manner of current had caught him, but there his progress ceased. The shore was set before him like a bit of scenery on a stage, and he looked at it and understood with his eyes each detail of it.

As the cook passed, much farther to the left, the captain was calling to him, "Turn over on your back, cook! Turn over on your back and use the oar."

"All right, sir." The cook turned on his back, and, paddling with an oar, went ahead as if he were a canoe.

Presently the boat also passed to the left of the correspondent with the captain clinging with one hand to the keel. He would have appeared like a man raising himself to look over a board fence, if it were not for the extraordinary gymnastics of the boat. The correspondent marvelled that the captain could still hold to it.

They passed on, nearer to shore—the oiler, the cook, the captain—and following them went the water-jar, bouncing gaily over the seas.

The correspondent remained in the grip of this strange new enemy—a current. The shore, with its white slope of sand and its green bluff, topped with little silent cottages, was spread like a picture before him. It was very near to him then, but he was impressed as one who in a gallery looks at a scene from Brittany or Holland.

He thought: "I am going to drown? Can it be possible? Can it be possible? Can it be possible?" Perhaps an individual must consider his own death to be the final phenomenon of nature.

But later a wave perhaps whirled him out of this small, deadly current, for he found suddenly that he could again make progress toward the shore. Later still, he was aware that the captain, clinging with one hand to the keel of the dingey, had his face turned away from the shore and toward him, and was calling his name. "Come to the boat! Come to the boat!"

In his struggle to reach the captain and the boat, he reflected that when one gets properly wearied, drowning must really be a comfortable arrangement, a cessation of hostilities accompanied by a large degree of relief, and he was glad of it, for the main thing in his mind for some months had been horror of the temporary agony. He did not wish to be hurt.

Presently he saw a man running along the shore. He was undressing with most remarkable speed. Coat, trousers, shirt, everything flew magically off him.

"Come to the boat," called the captain.

"All right, captain." As the correspondent paddled, he saw the captain let himself down to bottom and leave the boat. Then the correspondent performed his one little marvel of the voyage. A large wave caught him and flung him with ease and supreme speed completely over the boat and far beyond it. It struck him even then as an event in gymnastics, and a true miracle of the sea. An over-turned boat in the surf is not a plaything to a swimming man.

The correspondent arrived in water that reached only to his waist, but his condition did not enable him to stand for more than a moment. Each wave knocked him into a heap, and the under-tow pulled at him.

Then he saw the man who had been running and undressing, and undressing and running, come bounding into the water. He dragged ashore the cook, and then waded towards the captain, but the captain waved him away, and sent him to the correspondent. He was naked, naked as a tree in winter, but a halo was about his head, and he shone like a saint. He gave a strong pull, and a long drag, and a bully heave at the correspondent's hand. The correspondent, schooled in the minor formulæ, said: "Thanks, old man." But suddenly the man cried: "What's that?" He pointed a swift finger. The correspondent said: "Go."

In the shallows, face downward, lay the oiler. His forehead touched sand that was periodically, between each wave, clear of the sea.

The correspondent did not know all that transpired afterward. When he achieved safe ground he fell, striking the sand with each particular part of his body. It was as if he had dropped from a roof, but the thud was grateful to him.

It seems that instantly the beach was populated with men with blankets, clothes, and flasks, and women with coffeepots and all the remedies sacred to their minds. The welcome of the land to the men from the sea was warm and generous, but a still and dripping shape was carried slowly up the beach, and the land's welcome for it could only be the different and sinister hospitality of the grave.

When it came night, the white waves paced to and fro in the moonlight, and the wind brought the sound of the great sea's voice to the men on shore, and they felt that they could then be interpreters.

COMMENTARY

A great deal has been written about Stephen Crane, much of it beside the point. But even those who praise him ignorantly or reluctantly pay tribute, in spite of themselves, to his genius. H. G. Wells called "The Open Boat" "the finest short story in English." "The Beast in the Jungle" had not then appeared and it would be a long time before Joyce could secure publication for "Dubliners." Wells was right, for once, though he hardly knew why.

The fact is that Crane, during his short life, revolutionized the technique of the English and American short story by offering a stronger illusion of reality than any of his contemporaries were able to offer. Compared with him, the most gifted of them reads like the sports writer who is unable to get out to the ball park and tries to cover the game by telephone. And indeed, Crane's chief technical contribution is the result of a sort of inspired leg work.

He was gifted with an extraordinarily acute sensibility, eloquence, and a feeling for form, but many of his contemporaries had the same gifts. Crane distanced them by his superior agility and artistic courage. He "fought in" closer than Stendhal, Mérimée, Gautier, or even Flaubert. His chief strength is his masterly handling of the fundamental problem: on whose authority (see Appendix A, p. 621) is the story told?

Young writers, even geniuses, often start by emulating or even surpassing the masters. Crane tells us that the battle scenes in Stendhal's *La Chartreuse de Parme* inspired him to write his masterpiece, *The Red Badge of Courage.*

It is instructive to compare the battle scenes in *La Chartreuse* with almost any one of Crane's stories which deal with similar incidents. The passage in which Stendhal's hero, Fabrice, finally arrives at the battle may be the one which Crane, on the eve of a major technical discovery, found revolting in its inadequacy.

But just then the racket became so deafening that Fabrice was unable to reply. We must admit that our hero cut a very un-heroic figure at that moment; not that his fears troubled him, but he was annoyed by the tremendous din that threatened to burst his ear-drums. The cavalcade put spurs to their steeds and galloped off. Their course was across a plowed field that lay beyond the canal and was thickly strewn with corpses.

"The red-coats! see the red-coats!" the horsemen of the escort shouted joyously. Fabrice failed to understand at first; then he looked again and saw that the larger portion of the dead was uniformed in red. There was a circumstance that gave him a chill of horror: he noticed that many of those unhappy red-coats were still alive; they were evidently supplicating aid, and no one thought of stopping to give it them. Our hero, who was of a humane nature, strove to guide his mount so that he should not trample any of the mangled forms. The escort came to a halt: Fabrice, his faculties concentrated on the ghastly scene before him, gave no attention to the order and continued to gallop forward.

Here is an example of a failure by a master. The scene is not vivid. Events—even the hero's chill of horror—seem to be reported by some one who is standing at a little distance from the scene. (A person who mistakes a wounded man's blood for a red uniform is either not observing closely or is not very close to him.) Possibly Stendhal's instinct told him that his scene was not "coming off." He piles on more detail. The horsemen of the escort shout "joyously." Fabrice is "of a humane nature." The unfortunate red-coats are "supplicating aid." But each of these strokes makes the battle seem farther off. The omniscient viewpoint (see Appendix A, p. 623) will not serve here. *It does not bring us close enough to the scene.*

Crane solved the problem by putting his narrator in the heart of the battle. We register what goes on through his senses. The events seem to be enacted before our eyes. Sometimes we see a thing so clearly that we have time to reflect not only on what it is but what it is like:

> . . . the chest of the doomed soldier began to heave with a strained motion. It increased in violence until it was as if an animal was within and was kicking and tumbling furiously to be free. (From *The Red Badge of Courage*.)

But "The Open Boat," shorter than *The Red Badge* and, like it, a story of death and disaster, will serve us for comparisons.

Its opening paragraphs brought about a revolution in the writing of fiction, at least in the English-speaking world. Any beginning writer who realizes their full excellence will have learned a great deal about the fundamentals of the craft:

> None of them knew the color of the sky. Their eyes glanced level, and were fastened upon the waves that swept toward them. These waves were of the hue of slate, save for the tops, which were of foaming white, and all of the men knew the colors of the sea. The horizon narrowed and widened, and dipped and rose, and at all times its edge was jagged with waves that seemed thrust up in points like rocks.

Six hundred years ago a Greek poet, Callimachus, wrote of "the thin oak plank that separates the mariner from death." But the poet was safe on land when he composed his admirable line. Crane is *in* the boat with his shipwrecked men: "The correspondent, pulling at the other oar, watched the waves and wondered why he was there."

It is hard to find a more masterly use of the Roving Narrator (see Appendix A, p. 626) method. The correspondent functions dramatically throughout. His reflections, in fact, constitute the Enveloping Action (see Appendix A, p. 631) and advance the plot, but he performs a more intimate and necessary service. He *sees, hears, smells, tastes, and touches for us.*

> Their eyes glanced level, and were fastened upon the waves that swept toward them.

Let us see if we can paraphrase Crane's sentence:

> They looked straight ahead and fixed a desperate gaze on the waves that swept toward them.

Or:

> They fixed a desperate, level gaze on the waves that swept toward them.

In each of our paraphrases the narrator seems to be reporting events which he witnessed from a little distance, but if we read Crane's sentence as slowly and carefully as it is meant to be read we will feel in our own eyelids the slight increase of warmth that comes from gazing levelly at any object and if we gaze as intently as we are able we will achieve a relation with the object so close that the eye literally seems to be "fastened" rather than fixed upon it.

It is hardly possible to render sensation more faithfully. Throughout the paragraph Crane maintains the same faithfulness in rendition, coupled with an almost incredible agility. He is constantly changing his viewpoint, borrowing the eyes, ears, tactile senses of any one of the four men for the sake of intensity, but he is always mindful of another responsibility, the "over-all" pattern.

In the first sentence we identify ourselves with all of the men—a collective "we." In the second sentence we take up our post inside one of the men and look out through his eye sockets. But no individual exists alone in time or space, and in fiction, as in life, the seer's situation must be defined in terms of his relations to other objects or persons. Crane makes good use of this level gaze which he has induced us as well as his heroes to bend upon the scene. We see the waves coming toward us, the color of slate, "save for their tops, which were of foaming white." The same principle of relating one object to another which he has used in creating the whole scene is now invoked for the execution of one detail. The waves appear darker *because* of their white tops, the tops whiter because of the contrast with the dark wave, and both waves and the froth that crowns them seem more lifelike because Crane has set them in motion: the tops of the waves are "foaming" as they come. Having created the picture—what each man sees as he looks desperately around him—Crane sets the whole scene in even livelier motion. The horizon narrows and widens and dips and rises.

If the reader has ever been sea-sick that sentence will bring back a fleeting memory of his sensations. But "horizon" is a word in general use. The horizon we see in the desert is very different from the horizon we see in the mountains, say, or at sea. In order that you may fully realize the motion of this horizon Crane particularizes: his horizon is "at all times . . . jagged with waves that seemed thrust up in points like rocks." The naturalistic detail is here symbolic. Rocks thrust up in jagged points suggest a wall, the wall of a prison. These men are in prison, with the immense, wayward, cruel sea for a jailer.

Crane now turns rapidly from the general scene, the whole vast seascape, to the particular: the boat into which the men are crowded.

"Many a man ought to have a bath tub larger than the boat which here rode upon the sea." It is a small boat and it perches precariously, like an inexperienced rider, upon the back of the huge, restless sea. Crane borrows, at his need, not only the sensibilities of the men, but their faculties of moral judgment. This reflection seems to burst from one man; the use of the word "ought" conveys his indignation at Fate. The next sentence, one of the finest Crane ever wrote, not only renders what is going on, but continues to record the resentment the men feel—the resentment men have ever felt—at cruel fate:

> These waves were most wrongfully and barbarously abrupt and tall, and each froth top was a problem in small boat navigation.

Crane has not contented himself with telling us *how* each wave approached. He makes us see them as they come, by the use of the word "tall." After such a lively "close-up" it is a relief to be submerged for the moment in a panoramic view: "each froth top was a problem in small boat navigation."

But Crane's panoramic views (see Appendix A, p. 627) are used for their dramatic effect and are never prolonged. He returns to the immediate scene with a "close-up" of the cook, squatting in the bottom the boat and looking, like Callimachus's mariner, at "the six inches of gunwale that separated him from the ocean." But it is not enough for us to know that one of the men was a cook, squatting in the boat and looking out to sea. We must see him closer. There is a marvellous, almost geometrical, economy in Crane's portrayal of him. Two circles—"his sleeves were rolled over his fat fore-arms"—and two moving triangles—"the two flaps of his unbuttoned vest dangled as he bent to bail out the boat"—bring him before us. The illusion of life is completed by an appeal to the sense of sound. "Gawd, that was a narrow clip," he remarks and gazes eastward over the broken sea.

Again, the almost intolerably close view is relieved by a panoramic view. In the structure of the paragraph, the phrase, "gazed eastward over the broken sea," performs somewhat the same function as the *parodos* of the Greek chorus, a summing up whose dispassionateness comes as a kind of balm after the turbulence of the action.

In "The Open Boat" this masterly alternation of Long and Short Views (see Appendix A, p. 627) makes an important contribution to the tonal unity (see Appendix A, p. 632). The correspondent who, "pulling at the other oar, watched the waves and wondered why he was there," plays the part of a Central Intelligence, in much the same way that James's heroes do. Crane's symbolism (see Appendix A, p. 633) here is like that of James. On one level the Complication (see Appendix A, p. 630) of the story is the correspondent's facing death, the Resolution his escape from it. On another level, the symbolic level, the story is the way in which a man establishes relations with death. The correspondent, face to face with death, attains heroic stature, as men often do in such circumstances. He can speak for more than himself; he can speak for all men. But in a way he has experienced death in the death of his brother and comrade, the oiler; and he can speak for death, too, having become brother to its servant, the sea. "When it came night, the white waves paced to and fro in the moonlight, and the wind brought the sound of the great sea's voice to the men on the shore, and they felt that they could then be interpreters."

Thomas Mann

DISORDER AND EARLY SORROW

THE PRINCIPAL dish at dinner had been croquettes made of turnip greens. So there follows a trifle, concocted out of one of those dessert powders we use nowadays, that taste like almond soap. Xaver, the youthful manservant, in his outgrown striped jacket, white woollen gloves, and yellow sandals, hands it round, and the "big folk" take this opportunity to remind their father, tactfully, that company is coming today.

The "big folk" are two, Ingrid and Bert. Ingrid is brown-eyed, eighteen, and perfectly delightful. She is on the eve of her exams, and will probably pass them, if only because she knows how to wind masters, and even headmasters, round her finger. She does not, however, mean to use her certificate once she gets it; having leanings towards the stage, on the ground of her ingratiating smile, her equally ingratiating voice, and a marked and irresistible talent for burlesque. Bert is blond and seventeen. He intends to get done with school somehow, anyhow, and fling himself into the arms of life. He will be a dancer, or a cabaret actor, possibly even a waiter—but not a waiter anywhere else save at the Cairo, the night-club, whither he has once already taken flight, at five in the morning, and been brought back crestfallen. Bert bears a strong resemblance to the youthful manservant Xaver Kleinsgutl, of about the same age as himself; not because he looks common—in features he is strikingly like his father, Professor Cornelius—but by reason of an approximation of types, due in its turn to far-reaching compromises in matters of dress and bearing generally. Both lads wear their heavy hair very long on top, with a cursory parting in the middle, and give their heads the same characteristic toss to throw it off the forehead. When one of them leaves the house, by the garden gate, bareheaded in all weathers, in a blouse rakishly girt with a leather strap, and sheers off bent well over with his head on one side; or else mounts his push-bike—Xaver makes free with his employers', of both sexes, or even, in acutely irresponsible mood, with the Professor's own— Dr. Cornelius from his bedroom window cannot, for the life of him, tell whether he is looking at his son or his servant. Both, he thinks, look like young moujiks. And both are impassioned cigarette-smokers, though Bert has not the means to compete with Xaver, who smokes as many as thirty a day, of a brand named after a popular cinema star. The big folk call their father and mother the "old folk"—not behind their backs, but as a form of address and in all affection: "Hullo, old folks," they will say; though Cornelius is only forty-seven years old and his wife eight years younger. And the Professor's parents, who lead in his household the humble and hesitant life of the really old, are on the big folk's lips the "ancients." As for the "little folk," Ellie and Snapper, who take their meals upstairs with blue-faced Ann—so-called because of her prevailing facial hue—Ellie and Snapper follow their mother's example and address their father by his first name, Abel. Unutterably comic it sounds, in its pert, confiding familiarity; particularly on the lips, in the sweet accents, of five-year-old Eleanor, who is the image of Frau Cornelius's baby pictures and whom the Professor loves above everything else in the world.

"Darling old thing," says Ingrid affably, laying her large but shapely hand on his, as he presides in proper middle-class style over the family table, with her on his left and the mother opposite: "Parent mine, may I ever so gently jog your memory, for you have probably forgotten: this is the afternoon we were to have our little jollification, our turkey-trot with eats to match. You haven't a thing to do but just bear up and not funk it; everything will be over by nine o'clock."

"Oh—ah!" says Cornelius, his face falling. "Good!" he goes on, and nods his head to show himself in harmony with the inevitable. "I only meant—is this really the day? Thursday, yes. How time flies! Well, what time are they coming?"

"Half past four they'll be dropping in, I should say," answers Ingrid, to whom her brother leaves the major rôle in all dealings with the father. Upstairs, while he is resting, he will hear scarcely anything, and from seven to eight he takes his walk. He can slip out by the terrace if he likes.

"Tut!" says Cornelius deprecatingly, as who should say: "You exaggerate." But Bert puts in: "It's the one evening in the week Wanja doesn't have to play. Any other night he'd have to leave by half past six, which would be painful for all concerned."

Wanja is Ivan Herzl, the celebrated young leading man at the Stadttheater. Bert and Ingrid are on intimate terms with him, they often visit him in his dressing-room and have tea. He is an artist of the modern school, who stands on the stage in strange and, to the Professor's mind, utterly affected dancing attitudes, and shrieks lamentably. To a professor of history, all highly repugnant; but Bert has entirely succumbed to Herzl's influence, blackens the lower rim of his eyelids—despite painful but fruitless scenes with the father—and with youthful carelessness of the ancestral anguish declares that not only will he take Herzl for his model if he becomes a dancer, but in case he turns out to be a waiter at the Cairo he means to walk precisely thus.

Cornelius slightly raises his brows and makes his son a little bow—indicative of the unassumingness and self-abnegation that befits his age. You could not call it a mocking bow or suggestive in any special sense. Bert may refer it to himself or equally to his so talented friend.

"Who else is coming?" next inquires the master of the house. They mention various people, names all more or less familiar, from the city, from the suburban colony, from Ingrid's school. They still have some telephoning to do, they say. They have to phone Max. This is Max Hergesell, an engineering student; Ingrid utters his name in the nasal drawl which according to her is the traditional intonation of all the Hergesells. She goes on to parody it in the most abandonedly funny and lifelike way, and the parents laugh until they nearly choke over the wretched trifle. For even in these times when something funny happens people have to laugh.

From time to time the telephone bell rings in the Professor's study, and the big folk run across, knowing it is their affair. Many people had to give up their telephones the last time the price rose, but so far the Corneliuses have been able to keep theirs, just as they have kept their villa, which was built before the war, by dint of the salary Cornelius draws as professor of history—a million marks, and more or less adequate to the chances and changes of post-war life. The house is comfortable, even elegant, though sadly in need of repairs that cannot be made for lack of materials, and at present disfigured by iron stoves with long pipes. Even so, it is still the proper setting of the upper middle class, though they themselves look odd enough in it, with their worn and turned clothing and altered way of life. The children, of course, know nothing else; to them it is normal and regular, they belong by birth to the "villa proletariat." The problem of clothing troubles them not at all. They and their like have evolved a costume to fit the time, by poverty out of taste for innovation: in summer it consists of scarcely more than a belted linen smock and sandals. The middle-class parents find things rather more difficult.

The big folk's table-napkins hang over their chair-backs, they talk with their friends over the telephone. These friends are the invited guests who have rung up to accept or decline or arrange; and the conversation is carried on in the jargon of the clan, full of slang and high spirits, of which the old folk understand hardly a word. These consult together meantime about the hospitality to be offered to the impending guests. The Professor displays a middle-class ambitiousness: he wants to serve a sweet—or something that looks like a sweet—after the Italian salad and brown-bread sandwiches. But Frau Cornelius says that would be going too far. The guests would not expect it, she is sure—and the big folk, returning once more to their trifle, agree with her.

The mother of the family is of the same general type as Ingrid, though not so tall. She is languid; the fantastic difficulties of the housekeeping have broken and worn her. She really ought to go and take a cure, but feels incapable; the floor is always swaying under her feet, and everything seems upside down. She speaks of what is uppermost in her mind: the eggs, they simply must be bought today. Six thousand marks apiece they are, and just so many are to be had on this one day of the week at one single shop fifteen minutes' journey away. Whatever else they do, the big folk must go and fetch them immediately after luncheon, with Danny, their neighbour's son, who will soon be calling for them; and Xaver Kleinsgutl will don civilian garb and attend his young master and mistress. For no single household is allowed more than five eggs a week; therefore the young people will enter the shop singly, one after another, under assumed names, and thus wring twenty eggs from the shopkeeper for the Cornelius family. This enterprise is the sporting event of the week for all participants, not excepting the moujik Kleinsgutl, and most of all for Ingrid and Bert, who delight in misleading and mystifying their fellowmen and would revel in the performance even if it did not achieve one single egg. They adore impersonating fictitious characters; they love to sit in a bus and carry on long lifelike conversations in a dialect which they otherwise never speak, the most commonplace dialogue about politics and people and the price of food, while the whole bus listens open-mouthed to this incredibly ordinary prattle, though with a dark suspicion all the while that something is wrong somewhere. The conversation waxes ever more shameless, it enters into revolting detail about these people who do not exist. Ingrid can make her voice sound ever so common and twittering and shrill as she impersonates a shop-girl with an illegitimate child, said child being a son with sadistic tendencies, who lately out in the country treated a cow with such unnatural cruelty that no Christian could have borne to see it. Bert nearly explodes at her twittering, but restrains himself and displays a grisly sympathy; he and the unhappy shop-girl entering into a long, stupid, depraved, and shuddery conversation over the particular morbid cruelty involved; until an old gentleman opposite, sitting with his ticket folded between his index finger and his seal ring, can bear it no more and makes public protest against the nature of the themes these young folk are discussing with such particularity. He uses the Greek plural: "themata." Whereat Ingrid pretends to be dissolving in tears, and Bert behaves as though his wrath against the old gentleman was with difficulty being held in check and would probably burst out before long. He clenches his fists, he gnashes his teeth, he shakes from head to foot; and the unhappy old gentleman, whose intentions had been of the best, hastily leaves the bus at the next stop.

Such are the diversions of the big folk. The telephone plays a prominent part in them: they ring up any and everybody—members of government, opera singers, dignitaries of the Church—in the character of shop assistants, or perhaps as Lord or Lady Doolittle. They are only with difficulty persuaded that they have the wrong number. Once they emptied their parents' card-tray and distributed its contents among the neighbours' letter-boxes, wantonly, yet not without enough impish sense of the fitness of things to make it highly upsetting, God only knowing why certain people should have called where they did.

Xaver comes in to clear away, tossing the hair out of his eyes. Now that he has taken off his gloves you can see the yellow chain-ring on his left hand. And as the Professor finishes his watery eight-thousand-mark beer and lights a cigarette, the little folk can be heard scrambling down the stair, coming, by established custom, for their after-dinner call on Father and Mother. They storm the dining-room, after a struggle with the latch, clutched by both pairs of little hands at once; their clumsy small feet twinkle over the carpet, in red felt slippers with the socks falling down on them. With prattle and shoutings each makes for his own place: Snapper to Mother, to climb on her lap, boast of all he has eaten, and thump his fat little tum; Ellie to her Abel, so much hers because she is so very much his; because she consciously luxuriates in the deep tenderness—like all deep feeling, concealing a melancholy strain— with which he holds her small form embraced; in the love in his eyes as he kisses her little fairy hand or the sweet brow with its delicate tracery of tiny blue veins.

The little folk look like each other, with the strong undefined likeness of brother and sister. In clothing and hair-cut they are twins. Yet they are sharply distinguished after all, and quite on sex lines. It is a little Adam and a little Eve. Not only is Snapper the sturdier and more compact, he appears consciously to emphasize his four-year-old masculinity in speech, manner, and carriage, lifting his shoulders and letting the little arms hang down quite like a young American athlete, drawing down his mouth when he talks and seeking to give his voice a gruff and forthright ring. But all this masculinity is the result of effort rather than natively his. Born and brought up in these desolate, distracted times, he has been endowed by them with an unstable and hypersensitive nervous system and suffers greatly under life's dis- harmonies. He is prone to sudden anger and outbursts of bitter tears, stamp- ing his feet at every trifle; for this reason he is his mother's special nursling and care. His round, round eyes are chestnut brown and already inclined to squint, so that he will need glasses in the near future. His little nose is long, the mouth small—the father's nose and mouth they are, more plainly than ever since the Professor shaved his pointed beard and goes smooth-faced. The pointed beard has become impossible—even professors must make some con- cession to the changing times.

But the little daughter sits on her father's knee, his Eleonorchen, his little Eve, so much more gracious a little being, so much sweeter-faced than her brother—and he holds his cigarette away from her while she fingers his glasses with her dainty wee hands. The lenses are divided for reading and distance, and each day they tease her curiosity afresh.

At bottom he suspects that his wife's partiality may have a firmer basis than his own: that Snapper's refractory masculinity perhaps is solider stuff than his own little girl's more explicit charm and grace. But the heart will not be commanded, that he knows; and once and for all his heart belongs to the little one, as it has since the day she came, since the first time he saw her. Almost always when he holds her in his arms he remembers that first time: remembers the sunny room in the Women's Hospital, where Ellie first saw the light, twelve years after Bert was born. He remembers how he drew near, the mother smiling the while, and cautiously put aside the canopy of the diminutive bed that stood beside the large one. There lay the little miracle among the pillows: so well formed, so encompassed, as it were, with the harmony of sweet proportions, with little hands that even then, though so much tinier, were beautiful as now; with wide-open eyes blue as the sky and brighter than the sunshine—and almost in that very second he felt himself captured and held fast. This was love at first sight, love everlasting: a feeling unknown, unhoped for, unexpected—in so far as it could be a matter of conscious awareness; it took entire possession of him, and he understood, with joyous amazement, that this was for life.

But he understood more. He knows, does Dr. Cornelius, that there is something not quite right about this feeling, so unaware, so undreamed of, so involuntary. He has a shrewd suspicion that it is not by accident it has so utterly mastered him and bound itself up with his existence; that he had— even subconsciously—been preparing for it, or, more precisely, been prepared for it. There is, in short, something in him which at a given moment was ready to issue in such a feeling; and this something, highly extraordinary to relate, is his essence and quality as a professor of history. Dr. Cornelius, how- ever, does not actually say this, even to himself; he merely realizes it, at odd times, and smiles a private smile. He knows that history professors do not love history because it is something that comes to pass, but only because it is something that *has* come to pass; that they hate a revolution like the present one because they feel it is lawless, incoherent, irrelevant—in a word, unhis- toric; that their hearts belong to the coherent, disciplined, historic past. For the temper of timelessness, the temper of eternity—thus the scholar com- munes with himself when he takes his walk by the river before supper—that temper broods over the past; and it is a temper much better suited to the nervous system of a history professor than are the excesses of the present. The past is immortalized; that is to say, it is dead; and death is the root of all godliness and all abiding significance. Dr. Cornelius, walking alone in the dark, has a profound insight into this truth. It is this conservative instinct of his, his sense of the eternal, that has found in his love for his little daughter a way to save itself from the wounding inflicted by the times. For father love, and a little child on its mother's breast—are not these timeless, and thus very, very holy and beautiful? Yet Cornelius, pondering there in the dark, descries something not perfectly right and good in his love. Theoretically, in the interests of science, he admits it to himself. There is something ulterior about it, in the nature of it; that something is hostility, hostility against the history of today, which is still in the making and thus not history at all, in behalf of the genuine history that has already happened—that is to say, death. Yes, passing strange though all this is, yet it is true; true in a sense, that is. His devotion to this priceless little morsel of life and new growth has something to do with death, it clings to death as against life; and that is neither right nor beautiful—in a sense. Though only the most fanatical asceticism could be capable, on no other ground than such casual scientific perception, of tearing this purest and most precious of feelings out of his heart.

He holds his darling on his lap and her slim rosy legs hang down. He raises his brows as he talks to her, tenderly, with a half-teasing note of respect, and listens enchanted to her high, sweet little voice calling him Abel. He exchanges a look with the mother, who is caressing her Snapper and reading him a gentle lecture. He must be more reasonable, he must learn self-control; today again, under the manifold exasperations of life, he has given way to rage and behaved like a howling dervish. Cornelius casts a mistrustful glance at the big folk now and then, too; he thinks it not unlikely they are not unaware of those scientific preoccupations of his evening walks. If such be the case they do not show it. They stand there leaning their arms on their chair-backs and with a benevolence not untinctured with irony look on at the parental happiness.

The children's frocks are of a heavy brick-red stuff, embroidered in modern "arty" style. They once belonged to Ingrid and Bert and are precisely alike, save that little knickers come out beneath Snapper's smock. And both have their hair bobbed. Snapper's is a streaky blond, inclined to turn dark. It is bristly and sticky and looks for all the world like a droll, badly fitting wig. But Ellie's is chestnut brown, glossy and fine as silk, as pleasing as her whole little personality. It covers her ears—and these ears are not a pair, one of them being the right size, the other distinctly too large. Her father will sometimes uncover this little abnormality and exclaim over it as though he had never noticed it before, which both makes Ellie giggle and covers her with shame. Her eyes are now golden brown, set far apart and with sweet gleams in them—such a clear and lovely look! The brows above are blond; the nose still unformed, with thick nostrils and almost circular holes; the mouth large and expressive, with a beautifully arching and mobile upper lip. When she laughs, dimples come in her cheeks and she shows her teeth like loosely strung pearls. So far she has lost but one tooth, which her father gently twisted out with his handkerchief after it had grown very wobbling. During this small operation she had paled and trembled very much. Her cheeks have the softness proper to her years, but they are not chubby; indeed, they are rather concave, due to her facial structure, with its somewhat prominent jaw. On one, close to the soft fall of her hair, is a downy freckle.

Ellie is not too well pleased with her looks—a sign that already she troubles about such things. Sadly she thinks it is best to admit it once for all, her face is "homely"; though the rest of her, "on the other hand," is not bad at all. She loves expressions like "on the other hand"; they sound choice and grown-up to her, and she likes to string them together, one after the other: "very likely," "probably," "after all." Snapper is self-critical too, though more in the moral sphere: he suffers from remorse for his attacks of rage and considers himself a tremendous sinner. He is quite certain that heaven is not for such as he; he is sure to go to "the bad place" when he dies, and no persuasions will convince him to the contrary—as that God sees the heart and gladly makes allowances. Obstinately he shakes his head, with the comic, crooked little peruke, and vows there is no place for him in heaven. When he has a cold he is immediately quite choked with mucus;

rattles and rumbles from top to toe if you even look at him; his temperature flies up at once and he simply puffs. Nursy is pessimistic on the score of his constitution: such fat-blooded children as he might get a stroke any minute. Once she even thought she saw the moment at hand: Snapper had been in one of his berserker rages, and in the ensuing fit of penitence stood himself in the corner with his back to the room. Suddenly Nursy noticed that his face had gone all blue, far bluer, even, than her own. She raised the alarm, crying out that the child's all too rich blood had at length brought him to his final hour; and Snapper, to his vast astonishment, found himself, so far from being rebuked for evil-doing, encompassed in tenderness and anxiety— until it turned out that his colour was not caused by apoplexy but by the distempering on the nursery wall, which had come off on his tear-wet face.

Nursy has come downstairs too, and stands by the door, sleek-haired, owl-eyed, with her hands folded over her white apron, and a severely dignified manner born of her limited intelligence. She is very proud of the care and training she gives her nurslings and declares that they are "enveloping wonderfully." She has had seventeen suppurated teeth lately removed from her jaws and been measured for a set of symmetrical yellow ones in dark rubber gums; these now embellish her peasant face. She is obsessed with the strange conviction that these teeth of hers are the subject of general conversation, that, as it were, the sparrows on the housetops chatter of them. "Everybody knows I've had a false set put in," she will say; "there has been a great deal of foolish talk about them." She is much given to dark hints and veiled innuendo: speaks, for instance, of a certain Dr. Bleifuss, whom every child knows, and "there are even some in the house who pretend to be him." All one can do with talk like this is charitably to pass it over in silence. But she teaches the children nursery rhymes: gems like:

> "Puff, puff, here comes the train!
> Puff, puff, toot, toot,
> Away it goes again."

Or that gastronomical jingle, so suited, in its sparseness, to the times, and yet seemingly with a blitheness of its own:

> "Monday we begin the week,
> Tuesday there's a bone to pick.
> Wednesday we're half way through,
> Thursday what a great to-do!
> Friday we eat what fish we're able,
> Saturday we dance round the table.
> Sunday brings us pork and greens—
> Here's a feast for kings and queens!"

Also a certain four-line stanza with a romantic appeal, unutterable and unuttered:

"Open the gate, open the gate
And let the carriage drive in.
Who is it in the carriage sits?
A lordly sir with golden hair."

Or, finally that ballad about golden-haired Marianne who sat on a, sat on a, sat on a stone, and combed out her, combed out her, combed out her hair; and about bloodthirsty Rudolph who pulled out a, pulled out a, pulled out a knife—and his ensuing direful end. Ellie enunciates all these ballads charmingly, with her mobile little lips, and sings them in her sweet little voice—much better than Snapper. She does everything better than he does, and he pays her honest admiration and homage and obeys her in all things except when visited by one of his attacks. Sometimes she teaches him, instructs him upon the birds in the picture-book and tells him their proper names: "This is a chaffinch, Buddy, this is a bullfinch, this is a cowfinch." He has to repeat them after her. She gives him medical instruction too, teaches him the names of diseases, such as infammation of the lungs, infammation of the blood, infammation of the air. If he does not pay attention and cannot say the words after her, she stands him in the corner. Once she even boxed his ears, but was so ashamed that she stood herself in the corner for a long time. Yes, they are fast friends, two souls with but a single thought, and have all their adventures in common. They come home from a walk and relate as with one voice that they have seen two moollies and a teenty-weenty baby calf. They are on familiar terms with the kitchen, which consists of Xaver and the ladies Hinterhofer, two sisters once of the lower middle class who, in these evil days, are reduced to living *"au pair"* as the phrase goes and officiating as cook and housemaid for their board and keep. The little ones have a feeling that Xaver and the Hinterhofers are on much the same footing with their father and mother as they are themselves. At least sometimes, when they have been scolded, they go downstairs and announce that the master and mistress are cross. But playing with the servants lacks charm compared with the joys of playing upstairs. The kitchen could never rise to the height of the games their father can invent. For instance, there is "four gentlemen taking a walk." When they play it Abel will crook his knees until he is the same height with themselves and go walking with them, hand in hand. They never get enough of this sport; they could walk round and round the dining-room a whole day on end, five gentlemen in all, counting the diminished Abel.

Then there is the thrilling cushion game. One of the children, usually Ellie, seats herself, unbeknownst to Abel, in his seat at table. Still as a mouse she awaits his coming. He draws near with his head in the air, descanting in loud, clear tones upon the surpassing comfort of his chair; and sits down on top of Ellie. "What's this, what's this?" says he. And bounces about, deaf to the smothered giggles exploding behind him. "Why have they put a cushion in my chair? And what a queer, hard, awkward-shaped cushion it is!" he goes on. "Frightfully uncomfortable to sit on!" And keeps pushing and bouncing about more and more on the astonishing cushion and clutching behind him into the rapturous giggling and squeaking, until at last he turns round, and the game ends with a magnificent climax of discovery and recognition. They might go through all this a hundred times without diminishing by an iota its power to thrill.

Today is no time for such joys. The imminent festivity disturbs the atmosphere, and besides there is work to be done, and, above all, the eggs to be got. Ellie has just time to recite, "Puff, puff," and Cornelius to discover that her ears are not mates, when they are interrupted by the arrival of Danny, come to fetch Bert and Ingrid. Xaver, meantime, has exchanged his striped livery for an ordinary coat, in which he looks rather rough-and-ready, though as brisk and attractive as ever. So then Nursy and the children ascend to the upper regions, the Professor withdraws to his study to read, as always after dinner, and his wife bends her energies upon the sandwiches and salad that must be prepared. And she has another errand as well. Before the young people arrive she has to take her shopping-basket and dash into town on her bicycle, to turn into provisions a sum of money she has in hand, which she dares not keep lest it lose all value.

Cornelius reads, leaning back in his chair, with his cigar between his middle and index fingers. First he reads Macaulay on the origin of the English public debt at the end of the seventeenth century; then an article in a French periodical on the rapid increase in the Spanish debt towards the end of the sixteenth. Both these for his lecture on the morrow. He intends to compare the astonishing prosperity which accompanied the phenomenon in England with its fatal effects a hundred years earlier in Spain, and to analyse the ethical and psychological grounds of the difference in results. For that will give him a chance to refer back from the England of William III, which is the actual subject in hand, to the time of Philip II and the Counter-Reformation, which is his own special field. He has already written a valuable work on this period; it is much cited and got him his professorship. While his cigar burns down and gets strong, he excogitates a few pensive sentences in a key of gentle melancholy, to be delivered before his class next day: about the practically hopeless struggle carried on by the belated Philip against the whole trend of history: against the new, the kingdom-disrupting power of the Germanic ideal of freedom and individual liberty. And about the persistent, futile struggle of the aristocracy, condemned by God and rejected of man, against the forces of progress and change. He savours his sentences; keeps on polishing them while he puts back the books he has been using; then goes upstairs for the usual pause in his day's work, the hour with drawn blinds and closed eyes, which he so imperatively needs. But today, he recalls, he will rest under disturbed conditions, amid the bustle of preparations for the feast. He smiles to find his heart giving a mild flutter at the thought. Disjointed phrases on the theme of black-clad Philip and his times mingle with a confused consciousness that they will soon be dancing down below. For five minutes or so he falls asleep.

As he lies and rests he can hear the sound of the garden gate and the repeated ringing at the bell. Each time a little pang goes through him, of excitement and suspense, at the thought that the young people have begun to fill the floor below. And each time he smiles at himself again—though even his smile is slightly nervous, is tinged with the pleasurable anticipations people always feel before a party. At half past four—it is already dark—he gets up and washes at the wash-stand. The basin has been out of repair for two years. It is supposed to tip, but has broken away from its socket on one side and cannot be mended because there is nobody to mend it; neither replaced because no shop can supply another. So it has to be hung up above the vent and emptied by lifting in both hands and pouring out the water. Cornelius shakes his head over this basin, as he does several times a day—whenever, in fact, he has occasion to use it. He finishes his toilet with care, standing under the ceiling light to polish his glasses till they shine. Then he goes downstairs.

On his way to the dining-room he hears the gramophone already going, and the sound of voices. He puts on a polite, society air; at his tongue's end is the phrase he means to utter: "Pray don't let me disturb you," as he passes directly into the dining-room for his tea. "Pray don't let me disturb you"—it seems to him precisely the *mot juste;* towards the guests cordial and considerate, for himself a very bulwark.

The lower floor is lighted up, all the bulbs in the chandelier are burning save one that has burned out. Cornelius pauses on a lower step and surveys the entrance hall. It looks pleasant and cosy in the bright light, with its copy of Marées over the brick chimney-piece, its wainscoted walls—wainscoted in soft wood—and red-carpeted floor, where the guests stand in groups, chatting, each with his tea-cup and slice of bread-and-butter spread with anchovy paste. There is a festal haze, faint scents of hair and clothing and human breath come to him across the room, it is all characteristic and familiar and highly evocative. The door into the dressing-room is open, guests are still arriving.

A large group of people is rather bewildering at first sight. The Professor takes in only the general scene. He does not see Ingrid, who is standing just at the foot of the steps, in a dark silk frock with a pleated collar falling softly over the shoulders, and bare arms. She smiles up at him, nodding and showing her lovely teeth.

"Rested?" she asks, for his private ear. With a quite unwarranted start he recognizes her, and she presents some of her friends.

"May I introduce Herr Zuber?" she says. "And this is Fräulein Plaichinger."

Herr Zuber is insignificant. But Fräulein Plaichinger is a perfect Germania, blond and voluptuous, arrayed in floating draperies. She has a snub nose, and answers the Professor's salutation in the high, shrill pipe so many stout women have.

"Delighted to meet you," he says. "How nice of you to come! A classmate of Ingrid's, I suppose?"

And Herr Zuber is a golfing partner of Ingrid's. He is in business; he works in his uncle's brewery. Cornelius makes a few jokes about the thinness of the beer and professes to believe that Herr Zuber could easily do something about the quality if he would. "But pray don't let me disturb you," he goes on, and turns towards the dining-room.

"There comes Max," says Ingrid. "Max, you sweep, what do you mean by rolling up at this time of day?" For such is the way they talk to each other, offensively to an older ear; of social forms, of hospitable warmth, there is no faintest trace. They all call each other by their first names.

A young man comes up to them out of the dressing-room and makes his bow; he has an expanse of white shirt-front and a little black string tie. He is as pretty as a picture, dark, with rosy cheeks, clean-shaven of course, but with just a sketch of side-whisker. Not a ridiculous or flashy beauty, not like a gypsy fiddler, but just charming to look at, in a winning, well-bred way, with kind dark eyes. He even wears his dinner-jacket a little awkwardly.

"Please don't scold me, Cornelia," he say; "it's the idiotic lectures." And Ingrid presents him to her father as Herr Hergesell.

Well, and so this is Herr Hergesell. He knows his manners, does Herr Hergesell, and thanks the master of the house quite ingratiatingly for his invitation as they shake hands. "I certainly seem to have missed the bus," says he jocosely. "Of course I have lectures today up to four o'clock; I would have; and after that I had to go home to change." Then he talks about his pumps, with which he has just been struggling in the dressing-room.

"I brought them with me in a bag," he goes on. "Mustn't tramp all over the carpet in our brogues—it's not done. Well, I was ass enough not to fetch along a shoe-horn, and I find I simply can't get in! What a sell! They are the tightest I've ever had, the numbers don't tell you a thing, and all the leather today is just cast iron. It's not leather at all. My poor finger"—he confidingly displays a reddened digit and once more characterizes the whole thing as a "sell," and a putrid sell into the bargain. He really does talk just as Ingrid said he did, with a peculiar nasal drawl, not affectedly in the least, but merely because that is the way of all the Hergesells.

Dr. Cornelius says it is very careless of them not to keep a shoe-horn in the cloak-room and displays proper sympathy with the mangled finger. "But now you *really* must not let me disturb you any longer," he goes on. *"Auf wiedersehen!"* And he crosses the hall into the dining-room.

There are guests there too, drinking tea; the family table is pulled out. But the Professor goes at once to his own little upholstered corner with the electric light bulb above it—the nook where he usually drinks his tea. His wife is sitting there talking with Bert and two other young men, one of them

Herzl, whom Cornelius knows and greets; the other a typical "Wander-vogel" named Möller, a youth who obviously neither owns nor cares to own the correct evening dress of the middle classes (in fact, there is no such thing any more), nor to ape the manners of a gentleman (and, in fact, there is no such thing any more either). He has a wilderness of hair, horn spectacles, and long neck, and wears golf stockings and a belted blouse. His regular occupation, the Professor learns, is banking, but he is by way of being an amateur folk-lorist and collects folk-songs from all localities in all languages. He sings them, too, and at Ingrid's command has brought his guitar; it is hanging in the dressing-room in an oilcloth case. Herzl, the actor, is small and slight, but he has a strong growth of black beard, as you can tell by the thick coat of powder on his cheeks. His eyes are larger than life, with a deep and melancholy glow. He has put on rouge besides the powder—those dull carmine high-lights on the cheeks can be nothing but a cosmetic. "Queer," thinks the Professor. "You would think a man would be one thing or the other—not melancholic and use face paint at the same time. It's a psychological contradiction. How can a melancholy man rouge? But here we have a perfect illustration of the abnormality of the artist soul-form. It can make possible a contradiction like this—perhaps it even consists in the contradiction. All very interesting—and no reason whatever for not being polite to him. Politeness is a primitive convention—and legitimate. . . . Do take some lemon, Herr Hofschauspieler!

Court actors and court theatres—there are no such things any more, really. But Herzl relishes the sound of the title, notwithstanding he is a revolutionary artist. This must be another contradiction inherent in his soul-form; so, at least, the Professor assumes, and he is probably right. The flattery he is guilty of is a sort of atonement for his previous hard thoughts about the rouge.

"Thank you so much—it's really too good of you, sir," says Herzl, quite embarrassed. He is so overcome that he almost stammers; only his perfect enunciation saves him. His whole bearing towards his hostess and the master of the house is exaggeratedly polite. It is almost as though he had a bad conscience in respect of his rouge; as though an inward compulsion had driven him to put it on, but now, seeing it through the Professor's eyes, he disapproves of it himself, and thinks, by an air of humility towards the whole of unrouged society, to mitigate its effect.

They drink their tea and chat: about Möller's folk-songs, about Basque folk-songs and Spanish folk-songs; from which they pass to the new production of *Don Carlos* at the Stadttheater, in which Herzl plays the title-rôle. He talks about his own rendering of the part and says he hopes his conception of the character has unity. They go on to criticize the rest of the cast, the setting, and the production as a whole; and Cornelius is struck, rather painfully, to find the conversation trending towards his own special province, back to Spain and the Counter-Reformation. He has done nothing at all to give it this turn, he is perfectly innocent, and hopes it does not look as though he had sought an occasion to play the professor. He wonders, and falls silent, feeling relieved when the little folk come up to the table. Ellie and Snapper have on their blue velvet Sunday frocks; they are permitted to partake in the festivities up to bed-time. They look shy and large-eyed as they say how-do-you-do to the strangers and, under pressure, repeat their names and ages. Herr Möller does nothing but gaze at them solemnly, but Herzl is simply ravished. He rolls his eyes up to heaven and puts his hands over his mouth; he positively blesses them. It all, no doubt, comes from his heart, but he is so addicted to theatrical methods of making an impression and getting an effect that both words and behaviour ring frightfully false. And even his enthusiasm for the little folk looks too much like part of his general craving to make up for the rouge on his cheeks.

The tea-table has meanwhile emptied of guests, and dancing is going on in the hall. The children run off, the Professor prepares to retire. "Go and enjoy yourselves," he says to Möller and Herzl, who have sprung from their chairs as he rises from his. They shake hands and he withdraws into his study, his peaceful kingdom, where he lets down the blinds, turns on the desk lamp, and sits down to his work.

It is work which can be done, if necessary, under disturbed conditions: nothing but a few letters and a few notes. Of course, Cornelius's mind wanders. Vague impressions float through it: Herr Hergesell's refractory pumps, the high pipe in that plump body of the Plaichinger female. As he writes, or leans back in his chair and stares into space, his thoughts go back to Herr Möller's collection of Basque folk-songs, to Herzl's posings and humility, to "his" Carlos and the court of Philip II. There is something strange, he thinks, about conversations. They are so ductile, they will flow of their own accord in the direction of one's dominating interest. Often and often he has seen this happen. And while he is thinking, he is listening to the sounds next door—rather subdued, he finds them. He hears only voices, no sound of footsteps. The dancers do not glide or circle round the room; they merely walk about over the carpet, which does not hamper their movements in the least. Their way of holding each other is quite different and strange, and they move to the strains of the gramophone, to the weird music of the new world. He concentrates on the music and makes out that it is a jazz-band record, with various percussion instruments and the clack and clatter of castanets, which, however, are not even faintly suggestive of Spain, but merely jazz like the rest. No, not Spain. . . . His thoughts are back at their old round.

Half an hour goes by. It occurs to him it would be no more than friendly to go and contribute a box of cigarettes to the festivities next door. Too bad to ask the young people to smoke their own—though they have probably never thought of it. He goes into the empty dining-room and takes a box from his supply in the cupboard: not the best ones, nor yet the brand he himself prefers, but a certain long, thin kind he is not averse to getting rid of—after all, they are nothing but youngsters. He takes the box into the hall, holds it up with a smile, and deposits it on the mantel-shelf. After which he gives a look round and returns to his own room.

There comes a lull in dance and music. The guests stand about the room in groups or round the table at the window or are seated in a circle by the fireplace. Even the built-in stairs, with their worn velvet carpet, are crowded with young folk as in an amphitheatre: Max Hergesell is there, leaning back with one elbow on the step above and gesticulating with his free hand as he talks to the shrill, voluptuous Plaichinger. The floor of the hall is nearly empty, save just in the centre: there, directly beneath the chandelier, the two little ones in their blue velvet frocks clutch each other in an awkward embrace and twirl silently round and round, oblivious of all else. Cornelius, as he passes, strokes their hair, with a friendly word; it does not distract them from their small solemn preoccupation. But at his own door he turns to glance round and sees young Hergesell push himself off the stair by his elbow—probably because he noticed the Professor. He comes down into the arena, takes Ellie out of her brother's arms, and dances with her himself. It looks very comic, without the music, and he crouches down just as Cornelius does when he goes walking with the four gentlemen, holding the fluttered Ellie as though she were grown up and taking little "shimmy-ing" steps. Everybody watches with huge enjoyment, the gramophone is put on again, dancing becomes general. The Professor stands and looks, with his hand on the door-knob. He nods and laughs; when he finally shuts himself into his study the mechanical smile still lingers on his lips.

Again he turns over pages by his desk lamp, takes notes, attends to a few simple matters. After a while he notices that the guests have forsaken the entrance hall for his wife's drawing-room, into which there is a door from his own study as well. He hears their voices and the sounds of a guitar being tuned. Herr Möller, it seems, is to sing—and does so. He twangs the strings of his instrument and sings in a powerful bass a ballad in a strange tongue, possibly Swedish. The Professor does not succeed in identifying it, though he listens attentively to the end, after which there is great applause. The sound is deadened by the portière that hangs over the dividing door. The young bank-clerk begins another song. Cornelius goes softly in.

It is half-dark in the drawing-room; the only light is from the shaded standard lamp, beneath which Möller sits, on the divan, with his legs crossed, picking his strings. His audience is grouped easily about; as there are not enough seats, some stand, and more, among them many young ladies, are simply sitting on the floor with their hands clasped round their knees or even with their legs stretched out before them. Hergesell sits thus, in his dinner jacket, next the piano, with Fräulein Plaichinger beside him. Frau Cornelius is holding both children on her lap as she sits in her easy-chair opposite the singer. Snapper, the Bœotian, begins to talk loud and clear in the middle of the song and has to be intimidated with hushings and finger-shakings. Never, never would Ellie allow herself to be guilty of such con-duct. She sits there daintily erect and still on her mother's knee. The Professor tries to catch her eye and exchange a private signal with his little girl; but she does not see him. Neither does she seem to be looking at the singer. Her gaze is directed lower down.

Möller sings the "joli tambour":

> *"Sire, mon roi, donnez-moi votre*
> *fille—"*

They are all enchanted. "How good!" Hergesell is heard to say, in the odd, nasally condescending Hergesell tone. The next one is a beggar ballad, to a tune composed by young Möller himself; it elicits a storm of applause:

> "Gypsy lassie a-goin' to the fair,
> Huzza!
> Gypsy laddie a-goin' to be
>   there—
> Huzza, diddlety umpty dido!"

Laughter and high spirits, sheer reckless hilarity, reigns after this jovial ballad. "Frightfully good!" Hergesell comments again, as before. Follows another popular song, this time a Hungarian one; Möller sings it in its own outlandish tongue, and most effectively. The Professor applauds with ostentation. It warms his heart and does him good, this outcropping of artistic, historic, and cultural elements all amongst the shimmying. He goes up to young Möller and congratulates him, talks about the songs and their sources, and Möller promises to lend him a certain annotated book of folk-songs. Cornelius is the more cordial because all the time, as fathers do, he has been comparing the parts and achievements of this young stranger with those of his own son, and being gnawed by envy and chagrin. This young Möller, he is thinking, is a capable bank-clerk (though about Möller's capacity he knows nothing whatever) and has this special gift besides, which must have taken talent and energy to cultivate. "And here is my poor Bert, who knows nothing and can do nothing and thinks of nothing except playing the clown, without even talent for that!" He tries to be just; he tells himself that, after all, Bert has innate refinement; that probably there is a good deal more to him than there is to the successful Möller; that perhaps he has even something of the poet in him, and his dancing and table-waiting are due to mere boyish folly and the distraught times. But paternal envy and pessimism win the upper hand; when Möller begins another song, Dr. Cornelius goes back to his room.

He works as before, with divided attention, at this and that, while it gets on for seven o'clock. Then he remembers a letter he may just as well write, a short letter and not very important, but letter-writing is wonderful for the way it takes up the time, and it is almost half past when he has finished. At half past eight the Italian salad will be served; so now is the prescribed moment for the Professor to go out into the wintry darkness to post his letters and take his daily quantum of fresh air and exercise. They are dancing again, and he will have to pass through the hall to get his hat and coat; but they are used to him now, he need not stop and beg them not to be disturbed. He lays away his papers, takes up the letters he has written, and goes out. But he sees his wife sitting near the door of his room and pauses a little by her easy-chair.

She is watching the dancing. Now and then the big folk or some of their guests stop to speak to her; the party is at its height, and there are more onlookers than these two: blue-faced Ann is standing at the bottom of the stairs, in all the dignity of her limitations. She is waiting for the children, who simply cannot get their fill of these unwonted festivities, and watching over Snapper, lest his all too rich blood be churned to the danger-point by too much twirling round. And not only the nursery but the kitchen takes an interest: Xaver and the two ladies Hinterhofer are standing by the pantry door looking on with relish. Fräulein Walburga, the elder of the two sunken sisters (the culinary section—she objects to being called a cook), is a whimsical, good-natured sort, brown-eyed, wearing glasses with thick circular lenses; the nose-piece is wound with a bit of rag to keep it from pressing on her nose. Fräulein Cecilia is younger, though not so precisely young either. Her bearing is as self-assertive as usual, this being her way of sustaining her dignity as a former member of the middle class. For Fräulein Cecilia feels acutely her descent into the ranks of domestic service. She positively declines to wear a cap or other badge of servitude, and her hardest trial is on the Wednesday evening when she has to serve the dinner while Xaver has his afternoon out. She hands the dishes with averted face and elevated nose—a fallen queen; and so distressing is it to behold her degradation that one evening when the little folk happened to be at table and saw her they both with one accord burst into tears. Such anguish is unknown to young Xaver. He enjoys serving and does it with an ease born of practice as well as talent, for he was once a "piccolo." But otherwise he is a thorough-paced good-for-nothing and windbag—with quite distinct traits of character of his own, as his long-suffering employers are always ready to concede, but perfectly impossible and a bag of wind for all that. One must just take him as he is, they think, and not expect figs from thistles. He is the child and product of the disrupted times, a perfect specimen of his generation, follower of the revolution, Bolshevist sympathizer. The Professor's name for him is the "minute-man," because he is always to be counted on in any sudden crisis, if only it address his sense of humour or love of novelty, and will display therein amazing readiness and resource. But he utterly lacks a sense of duty and can as little be trained to the performance of the daily round and common task as some kinds of dog can be taught to jump over a stick. It goes so plainly against the grain that criticism is disarmed. One becomes resigned. On grounds that appealed to him as unusual and amusing he would be ready to turn out of his bed at any hour of the night. But he simply cannot get up before eight in the morning, he cannot do it, he will not jump over the stick. Yet all day long the evidence of this free and untrammelled existence, the sound of his mouth-organ, his joyous whistle, or his raucous but expressive voice lifted in song, rises to the hearing of the world above-stairs; and the smoke of his cigarettes fills the pantry. While the Hinterhofer ladies work he stands and looks on. Of a morning while the Professor is breakfasting, he tears the leaf off the study calendar—but does not lift a finger to dust the room. Dr. Cornelius has often told him to leave the calendar alone, for he tends to tear off two leaves at a time and thus to add to the general confusion. But young Xaver appears to find joy in this activity, and will not be deprived of it.

Again, he is fond of children, a winning trait. He will throw himself into games with the little folk in the garden, make and mend their toys with great ingenuity, even read aloud from their books—and very droll it sounds in his thick-lipped pronunciation. With his whole soul he loves the cinema; after an evening spent there he inclines to melancholy and yearning and talking to himself. Vague hopes stir in him that some day he may make his fortune in that gay world and belong to it by rights—hopes based on his shock of hair and his physical agility and daring. He likes to climb the ash tree in the front garden, mounting branch by branch to the very top and frightening everybody to death who sees him. Once there he lights a ciga-rette and smokes it as he sways to and fro, keeping a look-out for a cinema director who might chance to come along and engage him.

If he changed his striped jacket for mufti, he might easily dance with the others and no one would notice the difference. For the big folk's friends are rather anomalous in their clothing: evening dress is worn by a few, but it is by no means the rule. There is quite a sprinkling of guests, both male and female, in the same general style as Möller the ballad-singer. The Pro-fessor is familiar with the circumstances of most of this young generation he is watching as he stands beside his wife's chair; he has heard them spoken of by name. They are students at the high school or at the School of Applied Art; they lead, at least the masculine portion, that precarious and scrambling existence which is purely the product of the time. There is a tall, pale, spindling youth, the son of a dentist, who lives by speculation. From all the Professor hears, he is a perfect Aladdin. He keeps a car, treats his friends to champagne suppers, and showers presents upon them on every occasion, costly little trifles in mother-of-pearl and gold. So today he has brought gifts to the young givers of the feast: for Bert a gold lead-pencil, and for Ingrid a pair of ear-rings of barbaric size, great gold circlets that fortunately do not have to go through the little ear-lobe, but are fastened over it by means of a clip. The big folk come laughing to their parents to display these trophies; and the parents shake their heads even while they admire—Aladdin bowing over and over from afar.

The young people appear to be absorbed in their dancing—if the per-formance they are carrying out with so much still concentration can be called dancing. They stride across the carpet, slowly, according to some unfathomable prescript, strangely embraced; in the newest attitude, tummy advanced and shoulders high, waggling the hips. They do not get tired, because nobody could. There is no such thing as heightened colour or heaving bosoms. Two girls may dance together or two young men—it is all the same. They move to the exotic strains of the gramophone, played with the loudest needles to procure the maximum of sound: shimmies, foxtrots, one-steps, double foxes, African shimmies, Java dances, and Creole polkas, the wild musky melodies follow one another, now furious, now languishing, a monotonous Negro programme in unfamiliar rhythm, to a clacking, clashing, and strumming orchestral accompaniment.

"What is that record?" Cornelius inquires of Ingrid, as she passes him by in the arms of the pale young speculator, with reference to the piece then playing, whose alternate languors and furies he finds comparatively pleasing and showing a certain resourcefulness in detail.

"Prince of Pappenheim: 'Console thee, dearest child,' " she answers, and smiles pleasantly back at him with her white teeth.

The cigarette smoke wreathes beneath the chandelier. The air is blue with a festal haze compact of sweet and thrilling ingredients that stir the blood with memories of green-sick pains and are particularly poignant to those whose youth—like the Professor's own—has been over-sensitive. . . . The little folk are still on the floor. They are allowed to stop up until eight, so great is their delight in the party. The guests have got used to their presence; in their own way, they have their place in the doings of the evening. They have separated, anyhow: Snapper revolves all alone in the middle of the carpet, in his little blue velvet smock, while Ellie is running after one of the dancing couples, trying to hold the man fast by his coat. It is Max Hergesell and Fräulein Plaichinger. They dance well, it is a pleasure to watch them. One has to admit that these mad modern dances, when the right people dance them, are not so bad after all—they have something quite taking. Young Hergesell is a capital leader, dances according to rule, yet with individuality. So it looks. With what aplomb can he walk backwards— when space permits! And he knows how to be graceful standing still in a crowd. And his partner supports him well, being unsuspectedly lithe and buoyant, as fat people often are. They look at each other, they are talking, paying no heed to Ellie, though others are smiling to see the child's persistence. Dr. Cornelius tries to catch up his little sweetheart as she passes and draw her to him. But Ellie eludes him, almost peevishly; her dear Abel is nothing to her now. She braces her little arms against his chest and turns her face away with a persecuted look. Then escapes to follow her fancy once more.

The Professor feels an involuntary twinge. Uppermost in his heart is hatred for this party, with its power to intoxicate and estrange his darling child. His love for her—that not quite disinterested, not quite unexceptionable love of his—is easily wounded. He wears a mechanical smile, but his eyes have clouded, and he stares fixedly at a point in the carpet, between the dancers' feet.

"The children ought to go to bed," he tells his wife. But she pleads for another quarter of an hour; she has promised already, and they do love it so! He smiles again and shakes his head, stands so a moment and then goes across to the cloak-room, which is full of coats and hats and scarves and over-shoes. He has trouble in rummaging out his own coat, and Max Hergesell comes out of the hall, wiping his brow.

"Going out, sir?" he asks, in Hergesellian accents, dutifully helping the older man on with his coat. "Silly business this, with my pumps," he says. "They pinch like hell. The brutes are simply too tight for me, quite apart from the bad leather. They press just here on the ball of my great toe"—he stands on one foot and holds the other in his hand—"it's simply unbearable. There's nothing for it but to take them off; my brogues will have to do the business. . . . Oh, let me help you, sir."

"Thanks," says Cornelius. "Don't trouble. Get rid of your own tor-mentors. . . . Oh, thanks very much!" For Hergesell has gone on one knee to snap the fasteners of his snow-boots.

Once more the Professor expresses his gratitude; he is pleased and touched by so much sincere respect and youthful readiness to serve. "Go and enjoy yourself," he counsels. "Change your shoes and make up for what you have been suffering. Nobody can dance in shoes that pinch. Good-bye, I must be off to get a breath of fresh air."

"I'm going to dance with Ellie now," calls Hergesell after him. "She'll be a first-rate dancer when she grows up, and that I'll swear to."

"Think so?" Cornelius answers, already half out. "Well, you are a connoisseur, I'm sure. Don't get curvature of the spine with stooping."

He nods again and goes. "Fine lad," he thinks as he shuts the door. "Student of engineering. Knows what he's bound for, got a good clear head, and so well set up and pleasant too." And again paternal envy rises as he compares his poor Bert's status with this young man's, which he puts in the rosiest light that his son's may look the darker. Thus he sets out on his evening walk.

He goes up the avenue, crosses the bridge, and walks along the bank on the other side as far as the next bridge but one. The air is wet and cold, with a little snow now and then. He turns up his coat-collar and slips the crook of his cane over the arm behind his back. Now and then he ventilates his lungs with a long deep breath of the night air. As usual when he walks, his mind reverts to his professional preoccupations, he thinks about his lec-tures and the things he means to say tomorrow about Philip's struggle against the Germanic revolution, things steeped in melancholy and penetratingly just. Above all just, he thinks. For in one's dealings with the young it behooves one to display the scientific spirit, to exhibit the principles of enlightenment—not only for purposes of mental discipline, but on the human and individual side, in order not to wound them or indirectly offend their political sensibilities; particularly in these days, when there is so much tinder in the air, opinions are so frightfully split up and chaotic, and you may so easily incur attacks from one party or the other, or even give rise to scandal, by taking sides on a point of history. "And taking sides is unhistoric anyhow," so he muses. "Only justice, only impartiality is historic." And could not, properly considered, be otherwise. . . . For justice can have nothing of youthful fire and blithe, fresh, loyal conviction. It is by nature melancholy. And, being so, has secret affinity with the lost cause and the forlorn hope rather than with the fresh and blithe and loyal—perhaps this affinity is its very essence and without it it would not exist at all! . . . "And is there then no such thing as justice?" the Professor asks himself, and ponders the question so deeply that he absently posts his letters in the next box and turns round to go home. This thought of his is unsettling and disturbing to the scientific mind—but is it not after all itself scientific, psychological, conscientious, and therefore to be accepted without prejudice, no matter how upsetting? In the midst of which musings Dr. Cornelius finds himself back at his own door.

On the outer threshold stands Xaver, and seems to be looking for him.

"Herr Professor," says Xaver, tossing back his hair, "go upstairs to Ellie straight off. She's in a bad way."

"What's the matter?" asks Cornelius in alarm. "Is she ill?"

"No-o, not to say ill," answers Xaver. "She's just in a bad way and crying fit to bust her little heart. It's along o' that chap with the shirt-front that danced with her—Herr Hergesell. She couldn't be got to go upstairs peaceably, not at no price at all, and she's b'en crying bucketfuls."

"Nonsense," says the Professor, who has entered and is tossing off his things in the cloak-room. He says no more; opens the glass door and without a glance at the guests turns swiftly to the stairs. Takes them two at a time, crosses the upper hall and the small room leading into the nursery. Xaver follows at his heels, but stops at the nursery door.

A bright light still burns within, showing the gay frieze that runs all round the room, the large row of shelves heaped with a confusion of toys, the rocking-horse on his swaying platform, with red-varnished nostrils and raised hoofs. On the linoleum lie other toys—building blocks, railway trains, a little trumpet. The two white cribs stand not far apart, Ellie's in the window corner, Snapper's out in the room.

Snapper is asleep. He has said his prayers in loud, ringing tones, prompted by Nurse, and gone off at once into vehement, profound, and rosy slumber—from which a cannon-ball fired at close range could not rouse him. He lies with both fists flung back on the pillows on either side of the tousled head with its funny crooked little slumber-tossed wig.

A circle of females surrounds Ellie's bed: not only blue-faced Ann is there, but the Hinterhofer ladies too, talking to each other and to her. They make way as the Professor comes up and reveal the child sitting all pale among her pillows, sobbing and weeping more bitterly than he has ever seen her sob and weep in her life. Her lovely little hands lie on the coverlet in front of her, the nightgown with its narrow lace border has slipped down from her shoulder—such a thin, birdlike little shoulder—and the sweet head Cornelius loves so well, set on the neck like a flower on its stalk, her head is on one side, with the eyes rolled up to the corner between wall and ceiling above her head. For there she seems to envisage the anguish of her heart and even to nod to it—either on purpose or because her head wobbles as her body is shaken with the violence of her sobs. Her eyes rain down tears. The bow-shaped lips are parted, like a little *mater dolorosa's,* and from them issue long, low wails that in nothing resemble the unnecessary and exasperating shrieks of a naughty child, but rise from the deep extremity of her heart and wake in the Professor's own a sympathy that is well-nigh intolerable. He has never seen his darling so before. His feelings find immediate vent in an attack on the ladies Hinterhofer.

"What about the supper?" he asks sharply. "There must be a great deal to do. Is my wife being left to do it alone?"

For the acute sensibilities of the former middle class this is quite enough. The ladies withdraw in righteous indignation, and Xaver Kleingutl jeers at them as they pass out. Having been born to low life instead of achieving it, he never loses a chance to mock at their fallen state.

"Childie, childie," murmurs Cornelius, and sitting down by the crib enfolds the anguished Ellie in his arms. "What is the trouble with my darling?"

She bedews his face with her tears.

"Abel . . . Abel . . ." she stammers between sobs. "Why—isn't Max— my brother? Max ought to be—my brother!"

Alas, alas! What mischance is this? Is this what the party has wrought, with its fatal atmosphere? Cornelius glances helplessly up at blue-faced Ann standing there in all the dignity of her limitations with her hands before her on her apron. She purses up her mouth and makes a long face. "It's pretty young," she says, "for the female instincts to be showing up."

"Hold your tongue," snaps Cornelius, in his agony. He has this much to be thankful for, that Ellie does not turn from him now; she does not push him away as she did downstairs, but clings to him in her need, while she reiterates her absurd, bewildered prayer that Max might be her brother, or with a fresh burst of desire demands to be taken downstairs so that he can dance with her again. But Max, of course, is dancing with Fräulein Plaichinger, that behemoth who is his rightful partner and had every claim upon him; whereas Ellie—never, thinks the Professor, his heart torn with the violence of his pity, never has she looked so tiny and birdlike as now, when she nestles to him shaken with sobs and all unaware of what is happening in her little soul. No, she does not know. She does not comprehend that her suffering is on account of Fräulein Plaichinger, fat, overgrown, and utterly within her rights in dancing with Max Hergesell, whereas Ellie may only do it once, by way of a joke, although she is incomparably the more charming of the two. Yet it would be quite mad to reproach young Hergesell with the state of affairs or to make fantastic demands upon him. No, Ellie's suffering is without help or healing and must be covered up. Yet just as it is without understanding, so it is also without restraint—and that is what makes it so horribly painful. Xaver and blue-faced Ann do not feel this pain, it does not affect them—either because of native callousness or because they accept it as the way of nature. But the Professor's fatherly heart is quite torn by it, and by a distressful horror of this passion, so hopeless and so absurd.

Of no avail to hold forth to poor Ellie on the subject of the perfectly good little brother she already has. She only casts a distraught and scornful glance over at the other crib, where Snapper lies vehemently slumbering, and with fresh tears calls again for Max. Of no avail either the promise of a long, long walk tomorrow, all five gentlemen, round and round the dining-room table; or a dramatic description of the thrilling cushion games they will play. No, she will listen to none of all this, nor to lying down and going to sleep. She will not sleep, she will sit bolt upright and suffer. . . . But on a sudden they stop and listen, Abel and Ellie; listen to something miraculous that is coming to pass, that is approaching by strides, two strides to the nursery door, that now overwelmingly appears. . . .

It is Xaver's work, not a doubt of that. He has not remained by the door where he stood to gloat over the ejection of the Hinterhofers. No, he has bestirred himself, taken a notion; likewise steps to carry it out. Down-stairs he has gone, twitched Herr Hergesell's sleeve, and made a thick-lipped request. So here they both are. Xaver, having done his part, remains by the door; but Max Hergesell comes up to Ellie's crib; in his dinner-jacket, with his sketchy side-whisker and charming black eyes; obviously quite pleased with his rôle of swan knight and fairy prince, as one who should say: "See, here am I, now all losses are restored and sorrows end."

Cornelius is almost as much overcome as Ellie herself.

"Just look," he says feebly, "look who's here. This is uncommonly good of you, Herr Hergesell."

"Not a bit of it," says Hergesell. "Why shouldn't I come to say good-night to my fair partner?"

And he approaches the bars of the crib, behind which Ellie sits struck mute. She smiles blissfully through her tears. A funny, high little note that is half a sigh of relief comes from her lips, then she looks dumbly up at her swan knight with her golden-brown eyes—tear-swollen though they are, so much more beautiful than the fat Plaichinger's. She does not put up her arms. Her joy, like her grief, is without understanding; but she does not do that. The lovely little hands lie quiet on the coverlet, and Max Hergesell stands with his arms leaning over the rail as on a balcony.

"And now," he says smartly, "she need not 'sit the livelong night and weep upon her bed'!" He looks at the Professor to make sure he is receiving due credit of the quotation. "Ha ha!" he laughs, "she's beginning young.

'Console thee, dearest child!' Never mind, you're all right! Just as you are you'll be wonderful! You've only got to grow up. . . . And you'll lie down and go to sleep like a good girl, now I've come to say good-night? And not cry any more, little Lorelei?"

Ellie looks up at him, transfigured. One birdlike shoulder is bare; the Professor draws the lace-trimmed nighty over it. There comes into his mind a sentimental story he once read about a dying child who longs to see a clown he had once, with unforgettable ecstasy, beheld in a circus. And they bring the clown to the bedside marvellously arrayed, embroidered before and behind with silver butterflies; and the child dies happy. Max Hergesell is not embroidered, and Ellie, thank God, is not going to die, she has only "been in a bad way." But, after all, the effect is the same. Young Hergesell leans over the bars of the crib and rattles on, more for the father's ear than the child's, but Ellie does not know that—and the father's feelings towards him are a most singular mixture of thankfulness, embarrassment, and hatred.

"Good night, little Lorelei," says Hergesell, and gives her his hand through the bars. Her pretty, soft, white little hand is swallowed up in the grasp of his big, strong, red one. "Sleep well," he says, "and sweet dreams! But don't dream about me—God forbid! Not at your age—ha ha!" And then the fairy clown's visit is at an end. Cornelius accompanies him to the door. "No, no, positively, no thanks called for, don't mention it," he large-heartedly protests; and Xaver goes downstairs with him, to help serve the Italian salad.

But Dr. Cornelius returns to Ellie, who is now lying down, with her cheek pressed into her flat little pillow.

"Well, wasn't that lovely?" he says as he smoothes the covers. She nods, with one last little sob. For a quarter of an hour he sits beside her and watches while she falls asleep in her turn, beside the little brother who found the right way so much earlier than she. Her silky brown hair takes the enchanting fall it always does when she sleeps; deep, deep lie the lashes over the eyes that late so abundantly poured forth their sorrow; the angelic mouth with its bowed upper lip is peacefully relaxed and a little open. Only now and then comes a belated catch in her slow breathing.

And her small hands, like pink and white flowers, lie so quietly, one on the coverlet, the other on the pillow by her face—Dr. Cornelius, gazing, feels his heart melt with tenderness as with strong wine.

"How good," he thinks, "that she breathes in oblivion with every breath she draws! That in childhood each night is a deep, wide gulf between one day and the next. Tomorrow, beyond all doubt, young Hergesell will be a pale shadow, powerless to darken her little heart. Tomorrow, forgetful of all but present joy, she will walk with Abel and Snapper, all five gentlemen, round and round the table, will play the ever-thrilling cushion game."

Heaven be praised for that!

D. H. Lawrence

THE ROCKING-HORSE WINNER

THERE was a woman who was beautiful, who started with all the advantages, yet she had no luck. She married for love, and the love turned to dust. She had bonny children, yet she felt they had been thrust upon her, and she could not love them. They looked at her coldly, as if they were finding fault with her. And hurriedly she felt she must cover up some fault in herself. Yet what it was that she must cover up she never knew. Nevertheless, when her children were present, she always felt the centre of her heart go hard. This troubled her, and in her manner she was all the more gentle and anxious for her children, as if she loved them very much. Only she herself knew that at the centre of her heart was a hard little place that could not feel love, no, not for anybody. Everybody else said of her: "She is such a good mother. She adores her children." Only she herself, and her children themselves, knew it was not so. They read it in each other's eyes.

There were a boy and two little girls. They lived in a pleasant house, with a garden, and they had discreet servants, and felt themselves superior to anyone in the neighbourhood.

Although they lived in style, they felt always an anxiety in the house. There was never enough money. The mother had a small income, and the father had a small income, but not nearly enough for the social position which they had to keep up. The father went in to town to some office. But though he had good prospects, these prospects never materialized. There was always the grinding sense of the shortage of money, though the style was always kept up.

At last the mother said: "I will see if *I* can't make something." But she did not know where to begin. She racked her brains, and tried this thing and the other, but could not find anything successful. The failure made deep lines come into her face. Her children were growing up, they would have to go to school. There must be more money, there must be more money. The father, who was always very handsome and expensive in his tastes, seemed as if he never *would* be able to do anything worth doing. And the mother, who had a great belief in herself, did not succeed any better, and her tastes were just as expensive.

And so the house came to be haunted by the unspoken phrase: *There must be more money! There must be more money!* The children could hear it all the time, though nobody said it aloud. They heard it at Christmas, when the expensive and splendid toys filled the nursery. Behind the shining modern rocking-horse, behind the smart doll's-house, a voice would start whispering: "There *must* be more money! There *must* be more money!" And the children would stop playing, to listen for a moment. They would look into each other's eyes, to see if they had all heard. And each one saw in the eyes of the other two that they too had heard. "There *must* be more money! There *must* be more money!"

It came whispering from the springs of the still-swaying rocking-horse, and even the horse, bending his wooden, champing head, heard it. The big doll, sitting so pink and smirking in her new pram, could hear it quite plainly, and seemed to be smirking all the more self-consciously because of it. The foolish puppy, too, that took the place of the teddy-bear, he was looking so extraordinarily foolish for no other reason but that he heard the secret whisper all over the house: "There *must* be more money!"

Yet nobody ever said it aloud. The whisper was everywhere, and therefore no one spoke it. Just as no one ever says: "We are breathing!" in spite of the fact that breath is coming and going all the time.

"Mother," said the boy Paul one day, "why don't we keep a car of our own? Why do we always use uncle's, or else a taxi?"

"Because we're the poor members of the family," said the mother.

"But why *are* we, mother?"

"Well—I suppose," she said slowly and bitterly, "it's because your father has no luck."

The boy was silent for some time.

"Is luck money, mother?" he asked rather timidly.

"No, Paul. Not quite. It's what causes you to have money."

"Oh!" said Paul vaguely. "I thought when Uncle Oscar said *filthy lucker,* it meant money."

"*Filthy* lucre does mean money," said the mother. "But it's lucre, not luck."

"Oh!" said the boy. "Then what *is* luck, mother?"

"It's what causes you to have money. If you're lucky you have money. That's why it's better to be born lucky than rich. If you're rich, you may lose your money. But if you're lucky, you will always get more money."

"Oh! Will you? And is father not lucky?"

"Very unlucky, I should say," she said bitterly.

The boy watched her with unsure eyes.

"Why?" he asked.

"I don't know. Nobody ever knows why one person is lucky and another unlucky."

"Don't they? Nobody at all? Does *nobody* know?"

"Perhaps God. But He never tells."

"He ought to, then. And aren't you lucky either, mother?"

"I can't be, if I married an unlucky husband."

"But by yourself, aren't you?"

"I used to think I was, before I married. Now I think I am very unlucky indeed."

"Why?"

"Well—never mind! Perhaps I'm not really," she said.

The child looked at her, to see if she meant it. But he saw, by the lines of her mouth, that she was only trying to hide something from him.

"Well, anyhow," he said stoutly, "I'm a lucky person."

"Why?" said his mother, with a sudden laugh.

He stared at her. He didn't even know why he had said it.

"God told me," he asserted, brazening it out.

"I hope He did, dear!" she said, again with a laugh, but rather bitter.

"He did, mother!"

"Excellent!" said the mother, using one of her husband's exclamations.

The boy saw she did not believe him; or, rather, that she paid no attention to his assertion. This angered him somewhat, and made him want to compel her attention.

He went off by himself, vaguely, in a childish way, seeking for the clue to "luck." Absorbed, taking no heed of other people, he went about with a sort of stealth, seeking inwardly for luck. He wanted luck, he wanted it, he wanted it. When the two girls were playing dolls in the nursery, he would sit on his big rocking-horse, charging madly into space, with a frenzy that made the little girls peer at him uneasily. Wildly the horse careered, the waving dark hair of the boy tossed, his eyes had a strange glare in them. The little girls dared not speak to him.

When he had ridden to the end of his mad little journey, he climbed down and stood in front of his rocking-horse, staring fixedly into its lowered face. Its red mouth was slightly open, its big eye was wide and glassy-bright.

"Now!" he would silently command the snorting steed. "Now, take me to where there is luck! Now take me!"

And he would slash the horse on the neck with the little whip he had asked Uncle Oscar for. He *knew* the horse could take him to where there was luck, if only he forced it. So he would mount again, and start on his furious ride, hoping at last to get there. He knew he could get there.

"You'll break your horse, Paul!" said the nurse.

"He's always riding like that! I wish he'd leave off!" said his elder sister Joan.

But he only glared down on them in silence. Nurse gave him up. She could make nothing of him. Anyhow he was growing beyond her.

One day his mother and his Uncle Oscar came in when he was on one of his furious rides. He did not speak to them.

"Hallo, you young jockey! Riding a winner?" said his uncle.

"Aren't you growing too big for a rocking-horse? You're not a very little boy any longer, you know," said his mother.

But Paul only gave a blue glare from his big, rather close-set eyes. He would speak to nobody when he was in full tilt. His mother watched him with an anxious expression on her face.

At last he suddenly stopped forcing his horse into the mechanical gallop, and slid down.

"Well, I got there!" he announced fiercely, his blue eyes still flaring, and his sturdy long legs straddling apart.

"Where did you get to?" asked his mother.

"Where I wanted to go," he flared back at her.

"That's right, son!" said Uncle Oscar. "Don't you stop till you get there. What's the horse's name?"

"He doesn't have a name," said the boy.

"Gets on without all right?" asked the uncle.

"Well, he has different names. He was called Sansovino last week."

"Sansovino, eh? Won the Ascot. How did you know his name?"

"He always talks about horse-races with Bassett," said Joan.

The uncle was delighted to find that his small nephew was posted with all the racing news. Bassett, the young gardener, who had been wounded in the left foot in the war and had got his present job through Oscar Cresswell, whose batman he had been, was a perfect blade of the "turf." He lived in the racing events, and the small boy lived with him.

Oscar Cresswell got it all from Bassett.

"Master Paul comes and asks me, so I can't do more than tell him, sir," said Bassett, his face terribly serious, as if he were speaking of religious matters.

"And does he ever put anything on a horse he fancies?"

"Well—I don't want to give him away—he's a young sport, a fine sport, sir. Would you mind asking him himself? He sort of takes a pleasure in it, and perhaps he'd feel I was giving him away, sir, if you don't mind."

Bassett was serious as a church.

The uncle went back to his nephew and took him off for a ride in the car.

"Say, Paul, old man, do you ever put anything on a horse?" the uncle asked.

The boy watched the handsome man closely.

"Why, do you think I oughtn't to?" he parried.

"Not a bit of it! I thought perhaps you might give me a tip for the Lincoln."

The car sped on into the country, going down to Uncle Oscar's place in Hampshire.

"Honour bright?" said the nephew.

"Honour bright, son!" said the uncle.

"Well, then, Daffodil."

"Daffodil! I doubt it, sonny. What about Mirza?"

"I only know the winner," said the boy. "That's Daffodil."

"Daffodil, eh?"

There was a pause. Daffodil was an obscure horse comparatively.

"Uncle!"

"Yes, son?"

"You won't let it go any further, will you? I promised Bassett."

"Bassett be damned, old man! What's he got to do with it?"

"We're partners. We've been partners from the first. Uncle, he lent me my first five shillings, which I lost. I promised him, honour bright, it was only between me and him; only you gave me that ten-shilling note I started winning with, so I thought you were lucky. You won't let it go any further, will you?"

The boy gazed at his uncle from those big, hot, blue eyes, set rather close together. The uncle stirred and laughed uneasily.

"Right you are, son! I'll keep your tip private. Daffodil, eh? How much are you putting on him?"

"All except twenty pounds," said the boy. "I keep that in reserve."

The uncle thought it a good joke.

"You keep twenty pounds in reserve, do you, you young romancer? What are you betting, then?"

"I'm betting three hundred," said the boy gravely. "But it's between you and me, Uncle Oscar! Honour bright?"

The uncle burst into a roar of laughter.

"It's between you and me all right, you young Nat Gould," he said, laughing. "But where's your three hundred?"

"Bassett keeps it for me. We're partners."

"You are, are you! And what is Bassett putting on Daffodil?"

"He won't go quite as high as I do, I expect. Perhaps he'll go a hundred and fifty."

"What, pennies?" laughed the uncle.

"Pounds," said the child, with a surprised look at his uncle. "Bassett keeps a bigger reserve than I do."

Between wonder and amusement Uncle Oscar was silent. He pursued the matter no further, but he determined to take his nephew with him to the Lincoln races.

"Now, son," he said, "I'm putting twenty on Mirza, and I'll put five for you on any horse you fancy. What's your pick?"

"Daffodil, uncle."

"No, not the fiver on Daffodil!"

"I should if it was my own fiver," said the child.

"Good! Good! Right you are! A fiver for me and a fiver for you on Daffodil."

The child had never been to a race-meeting before, and his eyes were blue fire. He pursed his mouth tight, and watched. A Frenchman just in front had put his money on Lancelot. Wild with excitement, he flayed his arms up and down, yelling *"Lancelot! Lancelot!"* in his French accent.

Daffodil came in first, Lancelot second, Mirza third. The child, flushed and with eyes blazing, was curiously serene. His uncle brought him four five-pound notes, four to one.

"What am I to do with these?" he cried, waving them before the boy's eyes.

"I suppose we'll talk to Bassett," said the boy. "I expect I have fifteen hundred now; and twenty in reserve; and this twenty."

His uncle studied him for some moments.

"Look here, son!" he said. "You're not serious about Bassett and that fifteen hundred, are you?"

"Yes, I am. But it's between you and me, uncle. Honour bright!"

"Honour bright all right, son! But I must talk to Bassett."

"If you'd like to be a partner, uncle, with Bassett and me, we could all be partners. Only, you'd have to promise, honour bright, uncle, not to let it go beyond us three. Bassett and I are lucky, and you must be lucky, because it was your ten shillings I started winning with. . . ."

Uncle Oscar took both Bassett and Paul into Richmond Park for an afternoon, and there they talked.

"It's like this, you see, sir," Bassett said. "Master Paul would get me talking about racing events, spinning yarns, you know, sir. And he was always keen on knowing if I'd made or if I'd lost. It's about a year since, now, that I put five shilling on Blush of Dawn for him—and we lost. Then the luck turned, with that ten shillings he had from you, that we put on Singhalese. And since that time, it's been pretty steady, all things considering. What do you say, Master Paul?"

"We're all right when we're sure," said Paul. "It's when we're not quite sure that we go down."

"Oh, but we're careful then," said Bassett.

"But when are you *sure?*" smiled Uncle Oscar.

"It's Master Paul, sir," said Bassett, in a secret, religious voice. "It's as if he had it from heaven. Like Daffodil, now, for the Lincoln. That was as sure as eggs."

"Did you put anything on Daffodil?" asked Oscar Cresswell.

"Yes, sir. I made my bit."

"And my nephew?"

Bassett was obstinately silent, looking at Paul.

"I made twelve hundred, didn't I, Bassett? I told uncle I was putting three hundred on Daffodil."

"That's right," said Bassett, nodding.

"But where's the money?" asked the uncle.

"I keep it safe locked up, sir. Master Paul he can have it any minute he likes to ask for it."

"What, fifteen hundred pounds?"

"And twenty! And *forty,* that is, with the twenty he made on the course."

"It's amazing!" said the uncle.

"If Master Paul offers you to be partners, sir, I would, if I were you; if you'll excuse me," said Bassett.

Oscar Cresswell thought about it.

"I'll see the money," he said.

They drove home again, and sure enough, Bassett came round to the garden-house with fifteen hundred pounds in notes. The twenty pounds reserve was left with Joe Glee, in the Turf Commission deposit.

"You see, it's all right, uncle, when I'm *sure!* Then we go strong, for all we're worth. Don't we, Bassett?"

"We do that, Master Paul."

"And when are you sure?" said the uncle, laughing.

"Oh, well, sometimes I'm *absolutely* sure, like about Daffodil," said the boy; "and sometimes I have an idea; and sometimes I haven't even an idea, have I, Bassett? Then we're careful, because we mostly go down."

"You do, do you! And when you're sure, like about Daffodil, what makes you sure, sonny?"

"Oh, well, I don't know," said the boy uneasily. "I'm sure, you know, uncle; that's all."

"It's as if he had it from heaven, sir," Bassett reiterated.

"I should say so!" said the uncle.

But he became a partner. And when the Leger was coming on, Paul was "sure" about Lively Spark, which was a quite inconsiderable horse. The boy insisted on putting a thousand on the horse, Bassett went for five hundred, and Oscar Cresswell two hundred. Lively Spark came in first, and the betting had been ten to one against him. Paul had made ten thousand.

"You see," he said, "I was absolutely sure of him."

Even Oscar Cresswell had cleared two thousand.

"Look here, son," he said, "this sort of thing makes me nervous."

"It needn't, uncle! Perhaps I shan't be sure again for a long time."

"But what are you going to do with your money?" asked the uncle.

"Of course," said the boy, "I started it for mother. She said she had no luck, because father is unlucky, so I thought if *I* was lucky, it might stop whispering."

"What might stop whispering?"

"Our house. I *hate* our house for whispering."

"What does it whisper?"

"Why—why"—the boy fidgeted—"why, I don't know. But it's always short of money, you know, uncle."

"I know it, son, I know it."

"You know people send mother writs, don't you, uncle?"

"I'm afraid I do," said the uncle.

"And then the house whispers, like people laughing at you behind your back. It's awful, that is! I thought if I was lucky . . ."

"You might stop it," added the uncle.

The boy watched him with big blue eyes, that had an uncanny cold fire in them, and he said never a word.

"Well, then!" said the uncle. "What are we doing?"

"I shouldn't like mother to know I was lucky," said the boy.

"Why not, son?"

"She'd stop me."

"I don't think she would."

"Oh!"—and the boy writhed in an odd way—"I *don't* want her to know, uncle."

"All right, son! We'll manage it without her knowing."

They managed it very easily. Paul, at the other's suggestion, handed over five thousand pounds to his uncle, who deposited it with the family lawyer, who was then to inform Paul's mother that a relative had put five thousand pounds into his hands, which sum was to be paid out a thousand pounds at a time, on the mother's birthday, for the next five years.

"So she'll have a birthday present of a thousand pounds for five successive years," said Uncle Oscar. "I hope it won't make it all the harder for her later."

Paul's mother had her birthday in November. The house had been "whispering" worse than ever lately, and, even in spite of his luck, Paul could not bear up against it. He was very anxious to see the effect of the birthday letter, telling his mother about the thousand pounds.

When there were no visitors, Paul now took his meals with his parents, as he was beyond the nursery control. His mother went into town nearly every day. She had discovered that she had an odd knack of sketching furs and dress materials, so she worked secretly in the studio of a friend who was the chief "artist" for the leading drapers. She drew the figures of ladies in furs and ladies in silk and sequins for the newspaper advertisements. This young woman artist earned several thousand pounds a year, but Paul's mother only made several hundreds, and she was again dissatisfied. She so wanted to be first in something, and she did not succeed, even in making sketches for drapery advertisements.

She was down to breakfast on the morning of her birthday. Paul watched her face as she read her letters. He knew the lawyer's letter. As his mother read it, her face hardened and became more expressionless. Then a cold, determined look came on her mouth. She hid the letter under the pile of others, and said not a word about it.

"Didn't you have anything nice in the post for your birthday, mother?" said Paul.

"Quite moderately nice," she said, her voice cold and absent.

She went away to town without saying more.

But in the afternoon Uncle Oscar appeared. He said Paul's mother had had a long interview with the lawyer, asking if the whole five thousand could not be advanced at once, as she was in debt.

"What do you think, uncle?" said the boy.

"I leave it to you, son."

"Oh, let her have it, then! We can get some more with the other," said the boy.

"A bird in the hand is worth two in the bush, laddie!" said Uncle Oscar.

"But I'm sure to *know* for the Grand National; or the Lincolnshire; or else the Derby. I'm sure to know for *one* of them," said Paul.

So Uncle Oscar signed the agreement, and Paul's mother touched the whole five thousand. Then something very curious happened. The voices in the house suddenly went mad, like a chorus of frogs on a spring evening. There were certain new furnishings, and Paul had a tutor. He was *really* going to Eton, his father's school, in the following autumn. There were flowers in the winter, and a blossoming of the luxury Paul's mother had been used to. And yet the voices in the house, behind the sprays of mimosa and almond blossom, and from under the piles of iridescent cushions, simply trilled and screamed in a sort of ecstasy: "There *must* be more money! Oh-h-h; there *must* be more money. Oh, now, now-w! Now-w-w—there *must* be more money!—more than ever! More than ever!"

It frightened Paul terribly. He studied away at his Latin and Greek with his tutors. But his intense hours were spent with Bassett. The Grand National had gone by: he had not "known," and had lost a hundred pounds. Summer was at hand. He was in agony for the Lincoln. But even for the Lincoln he didn't "know," and he lost fifty pounds. He became wild-eyed and strange, as if something were going to explode in him.

"Let it alone, son! Don't you bother about it!" urged Uncle Oscar. But it was as if the boy couldn't really hear what his uncle was saying.

"I've got to know for the Derby! I've got to know for the Derby!" the child reiterated, his big blue eyes blazing with a sort of madness.

His mother noticed how overwrought he was.

"You'd better go to the seaside. Wouldn't you like to go now to the seaside, instead of waiting? I think you'd better," she said, looking down at him anxiously, her heart curiously heavy because of him.

But the child lifted his uncanny blue eyes.

"I couldn't possibly go before the Derby, mother!" he said. "I couldn't possibly!"

"Why not?" she said, her voice becoming heavy when she was opposed. "Why not? You can still go from the seaside to see the Derby with your Uncle Oscar, if that's what you wish. No need for you to wait here. Besides, I think you care too much about these races. It's a bad sign. My family has been a gambling family, and you won't know till you grow up how much damage it has done. But it has done damage. I shall have to send Bassett away, and ask Uncle Oscar not to talk racing to you, unless you promise to be reasonable about it; go away to the seaside and forget it. You're all nerves!"

"I'll do what you like, mother, so long as you don't send me away till after the Derby," the boy said.

"Send you away from where? Just from this house?"

"Yes," he said, gazing at her.

"Why, you curious child, what makes you care about this house so much, suddenly? I never knew you loved it."

He gazed at her without speaking. He had a secret within a secret, something he had not divulged, even to Bassett or to his Uncle Oscar.

But his mother, after standing undecided and a little bit sullen for some moments, said:

"Very well, then! Don't go to the seaside till after the Derby, if you don't wish it. But promise me you won't let your nerves go to pieces. Promise you won't think so much about horse-racing and *events,* as you call them!"

"Oh, no," said the boy casually. "I won't think much about them, mother. You needn't worry. I wouldn't worry, mother, if I were you."

"If you were me and I were you," said his mother, "I wonder what we *should* do!"

"But you know you needn't worry, mother, don't you?" the boy repeated.

"I should be awfully glad to know it," she said wearily.

"Oh, well, you *can,* you know. I mean, you *ought* to know you needn't worry," he insisted.

"Ought I? Then I'll see about it," she said.

Paul's secret of secrets was his wooden horse, that which had no name. Since he was emancipated from a nurse and a nursery-governess, he had had his rocking-horse removed to his own bedroom at the top of the house.

"Surely, you're too big for a rocking-horse!" his mother had remonstrated.

"Well, you see, mother, till I can have a *real* horse, I like to have *some* sort of animal about," had been his quaint answer.

"Do you feel he keeps you company?" she laughed.

"Oh, yes! He's very good, he always keeps me company, when I'm there," said Paul.

So the horse, rather shabby, stood in an arrested prance in the boy's bedroom.

The Derby was drawing near, and the boy grew more and more tense. He hardly heard what was spoken to him, he was very frail, and his eyes were really uncanny. His mother had sudden strange seizures of uneasiness about him. Sometimes, for half-an-hour, she would feel a sudden anxiety about him that was almost anguish. She wanted to rush to him at once, and know he was safe.

Two nights before the Derby, she was at a big party in town, when one of her rushes of anxiety about her boy, her first-born, gripped her heart till she could hardly speak. She fought with the feeling, might and main, for she believed in common-sense. But it was too strong. She had to leave the dance and go downstairs to telephone to the country. The children's nursery-governess was terribly surprised and startled at being rung up in the night.

"Are the children all right, Miss Wilmot?"

"Oh, yes, they are quite all right."

"Master Paul? Is he all right?"

"He went to bed as right as a trivet. Shall I run up and look at him?"

"No," said Paul's mother reluctantly. "No! Don't trouble. It's all right. Don't sit up. We shall be home fairly soon." She did not want her son's privacy intruded upon.

"Very good," said the governess.

It was about one o'clock when Paul's mother and father drove up to their house. All was still. Paul's mother went to her room and slipped off her white fur cloak. She had told her maid not to wait up for her. She heard her husband downstairs, mixing a whisky-and-soda.

And then, because of the strange anxiety at her heart, she stole upstairs to her son's room. Noiselessly she went along the upper corridor. Was there a faint noise? What was it?

She stood, with arrested muscles, outside his door, listening. There was a strange, heavy, and yet not loud noise. Her heart stood still. It was a sound-less noise, yet rushing and powerful. Something huge, in violent, hushed motion. What was it? What in God's name was it? She ought to know. She felt that she knew the noise. She knew what it was.

Yet she could not place it. She couldn't say what it was. And on and on it went, like a madness.

Softly, frozen with anxiety and fear, she turned the door-handle.

The room was dark. Yet in the space near the window, she heard and saw something plunging to and fro. She gazed in fear and amazament.

Then suddenly she switched on the light, and saw her son, in his green pyjamas, madly surging on the rocking-horse. The blaze of light suddenly lit him up, as he urged the wooden horse, and lit her up, as she stood, blonde, in her dress of pale green and crystal, in the doorway.

"Paul!" she cried. "Whatever are you doing?"

"It's Malabar!" he screamed, in a powerful, strange voice. "It's Malabar!"

His eyes blazed at her for one strange and senseless second, as he ceased urging his wooden horse. Then he fell with a crash to the ground, and she, all her tormented motherhood flooding upon her, rushed to gather him up.

But he was unconscious, and unconscious he remained, with some brain-fever. He talked and tossed, and his mother sat stonily by his side.

"Malabar! It's Malabar! Bassett, Bassett, I *know*! It's Malabar!"

So the child cried, trying to get up and urge the rocking-horse that gave him his inspiration.

"What does he mean by Malabar?" asked the heart-frozen mother.

"I don't know," said the father stonily.

"What does he mean by Malabar?" she asked her brother Oscar.

"It's one of the horses running for the Derby," was the answer.

And, in spite of himself, Oscar Cresswell spoke to Bassett, and himself put a thousand on Malabar: at fourteen to one.

The third day of the illness was critical: they were waiting for a change. The boy, with his rather long, curly hair, was tossing ceaselessly on the pillow. He neither slept nor regained consciousness, and his eyes were like blue stones. His mother sat, feeling her heart had gone, turned actually into a stone.

In the evening, Oscar Cresswell did not come, but Bassett sent a message, saying could he come up for one moment, just one moment? Paul's mother was very angry at the intrusion, but on second thought she agreed. The boy was the same. Perhaps Bassett might bring him to consciousness.

The gardener, a shortish fellow with a little brown moustache, and sharp little brown eyes, tip-toed into the room, touched his imaginary cap to Paul's mother, and stole to the bedside, staring with glittering, smallish eyes, at the tossing, dying child.

"Master Paul!" he whispered. "Master Paul! Malabar came in first all right, a clean win. I did as you told me. You've made over seventy thousand pounds, you have; you've got over eighty thousand. Malabar came in all right, Master Paul."

"Malabar! Malabar! Did I say Malabar, mother? Did I say Malabar? Do you think I'm lucky, mother? I knew Malabar, didn't I? Over eighty thousand pounds! I call that lucky, don't you, mother? Over eighty thousand pounds! I knew, didn't I know I knew? Malabar came in all right. If I ride my horse till I'm sure, then I tell you, Bassett, you can go as high as you like. Did you go for all you were worth, Bassett?"

"I went a thousand on it, Master Paul."

"I never told you, mother, that if I can ride my horse, and *get there,* then I'm absolutely sure—oh, absolutely! Mother, did I ever tell you? I *am* lucky!"

"No, you never did," said the mother.

But the boy died in the night.

And even as he lay dead, his mother heard her brother's voice saying to her: "My God, Hester, you're eighty-odd thousand to the good, and a poor devil of a son to the bad. But, poor devil, poor devil, he's best gone out of a life where he rides his rocking-horse to find a winner."

COMMENTARY

D. H. Lawrence believed that it was a misfortune for man when the Christian ideal of "Light" triumphed over "the dark gods of the blood," that modern civilization was founded on abstract values, and that man's only salvation was a return to a more primitive awareness of self.

His missionary zeal was often stronger than his artistic conscience; grave technical flaws mar some of his best work. "The Rocking-Horse Winner" approaches technical perfection; an artistic intelligence functions in it, con- sciously or unconsciously, giving the story a powerful dramatic impact.

The viewpoint is that of the Roving Narrator (see Appendix A, p. 626). There are a few Long Views (see Appendix A, p. 627), skillfully timed, but for the most part the story consists of "blocks" of action which seem to have the solidity and dimensions of life itself. There are one or two passages in which Lawrence sacrifices this objectivity and tells you what is going on in his young hero's mind instead of rendering it in terms of action, but these passages do not occur at crucial moments, as in "The Princess," for instance, and do not seem to weaken the pattern appreciably.

The Complication (see Appendix A, p. 630) is the situation of the hero, a little boy named Paul, who is unusually sensitive. For him the house he lives in is haunted; voices continually whisper: "There must be more money!" When he asks his mother why they haven't any more money she replies that it is because they are unlucky. Lawrence prepares for the Resolution (see Appendix A, p. 630) when Paul defies the supernatural voices, declaring stoutly, "Well, anyhow, I'm lucky."

In the Resolution Paul discovers, through association with a sporting gardener, that if he rides his rocking horse long enough and madly enough he "knows" the name of the winner of whatever horse race he and the gardener are interested in. The gardener places his bets for him. Paul amasses a little fortune and puts it at his mother's disposal, but the voices whisper more shrilly than ever. He places a few bets when he is not "sure" and goes down, determined to retrieve his fortunes with the Grand National and the Lincoln, but they both go by and he is not "sure." He is all the more determined to "know" for the Derby and, riding his rocking-horse harder than ever, rides across the boundary of the visible world and, screaming the name of the winner, collapses and dies.

It should be observed how one block of action springs out of the preceding block. When Uncle Oscar sees Paul riding his rocking horse he asks the horse's name. But the boy tells him that he has "different names. He was called Sansovino last week."

"Sansovino, eh? Won the Ascot. How did you know his name?"

"He always talks horse races with Bassett," Paul's elder sister, Joan, says. She has previously remarked to the nurse: "He's always riding like that. I wish he'd leave off." Thus, in an apparently casual interchange between a little girl and her nurse and an uncle and his nephew, important parts of the story's Complication are provided for. The uncle's man-of-the-world curiosity about his small nephew's interest in racing (the mechanism by which the action is made to unwind) is established and Joan's reference to Bassett prepares us for the partnership between Paul and the gardener, while her remark to the nurse indicates that Paul's behavior seems strange and even repellent to a normal child.

The Enveloping Action (see Appendix A, p. 631) is represented by the mother. It is her attitude towards life that fills the house with the whispers that start the boy on his race towards death. The envelopment not only furnishes the background but has its own dramatic action. At a key moment, midway of the story, the direct presentation is suspended and a Long View (see Appendix A, p. 627), belonging to the Enveloping Action, flows in and tightens the main current of the story so that it hurls itself faster towards its goal. This Long View—the occasion on which the boy puts five thousand pounds at his mother's disposal—is presented in brilliant detail, muted only by "distance." And yet the voices in the house, behind the sprays of mimosa and almond blossom, and from the piles of iridescent cushions, trilled and screamed in a kind of ecstasy: "There *must* be more money! . . . Now-w-w there *must* be more money!"

Again, action which sets forth the enveloping life of Paul's mother, comes to the front on an evening two nights before the Derby, when she has one of her "rushes of anxiety" about the boy and she and his father come home early from a party, and the mother, stealing along the corridor to the boy's room, hears a "strange, heavy, and yet not loud noise. . . . Something huge, in violent, hushed motion," and opening the door, sees and hears something plunging in the space near the window.

The Enveloping Action—that is, the life of the mother—also has the last word dramatically. As the boy lies dead his mother hears Uncle Oscar, who, "in spite of himself put a thousand on Malabar at fourteen to one," say to her: "My God, Hester, you're eighty-odd thousand pounds to the good, and a poor devil of a son to the bad, but poor devil, poor devil, he's best gone out of a life where he rides a rocking-horse to find a winner."

The details are beautifully rendered throughout the story. The pivot on which the action turns, the fact that the family does not have as much money as the mother thinks it should have, is presented with dramatic objectivity:

"Mother," said the boy Paul one day, "why don't we keep a car of our own? Why do we always use Uncle's, or else a taxi?"

Uncle Oscar—all we need to know about him is that he was handsome, had a fine car, a heart in his bosom and tongue in his head—speaks always admirably in character:

"Say, Paul, old man, do you ever put anything on a horse?" And when the boy, watching him closely, parries with, "Why, do you think I oughtn't to?" he replies with easy camaraderie, "Not a bit of it! I thought perhaps you might give me a tip for the Lincoln."

This remark arouses our admiration by its verisimilitude. It is exactly the kind of thing an amiable, sympathetic uncle might say to a small boy, but it also introduces an important part of the action: the fact that Paul cannot give his uncle a tip on the Lincoln contributes to his death. These solid, dimensional effects contribute a great deal to the dramatic impact of the story.

Many of the details have a double significance, playing their rôles in the action, even while they point it up. We see Paul descending from his first gallop and standing with "his blue eyes still flaring, and his sturdy long legs straddling apart." At the same time, the fact that his blue eyes are set rather close together prepares us for his fanatical pursuit of luck. Bassett, the gardener, has the serious demeanor of the well-trained upper servant. Lawrence's repeated use of the word "religious" in describing him prepares us by indirection for the revelation of the boy's being in the grip of a supernatural power.

At the climax of the story the mother opens her son's door and sees him "in his green pyjamas, madly surging on the rocking-horse." The blaze of light suddenly lit him up as he urged the wooden horse on and *lit her up* as she stood, blonde in her dress of pale green and crystal in the doorway.

Lawrence uses here—unconsciously, no doubt—a technique which is the solid underpinning (see Appendix B, p. 636) of all of Henry James's later work: the rendering of an object or person through reference to another object or person. We see the son through the eyes of the mother; we see the mother through the eyes of the son. The two viewpoints fuse to make a rounded whole.

Lawrence shows a rare objectivity in his use of symbolism (see Appendix A, p. 633) in this story. Again, he reminds us of James, seeming to be determined in this one instance, at least, to let his "message" present itself through symbolic action rather than through exhortation or preachment. The rocking horse is a link between the visible and invisible worlds and is his prime symbol. The horse behaves with traditional sibylline calm. When the boy stares appealingly into its face, its red mouth remains slightly open, its big eyes are wide and glassy-bright.

This story has extraordinary Tonal Unity (see Appendix A, p. 632). Carefully chosen cadences play their part in the dramatic effect. The first paragraph begins: "There was a woman who was beautiful, who started with all the advantages, and yet she had no luck," an admirable preparation for what follows.

The whispering voices also play an important part in the tonal effect, as does Bassett's speech to the dying boy which has the urgent, almost nonsensical quality of any speech made by the living to the dying. The name of the winner, too, is important.

"It's Malabar," he screamed, in a powerful, strange voice. "It's Malabar!"

Let the student substitute a name like "Little Andy" or "Sea Biscuit" for the winner and see what a difference such a substitution will make in the whole story. The combinations of short a's and broad a's has a tragic sound and the word "Malabar" itself strikes our ear strangely. (Joyce achieves the same effect with his title, "Araby.") To sum up: the boy, Paul, has invoked strange gods and pays the penalty with his death.

W. Somerset Maugham

RAIN

IT WAS nearly bed-time and when they awoke next morning land would be in sight. Dr Macphail lit his pipe and, leaning over the rail, searched the heavens for the Southern Cross. After two years at the front and a wound that had taken longer to heal than it should, he was glad to settle down quietly at Apia for twelve months at least, and he felt already better for the journey. Since some of the passengers were leaving the ship next day at Pago-Pago they had had a little dance that evening and in his ears hammered still the harsh notes of the mechanical piano. But the deck was quiet at last. A little way off he saw his wife in a long chair talking with the Davidsons, and he strolled over to her. When he sat down under the light and took off his hat you saw that he had very red hair, with a bald patch on the crown, and the red, freckled skin which accompanies red hair; he was a man of forty, thin, with a pinched face, precise and rather pedantic; and he spoke with a Scots accent in a very low, quiet voice.

Between the Macphails and the Davidsons, who were missionaries, there had arisen the intimacy of shipboard, which is due to propinquity rather than to any community of taste. Their chief tie was the disapproval they shared of the men who spent their days and nights in the smoking-room playing poker or bridge and drinking. Mrs Macphail was not a little flattered to think that she and her husband were the only people on board with whom the Davidsons were willing to associate, and even the doctor, shy but no fool, half unconsciously acknowledged the compliment. It was only because he was of an argumentative mind that in their cabin at night he permitted himself to carp.

"Mrs Davidson was saying she didn't know how they'd have got through the journey if it hadn't been for us," said Mrs Macphail, as she neatly brushed out her transformation. "She said we were really the only people on the ship they cared to know."

"I shouldn't have thought a missionary was such a big bug that he could afford to put on frills."

"It's not frills. I quite understand what she means. It wouldn't have been very nice for the Davidsons to have to mix with all that rough lot in the smoking-room."

"The founder of their religion wasn't so exclusive," said Dr Macphail with a chuckle.

"I've asked you over and over again not to joke about religion," answered his wife. "I shouldn't like to have a nature like yours, Alec. You never look for the best in people."

He gave her a sidelong glance with his pale, blue eyes, but did not reply. After many years of married life he had learned that it was more conducive to peace to leave his wife with the last word. He was undressed before she was, and climbing into the upper bunk he settled down to read himself to sleep.

When he came on deck next morning they were close to land. He looked at it with greedy eyes. There was a thin strip of silver beach rising quickly to hills covered to the top with luxuriant vegetation. The coconut trees, thick and green, came nearly to the water's edge, and among them you saw the grass houses of the Samoans; and here and there, gleaming white, a little church. Mrs Davidson came and stood beside him. She was dressed in black and wore round her neck a gold chain, from which dangled a small cross. She was a little woman, with brown, dull hair very elaborately arranged, and she had prominent blue eyes behind invisible *pince-nez*. Her face was long, like a sheep's, but she gave no impression of foolishness, rather of extreme alertness; she had the quick movements of a bird. The most remarkable thing about her was her voice, high, metallic, and without inflection; it fell on the ear with a hard monotony, irritating to the nerves like the pitiless clamour of the pneumatic drill.

"This must seem like home to you," said Dr Macphail, with his thin, difficult smile.

"Ours are low islands, you know, not like these. Coral. These are volcanic. We've got another ten days' journey to reach them."

"In these parts that's almost like being in the next street at home," said Dr Macphail facetiously.

"Well, that's rather an exaggerated way of putting it, but one does look at distances differently in the South Seas. So far you're right."

Dr Macphail sighed faintly.

"I'm glad we're not stationed here," she went on. "They say this is a terribly difficult place to work in. The steamers' touching makes the people unsettled; and then there's the naval station; that's bad for the natives. In our district we don't have difficulties like that to contend with. There are one or two traders, of course, but we take care to make them behave, and if they don't we make the place so hot for them they're glad to go."

Fixing the glasses on her nose she looked at the green island with a ruthless stare.

"It's almost a hopeless task for the missionaries here. I can never be sufficiently thankful to God that we are at least spared that."

Davidson's district consisted of a group of islands to the North of Samoa; they were widely separated and he had frequently to go long distances by canoe. At these times his wife remained at their headquarters and managed the mission. Dr Macphail felt his heart sink when he considered the efficiency with which she certainly managed it. She spoke of the depravity of the natives in a voice which nothing could hush, but with a vehemently unctuous horror. Her sense of delicacy was singular. Early in their acquaintance she had said to him:

"You know, their marriage customs when we first settled in the islands were so shocking that I couldn't possibly describe them to you. But I'll tell Mrs Macphail and she'll tell you."

Then he had seen his wife and Mrs Davidson, their deck-chairs close together, in earnest conversation for about two hours. As he walked past them backwards and forwards for the sake of exercise, he had heard Mrs Davidson's agitated whisper, like the distant flow of a mountain torrent, and he saw by his wife's open mouth and pale face that she was enjoying an alarming experience. At night in their cabin she repeated to him with bated breath all she had heard.

"Well, what did I say to you?" cried Mrs Davidson, exultant, next morning. "Did you ever hear anything more dreadful? You don't wonder that I couldn't tell you myself, do you? Even though you are a doctor."

Mrs Davidson scanned his face. She had a dramatic eagerness to see that she had achieved the desired effect.

"Can you wonder that when we first went there our hearts sank? You'll hardly believe me when I tell you it was impossible to find a single good girl in any of the villages."

She used the word *good* in a severely technical manner.

"Mr Davidson and I talked it over, and we made up our minds the first thing to do was to put down the dancing. The natives were crazy about dancing."

"I was not averse to it myself when I was a young man," said Dr Macphail.

"I guessed as much when I heard you ask Mrs Macphail to have a turn with you last night. I don't think there's any real harm if a man dances with his wife, but I was relieved that she wouldn't. Under the circumstances I thought it better that we should keep ourselves to ourselves."

"Under what circumstances?"

Mrs Davidson gave him a quick look through her *pince-nez,* but did not answer his question.

"But among white people it's not quite the same," she went on, "though I must say I agree with Mr Davidson, who says he can't understand how a husband can stand by and see his wife in another man's arms, and as far as I'm concerned I've never danced a step since I married. But the native dancing is quite another matter. It's not only immoral in itself, but it distinctly leads to immorality. However, I'm thankful to God that we stamped it out, and I don't think I'm wrong in saying that no one has danced in our district for eight years."

But now they came to the mouth of the harbour and Mrs Macphail joined them. The ship turned sharply and steamed slowly in. It was a great

land-locked harbour big enough to hold a fleet of battleships; and all around
it rose, high and steep, the green hills. Near the entrance, getting such breeze
as blew from the sea, stood the governor's house in a garden. The Stars and
Stripes dangled languidly from a flagstaff. They passed two or three trim
bungalows, and a tennis court, and then they came to the quay with its
warehouses. Mrs Davidson pointed out the schooner, moored two or three
hundred yards from the side, which was to take them to Apia. There was
a crowd of eager, noisy, and good-humoured natives come from all parts of
the island, some from curiosity, others to barter with the travellers on their
way to Sydney; and they brought pineapples and huge bunches of bananas,
tapa cloths, necklaces of shells or sharks' teeth, *kava*-bowls, and models of
war canoes. American sailors, neat and trim, clean-shaven and frank of face,
sauntered among them, and there was a little group of officials. While their
luggage was being landed the Macphails and Mrs Davidson watched the
crowd. Dr Macphail looked at the yaws from which most of the children and
the young boys seemed to suffer, disfiguring sores like torpid ulcers, and
his professional eyes glistened when he saw for the first time in his experience
cases of elephantiasis, men going about with a huge, heavy arm or dragging
along a grossly disfigured leg. Men and women wore the *lava-lava*.

"It's a very indecent costume," said Mrs Davidson. "Mr Davidson thinks
it should be prohibited by law. How can you expect people to be moral when
they wear nothing but a strip of red cotton round their loins?"

"It's suitable enough to the climate," said the doctor, wiping the sweat
off his head.

Now that they were on land the heat, though it was so early in the
morning, was already oppressive. Closed in by its hills, not a breath of air
came in to Pago-Pago.

"In our islands," Mrs Davidson went on in her high-pitched tones,
"we've practically eradicated the *lava-lava*. A few old men still continue to
wear it, but that's all. The women have all taken to the Mother Hubbard,
and the men wear trousers and singlets. At the very beginning of our stay
Mr Davidson said in one of his reports: the inhabitants of these islands will
never be thoroughly Christianised till every boy of more than ten years is
made to wear a pair of trousers."

But Mrs Davidson had given two or three of her birdlike glances at
heavy grey clouds that came floating over the mouth of the harbour. A few
drops began to fall.

"We'd better take shelter," she said.

They made their way with all the crowd to a great shed of corrugated
iron, and the rain began to fall in torrents. They stood there for some time
and then were joined by Mr Davidson. He had been polite enough to the
Macphails during the journey, but he had not his wife's sociability, and had
spent much of his time reading. He was a silent, rather sullen man, and you
felt that his affability was a duty that he imposed upon himself Christianly;
he was by nature reserved and even morose. His appearance was singular. He

was very tall and thin, with long limbs loosely jointed; hollow cheeks and curiously high cheek-bones; he had so cadaverous an air that it surprised you to notice how full and sensual were his lips. He wore his hair very long. His dark eyes, set deep in their sockets, were large and tragic; and his hands with their big, long fingers, were finely shaped; they gave him a look of great strength. But the most striking thing about him was the feeling he gave you of suppressed fire. It was impressive and vaguely troubling. He was not a man with whom any intimacy was possible.

He brought now unwelcome news. There was an epidemic of measles, a serious and often fatal disease among the Kanakas, on the island, and a case had developed among the crew of the schooner which was to take them on their journey. The sick man had been brought ashore and put in hospital on the quarantine station, but telegraphic instructions had been sent from Apia to say that the schooner would not be allowed to enter the harbour till it was certain no other member of the crew was affected.

"It means we shall have to stay here for ten days at least."

"But I'm urgently needed at Apia," said Dr Macphail.

"That can't be helped. If no more cases develop on board, the schooner will be allowed to sail with white passengers, but all native traffic is prohibited for three months."

"Is there a hotel here?" asked Mrs Macphail.

Davidson gave a low chuckle.

"There's not."

"What shall we do then?"

"I've been talking to the governor. There's a trader along the front who has rooms that he rents, and my proposition is that as soon as the rain lets up we should go along there and see what we can do. Don't expect comfort. You've just got to be thankful if we get a bed to sleep on and a roof over our heads."

But the rain showed no signs of stopping, and at length with umbrellas and waterproofs they set out. There was no town, but merely a group of official buildings, a store or two, and at the back, among the coconut trees and plantains, a few native dwellings. The house they sought was about five minutes' walk from the wharf. It was a frame house of two storeys, with broad verandahs on both floors and a roof of corrugated iron. The owner was a half-caste named Horn, with a native wife surrounded by little brown children, and on the ground-floor he had a store where he sold canned goods and cottons. The rooms he showed them were almost bare of furniture. In the Macphails' there was nothing but a poor, worn bed with a ragged mosquito net, a rickety chair, and a washstand. They looked round with dismay. The rain poured down without ceasing.

"I'm not going to unpack more than we actually need," said Mrs Macphail.

Mrs Davidson came into the room as she was unlocking a portmanteau. She was very brisk and alert. The cheerless surroundings had no effect on her.

"If you'll take my advice you'll get a needle and cotton and start right in to mend the mosquito net," she said, "or you'll not be able to get a wink of sleep to-night."

"Will they be very bad?" asked Dr Macphail.

"This is the season for them. When you're asked to a party at Government House at Apia you'll notice that all the ladies are given a pillow-slip to put their—their lower extremities in."

"I wish the rain would stop for a moment," said Mrs Macphail. "I could try to make the place comfortable with more heart if the sun were shining."

"Oh, if you wait for that, you'll wait a long time. Pago-Pago is about the rainiest place in the Pacific. You see, the hills, and that bay, they attract the water, and one expects rain at this time of year anyway."

She looked from Macphail to his wife, standing helplessly in different parts of the room, like lost souls, and she pursed her lips. She saw that she must take them in hand. Feckless people like that made her impatient, but her hands itched to put everything in the order which came so naturally to her.

"Here, you give me a needle and cotton and I'll mend that net of yours, while you go on with your unpacking. Dinner's at one. Dr Macphail, you'd better go down to the wharf and see that your heavy luggage has been put in a dry place. You know what these natives are, they're quite capable of storing it where the rain will beat in on it all the time."

The doctor put on his waterproof again and went downstairs. At the door Mr Horn was standing in conversation with the quartermaster of the ship they had just arrived in and a second-class passenger whom Dr Macphail had seen several times on board. The quartermaster, a little, shrivelled man, extremely dirty, nodded to him as he passed.

"This is a bad job about the measles, doc," he said. "I see you've fixed yourself up already."

Dr Macphail thought he was rather familiar, but he was a timid man and he did not take offence easily.

"Yes, we've got a room upstairs."

"Miss Thompson was sailing with you to Apia, so I've brought her along here."

The quartermaster pointed with his thumb to the woman standing by his side. She was twenty-seven perhaps, plump, and in a coarse fashion pretty. She wore a white dress and a large white hat. Her fat calves in white cotton stockings bulged over the tops of long white boots in glacé kid. She gave Macphail an ingratiating smile.

"The feller's tryin' to soak me a dollar and a half a day for the meanest sized room," she said in a hoarse voice.

"I tell you she's a friend of mine, Jo," said the quartermaster. "She can't pay more than a dollar, and you've sure got to take her for that."

The trader was fat and smooth and quietly smiling.

"Well, if you put it like that, Mr Swan, I'll see what I can do about it. I'll talk to Mrs Horn and if we think we can make a reduction we will."

"Don't try to pull that stuff with me," said Miss Thompson. "We'll settle this right now. You get a dollar a day for the room and not one bean more."

Dr Macphail smiled. He admired the effrontery with which she bargained. He was the sort of man who always paid what he was asked. He preferred to be over-charged than to haggle. The trader sighed.

"Well, to oblige Mr Swan I'll take it."

"That's the goods," said Miss Thompson. "Come right in and have a shot of hooch. I've got some real good rye in that grip if you'll bring it along, Mr Swan. You come along too, doctor."

"Oh, I don't think I will, thank you," he answered. "I'm just going down to see that our luggage is all right."

He stepped out into the rain. It swept in from the opening of the harbour in sheets and the opposite shore was all blurred. He passed two or three natives clad in nothing but the *lava-lava,* with huge umbrellas over them. They walked finely, with leisurely movements, very upright; and they smiled and greeted him in a strange tongue as they went by.

It was nearly dinner-time when he got back, and their meal was laid in the trader's parlour. It was a room designed not to live in but for purposes of prestige, and it had a musty, melancholy air. A suite of stamped plush was arranged neatly round the walls, and from the middle of the ceiling, protected from the flies by yellow tissue paper, hung a gilt chandelier. Davidson did not come.

"I know he went to call on the governor," said Mrs Davidson, "and I guess he's kept him to dinner."

A little native girl brought them a dish of Hamburger steak, and after a while the trader came up to see that they had everything they wanted.

"I see we have a fellow lodger, Mr Horn," said Dr Macphail.

"She's taken a room, that's all," answered the trader. "She's getting her own board."

He looked at the two ladies with an obsequious air.

"I put her downstairs so she shouldn't be in the way. She won't be any trouble to you."

"Is it someone who was on the boat?" asked Mrs Macphail.

"Yes, ma'am, she was in the second cabin. She was going to Apia. She has a position as cashier waiting for her."

"Oh!"

When the trader was gone Macphail said:

"I shouldn't think she'd find it exactly cheerful having her meals in her room."

"If she was in the second cabin I guess she'd rather," answered Mrs Davidson. "I don't exactly know who it can be."

"I happened to be there when the quartermaster brought her along. Her name's Thompson."

"It's not the woman who was dancing with the quartermaster last night?" asked Mrs Davidson.

"That's who it must be," said Mrs Macphail. "I wondered at the time what she was. She looked rather fast to me."

"Not good style at all," said Mrs Davidson.

They began to talk of other things, and after dinner, tired with their early rise, they separated and slept. When they awoke, though the sky was still grey and the clouds hung low, it was not raining and they went for a walk on the high road which the Americans had built along the bay.

On their return they found that Davidson had just come in.

"We may be here for a fortnight," he said irritably. "I've argued it out with the governor, but he says there is nothing to be done."

"Mr Davidson's just longing to get back to his work," said his wife, with an anxious glance at him.

"We've been away for a year," he said, walking up and down the verandah. "The mission has been in charge of native missionaries and I'm terribly nervous that they've let things slide. They're good men, I'm not saying a word against them, God-fearing, devout, and truly Christian men— their Christianity would put many so-called Christians at home to the blush —but they're pitifully lacking in energy. They can make a stand once, they can make a stand twice, but they can't make a stand all the time. If you leave a mission in charge of a native missionary, no matter how trustworthy he seems, in course of time you'll find he's let abuses creep in."

Mr Davidson stood still. With his tall, spare form, and his great eyes flashing out of his pale face, he was an impressive figure. His sincerity was obvious in the fire of his gestures and in his deep, ringing voice.

"I expect to have my work cut out for me. I shall act and I shall act promptly. If the tree is rotten it shall be cut down and cast into the flames."

And in the evening after the high tea which was their last meal, while they sat in the stiff parlour, the ladies working and Dr Macphail smoking his pipe, the missionary told them of his work in the islands.

"When we went there they had no sense of sin at all," he said. "They broke the commandments one after the other and never knew they were doing wrong. And I think that was the most difficult part of my work, to instil into the natives the sense of sin."

The Macphails knew already that Davidson had worked in the Solomons for five years before he met his wife. She had been a missionary in China, and they had become acquainted in Boston, where they were both spending part of their leave to attend a missionary congress. On their marriage they had been appointed to the islands in which they had laboured ever since.

In the course of all the conversations they had had with Mr Davidson one thing had shone out clearly and that was the man's unflinching courage. He was a medical missionary, and he was liable to be called at any time to one or other of the islands in the group. Even the whaleboat is not so very safe a conveyance in the stormy Pacific of the wet season, but often he would be sent for in a canoe, and then the danger was great. In cases of illness or accident he never hesitated. A dozen times he had spent the whole night baling for his life, and more than once Mrs Davidson had given him up for lost.

"I'd beg him not to go sometimes," she said, "or at least to wait till the weather was more settled, but he'd never listen. He's obstinate, and when he's once made up his mind, nothing can move him."

"How can I ask the natives to put their trust in the Lord if I am afraid to do so myself?" cried Davidson. "And I'm not, I'm not. They know that if they send for me in their trouble I'll come if it's humanly possible. And do you think the Lord is going to abandon me when I am on his business? The wind blows at his bidding and the waves toss and rage at his word."

Dr Macphail was a timid man. He had never been able to get used to the hurtling of the shells over the trenches, and when he was operating in an advanced dressing-station the sweat poured from his brow and dimmed his spectacles in the effort he made to control his unsteady hand. He shuddered a little as he looked at the missionary.

"I wish I could say that I've never been afraid," he said.

"I wish I could say that you believed in God," retorted the other.

But for some reason, that evening the missionary's thoughts travelled back to the early days he and his wife had spent on the islands.

"Sometimes Mrs Davidson and I would look at one another and the tears would stream down our cheeks. We worked without ceasing, day and night, and we seemed to make no progress. I don't know what I should have done without her then. When I felt my heart sink, when I was very near despair, she gave me courage and hope."

Mrs Davidson looked down at her work, and a slight colour rose to her thin cheeks. Her hands trembled a little. She did not trust herself to speak.

"We had no one to help us. We were alone, thousands of miles from any of our own people, surrounded by darkness. When I was broken and weary she would put her work aside and take the Bible and read to me till peace came and settled upon me like sleep upon the eyelids of a child, and when at last she closed the book she'd say: 'We'll save them in spite of themselves.' And I felt strong again in the Lord, and I answered: 'Yes, with God's help I'll save them. I must save them.'"

He came over to the table and stood in front of it as though it were a lectern.

"You see, they were so naturally depraved that they couldn't be brought to see their wickedness. We had to make sins out of what they thought were natural actions. We had to make it a sin, not only to commit adultery and to lie and thieve, but to expose their bodies, and to dance and not to come to church. I made it a sin for a girl to show her bosom and a sin for a man not to wear trousers."

"How?" asked Dr Macphail, not without surprise.

"I instituted fines. Obviously the only way to make people realise that an action is sinful is to punish them if they commit it. I fined them if they didn't come to church, and I fined them if they danced. I fined them if they were improperly dressed. I had a tariff, and every sin had to be paid for either in money or work. And at last I made them understand."

"But did they never refuse to pay?"

"How could they?" asked the missionary.

"It would be a brave man who tried to stand up against Mr Davidson," said his wife, tightening her lips.

Dr Macphail looked at Davidson with troubled eyes. What he heard shocked him, but he hesitated to express his disapproval.

"You must remember that in the last resort I could expel them from their church membership."

"Did they mind that?"

Davidson smiled a little and gently rubbed his hands.

"They couldn't sell their copra. When the men fished they got no share of the catch. It meant something very like starvation. Yes, they minded quite a lot."

"Tell him about Fred Ohlson," said Mrs Davidson.

The missionary fixed his fiery eyes on Dr Macphail.

"Fred Ohlson was a Danish trader who had been in the islands a good many years. He was a pretty rich man as traders go and he wasn't very pleased when we came. You see, he'd had things very much his own way. He paid the natives what he liked for their copra, and he paid in goods and whiskey. He had a native wife, but he was flagrantly unfaithful to her. He was a drunkard. I gave him a chance to mend his ways, but he wouldn't take it. He laughed at me."

Davidson's voice fell to a deep bass as he said the last words, and he was silent for a minute or two. The silence was heavy with menace.

"In two years he was a ruined man. He'd lost everything he'd saved in a quarter of a century. I broke him, and at last he was forced to come to me like a beggar and beseech me to give him a passage back to Sydney."

"I wish you could have seen him when he came to see Mr Davidson," said the missionary's wife. "He had been a fine, powerful man, with a lot of fat on him, and he had a great big voice, but now he was half the size, and he was shaking all over. He'd suddenly become an old man."

With abstracted gaze Davidson looked out into the night. The rain was falling again.

Suddenly from below came a sound, and Davidson turned and looked questioningly at his wife. It was the sound of a gramophone, harsh and loud, wheezing out a syncopated tune.

"What's that?" he asked.

Mrs Davidson fixed her *pince-nez* more firmly on her nose.

"One of the second-class passengers has a room in the house. I guess it comes from there."

They listened in silence, and presently they heard the sound of dancing. Then the music stopped, and they heard the popping of corks and voices raised in animated conversation.

"I daresay she's giving a farewell party to her friends on board," said Dr Macphail. "The ship sails at twelve, doesn't it?"

Davidson made no remark, but he looked at his watch.

"Are you ready?" he asked his wife.

She got up and folded her work.

"Yes, I guess I am," she answered.

"It's early to go to bed yet, isn't it?" said the doctor.

"We have a good deal of reading to do," explained Mrs Davidson. "Wherever we are, we read a chapter of the Bible before retiring for the night and we study it with the commentaries, you know, and discuss it thoroughly. It's a wonderful training for the mind."

The two couples bade one another good night. Dr and Mrs Macphail were left alone. For two or three minutes they did not speak.

"I think I'll go and fetch the cards," the doctor said at last.

Mrs Macphail looked at him doubtfully. Her conversation with the Davidsons had left her a little uneasy, but she did not like to say that she thought they had better not play cards when the Davidsons might come in at any moment. Dr Macphail brought them and she watched him, though with a vague sense of guilt, while he laid out his patience. Below the sound of revelry continued.

It was fine enough next day, and the Macphails, condemned to spend a fortnight of idleness at Pago-Pago, set about making the best of things. They went down to the quay and got out of their boxes a number of books. The doctor called on the chief surgeon of the naval hospital and went round the beds with him. They left cards on the governor. They passed Miss Thompson on the road. The doctor took off his hat, and she gave him a "Good morning, doc.," in a loud, cheerful voice. She was dressed as on the day before, in a white frock, and her shiny white boots with their high heels, her fat legs bulging over the tops of them, were strange things on that exotic scene.

"I don't think she's very suitably dressed, I must say," said Mrs Macphail. "She looks extremely common to me."

When they got back to their house, she was on the verandah playing with one of the trader's dark children.

"Say a word to her," Dr Macphail whispered to his wife. "She's all alone here, and it seems rather unkind to ignore her."

Mrs Macphail was shy, but she was in the habit of doing what her husband bade her.

"I think we're fellow lodgers here," she said, rather foolishly.

"Terrible, ain't it, bein' cooped up in a one-horse burg like this?" answered Miss Thompson. "And they tell me I'm lucky to have gotten a room. I don't see myself livin' in a native house, and that's what some have to do. I don't know why they don't have a hotel."

They exchanged a few more words. Miss Thompson, loud-voiced and garrulous, was evidently quite willing to gossip, but Mrs Macphail had a poor stock of small talk and presently she said:

"Well, I think we must go upstairs."

In the evening when they sat down to their high-tea Davidson on coming in said:

"I see that woman downstairs has a couple of sailors sitting there. I wonder how she's gotten acquainted with them."

"She can't be very particular," said Mrs Davidson.

They were all rather tired after the idle, aimless day.

"If there's going to be a fortnight of this I don't know what we shall feel like at the end of it," said Dr Macphail.

The only thing to do is to portion out the day to different activities," answered the missionary. "I shall set aside a certain number of hours to study and a certain number to exercise, rain or fine—in the wet season you can't afford to pay any attention to the rain—and a certain number to recreation."

Dr Macphail looked at his companion with misgiving. Davidson's programme oppressed him. They were eating Hamburger steak again. It seemed the only dish the cook knew how to make. Then below the gramophone began. Davidson started nervously when he heard it, but said nothing. Men's voices floated up. Miss Thompson's guests were joining in a well-known song and presently they heard her voice too, hoarse and loud. There was a good deal of shouting and laughing. The four people upstairs, trying to make conversation, listened despite themselves to the clink of glasses and the scrape of chairs. More people had evidently come. Miss Thompson was giving a party.

"I wonder how she gets them all in," said Mrs Macphail, suddenly breaking into a medical conversation between the missionary and her husband.

It showed whither her thoughts were wandering. The twitch of Davidson's face proved that, though he spoke of scientific things, his mind was busy in the same direction. Suddenly, while the doctor was giving some experience of practice on the Flanders front, rather prosily, he sprang to his feet with a cry.

"What's the matter, Alfred?" asked Mrs Davidson.

"Of course! It never occurred to me. She's out of Iwelei."

"She can't be."

"She came on board at Honolulu. It's obvious. And she's carrying on her trade here. Here."

He uttered the last word with a passion of indignation.

"What's Iwelei?" asked Mrs Macphail.

He turned his gloomy eyes on her and his voice trembled with horror.

"The plague spot of Honolulu. The Red Light district. It was a blot on our civilisation."

Iwelei was on the edge of the city. You went down side streets by the harbour, in the darkness, across a rickety bridge, till you came to a deserted road, all ruts and holes, and then suddenly you came out into the light. There was parking room for motors on each side of the road, and there were saloons, tawdry and bright, each one noisy with its mechanical piano, and there were barbers' shops and tobacconists. There was a stir in the air and a sense of expectant gaiety. You turned down a narrow alley, either to the right or to the left, for the road divided Iwelei into two parts, and you found yourself in the district. There were rows of little bungalows, trim and neatly painted in green, and the pathway between them was broad and straight. It was laid out like a garden-city. In its respectable regularity, its order and spruceness, it gave an impression of sardonic horror; for never can the search for love have been so systematised and ordered. The pathways were lit by a rare lamp, but they would have been dark except for the lights that came from the open windows of the bungalows. Men wandered about, looking at the women who sat at their windows, reading or sewing, for the most part taking no notice of the passers-by; and like the women they were of all nationalities. There were Americans, sailors from the ships in port, enlisted men off the gunboats, sombrely drunk, and soldiers from the regiments, white and black, quartered on the island; there were Japanese, walking in twos and threes; Hawaiians, Chinese in long robes, and Filipinos in preposterous hats. They were silent and as it were oppressed. Desire is sad.

"It was the most crying scandal of the Pacific," exclaimed Davidson vehemently. "The missionaries had been agitating against it for years, and at last the local press took it up. The police refused to stir. You know their argument. They say that vice is inevitable and consequently the best thing is to localise and control it. The truth is, they were paid. Paid. They were paid by the saloon-keepers, paid by the bullies, paid by the women themselves. At last they were forced to move."

"I read about it in the papers that came on board in Honolulu," said Dr Macphail.

"Iwelei, with its sin and shame, ceased to exist on the very day we arrived. The whole population was brought before the justices. I don't know why I didn't understand at once what that woman was."

"Now you come to speak of it," said Mrs Macphail, "I remember seeing her come on board only a few minutes before the boat sailed. I remember thinking at the time she was cutting it rather fine."

"How dare she come here!" cried Davidson indignantly. "I'm not going to allow it."

He strode towards the door.

"What are you going to do?" asked Macphail.

"What do you expect me to do? I'm going to stop it. I'm not going to have this house turned into—into . . ."

He sought for a word that should not offend the ladies' ears. His eyes were flashing and his pale face was paler still in his emotion.

"It sounds as though there were three or four men down there," said the doctor. "Don't you think it's rather rash to go in just now?"

The missionary gave him a contemptuous look and without a word flung out of the room.

"You know Mr Davidson very little if you think the fear of personal danger can stop him in the performance of his duty," said his wife.

She sat with her hands nervously clasped, a spot of colour on her high cheek bones, listening to what was about to happen below. They all listened. They heard him clatter down the wooden stairs and throw open the door. The singing stopped suddenly, but the gramophone continued to bray out its vulgar tune. They heard Davidson's voice and then the noise of something heavy falling. The music stopped. He had hurled the gramophone on the floor. Then again they heard Davidson's voice, they could not make out the words, then Miss Thompson's, loud and shrill, then a confused clamour as though several people were shouting together at the top of their lungs. Mrs Davidson gave a little gasp, and she clenched her hands more tightly. Dr Macphail looked uncertainly from her to his wife. He did not want to go down, but he wondered if they expected him to. Then there was something that sounded like a scuffle. The noise now was more distinct. It might be that Davidson was being thrown out of the room. The door was slammed. There was a moment's silence and they heard Davidson come up the stairs again. He went to his room.

"I think I'll go to him," said Mrs Davidson.

She got up and went out.

"If you want me, just call," said Mrs Macphail, and then when the other was gone: "I hope he isn't hurt."

"Why couldn't he mind his own business?" said Dr Macphail.

They sat in silence for a minute or two and then they both started, for the gramophone began to play once more, defiantly, and mocking voices shouted hoarsely the words of an obscene song.

Next day Mrs Davidson was pale and tired. She complained of headache, and she looked old and wizened. She told Mrs Macphail that the missionary had not slept at all; he had passed the night in a state of frightful agitation and at five had got up and gone out. A glass of beer had been thrown over him and his clothes were stained and stinking. But a sombre fire glowed in Mrs Davidson's eyes when she spoke of Miss Thompson.

"She'll bitterly rue the day when she flouted Mr Davidson," she said. "Mr Davidson has a wonderful heart and no one who is in trouble has ever gone to him without being comforted, but he has no mercy for sin, and when his righteous wrath is excited he's terrible."

"Why, what will he do?" asked Mrs Macphail.

"I don't know, but I wouldn't stand in that creature's shoes for anything in the world."

Mrs Macphail shuddered. There was something positively alarming in the triumphant assurance of the little woman's manner. They were going out together that morning, and they went down the stairs side by side. Miss Thompson's door was open, and they saw her in a bedraggled dressing-gown cooking something in a chafing-dish.

"Good morning," she called. "Is Mr Davidson better this morning?"

They passed her in silence, with their noses in the air, as if she did not exist. They flushed, however, when she burst into a shout of derisive laughter. Mrs Davidson turned on her suddenly.

"Don't you dare to speak to me," she screamed. "If you insult me I shall have you turned out of here."

"Say, did I ask Mr Davidson to visit with me?"

"Don't answer her," whispered Mrs Macphail hurriedly.

They walked on till they were out of earshot.

"She's brazen, brazen," burst from Mrs Davidson.

Her anger almost suffocated her.

And on their way home they met her strolling towards the quay. She had all her finery on. Her great white hat with its vulgar, showy flowers was an affront. She called out cheerily to them as she went by, and a couple of American sailors who were standing there grinned as the ladies set their faces to an icy stare. They got in just before the rain began to fall again.

"I guess she'll get her fine clothes spoilt," said Mrs Davidson with a bitter sneer.

Davidson did not come in till they were half way through dinner. He was wet through, but he would not change. He sat, morose and silent, refusing to eat more than a mouthful, and he stared at the slanting rain. When Mrs Davidson told him of their two encounters with Miss Thompson he did not answer. His deepening frown alone showed that he had heard.

"Don't you think we ought to make Mr Horn turn her out of here?" asked Mrs Davidson. "We can't allow her to insult us."

"There doesn't seem to be any other place for her to go," said Macphail.

"She can live with one of the natives."

"In weather like this a native hut must be a rather uncomfortable place to live in."

"I lived in one for years," said the missionary.

When the little native girl brought in the fried bananas which formed the sweet they had every day, Davidson turned to her.

"Ask Miss Thompson when it would be convenient for me to see her," he said.

The girl nodded shyly and went out.

"What do you want to see her for, Alfred?" asked his wife.

"It's my duty to see her. I won't act till I've given her every chance."

"You don't know what she is. She'll insult you."

"Let her insult me. Let her spit on me. She has an immortal soul, and I must do all that is in my power to save it."

Mrs Davidson's ears rang still with the harlot's mocking laughter.

"She's gone too far."

"Too far for the mercy of God?" His eyes lit up suddenly and his voice grew mellow and soft. "Never. The sinner may be deeper in sin than the depth of hell itself, but the love of the Lord Jesus can reach him still."

The girl came back with the message.

"Miss Thompson's compliments and as long as Rev. Davidson don't come in business hours she'll be glad to see him any time."

The party received it in stony silence, and Dr Macphail quickly effaced from his lips the smile which had come upon them. He knew his wife would be vexed with him if he found Miss Thompson's effrontery amusing.

They finished the meal in silence. When it was over the two ladies got up and took their work, Mrs Macphail was making another of the innumerable comforters which she had turned out since the beginning of the war, and the doctor lit his pipe. But Davidson remained in his chair and with abstracted eyes stared at the table. At last he got up and without a word went out of the room. They heard him go down and they heard Miss Thompson's defiant "Come in" when he knocked at the door. He remained with her for an hour. And Dr Macphail watched the rain. It was beginning to get on his nerves. It was not like our soft English rain that drops gently on the earth; it was unmerciful and somehow terrible; you felt in it the malignancy of the primitive powers of nature. It did not pour, it flowed. It was like a deluge from heaven, and it rattled on the roof of corrugated iron with a steady persistence that was maddening. It seemed to have a fury of its own. And sometimes you felt that you must scream if it did not stop, and then suddenly you felt powerless, as though your bones had suddenly become soft; and you were miserable and hopeless.

Macphail turned his head when the missionary came back. The two women looked up.

"I've given her every chance. I have exhorted her to repent. She is an evil woman."

He paused, and Dr Macphail saw his eyes darken and his pale face grow hard and stern.

"Now I shall take the whips with which the Lord Jesus drove the usurers and the money changers out of the Temple of the Most High."

He walked up and down the room. His mouth was close set, and his black brows were frowning.

"If she fled to the uttermost parts of the earth I should pursue her."

With a sudden movement he turned round and strode out of the room. They heard him go downstairs again.

"What is he going to do?" asked Mrs Macphail.

"I don't know." Mrs Davidson took off her *pince-nez* and wiped them. "When he is on the Lord's work I never ask him questions."

She sighed a little.

"What is the matter?"

"He'll wear himself out. He doesn't know what it is to spare himself."

Dr Macphail learnt the first results of the missionary's activity from the half-caste trader in whose house they lodged. He stopped the doctor when he passed the store and came out to speak to him on the stoop. His fat face was worried.

"The Rev. Davidson has been at me for letting Miss Thompson have a room here," he said, "but I didn't know what she was when I rented it to her. When people come and ask if I can rent them a room all I want to know is if they've the money to pay for it. And she paid me for hers a week in advance."

Dr Macphail did not want to commit himself.

"When all's said and done it's your house. We're very much obliged to you for taking us in at all."

Horn looked at him doubtfully. He was not certain yet how definitely Macphail stood on the missionary's side.

"The missionaries are in with one another," he said, hesitatingly. "If they get it in for a trader he may just as well shut up his store and quit."

"Did he want you to turn her out?"

"No, he said so long as she behaved herself he couldn't ask me to do that. He said he wanted to be just to me. I promised she shouldn't have no more visitors. I've just been and told her."

"How did she take it?"

"She gave me Hell."

The trader squirmed in his old ducks. He had found Miss Thompson a rough customer.

"Oh, well, I daresay she'll get out. I don't suppose she wants to stay here if she can't have anyone in."

"There's nowhere she can go, only a native house, and no native'll take her now, not now that the missionaries have got their knife in her."

Dr Macphail looked at the falling rain

"Well, I don't suppose it's any good waiting for it to clear up."

In the evening when they sat in the parlour Davidson talked to them of his early days at college. He had had no means and had worked his way through by doing odd jobs during the vacations. There was silence downstairs. Miss Thompson was sitting in her little room alone. But suddenly the gramophone began to play. She had set it on in defiance, to cheat her loneliness, but there was no one to sing, and it had a melancholy note. It was like a cry for help. Davidson took no notice. He was in the middle of a long anecdote and without change of expression went on. The gramophone continued. Miss Thompson put on one reel after another. It looked as though the silence of the night were getting on her nerves. It was breathless and sultry. When the Macphails went to bed they could not sleep. They lay side by side with their eyes wide open, listening to the cruel singing of the mosquitoes outside their curtain.

"What's that?" whispered Mrs Macphail at last.

They heard a voice, Davidson's voice, through the wooden partition. It went on with a monotonous, earnest insistence. He was praying aloud. He was praying for the soul of Miss Thompson.

Two or three days went by. Now when they passed Miss Thompson on the road she did not greet them with ironic cordiality or smile; she passed with her nose in the air, a sulky look on her painted face, frowning, as though she did not see them. The trader told Macphail that she had tried to get lodging elsewhere, but had failed. In the evening she played through the various reels of her gramophone, but the pretence of mirth was obvious now. The ragtime had a cracked, heart-broken rhythm as though it were a one-step of despair. When she began to play on Sunday Davidson sent Horn to beg her to stop at once since it was the Lord's day. The reel was taken off and the house was silent except for the steady pattering of the rain on the iron roof.

"I think she's getting a bit worked up," said the trader next day to Macphail. "She don't know what Mr Davidson's up to and it makes her scared."

Macphail had caught a glimpse of her that morning and it struck him that her arrogant expression had changed. There was in her face a hunted look. The half-caste gave him a sidelong glance.

"I suppose you don't know what Mr Davidson is doing about it?" he hazarded.

"No, I don't."

It was singular that Horn should ask him that question, for he also had the idea that the missionary was mysteriously at work. He had an impression that he was weaving a net around the woman, carefully, systematically, and suddenly, when everything was ready would pull the strings tight.

"He told me to tell her," said the trader, "that if at any time she wanted him she only had to send and he'd come."

"What did she say when you told her that?"

"She didn't say nothing. I didn't stop. I just said what he said I was to and then I beat it. I thought she might be going to start weepin'."

"I have no doubt the loneliness is getting on her nerves," said the doctor. "And the rain—that's enough to make anyone jumpy," he continued irritably. "Doesn't it ever stop in this confounded place?"

"It goes on pretty steady in the rainy season. We have three hundred inches in the year. You see, it's the shape of the bay. It seems to attract the rain from all over the Pacific."

"Damn the shape of the bay," said the doctor.

He scratched his mosquito bites. He felt very short-tempered. When the rain stopped and the sun shone, it was like a hothouse, seething, humid,

sultry, breathless, and you had a strange feeling that everything was growing with a savage violence. The natives, blithe and childlike by reputation,
seemed then, with their tattooing and their dyed hair, to have something
sinister in their appearance; and when they pattered along at your heels
with their naked feet you looked back instinctively. You felt they might
at any moment come behind you swiftly and thrust a long knife between
your shoulder blades. You could not tell what dark thoughts lurked behind
their wide-set eyes. They had a little the look of ancient Egyptians painted
on a temple wall, and there was about them the terror of what is immeasur-
ably old.

The missionary came and went. He was busy, but the Macphails did not
know what he was doing. Horn told the doctor that he saw the governor
every day, and once Davidson mentioned him.

"He looks as if he had plenty of determination," he said, "but when
you come down to brass tacks he has no backbone."

"I suppose that means he won't do exactly what you want," suggested
the doctor facetiously.

The missionary did not smile.

"I want him to do what's right. It shouldn't be necessary to persuade a
man to do that."

"But there may be differences of opinion about what is right."

"If a man had a gangrenous foot would you have patience with anyone
who hesitated to amputate it?"

"Gangrene is a matter of fact."

"And Evil?"

What Davidson had done soon appeared. The four of them had just
finished their midday meal, and they had not yet separated for the siesta
which the heat imposed on the ladies and on the doctor. Davidson had little
patience with the slothful habit. The door was suddenly flung open and Miss
Thompson came in. She looked round the room and then went up to
Davidson.

"You low-down skunk, what have you been saying about me to the
governor?"

She was spluttering with rage. There was a moment's pause. Then the
missionary drew forward a chair.

"Won't you be seated, Miss Thompson? I've been hoping to have
another talk with you."

"You poor low-life bastard."

She burst into a torrent of insult, foul and insolent. Davidson kept his
grave eyes on her.

"I'm indifferent to the abuse you think fit to heap on me, Miss Thompson," he said, "but I must beg you to remember that ladies are present."

Tears by now were struggling with her anger. Her face was red and
swollen as though she were choking.

"What has happened?" asked Dr Macphail.

"A feller's just been in here and he says I gotter beat it on the next boat."

Was there a gleam in the missionary's eyes? His face remained impassive.

"You could hardly expect the governor to let you stay here under the circumstances."

"You done it," she shrieked. "You can't kid me. You done it."

"I don't want to deceive you. I urged the governor to take the only possible step consistent with his obligations."

"Why couldn't you leave me be? I wasn't doin' you no harm."

"You may be sure that if you had I should be the last man to resent it."

"Do you think I want to stay on in this poor imitation of a burg? I don't look no busher, do I?"

"In that case I don't see what cause of complaint you have," he answered.

She gave an inarticulate cry of rage and flung out of the room. There was a short silence.

"It's a relief to know that the governor has acted at last," said Davidson finally. "He's a weak man and he shilly-shallied. He said she was only here for a fortnight anyway, and if she went on to Apia that was under British jurisdiction and had nothing to do with him."

The missionary sprang to his feet and strode across the room.

"It's terrible the way the men who are in authority seek to evade their responsibility. They speak as though evil that was out of sight ceased to be evil. The very existence of that woman is a scandal and it does not help matters to shift it to another of the islands. In the end I had to speak straight from the shoulder."

Davidson's brow lowered, and he protruded his firm chin. He looked fierce and determined.

"What do you mean by that?"

"Our mission is not entirely without influence at Washington. I pointed out to the governor that it wouldn't do him any good if there was a complaint about the way he managed things here."

"When has she got to go?" asked the doctor, after a pause.

"The San Francisco boat is due here from Sydney next Tuesday. She's to sail on that."

That was in five days' time. It was next day, when he was coming back from the hospital where for want of something better to do Macphail spent most of his mornings, that the half-caste stopped him as he was going upstairs.

"Excuse me, Dr Macphail, Miss Thompson's sick. Will you have a look at her."

"Certainly."

Horn led him to her room. She was sitting in a chair idly, neither reading nor sewing, staring in front of her. She wore her white dress and the large hat with the flowers on it. Macphail noticed that her skin was yellow and muddy under her powder, and her eyes were heavy.

"I'm sorry to hear you're not well," he said.

"Oh, I ain't sick really. I just said that, because I just had to see you. I've got to clear on a boat that's going to 'Frisco."

She looked at him and he saw that her eyes were suddenly startled. She opened and clenched her hands spasmodically. The trader stood at the door, listening.

"So I understand," said the doctor.

She gave a little gulp.

"I guess it ain't very convenient for me to go to 'Frisco just now. I went to see the governor yesterday afternoon, but I couldn't get to him. I saw the secretary, and he told me I'd got to take that boat and that was all there was to it. I just had to see the governor, so I waited outside his house this morning, and when he come out I spoke to him. He didn't want to speak to me, I'll say, but I wouldn't let him shake me off, and at last he said he hadn't no objection to my staying here till the next boat to Sydney if the Rev. Davidson will stand for it."

She stopped and looked at Dr Macphail anxiously.

"I don't know exactly what I can do," he said.

"Well, I thought maybe you wouldn't mind asking him. I swear to God I won't start anything here if he'll just only let me stay. I won't go out of the house if that'll suit him. It's no more'n a fortnight."

"I'll ask him."

"He won't stand for it," said Horn. "He'll have you out on Tuesday, so you may as well make up your mind to it."

"Tell him I can get work in Sydney, straight stuff, I mean. 'Tain't asking very much."

"I'll do what I can."

"And come and tell me right away, will you? I can't set down to a thing till I get the dope one way or the other."

It was not an errand that much pleased the doctor, and, characteristically perhaps, he went about it indirectly. He told his wife what Miss Thompson had said to him and asked her to speak to Mrs Davidson. The missionary's attitude seemed rather arbitrary and it could do no harm if the girl were allowed to stay in Pago-Pago another fortnight. But he was not prepared for the result of his diplomacy. The missionary came to him straightway.

"Mrs Davidson tells me that Thompson has been speaking to you."

Dr Macphail, thus directly tackled, had the shy man's resentment at being forced out into the open. He felt his temper rising, and he flushed.

"I don't see that it can make any difference if she goes to Sydney rather than to San Francisco, and so long as she promises to behave while she's here it's dashed hard to persecute her."

The missionary fixed him with his stern eyes.

"Why is she unwilling to go back to San Francisco?"

"I didn't enquire," answered the doctor with some asperity. "And I think one does better to mind one's own business."

Perhaps it was not a very tactful answer.

"The governor has ordered her to be deported by the first boat that leaves the island. He's only done his duty and I will not interfere. Her presence is a peril here."

"I think you're very harsh and tyrannical."

The two ladies looked up at the doctor with some alarm, but they need not have feared a quarrel, for the missionary smiled gently.

"I'm terribly sorry you should think that of me, Dr Macphail. Believe me, my heart bleeds for that unfortunate woman, but I'm only trying to do my duty."

The doctor made no answer. He looked out of the window sullenly. For once it was not raining and across the bay you saw nestling among the trees the huts of a native village.

"I think I'll take advantage of the rain stopping to go out," he said.

"Please don't bear me malice because I can't accede to your wish," said Davidson, with a melancholy smile. "I respect you very much, doctor, and I should be sorry if you thought ill of me."

"I have no doubt you have a sufficiently good opinion of yourself to bear mine with equanimity," he retorted.

"That's one on me," chuckled Davidson.

When Dr Macphail, vexed with himself because he had been uncivil to no purpose, went downstairs, Miss Thompson was waiting for him with her door ajar.

"Well," she said, "have you spoken to him?"

"Yes, I'm sorry, he won't do anything," he answered, not looking at her in his embarrassment.

But then he gave her a quick glance, for a sob broke from her. He saw that her face was white with fear. It gave him a shock of dismay. And suddenly he had an idea.

"But don't give up hope yet. I think it's a shame the way they're treating you and I'm going to see the governor myself."

"Now?"

He nodded. Her face brightened.

"Say, that's real good of you. I'm sure he'll let me stay if you speak for me. I just won't do a thing I didn't ought all the time I'm here."

Dr Macphail hardly knew why he had made up his mind to appeal to the governor. He was perfectly indifferent to Miss Thompson's affairs, but the missionary had irritated him, and with him temper was a smouldering thing. He found the governor at home. He was a large, handsome man, a sailor with a grey toothbrush moustache; and he wore a spotless uniform of white drill.

"I've come to see you about a woman who's lodging in the same house as we are," he said. "Her name's Thompson."

"I guess I've heard nearly enough about her, Dr Macphail," said the governor, smiling. "I've given her the order to get out next Tuesday and that's all I can do."

"I wanted to ask you if you couldn't stretch a point and let her stay here till the boat comes in from San Francisco so that she can go to Sydney. I will guarantee her good behaviour."

The governor continued to smile, but his eyes grew small and serious.

"I'd be very glad to oblige you, Dr Macphail, but I've given the order and it must stand."

The doctor put the case as reasonably as he could, but now the governor ceased to smile at all. He listened sullenly, with averted gaze. Macphail saw that he was making no impression.

"I'm sorry to cause any lady inconvenience, but she'll have to sail on Tuesday and that's all there is to it."

"But what difference can it make?"

"Pardon me, doctor, but I don't feel called upon to explain my official actions except to the proper authorities."

Macphail looked at him shrewdly. He remembered Davidson's hint that he had used threats, and in the governor's attitude he read a singular embarrassment.

"Davidson's a damned busybody," he said hotly.

"Between ourselves, Dr Macphail, I don't say that I have formed a very favourable opinion of Mr Davidson, but I am bound to confess that he was within his rights in pointing out to me the danger that the presence of a woman of Miss Thompson's character was to a place like this where a number of enlisted men are stationed among a native population."

He got up and Dr Macphail was obliged to do so too.

"I must ask you to excuse me. I have an engagement. Please give my respects to Mrs Macphail."

The doctor left him crest-fallen. He knew that Miss Thompson would be waiting for him, and unwilling to tell her himself that he had failed, he went into the house by the back door and sneaked up the stairs as though he had something to hide.

At supper he was silent and ill-at-ease, but the missionary was jovial and animated. Dr Macphail thought his eyes rested on him now and then with triumphant good-humour. It struck him suddenly that Davidson knew of his visit to the governor and of its ill success But how on earth could he have heard of it? There was something sinister about the power of that man. After supper he saw Horn on the verandah and, as though to have a casual word with him, went out.

"She wants to know if you've seen the governor," the trader whispered.

"Yes. He wouldn't do anything. I'm awfully sorry, I can't do anything more."

"I knew he wouldn't. They daren't go against the missionaries."

"What are you talking about?" said Davidson affably, coming out to join them.

"I was just saying there was no chance of your getting over to Apia for at least another week," said the trader glibly.

He left them, and the two men returned into the parlour. Mr Davidson devoted one hour after each meal to recreation. Presently a timid knock was heard at the door.

"Come in," said Mrs Davidson, in her sharp voice.

The door was not opened. She got up and opened it. They saw Miss Thompson standing at the threshold. But the change in her appearance was extraordinary. This was no longer the flaunting hussy who had jeered at them in the road, but a broken, frightened woman. Her hair, as a rule so elaborately arranged, was tumbling untidily over her neck. She wore bed-room slippers and a skirt and blouse. They were unfresh and bedraggled. She stood at the door with the tears streaming down her face and did not dare to enter.

"What do you want?" said Mrs Davidson harshly.

"May I speak to Mr Davidson?" she said in a choking voice.

The missionary rose and went towards her.

"Come right in, Miss Thompson," he said in cordial tones. "What can I do for you?"

She entered the room.

"Say, I'm sorry for what I said to you the other day an' for—for every-thin' else. I guess I was a bit lit up. I beg pardon."

"Oh, it was nothing. I guess my back's broad enough to bear a few hard words."

She stepped towards him with a movement that was horribly cringing.

"You've got me beat. I'm all in. You won't make me go back to 'Frisco?"

His genial manner vanished and his voice grew on a sudden hard and stern.

"Why don't you want to go back there?"

She cowered before him.

"I guess my people live there. I don't want them to see me like this. I'll go anywhere else you say."

"Why don't you want to go back to San Francisco?"

"I've told you."

He leaned forward, staring at her, and his great, shining eyes seemed to try to bore into her soul. He gave a sudden gasp.

"The penitentiary."

She screamed, and then she fell at his feet, clasping his legs.

"Don't send me back there. I swear to you before God I'll be a good woman. I'll give all this up."

She burst into a torrent of confused supplication and the tears coursed down her painted cheeks. He leaned over her and, lifting her face, forced her to look at him.

"Is that it, the penitentiary?"

"I beat it before they could get me," she gasped. "If the bulls grab me it's three years for mine."

He let go his hold of her and she fell in a heap on the floor, sobbing bitterly. Dr Macphail stood up.

"This alters the whole thing," he said. "You can't make her go back when you know this. Give her another chance. She wants to turn over a new leaf."

"I'm going to give her the finest chance she's ever had. If she repents let her accept her punishment."

She misunderstood the words and looked up. There was a gleam of hope in her heavy eyes.

"You'll let me go?"

"No. You shall sail for San Francisco on Tuesday."

She gave a groan of horror and then burst into low, hoarse shrieks which sounded hardly human, and she beat her head passionately on the ground. Dr Macphail sprang to her and lifted her up.

"Come on, you mustn't do that. You'd better go to your room and lie down. I'll get you something."

He raised her to her feet and partly dragging her, partly carrying her, got her downstairs. He was furious with Mrs Davidson and with his wife because they made no effort to help. The half-caste was standing on the landing and with his assistance he managed to get her on the bed. She was moaning and crying. She was almost insensible. He gave her a hypodermic injection. He was hot and exhausted when he went upstairs again.

"I've got her to lie down."

The two women and Davidson were in the same positions as when he had left them. They could not have moved or spoken since he went.

"I was waiting for you," said Davidson, in a strange, distant voice. "I want you all to pray with me for the soul of our erring sister."

He took the Bible off a shelf, and sat down at the table at which they had supped. It had not been cleared, and he pushed the tea-pot out of the way. In a powerful voice, resonant and deep, he read to them the chapter in which is narrated the meeting of Jesus Christ with the woman taken in adultery.

"Now kneel with me and let us pray for the soul of our dear sister, Sadie Thompson."

He burst into a long, passionate prayer in which he implored God to have mercy on the sinful woman. Mrs Macphail and Mrs Davidson knelt with covered eyes. The doctor, taken by surprise, awkward and sheepish, knelt too. The missionary's prayer had a savage eloquence. He was extraordinarily moved, and as he spoke the tears ran down his cheeks. Outside, the pitiless rain fell, fell steadily, with a fierce malignity that was all too human.

At last he stopped. He paused for a moment and said:

"We will now repeat the Lord's prayer."

They said it and then, following him, they rose from their knees. Mrs

Davidson's face was pale and restful. She was comforted and at peace, but the Macphails felt suddenly bashful. They did not know which way to look.

"I'll just go down and see how she is now," said Dr Macphail.

When he knocked at her door it was opened for him by Horn. Miss Thompson was in a rocking-chair, sobbing quietly.

"What are you doing there?" exclaimed Macphail. "I told you to lie down."

"I can't lie down. I want to see Mr Davidson."

"My poor child, what do you think is the good of it? You'll never move him."

"He said he'd come if I sent for him."

Macphail motioned to the trader.

"Go and fetch him."

He waited with her in silence while the trader went upstairs. Davidson came in.

"Excuse me for asking you to come here," she said, looking at him sombrely.

"I was expecting you to send for me. I knew the Lord would answer my prayer."

They stared at one another for a moment and then she looked away. She kept her eyes averted when she spoke.

"I've been a bad woman. I want to repent."

"Thank God! thank God! He has heard our prayers."

He turned to the two men.

"Leave me alone with her. Tell Mrs Davidson that our prayers have been answered."

They went out and closed the door behind them.

"Gee whiz," said the trader.

That night Dr Macphail could not get to sleep till late, and when he heard the missionary come upstairs he looked at his watch. It was two o'clock. But even then he did not go to bed at once, for through the wooden partition that separated their rooms he heard him praying aloud, till he himself, exhausted, fell asleep.

When he saw him next morning he was surprised at his appearance. He was paler than ever, tired, but his eyes shone with an inhuman fire. It looked as though he were filled with an overwhelming joy.

"I want you to go down presently and see Sadie," he said. "I can't hope that her body is better, but her soul—her soul is transformed."

The doctor was feeling wan and nervous.

"You were with her very late last night," he said.

"Yes, she couldn't bear to have me leave her."

"You look as pleased as Punch," the doctor said irritably.

Davidson's eyes shone with ecstasy.

"A great mercy has been vouchsafed me. Last night I was privileged to bring a lost soul to the loving arms of Jesus."

Miss Thompson was again in the rocking-chair. The bed had not been made. The room was in disorder. She had not troubled to dress herself, but wore a dirty dressing-gown, and her hair was tied in a sluttish knot. She had given her face a dab with a wet towel, but it was all swollen and creased with crying. She looked a drab.

She raised her eyes dully when the doctor came in. She was cowed and broken.

"Where's Mr Davidson?" she asked.

"He'll come presently if you want him," answered Macphail acidly. "I came here to see how you were."

"Oh, I guess I'm O. K. You needn't worry about that."

"Have you had anything to eat?"

"Horn brought me some coffee."

She looked anxiously at the door.

"D'you think he'll come down soon? I feel as if it wasn't so terrible when he's with me."

"Are you still going on Tuesday?"

"Yes, he says I've got to go. Please tell him to come right along. You can't do me any good. He's the only one as can help me now."

"Very well," said Dr Macphail.

During the next three days the missionary spent almost all his time with Sadie Thompson. He joined the others only to have his meals. Dr Macphail noticed that he hardly ate.

"He's wearing himself out," said Mrs Davidson pitifully. "He'll have a breakdown if he doesn't take care, but he won't spare himself."

She herself was white and pale. She told Mrs Macphail that she had no sleep. When the missionary came upstairs from Miss Thompson he prayed till he was exhausted, but even then he did not sleep for long. After an hour or two he got up and dressed himself, and went for a tramp along the bay. He had strange dreams.

"This morning he told me that he'd been dreaming about the mountains of Nebraska," said Mrs Davidson.

"That's curious," said Dr Macphail.

He remembered seeing them from the windows of the train when he crossed America. They were like huge mole-hills, rounded and smooth, and they rose from the plain abruptly. Dr Macphail remembered how it struck him that they were like a woman's breasts.

Davidson's restlessness was intolerable even to himself. But he was buoyed up by a wonderful exhilaration. He was tearing out by the roots the last vestiges of sin that lurked in the hidden corners of that poor woman's heart. He read with her and prayed with her.

"It's wonderful," he said to them one day at supper. "It's a true rebirth. Her soul, which was black as night, is now pure and white like the new-fallen snow. I am humble and afraid. Her remorse for all her sins is beautiful. I am not worthy to touch the hem of her garment."

"Have you the heart to send her back to San Francisco?" said the doctor. "Three years in an American prison. I should have thought you might have saved her from that."

"Ah, but don't you see? It's necessary. Do you think my heart doesn't bleed for her? I love her as I love my wife and my sister. All the time that she is in prison I shall suffer all the pain that she suffers."

"Bunkum," cried the doctor impatiently.

"You don't understand because you're blind. She's sinned, and she must suffer. I know what she'll endure. She'll be starved and tortured and humiliated. I want her to accept the punishment of man as a sacrifice to God. I want her to accept it joyfully. She has an opportunity which is offered to very few of us. God is very good and very merciful."

Davidson's voice trembled with excitement. He could hardly articulate the words that tumbled passionately from his lips.

"All day I pray with her and when I leave her I pray again, I pray with all my might and main, so that Jesus may grant her this great mercy. I want to put in her heart the passionate desire to be punished so that at the end, even if I offered to let her go, she would refuse. I want her to feel that the bitter punishment of prison is the thank-offering that she places at the feet of our Blessed Lord, who gave his life for her."

The days passed slowly. The whole household, intent on the wretched, tortured woman downstairs, lived in a state of unnatural excitement. She was like a victim that was being prepared for the savage rites of a bloody idolatry. Her terror numbed her. She could not bear to let Davidson out of her sight; it was only when he was with her that she had courage, and she hung upon him with a slavish dependence. She cried a great deal, and she read the Bible, and prayed. Sometimes she was exhausted and apathetic. Then she did indeed look forward to her ordeal, for it seemed to offer an escape, direct and concrete, from the anguish she was enduring. She could not bear much longer the vague terrors which now assailed her. With her sins she had put aside all personal vanity, and she slopped about her room, unkempt and dishevelled, in her tawdry dressing-gown. She had not taken off her night-dress for four days, nor put on stockings. Her room was littered and untidy. Meanwhile the rain fell with a cruel persistence. You felt that the heavens must at last be empty of water, but still it poured down, straight and heavy, with a maddening iteration, on the iron roof. Everything was damp and clammy. There was mildew on the walls and on the boots that stood on the floor. Through the sleepless nights the mosquitoes droned their angry chant.

"If it would only stop raining for a single day it wouldn't be so bad," said Dr Macphail.

They all looked forward to the Tuesday when the boat for San Francisco was to arrive from Sydney. The strain was intolerable. So far as Dr Macphail was concerned, his pity and his resentment were alike extinguished by his desire to be rid of the unfortunate woman. The inevitable must be accepted. He felt he would breathe more freely when the ship had sailed. Sadie Thomp-

son was to be escorted on board by a clerk in the governor's office. This
person called on the Monday evening and told Miss Thompson to be prepared at eleven in the morning. Davidson was with her.

"I'll see that everything is ready. I mean to come on board with her
myself."

Miss Thompson did not speak.

When Dr Macphail blew out his candle and crawled cautiously under his
mosquito curtains, he gave a sigh of relief.

"Well, thank God that's over. By this time tomorrow she'll be gone."

"Mrs Davidson will be glad too. She says he's wearing himself to a
shadow," said Mrs Macphail. "She's a different woman."

"Who?"

"Sadie. I should never have thought it possible. It makes one humble."

Dr Macphail did not answer, and presently he fell asleep. He was tired
out, and he slept more soundly than usual.

He was awakened in the morning by a hand placed on his arm, and,
starting up, saw Horn by the side of his bed. The trader put his finger on his
mouth to prevent any exclamation from Dr Macphail and beckoned to him to
come. As a rule he wore shabby ducks, but now he was barefoot and wore
only the *lava-lava* of the natives. He looked suddenly savage, and Dr Macphail, getting out of bed, saw that he was heavily tattooed. Horn made him
a sign to come on to the verandah. Dr Macphail got out of bed and followed
the trader out.

"Don't make a noise," he whispered. "You're wanted. Put on a coat and
some shoes. Quick."

Dr Macphail's first thought was that something had happened to Miss
Thompson.

"What is it? Shall I bring my instruments?"

"Hurry, please, hurry."

Dr Macphail crept back into the bedroom, put on a waterproof over
his pyjamas, and a pair of rubber-soled shoes. He rejoined the trader, and
together they tiptoed down the stairs. The door leading out to the road was
open and at it were standing half a dozen natives.

"What is it?" repeated the doctor.

"Come along with me," said Horn.

He walked out and the doctor followed him. The natives came after them
in a little bunch. They crossed the road and came on to the beach. The doctor
saw a group of natives standing round some object at the water's edge. They
hurried along, a couple of dozen yards perhaps, and the natives opened out
as the doctor came up. The trader pushed him forwards. Then he saw, lying
half in the water and half out, a dreadful object, the body of Davidson. Dr
Macphail bent down—he was not a man to lose his head in an emergency—
and turned the body over. The throat was cut from ear to ear, and in the
right hand was still the razor with which the deed was done.

"He's quite cold," said the doctor. "He must have been dead some time."

"One of the boys saw him lying there on his way to work just now and came and told me. Do you think he did it himself?"

"Yes. Someone ought to go for the police."

Horn said something in the native tongue, and two youths started off.

"We must leave him here till they come," said the doctor.

"They mustn't take him into my house. I won't have him in my house."

"You'll do what the authorities say," replied the doctor sharply. "In point of fact I expect they'll take him to the mortuary."

They stood waiting where they were. The trader took a cigarette from a fold in his *lava-lava* and gave one to Dr Macphail. They smoked while they stared at the corpse. Dr Macphail could not understand.

"Why do you think he did it?" asked Horn.

The doctor shrugged his shoulders. In a little while native police came along, under the charge of a marine, with a stretcher, and immediately afterwards a couple of naval officers and a naval doctor. They managed everything in a businesslike manner.

"What about the wife?" said one of the officers.

"Now that you've come I'll go back to the house and get some things on. I'll see that it's broken to her. She'd better not see him till he's been fixed up a little."

"I guess that's right," said the naval doctor.

When Dr Macphail went back he found his wife nearly dressed.

"Mrs Davidson's in a dreadful state about her husband," she said to him as soon as he appeared. "He hasn't been to bed all night. She heard him leave Miss Thompson's room at two, but he went out. If he's been walking about since then he'll be absolutely dead."

Dr Macphail told her what had happened and asked her to break the news to Mrs Davidson.

"But why did he do it?" she asked, horror-stricken.

"I don't know."

"But I can't. I can't."

"You must."

She gave him a frightened look and went out. He heard her go into Mrs Davidson's room. He waited a minute to gather himself together and then began to shave and wash. When he was dressed he sat down on the bed and waited for his wife. At last she came.

"She wants to see him," she said.

"They've taken him to the mortuary. We'd better go down with her. How did she take it?"

"I think she's stunned. She didn't cry. But she's trembling like a leaf."

"We'd better go at once."

When they knocked at her door Mrs Davidson came out. She was very pale, but dry-eyed. To the doctor she seemed unnaturally composed. No word was exchanged, and they set out in silence down the road. When they arrived at the mortuary Mrs Davidson spoke.

"Let me go in and see him alone."

They stood aside. A native opened a door for her and closed it behind her. They sat down and waited. One or two white men came and talked to them in undertones. Dr Macphail told them again what he knew of the tragedy. At last the door was quietly opened and Mrs Davidson came out. Silence fell upon them.

"I'm ready to go back now," she said.

Her voice was hard and steady. Dr Macphail could not understand the look in her eyes. Her pale face was very stern. They walked back slowly, never saying a word, and at last they came round the bend on the other side of which stood their house. Mrs Davidson gave a gasp, and for a moment they stopped still. An incredible sound assaulted their ears. The gramophone which had been silent for so long was playing, playing ragtime loud and harsh.

"What's that?" cried Mrs Macphail with horror.

"Let's go on," said Mrs Davidson.

They walked up the steps and entered the hall. Miss Thompson was standing at her door, chatting with a sailor. A sudden change had taken place in her. She was no longer the cowed drudge of the last days. She was dressed in all her finery, in her white dress, with the high shiny boots over which her fat legs bulged in their cotton stockings; her hair was elaborately arranged; and she wore that enormous hat covered with gaudy flowers. Her face was painted, her eyebrows were boldly black, and her lips were scarlet. She held herself erect. She was the flaunting quean that they had known at first. As they came in she broke into a loud, jeering laugh; and then, when Mrs Davidson involuntarily stopped, she collected the spittle in her mouth and spat. Mrs Davidson cowered back, and two red spots rose suddenly to her cheeks. Then, covering her face with her hands, she broke away and ran quickly up the stairs. Dr Macphail was outraged. He pushed past the woman into her room.

"What the devil are you doing?" he cried. "Stop that damned machine."

He went up to it and tore the record off. She turned on him.

"Say, doc, you can that stuff with me. What the hell are you doin' in my room?"

"What do you mean?" he cried. "What d'you mean?"

She gathered herself together. No one could describe the scorn of her expression or the contemptuous hatred she put into her answer.

"You men! You filthy, dirty pigs! You're all the same, all of you. Pigs! Pigs!"

Dr Macphail gasped. He understood.

COMMENTARY

The provocative remarks with which Mr. Somerset Maugham prefaces collections of his works have set almost as bad an example for young writers as the works themselves. These discussions are ingenious, subtle, often learned pleas to the artist to do only as well as it lies in him easily to do, and as a rule, they set forth reasons why he should stop short of the final, exhausting, almost superhuman efforts which result in the production of masterpieces.

In one of his most stimulating discussions Mr. Maugham considers how Chekhov and Maupassant differ as writers. The differences, he feels, lie largely in their gifts. He says:

> On the face of it it is easier to write stories like Chekhov's than stories like Maupassant's. To invent a story interesting in itself apart from the telling is a difficult thing, the power to do it is a gift of nature, it cannot be acquired by taking thought, and it is a gift that few people have . . .

Mr. Maugham feels that Chekhov is lacking in this gift which Maupassant possessed in abundance. In his own work he has followed the paths indicated by Maupassant rather than Chekhov. The kernel of any one of his plots would make an interesting newspaper item, and the interest is heightened by the exotic settings, an island in the South Seas, an out-station of the British Empire, some city whose very name calls up glamorous images. "Sadie Thompson," perhaps Mr. Maugham's most famous story, which, under the name of "Rain" (the title now usually applied to the story, too), enjoyed enormous popularity as a stage presentation not too long after its publication, employs such a setting. Its neat, clipped representations, in which there are no grays, only sharp blacks and whites, was peculiarly congenial to the mood of the twenties. Even more congenial was the hedonistic philosophy which pervaded the action. One is given to understand that the natives on Pago Pago were perfectly happy until the missionary, Mr. Davidson, made "sins" for them out of "natural actions." "We had to make it a sin not only to commit adultery and to lie and to thieve, but to expose their bodies and to dance and not to come to church," Mrs. Davidson says. Similarly, one infers that the prostitute, Miss Thompson, would have gone on being happy in her natural state, if only Mr. Davidson had let her alone, and he, sinning by seeing sin where there was no sin, is properly punished by death while Miss Thompson reverts to the state she was in when she met him.

In "Rain" Mr. Maugham comes as near attaining perfection of form as he has ever come. (Most of his other stories, with the exception of the Ashenden series, which are high-class thrillers, are dilutions of this basic formula.) "Rain," which established him, in the minds of the public and of some critics, as a master of the art form, has influenced a whole generation of writers. The serious student of today finds it perhaps more interesting as an historical document than as a work of art. It affords the dramatic spectacle of an artist engaged in the struggle which will decide his fate, for its five or six thousand words seem at once to recapitulate and foreshadow the artist's working life.

In the first paragraphs of his story, Mr. Maugham presents a brilliant solution of the question of Authority (see Appendix A, p. 621). We see events through the eyes of Dr. Macphail, who is a keen observer, by nature and training. He is also a man who knows a good deal more about life than he can put into words: in the last few years he has suffered a slow sapping of his moral and physical forces as the result of a wound that "had taken longer to heal than it should." We find such precise and at the same time cryptic observations on every page of the first half of the story. The author takes up his post of observation (see Appendix A, p. 626) at the doctor's shoulder. We, too, stand beside him on the deck to watch the strip of silver beach which is Pago Pago rise out of the water, or turn with him to receive an ingratiating smile from Miss Thompson, plump and in a coarse fashion pretty, with her fat calves in their white stockings bulging over the tops of long white boots in glacé kid. The first half of the story is vivid with such sensuous details and the doctor's ironical reflections playing over the scene give the whole surface a peculiarly lively glow.

Effects like these are usually the result of the joint workings of an admirable literary talent and a fine literary conscience. One reads the first half of "Rain" with mounting excitement, but halfway through, the literary conscience seems to go on vacation. The point of view is not held to with the same strictness. The doctor deserts his vantage post, moves away from the center of the stage and from then on we see events less clearly.

The first example of this change of method is the description of Iwelei:

> Iwelei was on the edge of the city. You went down side streets by the harbour, in the darkness, across a rickety bridge, till you came to a deserted road, all ruts and holes, and then suddenly you came out into the light. There was parking room for motors on each side of the road, and there were saloons, tawdry and bright, each one noisy with its mechanical piano, and there were barbers' shops and tobacconists. There was a stir in the air and a sense of expectant gaiety. You turned down a narrow alley, either to the right or to the left, for the road divided Iwelei into two parts, and you found yourself in the district. There were rows of little bungalows, trim and neatly painted in green, and the pathway between them was broad and straight. It was laid out like a garden-city. In its respectable regularity, its order and spruceness, it gave an impression of sardonic horror; for never can the search for love have been so systematised and ordered. . . .

This kind of writing does not impose a severe strain upon either the author or the reader. We do not even know whether the "you" who looks into the bungalows of Iwelei is a man or a woman, British or American or Hawaiian. His history and his present situation would appear to be none of our concern. It would seem that when author and reader are freed from the burden of attending, the narrator would have more energy to give to the task of rendering sensuous impressions. But this change of method, which may be compared to the soft focus that photographers use when they want to lend a subject easy glamour, has the effect of dissipating rather than enhancing interest. The subject may appear more glamorous at the first glance, but a second glance will hardly reveal more than the first. The scene is blurred; we are never sharply aware of what is going on. The burden which has been cast aside is found to be an important part of the artist's equipment; the doctor's sensuous impressions, underpinning his ironic reflections, have all along added another dimension to the scene, and without that dimension events do not show as clear. The doctor will continue to appear in the action, but—with the exception of his dramatic soliloquy in which the low, round hills of Nevada have the same shape as a woman's breasts—he no longer serves as the instrument of perception, and at the climax of the story he is so far off stage that his words come to us muffled, as it were, from the wings. The author, evidently aware that something has gone wrong, but unable or unwilling to discard his "soft focus" lens, resorts to auctorial comments:

> Miss Thompson was standing at her door, chatting with a sailor. . . . A sudden change had taken place in her. She was no longer the cowed drudge of the last days.

But these remarks do not have the dramatic impact that the doctor's observations have, and the last half of the story lacks the objectivity and the drama of the first half. The author, hard pressed, at the last turns from auctorial comment to melodrama: Miss Thompson spits in Mrs. Davidson's face. And when that does not serve, he calls desperately on his former narrator. Dr. Macphail, recalled from the wings, is pushed into the center of the stage and the limelight is turned full on him. But the doctor, deprived of his rôle, no longer speaks with authority. The words he emits are not his own but lines which the author-commentator has hurriedly put into his mouth and his voice is too feeble to carry past the first rows.

Mr. Maugham's is a baffling case. In the end, the stroke which in this story carried him out of the main current into the shallows, seems as decisive as the stroke which severed the missionary's jugular vein, but one wonders why he should ever have swum so strongly upstream if he is content to disport himself in the shallows. Perhaps the key to the enigma may be found in a much-quoted remark of Mr. Maugham's, to the effect that an artist needs to work only a certain number of hours a day. The remark might be more valuable if it were amended so that it set forth the disconcerting but inescapable fact: the artist needs to work.

Colette

THE SICK CHILD

THE CHILD wanted to prop himself higher on his pillow but could not. His mother heard his prayer without words and lifted him up. He had thought she was no longer watching him, the child promised to death, yet here was the maternal face bending over him again, the chestnut hair drawn over the temples in old-fashioned wings, the thinnish cheeks barely touched with powder, the candidly set brown eyes so confident of mastery over their fears that often they forgot to be on guard. . . .

"You are nice and rosy this evening, little boy," she said gaily.

But her brown eyes kept a worried fixity that the little boy had come to know well. To avoid any tiring movement of his neck, he raised the pupils of his sea-green eyes upward against their lids and gravely made a correction:

"I'm rosy because of the lamp shade."

Lady Mother looked sorrowfully at her son, inwardly reproaching him for the word that had erased the color she had seen in his face. He had closed his eyes, and again with the appearance of sleep he was a ten-year-old. "She believes that I am sleeping." With a gentle guile, his mother turned away from the bed, as though she could now concern herself elsewhere. "He believes that I believe he is sleeping." Many a time they played this game of outpretending each other. "She believes that I'm not in pain," Jean would think, his lashes crisping against his hot cheekbones. While Lady Mother would be thinking: "How well he knows how to imitate a child who is not in pain. Any other mother would be taken in. But I . . ."

"Doesn't the lavender spray make the most delicious fragrance? Your room smells so good."

The child agreed without speaking. Practice and the need to spare his strength had gradually provided him with a repertory of intricate little signs, a mimicry as delicate as the language of the animals. He excelled in putting his senses to a fantastic and magical use. For example, he could hear the morning sunlight make a pink sound as it came through the curtains of white muslin. He could hold his battered old *Voyage Up the Amazon* under his nose, and the smell of the calfskin binding became the taste of steaming pancakes. . . . Three blinks of his eyelids meant that he wanted water. And for food . . . oh, but somehow he never seemed to want food, it hardly needed a sign. The other wants of his soft and wasted little body

Reprinted from *Mademoiselle*, July, 1947, and used with the kind permission of the author, Colette, *Mademoiselle*, Jacques Chambrun, Inc., and the translator, George Davis.

made themselves known by a modest telegraphy. But for anything that was not actually necessary, anything that could still represent pleasure and play in the life of a condemned child, Jean clung to human speech, sought words that were exact and varied, spoke them in a voice to which pain had given its own wan harmony.

"No, it isn't really such a delicious smell," he thought. "I don't remember lavender quite that way. It seems to me that when I used to live standing up . . ."

At that moment a cloud of scent passed under his pinched white nostrils. Swiftly Jean leaped on and galloped away. It was just one of the wonderful stunts he had learned during the long hours in bed, though he never breathed a word about them to his mother.

Bored after a moment with his room, he headed his perfumed steed out through the frosted transom and down the hall. A big silvery moth followed sneezing in their wake, but Jean outdistanced him easily by giving Lavender a few digs with his knees. While people were around, those long legs of Jean's would only lie still, but now they gave him all the strength and skill a rider needed. At times like this, escaped from his bed, he could ride a horse—and right through a wall, too. But best of all he could fly! Bending his body forward like a diver plunging into space, he could feel his forehead cleaving an element that had yielded its every resource to him. Arms spread, he had only to raise one or the other shoulder to shift the direction of his flight. An extra little shove forward always eased the shock of landing.

Not that he landed often. . . . Once he was careless enough to swoop too low, over a cow pasture. Suddenly there he was, right up against the astonished gaze of a beautiful tan cow, her horns sprouting toward him, her eyes like two magnifying lenses whirling bigger and bigger, while from the grass yellow dandelions sped up like bursting planets. Just in the nick of time he managed to grab hold of her horns with his bare hands and vault back into the air. He could still recall the warm glossy feel of the horns, with their blunt and somehow kindly tips, and hear the barking of the shepherd dog grow fainter as the flying boy climbed back into his familiar sky. That morning he had to use all the strength in his arm-feathers to retrace his way across the periwinkle dawn, glide over the slumbering city and tumble into his lacquered bed. The rumples in the blanket had hurt him terribly, with a tenacious hurt that burned along his back and down his thighs, so that he was unable to hide the traces of his tears. . . .

"Did something make you cry, Jean darling?"

"No, Lady Mother, only in a dream. . . ."

Now Lavender had reached the end of the hall and was butting against the door that led to the kitchen. "Ho ho! Ho ho! What a stupid beast! I knew she wasn't a thoroughbred. These mongrel ponies will always break your neck if you don't hold tight. . . ." Jean dug severely into her penitent flanks and guided her into the warm upper region of the kitchen where the wash was drying. Lowering his head to pass between two clotheslines, he neatly snipped off an apron string and slipped it into Lavender's mouth.

"Where are we heading? We must get back in time for dinner, and it's already late. . . . Giddyap, Lavender, giddyap. . . ."

They were out the service door, and Jean invented a new game of racing down the stairs head first, with a couple of spins thrown in for fun. Lavender was terrified by her master's commands and tried to balk. "Oh, you big dumb filly!" cried the child, and he burst into laughter, he who never laughed in his sheltered other life. As they flew madly down, they came on a small dog, the one who "knew how to do his business all alone," then go back and scratch on the door. Jean reached out to pull his tail.

"Want a ride, Riki? You can sit behind me!"

Jean swept up the dog with his powerful little hand, bounced him on to the bulging rump of Lavender, who, spurred by Riki's frantic clawings, went tumbling down the last two flights. There Riki leaped from the eiderdown rump and ran off howling.

"You don't know what you're missing!" shouted Jean. "I used to be scared at first too, but now . . . watch me, Riki!"

Rider and mount flung themselves against the stout street door. To Jean's astonishment, they were met not with the usual surrender of obliging oak, melting locks and big bolts which said, "Yes, yes," as they slid tamely back, but by the inflexible barrier of a chiseled voice whispering: ". . . back to slumberland . . ."

Breathless with the shock, shaken from head to foot, Jean could feel the cruelly sharp words "back to, Baktu, Baktu" cutting like a razor. Behind them the word "slumberland" lay severed in three pieces.

"Slum . . . ber . . . land . . . " murmured Jean. "It's all over, my horseback ride. Now it's slum . . . ber . . . land, rolled into a ball. Good-by . . . good-by . . ."

He had no chance to find out to whom he was saying good-by. Time was getting horribly short. He miscalculated the landing. The exhausted Lavender missed the four feet she never had; before vanishing forever into cold droplets she threw her rider from her non-existent back into his lacquered bed, and Jean groaned as he crashed. . . .

"You were sleeping so well . . ." said the voice of Lady Mother.

A voice, thought her son, that was made up of a mixture of straight and curved lines—a curved, a straight—a dry line, a wet line. . . . But there would never be any use in trying to explain this to Lady Mother.

"You woke up as though something were the matter, my darling. Were you in pain?"

He made his "no" sign, wagging from right to left his thin white index finger. Besides, his suffering was not so bad now. He wished the bed were not quite so hard, but he was getting used to his falls. As for Lavender, well, what could you expect from a stinky old nag?

"The next time," thought Jean, "I'll take a ride on Big Scooter." That was his nighttime name for an ennnormous nickel-plated paper cutter; it always took those three n's and sometimes four, to give an idea of its size.

"Lady Mother, would you please push Big Scoot—I mean the big paper cutter—over here under the lamp?"

To make sure that everything would be ready for his next expedition, Jean turned on his pillow toward his mother. His hair was cut short in back to keep it from matting. On top and over his forehead and ears he had soft yellow curls with a faint greenish tint, the color of a winter moon, well matched with the sea green of his eyes, the petal white of his face. He watched his mother's practiced hand place the lamp and the paper cutter where he wanted them, so that the polished blade caught a reflection that was like snow at sunset, with bluish streaks; a strange landscape that he loved. He half closed his eyes.

"Jean dearest, it will soon be time for your dinner," said Lady Mother hesitatingly.

The sick child smiled indulgently at his mother. People who are well must be forgiven everything. And he really did feel rather bruised from his fall. "I have lots of time," he thought, and accentuated his smile at the risk of seeing Lady Mother—as whenever his smiles were too accomplished, too charged with a serenity to which she gave only one meaning—break down and rush from the room.

"If you don't mind, dearest, I'll have my dinner all alone in the dining-room, after you have finished with your tray. . . ."

"Okay, okay," answered the index finger condescendingly, closing twice.

Lady Mother bent over him, and he reached up his arms and clasped them according to ritual around her neck. Thus proudly charged, she hauled up the meager body of her child, too tall for his age, the slender torso followed by the long legs, inert now but which knew how to grip and master the flanks of a skittish cloud steed. . . . Lady Mother gazed at her graceful and ailing creation, sitting against his hard, pulpit-shaped pillow.

"There we are! Your tray will be right along. Just the same, I think I'll go and hurry Mandore. She never manages to be on time!"

And out she went once more.

"She goes, she comes. . . . Mostly she goes. She doesn't want to leave me alone, but she is always running out of my room. Probably she was thinking of me and has tears she wants to wipe away. Won't she ever get used to me? Won't she ever learn to be sensible? She has a hundred reasons for leaving my room and if by luck she didn't, I could give her a thousand. . . . Mandore is never late."

Turning his neck cautiously, he watched Mandore enter. "If it weren't for me," thought Jean, "she would still be calling herself Angelina." But wasn't Mandore the perfect, inevitable name for her, so round-bellied and golden, sounding tunefully to every touch, harmony in her beautiful voice and in her eyes that gleamed like the precious wood of lutes? Mandore, Mandore . . .

She crossed the room, and as her yellow-and-chestnut-striped skirt brushed against the furniture, Jean heard the full cello notes that his ear alone could catch. She put over the bed a little table covered with an embroidered napkin and holding a steaming bowl.

"Here's your dinner, young man!"

"What have you got?"

"Your phosphate salts to start off with, right here! Then . . . well, you'll see."

Over the reclining body of the sick child poured a glance that was like a consoling flood of foamy, thirst-quenching liquid. "How good, how good the dark beer of Mandore's eyes! How kind she is! How kind everybody is to me. . . . If only sometimes they wouldn't be quite so much so. . . ." Exhausted by the burden of universal kindness, he shut his eyes, reopening them to the clinking of the spoons. Spoons for his medicine, for his soup, for his desserts. . . . Jean hated spoons, except for one wonderful spoon with a long handle and an ornamented ring on the end. "It's a sugar crusher," was Lady Mother's explanation. "And what's the other end for?" "I'm not quite sure, precious. I believe it is an absinthe spoon. . . ." And her glance had a way of slipping toward a photograph of Jean's father, the husband she had lost so young, "Your dear papa, Jean darling," and to whom Jean referred coldly—with words out of a silence, out of a secret—as "that gentleman hanging in the parlor."

"Now, Jean my pet, open wide. . . ."

He obeyed, gulping down the medicine that was inoffensive enough except for a quick musky taste that seemed to disguise a horror. In Jean's secret vocabulary, this potion was called "the gully of the corpses."

The phosphated soup followed inescapably, with a flavor like the seedy sweepings from a granary. All that saved it was a magical something floating in its depths like a floral breeze; the perfumed powder of cornflowers that Mandore had bought for him last July from a pushcart. . . . A small cube of grilled lamb took no time at all. "Hurry, lamb, hurry, I won't make a face at you, as long as you roll down quick to my stomach. But I wouldn't chew you for the world, I can still hear you saying baaa, and your insides are pink!"

"Aren't you eating faster than usual this evening, Jean?"

Lady Mother's voice came floating down from the shadows overhead, perhaps from the plaster shell cornice, perhaps from somewhere high in the huge wardrobe. By special grant from Jean, Lady Mother had been given the power to penetrate the lofty reaches of the wardrobe, realm of the household linen. Up she would go on a double ladder that was invisible behind the right-hand door, and climb down again carrying great snowy slabs that she had hewed from above. Her ambition was satisfied with this harvest. Jean went farther, higher, leaping ever on toward the pure summits, plunging through an unmatched pair of sheets, reappearing through the even folds of a matched pair—with a perilous slip or two, a dizzy spell, among the stiff damask napkins—then a pause on an Alp to admire the Greek scrolls and the glazed foliage, the sprigs of dried lavender, the big and creamy iris roots. . . . At dawn he would have made the descent again, rigid with cold, white and utterly done in, but still devilish. "Jean! Heavens, he must have thrown off the covers during his sleep. Mandore, quick, the hot-water bottle!" . . . While Jean was congratulating himself on getting back in time. . . .

"I'm eating fast, Lady Mother, because I'm hungry." He was an old hand at sly tricks, and Lady Mother had only to hear him say, "I'm hungry," to blush with delight.

"If that's so, precious, I feel dreadful that I have only applesauce for your dessert. But I told Mandore to give it a dash of lemon and a stick of vanilla for perfume."

Jean turned stoutly on the applesauce, sour provincial maiden of fifteen summers, who like all girls her age scorns and despises little boys of ten. But Jean could give as good as he took. Couldn't he get around nimbly, with the aid of his vanilla stick? "Too short, always too short, this little stick," he muttered under his breath.

Mandore was back, her skirt billowing out on all sides, so that with the large stripes she looked like a melon. With every step she plucked—zroom, zzrroomm, for Jean alone to hear—those interior chords that were the very soul, the rich harmony of Mandore.

"You've got your dinner finished already? It's not good to eat so fast, you'll only bring it up later. That's not your usual way."

Lady Mother on the one side, Mandore on the other, standing beside his bed. "How big they are!" Not that Lady Mother took up very much room, in her little claret-colored dress. But Mandore, already like a giant fiddle box, added two curved handles by putting her arms akimbo. Jean got rid of the last of the applesauce, scattered in tiny festoons among the gilt curlicues on his plate. Once more the question of dinner was settled.

The winter night had long since fallen. Lingering over his half glass of mineral water, which he thought was green because he drank it from a pale green tumbler, Jean calculated that he still needed a little courage to bring his invalid's day to a close. There was still his toilet for the night, the minute and inescapable chores which called on Lady Mother and even—zroom, zzrroomm—the gay, tuneful assistance of Mandore; still the toothbrush, the sponge glove, the special soap and the luke-warm water; still the tender maternal inquisitions. . . .

"Now, little boy, you won't be able to sleep like this, with your big picture book sticking into your side. And look at all those little books everywhere in your bed, with their sharp corners. Don't you want the night table closer?"

"No, Lady Mother, thank you, I'm fine just the way I am."

His toilet over, Jean fought the drunken fatigue creeping over him. He knew the limits of his strength and was anxious not to miss the capricious wonders that the night might set as its program. He was afraid that the solicitude of Lady Mother would prolong the day unbearably, ruining his structure of books and furniture, his balance of light and shadows, so reverently assembled. It was already ten o'clock, and he was utterly used up. "If she stays, if she insists, if she is still taking care of me when the big hand leans to the other side of XII, I'll just get whiter and whiter, my eyes will sink in, I won't be able to say any more of the no-thank-you-I'm-just-fine-Lady-Mother-good-nights that she must always have, and . . . and . . . it will be awful, she'll begin sobbing. . . ."

He smiled at his mother, and the majesty which suffering bestows on her chosen children was born in a blazing curl of his hair, descended to his eyelids and settled bitterly on his lips. This was the hour when Lady Mother could have lost herself forever in adoration of her shattered and exquisite creation. . . .

"Good night, Lady Mother," whispered Jean.

"Are you tired, dear? Would you like me to leave you alone?"

He made another effort, opened wide his sea green eyes, courageously pulled back his high shoulders. "Do I look like a tired boy? Lady Mother, I ask you!"

She answered with a mischievous shake of her head, kissed him and went away carrying the suppressed cries of love, the stifled entreaties, the hushed litanies that pleaded with the pain to release her son, to unshackle the fetters from his long legs and his wasted but not deformed hips, to let the impoverished blood run freely through the green branches of his veins.

"I have left two oranges on the plate. Should I turn out your lamp for you?"

"I'll turn it out myself, Lady Mother."

"Heavens, where is my head? I've forgotten to take your temperature tonight."

A haze came between Lady Mother's claret dress and her son. Tonight, Jean burned with a fever that had been sending out a thousand warnings; a little fire smoldering in his palms, a wou-wou-wou throbbing inside his ears, a hot crown against his temples. . . .

"We'll take it tomorrow without fail, Lady Mother."

"The buzzer is right beside your wrist. Are you sure you wouldn't like to have a night light for company, when you are alone? You know, one of those pretty night . . ."

The last syllable of the word tumbled into a dark corner, but Lady Mother never even noticed. "She is too busy with all that she has gathered up in her skirt," thought Jean. "She can only worry about her little prayers, the things she wants to tell the doctor, the sadness she feels because I don't want anybody to stay with me at night. . . . And all that, she tries to carry in her skirt, no wonder something falls out and rolls on the carpet. Poor Lady Mother . . . how can I make her understand that I'm not unhappy? It seems that a boy my age can't lie in bed, can't be pale and unable to use his legs, can't feel pain, without being unhappy. Yes, I was unhappy when they used to take me out for a ride, and everybody used to look at me and I could hear them saying, 'Such a beautiful child, isn't it a dreadful pity?' Now I'm only unhappy when my cousin Charlie comes to visit me, with his scraped knees, his hob-nail shoes and that word 'boy scout,' half steel and half rubber, he is always pestering me with. . . . But when night comes and I'm alone, everything is fine. . . ."

He turned out the lamp and watched peacefully while his nocturnal visitors rose to greet him in a chorus of forms and colors. He awaited a symphonic blaze and the troupe that Lady Mother called his loneliness. He reached for the luminous buzzer, and put it on the bedside table. "Now shine!" he commanded.

It did not obey immediately. The night outside was not too black to distinguish, tapping against one of the panes, the farthest branch of a chestnut tree, stripped of its leaves and imploring help. Its swollen tip was trying hard to look like a sickly rosebud. "Yes, you are still trying to work on my sympathy by pretending to be the first bud of spring. You should know by now that I don't want any talk about next year. Stay outside. Vanish! As Charlie would say, 'Get the hell out!'"

His purity drew itself up to its full height, inflicting yet another rebuke on his cousin with the scratched and purplish knees, and his vocabulary studded with "Says you!" and "I get it!"—as though thought and comprehension would not have fled in terror, as fast as their wise old cricket legs could carry them, from such a boy with his hobnails and dried mud. . . .

Just at the sight of his cousin Charlie, Jean would wipe his fingers with his handkerchief as if to rid them of some filth. Because Lady Mother and Mandore, standing between the child and ugliness, the child and abusive language, the child and coarse reading, had taught him to know and cherish only two luxuries: fastidiousness and suffering. Protected, precocious, he had mastered the hieroglyphics of print, racing as madly through books as over clouds, uncovering countrysides inscribed under glossy surfaces and gathering around him all that, for privileged folk like him, secretly people the air.

But he no longer used the silver fountain pen engraved with his initials, since the day his agile handwriting had surprised and somehow antagonized the doctor with the cold hands. "Is this the writing of a young child, Madam?" "Yes, yes, Doctor, my son has a grownup way of writing. . . ." And the worried eyes of Lady Mother seemed to ask, apologetically: "At least, it isn't a dangerous symptom, Doctor?"

"Wouldn't you like a drawing book, my young friend, with a box of crayons? They are an excellent pastime and just the thing for a boy your age." This extramedical suggestion Jean answered with a narrowed look between his lashes, a grave and virile look that took the measure of this doctor so free with his advice: "It wouldn't be my nice barber who would talk such nonsense!" He had never forgiven the doctor for asking, out of the maternal presence: "And why the devil do you call your mother, *Lady Mother*?" This time the angered male look, the weak musical voice merged in: "I didn't think it would be the devil's business."

The nice barber went about his task quite differently. It was the account of his dominical activities that absorbed Jean. Every Sunday he went fishing with a bamboo rod and line. With a dazzling wave of the scissors, he would demonstrate to Jean how he cast the bobber and bait. Jean could always see the cool spray fly up, then the expanding circles as the victorious fisherman drew up his catch.

"When you are well, Master Jean, I'll take you with me up the river."

"Yes, yes . . ." Why did they all want him to get well? He *was* up the river now. And what would he do with a bass-as-big-as-my-hand-here and a pickerel-as-long-as-that-paper-cutter? "Tell me some more. . . ."

And then he would hear the tall tale of the cloud of fish flies that the barber had spied sticking under the little bridge, an impromptu bait that had landed a wagonful of trout, calling for the biggest stringer the barber could find, and three lengths of cord knotted one to the other. The story began to the edgy refrain of the clipping scissors: "You follow the river until you get to a little branch that begins big-as-my-behind, then spreads out as you go up the meadow. You see two, three willow trees together and a clump of bushes. Well, sir, that's the spot. . . ."

Around the two, three willows, Jean had transplanted, the first day he saw them, some thick-spiked agrimony *eupatoria,* dug from his big botanical album, and a bed of hemp, whose pink blossoms put butterflies and tired children to sleep. The raggedly pruned face of the oldest willow winks monstrously at Jean from under a crown of white morning-glories. A fish leaps through the mirrored surface of the river, then two more. . . . The kind barber, busy with his bait, turns around:

"They think they can tease me! I'll have 'em on my hook!"

"No, no," protests Jean, "it was just me throwing pebbles. . . ."

A frog sings, the imaginary afternoon drowses away. . . . "The frog sings," dreams Jean, "because he begins with *fr* and hides under his lily pad . . . but if he began with *l* he would be a log instead, and he wouldn't be able to sing, just float where the river carried him. . . ."

The barber-fisherman, the river and the meadow faded like a daydream, their only trace a sweetish perfume on Jean's forehead, a wind-blown tuft of blond hair. . . . Wide awake, Jean heard a long whispering, coming from the parlor, a low-voiced conference between Lady Mother and the doctor. A word escaped and ran, frizzled and frisky, to find Jean: *crisis.* It appeared again, but ceremoniously this time, like a girl receiving a prize at school. She had an *h* behind her ear and a *y* in her corsage: Chrysis, Chrysis Turnapoynt. "Truly? truly?" pressed the voice of Lady Mother. "I said *perhaps,*" replied the voice of the doctor, a voice unable to stand straight on its two legs. "A crisis . . . turning point . . ." Chrysis Turnapoynt, a young West Indian girl in flowing white veils, flitting through the forest. . . .

The subtle ear of the sick child caught another name, one he was positive they did not wish him to hear. It was only part of the name—something like Infanta Peralla, Fantil Lysis. . . . Jean concluded finally that she was a little girl who had to lie painfully still, like him, her long legs stretched out on the bed. They never mentioned her name in front of him because they were afraid he might be jealous. . . .

Obedient to his harsh command, the branch of the chestnut tree, with its false message of spring, had sunk into the night. But the buzzer had disobeyed a second time, refusing to shed its faint opaline glow over the night table where Lady Mother had arranged the green tumbler, the oranges, the paper cutter, the myopic watch with its bulging crystal.

None of Jean's books were on the table. No matter what their size or weight, whether they were sleeping tight or keeping watch, they were lodged in the sick child's bed. Down at the foot, one big volume heavy as a tile weighed against those legs in which life moved in a miserly flow, but Jean had no complaint. With his still active arms, he groped around him, bringing up paper-covered books, tattered and warm. These he heaped into a prop alongside his meager hips, while he pressed his cheek against a tan calfskin binding a century old. Under his left shoulder, Jean felt the presence of a favorite companion, a book chunky as a paving stone.

Cardboard corners fitted against the frail body in boon companionship. A momentary bruise taught patience for the chronic pain. Certain little tortures inflicted between the ear and the shoulder by a tan calfskin horn seemed to ease the larger torment in the same region and around his winged shoulder blades. . . . "What do you have here?" Lady Mother would say, suddenly. "Really, it's beyond my understanding what happens. As though you had been hit. . . ." In truth, the bruised child would have to reflect for a moment before he told himself: "There . . . but let's see, yes. . . . It must have been that tree I flew against. It might have been that roof I was leaning on, watching the sheep being brought in. Or maybe that big rake that fell on me while I was drinking at the fountain. At that, it's lucky Lady Mother didn't see the nick in the corner of my eye, where that swallow's beak caught me. . . . I didn't have time to get out of his way. . . . It's true that the sky is such a small place. . . ."

Around him rose the nocturnal hum, expected if not always familiar, varying according to the dreams, the fever, the weakness, the fancies that had made up a day that Lady Mother had sadly thought must be like all the others. But this night bore no resemblance to yesterday's. Darkness can be many, many blacks. "Now tonight black is like purple. I have a terrible pain . . . but where? In my forehead. No, what am I saying? It must be in my back, as always. . . . No, though, it's a weight, two weights, hanging from my hips, two weights like the pine cones on the cuckoo clock in the kitchen. Aren't you going to shine, you buzzer you?"

In order to snap another command to the buzzer, he leaned his temple against the tan calfskin binding and shivered to find it so cold. "It must be me that's on fire." No light came from the buzzer on the night table. "What's wrong with it? And what's wrong with me, that the service door wouldn't let me fly through, this afternoon?" He reached out in the swarming blackness and without a fumble managed to find the buzzer. But now the light played a mischievous trick on him and shone suddenly from the fat, myopic face of the spherical watch. "What are you sticking your nose in for?" murmured Jean.

Mortified, the watch dimmed its light, and Jean breathed a sigh of appeased power. But from his stiffened sides he was able to wrest no more than a moan. Now a wind was rising that was the one Jean knew best; the wind that blows down the pines, dishevels the larches, builds and tears down the dunes. Its roar filled Jean's ears, and images that his ordinary daydreams could never summon up, that could not push past the lashes of his poor eyelids, now burst into rebellion, leaped free to roam the vast reaches of the room. Queerly horizontal ones crossed others that had bolted straight up, making a luminous quivering plaid. "Those must be Scotch," thought Jean.

His bed trembled slightly, shaken by the vibrant rise of the Great Fever. He felt three or four years slipping away from him, and suddenly, almost for the first time in his life, he knew fear. He was on the point of calling: "Help, help, Lady Mother! Your little boy is being kidnaped!"

Not in his wildest rides, not in his rich domain of strange sounds—hunchbacked sounds wearing radio tubes on their heads, sounds with pointed snouts like weasels—never anywhere had Jean envisioned such a mad swarm. His hearing drank them in like a mouth, his sight was held in a kind of enraptured agony. "Help me, Lady Mother! You know that I can't walk! I only know how to fly, to swim, to glide from cloud to cloud. . . ." At that moment, something indescribable and long forgotten, stirred within his body, far off, infinitely far off, at the very end of his useless legs, something like a frantic scatter of lost ants. "Help me, Mother!"

But another being, whose decisions did not defer to maternal hope or despair, made an imperious sign that imposed silence. A magic spell held Lady Mother in her room, dreaming timidly of a time when she might be as grownup as her own little boy.

So he did not cry out. Already his fabulous, unknown visitors had begun their assault. Surging up everywhere, they poured fire and ice over him, a shrilling torture. Lying in motionless agony, listening in vain for the maternal footsteps, Jean made a sudden decision and flung himself into a headlong flight that shot him over meteors, above the battle of thunderbolts, through mists that hid and shielded him. Now the boy who had been so gay and so spoiled, so at home in his loneliness, so wrapped up in his privileges as a fatherless invalid, knew that only a sad little sound, as of crystal breaking, remained between him and a happiness whose hollow name he had still to learn: death. A sad, frail little breaking sound, coming from a planet he might never see again . . . a clear and grieving sound, somehow connected with the child who might die, and so penetrating that Jean could not outdistance it in his dazzling flight.

Perhaps his journey lasted a long time. He had lost all sense of time passing, so he could only judge by what he experienced. Often he believed that he was following a shadowy guide, one who had difficulty himself in finding the trail. Then he whimpered because he could not take the lead and, hearing his own wail of humbled pride or of utter exhaustion, he wheeled sharply, plunged through the wake of a cyclone, in search of a corner where he might find refuge. Now he was gripped with the agony of inhabiting a country where there were no corners, only a freezing current of dark air, a night on whose breast he was nothing more than a lost and weeping lad. Then he stood up, on legs that suddenly grew in number, that stretched to stilts through which pain cut like a scythe. Then everything vanished, and he had only the blind wind rushing past to tell him how fast was his speed. As he fled from a familiar continent over an uncharted sea, he caught a few words spoken in a language he was surprised to understand:
"The noise of the green tumbler breaking woke me . . ."
"Look, Madam, he's moving his lips like he's thirsty. Would he be wanting some water?"
He would have loved to know whose voice he had heard last . . . *thirsty . . . water.* . . . But already the words and his memory of them were swallowed up by time and space. Once again during the night, after a sudden halt that set his temples throbbing, he overheard a snatch of human talk and longed to say over the fragmentary syllables. He had been brought up abruptly and achingly against a rough, solid object that seemed to arrive from nowhere; it was finely striped, shaggy, mysteriously allied—he was to discover later—to horrid *my-young-friends.* "It's a . . . I know . . . a sleeve. . . ." With that he winged out again, head lowered, into chaos.
Another time he saw a hand. With slender fingers, skin slightly chapped, and white spots on the nails, it was repelling some strange monster will make a mouthful of it. And it's Jean began to laugh. "Poor little hand, the monster will make a mouthful of it. And it's such a clever-looking monster, with those black and yellow stripes!" The weak little hand was fighting as hard as it could, fingers outstretched, and the parallel stripes began to swell out, to diverge, to bend like molten bars. A great opening appeared between them and swallowed the frail hand. Somehow the spectacle had filled Jean with a vague grief, and he found it difficult to strike out on his travels. The grief went along with him, like the obstinate tinkling of shattered green glass, in an age long, long past. From that time on, through the cradling giddiness of

swirling eddy and sudden fall, Jean's journey was troubled by echoes, the sound of weeping, the anxious try at something like a thought, by a strangely insistent pity.

A sharp barking ripped through space, and Jean murmured, "Riki. . . ." Far away he heard a kind of sob: "Riki! Madam, he said Riki!" And another voice stammered, "He said Riki . . . Oh, God, he said Riki . . ."

Some obstinate, quivering force seemed to be tugging under his arms, trying to lift him high, high, toward an unknown peak. The pressure was hurting him, and he grumbled. Things were simply not done that way to a traveler who was used to motors without engines, steeds that had never been shod, sleighs that sped down the multicolored ways of the rainbow. . . . He must not be bothered by outsiders . . . only if the night had unleashed and commanded them. For example, the pigeon that was just now snuggling its breast against his cheek had no right. . . . Not that it *could* be a bird's breast, because it wasn't feathered, only bordered with a lock of long hair. "It would be a cheek," he thought, "if there were another cheek besides mine in the universe . . . but it's an impostor. . . . I forbid anybody touching me, I forbid . . ."

To find the strength to speak, Jean drew in deep breaths. With the air entered the wonder, the enchantment of memory, the fragrance of hair and skin that he had forgotten on the other side of the world and which set loose within him now a torrent of remembrance. He coughed, trying to keep down something that was knotting his throat, moistening his dry lips, overflowing his eyes . . . and mercifully veiling his descent to the hard bed. Next he heard a voice, echoing to infinity: "He's crying . . . dear, dear God, he's crying. . . ." The voice subsided into a kind of storm, over which rose disjointed syllables, calls to someone hidden in the room: "Come, come quickly!"

"So noisy, so noisy," thought the child reproachfully. But he pressed his cheek more and more against the smooth, soft surface framed with hair and felt against his mouth a briny dew. He turned away his head, meeting on the way a narrow valley, a nest molded to his measure. He just had time to say to himself what it was—"Lady Mother's shoulder"—before he lost consciousness. Or did he only fall asleep?

It was his own voice, clear and teasing, that brought him back. "Where have you been all this time, Lady Mother?"

There was no answer, but a slice of orange slipped between his lips, told him of the presence of the one he had sought. He knew that she was bending over him, submissive, unmindful of her own comfort. Completely exhausted, Jean lay still. But already a thousand worries were plaguing him, and he momentarily conquered his faintness to settle the most urgent: "Did you change my pajamas, Lady Mother, while I was sleeping? When I went to bed last night I had on my blue ones and now these are the green. . . ."

"Can you believe it, Madam? He remembers that he was wearing his blue pajamas, the night when . . ."

He did not listen to the rest of the sentence whispered in a warm, husky voice but gave himself over to the hands that were removing his damp garments, hands as nimble as a cloud steed, rocking him weightlessly.

"He is soaked. Wrap him in the big bathrobe, Mandore, but don't bother with the sleeves."

"The furnace is sending up heat, Madam, don't worry. And I've just given him another hot-water bottle. He's all damp, bless him. . . ."

"If they knew where I've come from . . . getting a little damp would be the least of it," thought Jean. "I wish I could scratch my legs or else that they would get rid of those ants. Lady Mother . . ."

He recognized, absorbed, the silence, the still vigilance that was Lady Mother's guarded reply.

"Would you please . . . would you scratch above my ankles, where the ants have been crawling? . . ."

Out of the depths of silence, someone murmured, with a queer awe: "He says there are ants. That's what he said, ants."

Snug within the oversized bathrobe, he tried to raise his shoulders. Why, naturally, he said ants. What was there so amazing just because he said Riki and ants? An airy, carefree dream bore him off to the borderline between waking and sleep, until he was revived by something brushing against him. Through his lashes he saw that it was the hateful sleeve, right there beside him, with its blue stripes, its woolen hairs. Resentment brought him wide awake. He refused to see more, but then he heard a voice that made him open his eyes, a voice saying: "Well, my young friend. . . ."

"I'll drive him out!" cried Jean to himself. "Yes, him, his sleeve, his *my-young-friend,* his mean little eyes, I hate them and I'll drive them all out!" In his fury he began gasping.

"Well, well, what's this? Yes, there's really movement. . . . There . . . there . . ."

A hand rested on Jean's head. Powerless to rebel, the child hoped to crush the aggressor with a glance. But his eyes discovered, in the bedside chair that was reserved for Lady Mother, a man who wasn't so bad after all, heavyish, rather bald, whose eyes moistened when they met Jean's.

"Well, my boy, well, well. . . . Is it true you can feel ants crawling on your legs? Honest to goodness? That's good news, on my word. . . . Would you like to have a glass of orange juice? Or a few spoonfuls of lemon ice? Or maybe a few swallows of milk?"

Jean's hand let itself go in the clasp of the gentle big fingers, the pleasantly warm palm. He murmured confused acceptance, not sure whether he had said he wanted or did not want the orange juice, the lemon ice, the milk. . . . With eyes faded to a pale gray, between deeply creased circles and dark eyebrows, he greeted eyes that were gaily blue, twinkling, tender. . . .

The remainder of this new time in Jean's life passed in a succession of jumbled moments, in a mixture of short naps and tight slumbers, of quickening urges and hazy thrills. The good doctor spent himself in a holiday of well-wells and there-theres, satisfied harrumphings and repetitions of "Happy days, my dear lady! We're out of the woods now!" Indeed, if Jean had not been in a state of sublime indifference, he would surely have asked what was the joyous occasion. As it was, the hours slipped away, with only the arrival of a glass of milk or a dish of stewed berries, to mark them off. A boiled egg would tip its lid, revealing a yellow as gay as a gold button.

Through the half-opened window entered a heady breeze, a wine of spring, while outside the rosy chestnut buds swelled more and more each day. Up and down Jean's legs ran ants armed with tiny pincers. "This time I've caught one, Lady Mother!" But it was his own transparent skin that he was pinching; the ant had escaped to the other side of his tree of veins. The eighth day of this new time, a long scarf of sunlight wound across the bed, arousing in Jean an emotion stronger than he could bear. He made up his mind that in his nocturnal fever he would retrieve all that he had missed for the past week; his periods of sleep had become like blocks of black stone, separating him from his faceless companions, his wild flights, his round of firmaments, his security as a soaring angel. . . .

"Lady Mother, if you please, I'd like my books."

"But darling, the doctor said that . . ."

"Oh, but I don't want to read them, Lady Mother. I just want them to get used to me again. . . ."

She protested no more, but brought him somewhat apprehensively his tattered books—the surly old paving stone, the one bound in tan calf smooth as his own cheek, his *Horticulture* with its lusciously colored fruits, his *Zoology* with its flat-faced lion and duck-bill platypuses cowering under beetles bigger than islands. . . .

Evening, and he had stuffed himself greedily with all the food Mandore had brought on his tray. He pretended that he was ready to drowse off, crooned his good nights in a wandering sly song. Having attended to the departure of Lady Mother and Mandore, he took command of his raft of folios and atlases and embarked. A new moon behind the branch of the chestnut tree revealed that, thanks to an indulgent April, the buds were about to burst into forked leaves.

He sat up without help, dragging along legs that were still heavy and swarming with ants. Beyond the window, in the heavenly waters of the night, bathed a curved moon and the blurred reflection of a child with long hair, to whom Jean beckoned. The other child docilely repeated the gesture. Intoxicated with his old sense of power and wonder, he summoned back his companions of the cruel and privileged hours he used to know, the visible sounds, the tangible images, the breathable seas, the nourishing and navigable air, the defiant wings, the laughing stars. . . .

Above all, he summoned back a certain impetuous boy who used to shake with secret mirth as he hurtled into the air, who as lord and master of Lady Mother's every emotion made her the victim of a hundred tender hoaxes.

He waited, but nothing came. Not that night, nor the next; nothing came again ever. The landscape of pink snow had vanished from the nickel paper cutter, and nevermore would Jean glide through a periwinkle dawn, skimming the sharp horns of cattle blue with morning mist. . . . Nevermore would a yellow and brown Mandore entrance him—zzroom, zzrroomm— with the melodies of her expansive skirts. Never more would the damask Alp indulge the child, who was soon to be cured, in the hardy exploits that had been his as a helpless lad, leaping over imaginary glaciers. . . .

A time comes to give oneself to life. A time comes to turn away utterly, irrevocably, from death. Jean waved farewell to his haloed reflection, and the salute was returned to him from a night that had lost its magic, the meek and disenchanted night that is the lot of children on whom death has no more claim.

Ernest Hemingway

THE SNOWS OF KILIMANJARO

Kilimanjaro is a snow-covered mountain 19,710 feet high, and is said to be the highest mountain in Africa. Its western summit is called the Masai "Ngàje Ngàji," the House of God. Close to the western summit there is the dried and frozen carcass of a leopard. No one has explained what the leopard was seeking at that altitude.

"THE MARVELLOUS thing is that it's painless," he said. "That's how you know when it starts."

"Is it really?"

"Absolutely. I'm awfully sorry about the odor though. That must bother you."

"Don't! Please don't."

"Look at them," he said. "Now is it sight or is it scent that brings them like that?"

The cot the man lay on was in the wide shade of a mimosa tree and as he looked out past the shade onto the glare of the plain there were three of the big birds squatted obscenely, while in the sky a dozen more sailed, making quick-moving shadows as they passed.

"They've been there since the day the truck broke down," he said. "Today's the first time any have lit on the ground. I watched the way they sailed very carefully at first in case I ever wanted to use them in a story. That's funny now."

"I wish you wouldn't," she said.

"I'm only talking," he said. "It's much easier if I talk. But I don't want to bother you."

"You know it doesn't bother me," she said. "It's that I've gotten so very nervous not being able to do anything. I think we might make it as easy as we can until the plane comes."

"Or until the plane doesn't come."

"Please tell me what I can do. There must be something I can do."

"You can take the leg off and that might stop it, though I doubt it. Or you can shoot me. You're a good shot now. I taught you to shoot didn't I?"

"Please don't talk that way. Couldn't I read to you?"

"Read what?"

"Anything in the book bag that we haven't read."

"I can't listen to it," he said. "Talking is the easiest. We quarrel and that makes the time pass."

"I don't quarrel. I never want to quarrel. Let's not quarrel any more. No matter how nervous we get. Maybe they will be back with another truck today. Maybe the plane will come."

"I don't want to move," the man said. "There is no sense in moving now except to make it easier for you."

"That's cowardly."

"Can't you let a man die as comfortably as he can without calling him names? What's the use of slanging me?"

"You're not going to die."

"Don't be silly. I'm dying now. Ask those bastards." He looked over to where the huge, filthy birds sat, their naked heads sunk in the hunched feathers. A fourth planed down, to run quick-legged and then waddle slowly toward the others.

"They are around every camp. You never notice them. You can't die if you don't give up."

"Where did you read that? You're such a bloody fool."

"You might think about some one else."

"For Christ's sake," he said, "That's been my trade."

He lay then and was quiet for a while and looked across the heat shimmer of the plain to the edge of the bush. There were a few Tommies that showed minute and white against the yellow and, far off, he saw a herd of zebra, white against the green of the bush. This was a pleasant camp under big trees against a hill, with good water, and close by, a nearly dry water-hole where sand grouse flighted in the mornings.

"Wouldn't you like me to read?" she asked. She was sitting on a canvas chair beside his cot. "There's a breeze coming up."

"No thanks."

"Maybe the truck will come."

"I don't give a damn about the truck."

"I do."

"You give a damn about so many things that I don't."

"Not so many, Harry."

"What about a drink?"

"It's supposed to be bad for you. It said in Black's to avoid all alcohol. You shouldn't drink."

"Molo!" he shouted.

"Yes Bwana."

"Bring whiskey-soda."

"Yes Bwana."

"You shouldn't," she said. "That's what I mean by giving up. It says it's bad for you. I know it's bad for you."

"No," he said. "It's good for me."

So now it was all over, he thought. So now he would never have a chance to finish it. So this was the way it ended in a bickering over a drink. Since the gangrene started in his right leg he had no pain and with the pain the horror had gone and all he felt now was a great tiredness and anger that this was the end of it. For this, that now was coming, he had very little curiosity. For years it had obsessed him; but now it meant nothing in itself. It was strange how easy being tired enough made it.

Now he would never write the things that he had saved to write until he knew enough to write them well. Well, he would not have to fail at trying to write them either. Maybe you could never write them, and that was why you put them off and delayed the starting. Well he would never know, now.

"I wish we'd never come," the woman said. She was looking at him holding the glass and biting her lip. "You never would have gotten anything like this in Paris. You always said you loved Paris. We could have stayed in Paris or gone anywhere. I'd have gone anywhere. I said I'd go anywhere you wanted. If you wanted to shoot we could have gone shooting in Hungary and been comfortable."

"Your bloody money," he said.

"That's not fair," she said. "It was always yours as much as mine. I left everything and I went wherever you wanted to go and I've done what you wanted to do. But I wish we'd never come here."

"You said you loved it."

"I did when you were all right. But now I hate it. I don't see why that had to happen to your leg. What have we done to have that happen to us?"

"I suppose what I did was to forget to put iodine on it when I first scratched it. Then I didn't pay any attention to it because I never infect. Then, later, when it got bad, it was probably using that weak carbolic solution when the other antiseptics ran out that paralyzed the minute blood vessels and started the gangrene." He looked at her, "What else?"

"I don't mean that."

"If we would have hired a good mechanic instead of a half baked kikuyu driver, he would have checked the oil and never burned out that bearing in the truck."

"I don't mean that."

"If you hadn't left your own people, your goddamned Old Westbury, Saratoga, Palm Beach people to take me on——"

"Why, I loved you. That's not fair. I love you now. I'll always love you. Don't you love me?"

"No," said the man. "I don't think so. I never have."

"Harry, what are you saying? You're out of your head."

"No. I haven't any head to go out of."

"Don't drink that," she said. "Darling, please don't drink that. We have to do everything we can."

"You do it," he said. "I'm tired."

Now in his mind he saw a railway station at Karagatch and he was standing with his pack and that was the headlight of the Simplon-Orient cutting the dark now and he was leaving Thrace then after the retreat. That was one of the things he had saved to write, with, in the morning at breakfast, looking out the window and seeing snow on the mountains in Bulgaria and Nansen's Secretary asking the old man if it were snow and the old man looking at it and saying, No, that's not snow. It's too early for snow. And the Secretary repeating to the other girls, No, you see.. It's not snow and them all saying, It's not snow we were mistaken. But it was the snow all right and he sent them on into it when he evolved exchange of populations. And it was snow they tramped along in until they died that winter.

It was snow too that fell all Christmas week that year up in the Gauertal, that year they lived in the woodcutter's house with the big square porcelain stove that filled half the room, and they slept on mattresses filled with beech leaves, the time the deserter came with his feet bloody in the snow. He said the police were right behind him and they gave him woolen socks and held the gendarmes talking until the tracks had drifted over.

In Schrunz, on Christmas day, the snow was so bright it hurt your eyes when you looked out from the weinstube and saw every one coming home from church. That was where they walked up the sleigh-smoothed urine-yellowed road along the river with the steep pine hills, skis heavy on the shoulder, and where they ran that great run down the glacier above the Madlener-haus, the snow as smooth to see as cake frosting and as light as powder and he remembered the noiseless rush the speed made as you dropped down like a bird.

They were snow-bound a week in the Madlener-haus that time in the blizzard playing cards in the smoke by the lantern light and the stakes were higher all the time as Herr Lent lost more. Finally he lost it all. Everything, the skischule money and all the season's profit and then his capital. He could see him with his long nose, picking up the cards and then opening, "Sans Voir." There was always gambling then. When there was no snow you gambled and when there was too much you gambled. He thought of all the time in his life he had spent gambling.

But he had never written a line of that, nor of that cold, bright Christmas day with the mountains showing across the plain that Barker had flown across the lines to bomb the Austrian officers' leave train, machine-gunning them as they scattered and ran. He remembered Barker afterwards coming into the mess and starting to tell about it. And how quiet it got and then somebody saying, "You bloody murderous bastard."

Those were the same Austrians they killed then that he skied with later. No not the same. Hans, that he skied with all that year, had been in the Kaiser-Jägers and when they went hunting hares together up the little valley above the saw-mill they had talked of the fighting on Pasubio and of the attack on Pertica and Asalone and he had never written a word of that. Nor of Monte Corno, nor the Siete Commun, nor of Arsiedo.

How many winters had he lived in the Voralberg and the Arlberg? It was four and then he remembered the man who had the fox to sell when they had walked into Bludenz, that time to buy presents, and the cherry-pit taste of good kirsch, the fast-slipping rush of running powder-snow on crust,

*singing "Hi! Ho! said Rolly!" as you ran down the last stretch to the steep
drop, taking it straight, then running the orchard in three turns and out
across the ditch and onto the icy road behind the inn. Knocking your bind-
ings loose, kicking the skis free and leaning them up against the wooden
wall of the inn, the lamplight coming from the window, where inside, in the
smoky, new-wine smelling warmth, they were playing the accordion.*

"Where did we stay in Paris?" he asked the woman who was sitting by
him in a canvas chair, now, in Africa.

"At the Crillon. You know that."

"Why do I know that?"

"That's where we always stayed."

"No. Not always."

"There and at the Pavilion Henri-Quatre in St. Germain. You said you
loved it there."

"Love is a dunghill," said Harry. "And I'm the cock that gets on it to
crow."

"If you have to go away," she said, "is it absolutely necessary to kill off
everything you leave behind? I mean do you have to take away everything?
Do you have to kill your horse, and your wife and burn your saddle and
your armour?"

"Yes," he said. "Your damned money was my armour. My Swift and my
Armour."

"Don't."

"All right. I'll stop that. I don't want to hurt you."

"It's a little bit late now."

"All right then. I'll go on hurting you. It's more amusing. The only
thing I ever really liked to do with you I can't do now."

"No, that's not true. You liked to do many things and everything you
wanted to do I did."

"Oh, for Christ sake stop bragging, will you?"

He looked at her and saw her crying.

"Listen," he said. "Do you think that it is fun to do this? I don't know
why I'm doing it. It's trying to kill to keep yourself alive, I imagine. I was
all right when we started talking. I didn't mean to start this, and now I'm
crazy as a coot and being as cruel to you as I can be. Don't pay any attention,
darling, to what I say. I love you, really. You know I love you. I've never
loved any one else the way I love you."

He slipped into the familiar lie he made his bread and butter by.

"You're sweet to me."

"You bitch," he said. "You rich bitch. That's poetry. I'm full of poetry
now. Rot and poetry. Rotten poetry."

"Stop it. Harry, why do you have to turn into a devil now?"

"I don't like to leave anything," the man said. "I don't like to leave
things behind."

It was evening now and he had been asleep. The sun was gone behind the hill and there was a shadow all across the plain and the small animals were feeding close to camp; quick dropping heads and switching tails, he watched them keeping well out away from the bush now. The birds no longer waited on the ground. They were all perched heavily in a tree. There were many more of them. His personal boy was sitting by the bed.

"Memsahib's gone to shoot," the boy said. "Does Bwana want?"

"Nothing."

She had gone to kill a piece of meat and, knowing how he liked to watch the game, she had gone well away so she would not disturb this little pocket of the plain that he could see. She was always thoughtful, he thought. On anything she knew about, or had read, or that she had ever heard.

It was not her fault that when he went to her he was already over. How could a woman know that you meant nothing that you said; that you spoke only from habit and to be comfortable? After he no longer meant what he said, his lies were more successful with women than when he had told them the truth.

It was not so much that he lied as that there was no truth to tell. He had had his life and it was over and then he went on living it again with different people and more money, with the best of the same places, and some new ones.

You kept from thinking and it was all marvellous. You were equipped with good insides so that you did not go to pieces that way, the way most of them had, and you made an attitude that you cared nothing for the work you used to do, now that you could no longer do it. But, in yourself, you said that you would write about these people; about the very rich; that you were really not of them but a spy in their country; that you would leave it and write of it and for once it would be written by some one who knew what he was writing of. But he would never do it, because each day of not writing, of comfort, or being that which he despised, dulled his ability and softened his will to work, so that, finally, he did no work at all. The people he knew now were all much more comfortable when he did not work. Africa was where he had been happiest in the good time of his life, so he had come out here to start again. They had made this safari with the minimum of comfort. There was no hardship; but there was no luxury and he had thought that he could get back into training that way. That in some way he could work the fat off his soul the way a fighter went into the mountains to work and train in order to burn it out of his body.

She had liked it. She said she loved it. She loved anything that was exciting, that involved a change of scene, where there were new people and where things were pleasant. And he had felt the illusion of returning strength of will to work. Now if this was how it ended, and he knew it was, he must not turn like some snake biting itself because its back was broken. It wasn't this woman's fault. If it had not been she it would have been another. If he lived by a lie he should try to die by it. He heard a shot beyond the hill.

She shot very well this good, this rich bitch, this kindly caretaker and destroyer of his talent. Nonsense. He had destroyed his talent himself. Why should he blame this woman because she kept him well? He had destroyed his talent by not using it, by betrayals of himself and what he believed in, by drinking so much that he blunted the edge of his perceptions, by laziness, by sloth, and by snobbery, by pride and by prejudice, by hook and and by crook. What was this? A catalogue of old books? What was his talent anyway? It was a talent all right but instead of using it, he had traded on it. It was never what he had done, but always what he could do. And he had chosen to make his living with something else instead of a pen or a pencil. It was strange, too, wasn't it, that when he fell in love with another woman, that woman should always have more money than the last one? But when he no longer was in love, when he was only lying, as to this woman, now, who had the most money of all, who had all the money there was, who had had a husband and children, who had taken lovers and been dissatisfied with them, and who loved him dearly as a writer, as a man, as a companion and as a proud possession; it was strange that when he did not love her at all and was lying, that he should be able to give her more for her money than when he had really loved.

We must all be cut out for what we do, he thought. However you make your living is where your talent lies. He had sold vitality, in one form or another, all his life and when your affections are not too involved you give much better value for the money. He had found that out but he would never write that, now, either. No, he would not write that, although it was well worth writing.

Now she came in sight, walking across the open toward the camp. She was wearing jodphurs and carrying her rifle. The two boys had a Tommie slung and they were coming along behind her. She was still a good-looking woman, he thought, and she had a pleasant body. She had a great talent and appreciation for the bed, she was not pretty, but he liked her face, she read enormously, liked to ride and shoot and, certainly, she drank too much. Her husband had died when she was still a comparatively young woman and for a while she had devoted herself to her two just-grown children, who did not need her and were embarrassed at having her about, to her stable of horses, to books, and to bottles. She liked to read in the evening before dinner and she drank Scotch and soda while she read. By dinner she was fairly drunk and after a bottle of wine at dinner she was usually drunk enough to sleep.

That was before the lovers. After she had the lovers she did not drink so much because she did not have to be drunk to sleep. But the lovers bored her. She had been married to a man who had never bored her and these people bored her very much.

Then one of her two children was killed in a plane crash and after that was over she did not want the lovers, and drink being no anæsthetic she had to make another life. Suddenly, she had been acutely frightened of being alone. But she wanted some one that she respected with her.

It had begun very simply. She liked what he wrote and she had always envied the life he led. She thought he did exactly what he wanted to. The steps by which she had acquired him and the way in which she had finally fallen in love with him were all part of a regular progression in which she had built herself a new life and he had traded away what remained of his old life.

He had traded it for security, for comfort too, there was no denying that, and for what else? He did not know. She would have bought him anything he wanted. He knew that. She was a damned nice woman too. He would as soon be in bed with her as any one; rather with her, because she was richer, because she was very pleasant and appreciative and because she never made scenes. And now this life that she had built again was coming to a term because he had not used iodine two weeks ago when a thorn had scratched his knee as they moved forward trying to photograph a herd of waterbuck standing, their heads up, peering while their nostrils searched the air, their ears spread wide to hear the first noise that would send them rushing into the bush. They had bolted, too, before he got the picture.

Here she came now.

He turned his head on the cot to look toward her. "Hello," he said.

"I shot a Tommy ram," she told him. "He'll make you good broth and I'll have them mash some potatoes with the Klim. How do you feel?"

"Much better."

"Isn't that lovely? You know I thought perhaps you would. You were sleeping when I left."

"I had a good sleep. Did you walk far?"

"No. Just around behind the hill. I made quite a good shot on the Tommy."

"You shoot marvellously, you know."

"I loved it. I've loved Africa. Really. If *you're* all right it's the most fun that I've ever had. You don't know the fun it's been to shoot with you. I've loved the country."

"I love it too."

"Darling, you don't know how marvellous it is to see you feeling better. I couldn't stand it when you felt that way. You won't talk to me like that again, will you? Promise me?"

"No," he said. "I don't remember what I said."

"You don't have to destroy me. Do you? I'm only a middle-aged woman who loves you and wants to do what you want to do. I've been destroyed two or three times already. You wouldn't want to destroy me again, would you?"

"I'd like to destroy you a few times in bed," he said.

"Yes. That's the good destruction. That's the way we're made to be destroyed. The plane will be here tomorrow."

"How do you know?"

"I'm sure. It's bound to come. The boys have the wood all ready and the grass to make the smudge. I went down and looked at it again today. There's plenty of room to land and we have the smudges ready at both ends."

"What makes you think it will come tomorrow?"

"I'm sure it will. It's overdue now. Then, in town, they will fix up your leg and then we will have some good destruction. Not that dreadful talking kind."

"Should we have a drink? The sun is down."

"Do you think you should?"

"I'm having one."

"We'll have one together. *Molo, letti dui whiskey-soda!*" she called.

"You'd better put on your mosquito boots," he told her.

"I'll wait till I bathe . . ."

While it grew dark they drank and just before it was dark and there was no longer enough light to shoot, a hyena crossed the open on his way around the hill.

"That bastard crosses there every night," the man said. "Every night for two weeks."

"He's the one makes the noise at night. I don't mind it. They're a filthy animal though."

Drinking together, with no pain now except the discomfort of lying in the one position, the boys lighting a fire, its shadow jumping on the tents, he could feel the return of acquiescence in this life of pleasant surrender. She *was* very good to him. He had been cruel and unjust in the afternoon. She was a fine woman, marvellous really. And just then it occurred to him that he was going to die.

It came with a rush; not as a rush of water nor of wind; but of a sudden evil-smelling emptiness and the odd thing was that the hyena slipped lightly along the edge of it.

"What is it, Harry?" she asked him.

"Nothing," he said. "You had better move over to the other side. To windward."

"Did Molo change the dressing?"

"Yes. I'm just using the boric now."

"How do you feel?"

"A little wobbly."

"I'm going in to bathe," she said. "I'll be right out. I'll eat with you and then we'll put the cot in."

So, he said to himself, we did well to stop the quarrelling. He had never quarrelled much with this woman, while with the women that he loved he had quarrelled so much they had finally, always, with the corrosion of the quarrelling, killed what they had together. He had loved too much, demanded too much, and he wore it all out.

He thought about alone in Constantinople that time, having quarrelled in Paris before he had gone out. He had whored the whole time and then, when that was over, and he had failed to kill his loneliness, but only made it worse, he had written her, the first one, the one who left him, a letter telling her how he had never been able to kill it. . . . How when he thought he saw her outside the Regence one time it made him go all faint and sick inside, and that he would follow a woman who looked like her in some way, along the Boulevard, afraid to see it was not she, afraid to lose the feeling it gave him. How every one he had slept with had only made him miss her more. How what she had done could never matter since he knew he could not cure himself of loving her. He wrote this letter at the Club, cold sober, and mailed it to New York asking her to write him at the office in Paris. That seemed safe. And that night missing her so much it made him feel hollow sick inside, he wandered up past Taxim's, picked a girl up and took her out to supper. He had gone to a place to dance with her afterward, she danced badly, and left her for a hot Armenian slut, that swung her belly against him so it almost scalded. He took her away from a British gunner subaltern after a row. The gunner asked him outside and they fought in the street on the cobbles in the dark. He'd hit him twice, hard, on the side of the jaw and when he didn't go down he knew he was in for a fight. The gunner hit him in the body, then beside his eye. He swung with his left again and landed and the gunner fell on him and grabbed his coat and tore the sleeve off and he clubbed him twice behind the ear and then smashed him with his right as he pushed him away. When the gunner went down his head hit first and he ran with the girl because they heard the M. P.'s coming. They got into a taxi and drove out to Rimmily Hissa along the Bosphorus, and around, and back in the cool night and went to bed and she felt as over-ripe as she looked but smooth, rose-petal, syrupy, smooth-bellied, big-breasted and needed no pillow under her buttocks, and he left her before she was awake looking blowzy enough in the first daylight and turned up at the Pera Palace with a black eye, carrying his coat because one sleeve was missing.

That same night he left for Anatolia and he remembered, later on that trip, riding all day through fields of the poppies that they raised for opium and how strange it made you feel, finally, and all the distances seemed wrong, to where they had made the attack with the newly arrived Constantine officers, that did not know a god-damned thing, and the artillery had fired into the troops and the British observer had cried like a child.

That was the day he'd first seen dead men wearing white ballet skirts and upturned shoes with pompons on them. The Turks had come steadily and lumpily and he had seen the skirted men running and the officers shooting into them and running then themselves and he and the British observer had run too until his lungs ached and his mouth was full of the taste of

pennies and they stopped behind some rocks and there were the Turks com-
ing as lumpily as ever. Later he had seen the things that he could never think
of and later still he had seen much worse. So when he got back to Paris that
time he could not talk about it or stand to have it mentioned. And there in
the café as he passed was that American poet with a pile of saucers in front of
him and a stupid look on his potato face talking about the Dada movement
with a Roumanian who said his name was Tristan Tzara, who always wore a
monocle and had a headache, and, back at the apartment with his wife that
now he loved again, the quarrel all over, the madness all over, glad to be
home, the office sent his mail up to the flat. So then the letter in answer to the
one he'd written came in on a platter one morning and when he saw the
handwriting he went cold all over and tried to slip the letter underneath an-
other. But his wife said, "Who is that letter from, dear?" and that was the end
of the beginning of that.

He remembered the good times with them all, and the quarrels. They
always picked the finest places to have the quarrels. And why had they always
quarrelled when he was feeling best? He had never written any of that
because, at first, he never wanted to hurt any one and then it seemed as
though there was enough to write without it. But he had always thought that
he would write it finally. There was so much to write. He had seen the world
change; not just the events; although he had seen many of them and had
watched the people, but he had seen the subtler change and he could remem-
ber how the people were at different times. He had been in it and he had
watched it and it was his duty to write of it; but now he never would.

"How do you feel?" she said. She had come out from the tent now after
her bath.

"All right."

"Could you eat now?" He saw Molo behind her with the folding table
and the other boy with the dishes.

"I want to write," he said.

"You ought to take some broth to keep your strength up."

"I'm going to die tonight," he said. "I don't need my strength up."

"Don't be melodramatic, Harry, please," she said.

"Why don't you use your nose? I'm rotted half way up my thigh now.
What the hell should I fool with broth for? Molo bring whiskey-soda."

"Please take the broth," she said gently.

"All right."

The broth was too hot. He had to hold it in the cup until it cooled
enough to take it and then he just got it down without gagging.

"You're a fine woman," he said. "Don't pay any attention to me."

She looked at him with her well-known, well-loved face from *Spur* and
Town and Country, only a little the worse for drink, only a little the worse
for bed, but *Town and Country* never showed those good breasts and those
useful thighs and those lightly small-of-back-caressing hands, and as he looked

and saw her well known pleasant smile, he felt death come again. This time there was no rush. It was a puff, as of a wind that makes a candle flicker and the flame go tall.

"They can bring my net out later and hang it from the tree and build the fire up. I'm not going in the tent tonight. It's not worth moving. It's a clear night. There won't be any rain."

So this was how you died, in whispers that you did not hear. Well, there would be no more quarrelling. He could promise that. The one experience that he had never had he was not going to spoil now. He probably would. You spoiled everything. But perhaps he wouldn't.

"You can't take dictation, can you?"

"I never learned," she told him.

"That's all right."

There wasn't time, of course, although it seemed as though it telescoped so that you might put it all into one paragraph if you could get it right.

There was a log house, chinked white with mortar, on a hill above the lake. There was a bell on a pole by the door to call the people in to meals. Behind the house were fields and behind the fields was the timber. A line of lombardy poplars ran from the house to the dock. Other poplars ran along the point. A road went up to the hills along the edge of the timber and along that road he picked blackberries. Then that log house was burned down and all the guns that had been on deer foot racks above the open fire place were burned and afterwards their barrels, with the lead melted in the magazines, and the stocks burned away, lay out on the heap of ashes that were used to make lye for the big iron soap kettles, and you asked Grandfather if you could have them to play with, and he said, no. You see they were his guns still and he never bought any others. Nor did he hunt any more. The house was rebuilt in the same place out of lumber now and painted white and from its porch you saw the poplars and the lake beyond; but there were never any more guns. The barrels of the guns that had hung on the deer feet on the wall of the log house lay out there on the heap of ashes and no one ever touched them.

In the Black Forest, after the war, we rented a trout stream and there were two ways to walk to it. One was down the valley from Triberg and around the valley road in the shade of the trees that bordered the white road, and then up a side road that went up through the hills past many small farms, with the big Schwarzwald houses, until that road crossed the stream. That was where our fishing began.

The other way was to climb steeply up to the edge of the woods and then go across the top of the hills through the pine woods, and then out to the edge of a meadow and down across this meadow to the bridge. There were birches along the stream and it was not big, but narrow, clear and fast, with pools where it had cut under the roots of the birches. At the Hotel in Triberg the proprietor had a fine season. It was very pleasant and we were all great friends. The next year came the inflation and the money he had made the year before was not enough to buy supplies to open the hotel and he hanged himself.

You could dictate that, but you could not dictate the Place Contrescarpe where the flower sellers dyed their flowers in the street and the dye ran over the paving where the autobus started and the old men and the women, always drunk on wine and bad marc; and the children with their noses running in the cold; the smell of dirty sweat and poverty and drunkenness at the Café des Amateurs and the whores at the Bal Musette they lived above. The Concierge who entertained the trooper of the Garde Republicaine in her loge, his horse-hair-plumed helmet on a chair. The locataire across the hall whose husband was a bicycle racer and her joy that morning at the Cremerie when she had opened L'Auto and seen where he placed third in Paris-Tours, his first big race. She had blushed and laughed and then gone upstairs crying with the yellow sporting paper in her hand. The husband of the woman who ran the Bal Musette drove a taxi and when he, Harry, had to take an early plane the husband knocked upon the door to wake him and they each drank a glass of white wine at the zinc of the bar before they started. He knew his neighbors in that quarter then because they all were poor.

Around that Place *there were two kinds; the drunkards and the sportifs. The drunkards killed their poverty that way; the sportifs took it out in exercise. They were the descendants of the Communards and it was no struggle for them to know their politics. They knew who had shot their fathers, their relatives, their brothers, and their friends when the Versailles troops came in and took the town after the Commune and executed any one they could catch with calloused hands, or who wore a cap, or carried any other sign he was a working man. And in that poverty, and in that quarter across the street from a Boucherie Chevaline and a wine co-operative he had written the start of all he was to do. There never was another part of Paris that he loved like that, the sprawling trees, the old white plastered houses painted brown below, the long green of the autobus in that round square, the purple flower dye upon the paving, the sudden drop down the hill of the rue Cardinal Lemoine to the River, and the other way the narrow crowded world of the rue Mouffetard. The street that ran up toward the Pantheon and the other that he always took with the bicycle, the only asphalted street in all that quarter, smooth under the tires, with the high narrow houses and the cheap tall hotel where Paul Verlaine had died. There were only two rooms in the apartments where they lived and he had a room on the top floor of that hotel that cost him sixty francs a month where he did his writing, and from it he could see the roofs and chimney pots and all the hills of Paris.*

From the apartment you could only see the wood and coal man's place. He sold wine too, bad wine. The golden horse's head outside the Boucherie Chevaline where the carcasses hung yellow gold and red in the open window, and the green painted co-operative where they bought their wine; good wine and cheap. The rest was plaster walls and the windows of the neighbors. The neighbors who, at night, when some one lay drunk in the street, moaning and groaning in that typical French ivresse *that you were propaganded to believe did not exist, would open their windows and then the murmur of talk.*

"Where is the policeman? When you don't want him the bugger is always there. He's sleeping with some concierge. Get the Agent.*" Till some one threw a bucket of water from a window and the moaning stopped. "What's that? Water. Ah, that's intelligent." And the windows shutting. Marie, his femme de menage, protesting against the eight-hour day saying, "If a husband works until six he gets only a little drunk on the way home and does not waste too much. If he works only until five he is drunk every night and one has no money. It is the wife of the working man who suffers from this shortening of hours."*

"Wouldn't you like some more broth?" the woman asked him now.

"No, thank you very much. It is awfully good."

"Try just a little."

"I would like a whiskey-soda."

"It's not good for you."

"No. It's bad for me. Cole Porter wrote the words and the music. This knowledge that you're going mad for me."

"You know I like you to drink."

"Oh yes. Only it's bad for me."

When she goes, he thought. I'll have all I want. Not all I want but all there is. Ayee he was tired. Too tired. He was going to sleep a little while. He lay still and death was not there. It must have gone around another street. It went in pairs, on bicycles, and moved absolutely silently on the pavements.

No, he had never written about Paris. Not the Paris that he cared about. But what about the rest that he had never written?

What about the ranch and the silvered gray of the sage brush, the quick, clear water in the irrigation ditches, and the heavy green of the alfalfa. The trail went up into the hills and the cattle in the summer were shy as deer. The bawling and the steady noise and slow moving mass raising a dust as you brought them down in the fall. And behind the mountains, the clear sharpness of the peak in the evening light and, riding down along the trail in the moonlight, bright across the valley. Now he remembered coming down through the timber in the dark holding the horse's tail when you could not see and all the stories that he meant to write.

About the half-wit chore boy who was left at the ranch that time and told not to let any one get any hay, and that old bastard from the Forks who had beaten the boy when he had worked for him stopping to get some feed. The boy refusing and the old man saying he would beat him again. The boy got the rifle from the kitchen and shot him when he tried to come into the barn and when they came back to the ranch he'd been dead a week, frozen in the corral, and the dogs had eaten part of him. But what was left you packed on a sled wrapped in a blanket and roped on and you got the boy to help you haul it, and the two of you took it out over the road on skis, and sixty miles down to town to turn the boy over. He having no idea that he would be arrested. Thinking he had done his duty and that you were his friend and he would be rewarded. He'd helped to haul the old man in so everybody could know how bad the old man had been and how he'd tried to steal some feed that didn't belong to him, and when the sheriff put the handcuffs on the boy he couldn't believe it. Then he'd started to cry. That was one story he had saved to write. He knew at least twenty good stories from out there and he had never written one. Why?

"You tell them why," he said.

"Why what, dear?"

"Why nothing."

She didn't drink so much, now, since she had him. But if he lived he would never write about her, he knew that now. Nor about any of them. The rich were dull and they drank too much, or they played too much backgammon. They were dull and they were repetitious. He remembered poor Julian and his romantic awe of them and how he had started a story once that began, "The very rich are different from you and me." And how some one had said to Julian, Yes, they have more money. But that was not humorous to Julian. He thought they were a special glamorous race and when he found they weren't it wrecked him just as much as any other thing that wrecked him.

He had been contemptuous of those who wrecked. You did not have to like it because you understood it. He could beat anything, he thought, because no thing could hurt him if he did not care.

All right. Now he would not care for death. One thing he had always dreaded was the pain. He could stand pain as well as any man, until it went on too long, and wore him out, but here he had something that had hurt frightfully and just when he had felt it breaking him, the pain had stopped.

He remembered long ago when Williamson, the bombing officer, had been hit by a stick bomb some one in a German patrol had thrown as he was coming in through the wire that night and, screaming, had begged every one to kill him. He was a fat man, very brave, and a good officer, although addicted to fantastic shows. But that night he was caught in the wire, with a flare lighting him up and his bowels spilled out into the wire, so when they brought him in, alive, they had to cut him loose. Shoot me, Harry. For Christ sake shoot me. They had had an argument one time about our Lord never sending you anything you could not bear and some one's theory had been that meant that at a certain time the pain passed you out automatically. But he had always remembered Williamson, that night. Nothing passed out Williamson until he gave him all his morphine tablets that he had always saved to use himself and then they did not work right away.

Still this now, that he had, was very easy; and if it was no worse as it went on there was nothing to worry about. Except that he would rather be in better company.

He thought a little about the company that he would like to have.

No, he thought, when everything you do, you do too long, and do too late, you can't expect to find the people still there. The people all are gone. The party's over and you are with your hostess now.

I'm getting as bored with dying as with everything else, he thought.

"It's a bore," he said out loud.

"What is, my dear?"

"Anything you do too bloody long."

He looked at her face between him and the fire. She was leaning back in the chair and the firelight shone on her pleasantly lined face and he could see that she was sleepy. He heard the hyena make a noise just outside the range of the fire.

"I've been writing," he said. "But I got tired."

"Do you think you will be able to sleep?"

"Pretty sure. Why don't you turn in?"

"I like to sit here with you."

"Do you feel anything strange?" he asked her.

"No. Just a little sleepy."

"I do," he said.

He had just felt death come by again.

"You know the only thing I've never lost is curiosity," he said to her.

"You've never lost anything. You're the most complete man I've ever known."

"Christ," he said. "How little a woman knows. What is that? Your intuition?"

Because, just then, death had come and rested its head on the foot of the cot and he could smell its breath.

"Never believe any of that about a scythe and a skull," he told her. "It can be two bicycle policemen as easily, or be a bird. Or it can have a wide snout like a hyena."

It had moved up on him now, but it had no shape any more. It simply occupied space.

"Tell it to go away."

It did not go away but moved a little closer.

"You've got a hell of a breath," he told it. "You stinking bastard."

It moved up closer to him still and now he could not speak to it, and when it saw he could not speak it came a little closer, and now he tried to send it away without speaking, but it moved in on him so its weight was all upon his chest, and while it crouched there and he could not move, or speak, he heard the woman say, "Bwana is asleep now. Take the cot up very gently and carry it into the tent."

He could not speak to tell her to make it go away and it crouched now, heavier, so he could not breathe. And then, while they lifted the cot, suddenly it was all right and the weight went from his chest.

It was morning and had been morning for some time and he heard the plane. It showed very tiny and then made a wide circle and the boys ran out and lit the fires, using kerosene, and piled on grass so there were two big smudges at each end of the level place and the morning breeze blew them toward the camp and the plane circled twice more, low this time, and then glided down and levelled off and landed smoothly and, coming walking toward him, was old Compton in slacks, a tweed jacket and a brown felt hat.

"What's the matter, old cock?" Compton said.

"Bad leg," he told him. "Will you have some breakfast?"

"Thanks. I'll just have some tea. It's the Puss Moth you know. I won't be able to take the Memsahib. There's only room for one. Your lorry is on the way."

Helen had taken Compton aside and was speaking to him. Compton came back more cheery than ever.

"We'll get you right in," he said. "I'll be back for the Mem. Now I'm afraid I'll have to stop at Arusha to refuel. We'd better get going."

"What about the tea?"

"I don't really care about it you know."

The boys had picked up the cot and carried it around the green tents and down along the rock and out onto the plain and along past the smudges that were burning brightly now, the grass all consumed, and the wind fanning the fire, to the little plane. It was difficult getting him in, but once in he lay back in the leather seat, and the leg was stuck straight out to one side of the seat where Compton sat. Compton started the motor and got in. He waved to Helen and to the boys and, as the clatter moved into the old familiar roar, they swung around with Compie watching for wart-hog holes and roared, bumping, along the stretch between the fires and with the last bump rose and he saw them all standing below, waving, and the camp beside the hill, flattening now, and the plain spreading, clumps of trees, and the bush flattening, while the game trails ran now smoothly to the dry water-holes, and there was a new water that he had never known of. The zebra, small rounded backs now, and the wildebeeste, big-headed dots seeming to climb as they moved in long fingers across the plain, now scattering as the shadow came toward them, they were tiny now, and the movement had no gallop, and the plain as far as you could see, grey-yellow now and ahead old Compie's tweed back and the brown felt hat. Then they were over the first hills and the wildebeeste were trailing up them, and then they were over mountains with sudden depths of green-rising forest and the solid bamboo slopes, and then the heavy forest again, sculptured into peaks and hollows until they crossed, and hills sloped down and then another plain, hot now, and purple brown, bumpy with heat and Compie looking back to see how he was riding. Then there were other mountains dark ahead.

And then instead of going on to Arusha they turned left, he evidently figured that they had the gas, and looking down he saw a pink sifting cloud, moving over the ground, and in the air, like the first snow in a blizzard, that comes from nowhere, and he knew the locusts were coming up from the South. Then they began to climb and they were going to the East it seemed, and then it darkened and they were in a storm, the rain so thick it seemed like flying through a waterfall, and then they were out and Compie turned his head and grinned and pointed and there, ahead, all he could see, as wide as all the world, great, high, and unbelievably white in the sun, was the square top of Kilimanjaro. And then he knew that there was where he was going.

Just then the hyena stopped whimpering in the night and started to make a strange, human, almost crying sound. The woman heard it and stirred uneasily. She did not wake. In her dream she was at the house on Long Island and it was the night before her daughter's début. Somehow her father was there and he had been very rude. Then the noise the hyena made was so loud she woke and for a moment she did not know where she was and she was very afraid. Then she took the flashlight and shone it on the other cot that they had carried in after Harry had gone to sleep. She could see his bulk under the mosquito bar but somehow he had gotten his leg out and it hung down alongside the cot. The dressings had all come down and she could not look at it.

"Molo," she called, "Molo! Molo!"

Then she said, "Harry, Harry!" Then her voice rising, "Harry! Please, Oh Harry!"

There was no answer and she could not hear him breathing.

Outside the tent the hyena made the same strange noise that had awakened her. But she did not hear him for the beating of her heart.

COMMENTARY

Edgar Allan Poe, in his review of Hawthorne's *Twice-Told Tales* in *Graham's Magazine* of May, 1842, laid down a fundamental principle for the construction of the "tale" or short fiction:

A skillful literary artist has fashioned a tale. If wise, he has not fashioned his thought to accommodate his incidents; but having conceived, with deliberate care, a certain unique or single *effect* to be wrought out, he then invents such incidents—he then combines such events as may best aid him in establishing this preconceived effect. If his very initial sentence tend not to the outbringing of this effect, then he has failed in the first step. In the whole composition there should be no word written, of which the tendency, direct or indirect, is not to the preestablished design.

Ernest Hemingway's *A Farewell to Arms* begins:

> In the late summer of that year we lived in a house in a village that looked across the river and the plains to the mountains. In the bed of the river there were pebbles and boulders, dry and white in the sun, and the water was clear and swiftly moving and blue in the channels. Troops went by the house and down the road and the dust they raised powdered the leaves of the trees. The trunks of the trees were dusty and the leaves fell early that year and we saw troops marching along the road and the dust rising and leaves, stirred by the breeze, falling and the soldiers marching and afterward the road bare and white except for the leaves.

The tone (see Appendix A, p. 632) of the whole book is set in the first paragraph. The tone, in this case, is a mood, a dramatization of the wistful rebellion of youth, confronted with the hard facts of life, love, and death. This mood, evoked by the very sound of the words in the first sentence: "In the late summer of that year . . ." and persisting throughout the action, swells up at the climax in a crescendo that is so perfectly timed that when one re-reads the book tears spring always to the eyes at the same passage—provided that one is capable of shedding tears over the sorrows of fictional characters.

Another master, Chekhov, might have admired the rendering of the rest of the passage. The action of the sun *shows* the pebbles and boulders that lie in the bed of the river to be *dry* and *white*. The river is clear and moves swiftly; the further specification that it was blue where the water was deepest (in the channels) makes us *see* it flow. We are convinced that the troops passed the house by the fact that enough dust was raised to powder the leaves of the trees and even the trunks. The passage could stand as an amplification of some advice that Chekhov once wrote to his good-for-nothing brother, Alexander:

> Descriptions of Nature should be very brief and have an incidental character. Commonplaces like "The setting sun, bathing in the waves of the darkening sea, flooded with purple and gold . . . The swallows, flying over the surface of the water, chirped merrily"—such commonplaces should be finished with. In descriptions of Nature one has to snatch at small details, grouping them in such a manner that after reading them one can obtain the picture on closing one's eyes.
>
> For instance, you will get a moonlight night if you write that on the dam of the mill a fragment of broken bottle flashed like a small bright star, and there rolled by, like a ball, the black shadow of a dog or a wolf—and so on.

One is reminded of another piece of advice that Chekhov gave:
"If a gun hangs on the wall in the first paragraph of your story it must be discharged at the end"—which is only another way of saying the same thing

that Poe said. The phrase, "The leaves fell early that year," is an admirable preparation for the climax of the action; that is to say, "My love died young." The whole Resolution (see Appendix A, p. 630) is, in fact, both prepared for and symbolized in this passage: "We saw troops marching along the road and the dust rising and leaves, stirred by the breeze, falling and afterward the road bare and white except for the leaves." A human heart, ravaged by grief, will ultimately become as bare and as quiet as the white road that the soldiers have passed over.

This kind of writing was rare in the twenties and, indeed, is rare at any time. It calls for a particular kind of response to the natural world, the kind of response that Turgenev, for instance, gave. But we sometimes say that in order to write like Turgenev one would have to be Turgenev. And that, in a measure, was true, up to Hemingway's time. Hemingway has not the range or the depth of the Russian, but possessing a sensory apparatus capable of the same exquisite response to the natural world, he is more deeply grounded in his craft, more athletic. He is, in short, the kind of writer one can learn from as distinguished from the kind of writer, like Turgenev or Tolstoy, who can be safely followed only at a distance. Developing a high degree of technical proficiency, Hemingway fulfilled the promise of early American realistic writers, such as Frank Norris, Ambrose Bierce, Sarah Orne Jewett, and became, like Stephen Crane, a master of naturalism.

There had been masters of naturalism before him, notably in France. Indeed, it might be claimed that the mantle of Flaubert's great disciple, Maupassant, has fallen on Hemingway's shoulders. Some remarks which Henry James once made about Maupassant apply equally well to Hemingway:

"Nothing can exceed the masculine firmness, the quiet force of his style, in which every phrase is a close sequence, every epithet a paying piece, and the ground is completely cleared of the vague, the ready-made and the second-best. Less than any one today does he beat the air; more than any one does he hit out from the shoulder."

"The Snows of Kilimanjaro," one of Hemingway's late and most ambitious stories, exhibits both the virtues and the limitations of his method. He is hitting out from the shoulder as hard—or nearly as hard—as he hits out in his early stories, but his reach isn't long enough. He has chosen an ineffable subject: a man approaching the moment of his death. He uses the snow-covered mountain of Kilimanjaro as the symbol of death, but the symbolism (see Appendix A, p. 633) is not a part of the action and therefore does not operate as a controlling image, as in the stories of Joyce, James, and Kafka. The result is a lack of dramatic force. The symbolism seems something the writer has tacked on, rather than an integral part of the story.

As a substitute for the kind of incidents James and Joyce use, incidents which are at once naturalistic and symbolic, Hemingway uses two levels of action: a man who is dying of gangrene alternately talks with those around him and communes with his soul. The incidents are all seen through the eyes of the chief character. The surface pattern of action, the man's bickerings with his wife, his memories of their past life together, his thoughts about the life they lead together now, his few exchanges with the native servants, are all rendered with precision and fidelity to reality. His reveries about his own life before he met his present wife, his communings, so to speak, with his soul, make an effective contrast to the smooth pattern of their day and also prepare for the Resolution. He not only scents the approach of death, who comes now as a hyena or riding on a bicycle, but he realizes when he first began to die: the day he traded his integrity for security. (The story is, to that extent, a parable of the situation of the artist in the world.) Some of the passages are as lucid and beautiful as any Hemingway has written:

> What about the ranch and the silvered gray of the sage brush, the quick, clear water in the irrigation ditches, and the heavy green of the alfalfa? The trail went up into the hills and the cattle in the summer were shy as deer . . .

The African countryside constitutes the Enveloping Action (see Appendix A, p. 631) of the story:

> He lay then and was quiet for a while and looked across the heat shimmer of the plain to the edge of the bush. There were a few Tommies that showed minute and white against the yellow and, far off, he saw a herd of zebra, white against the green of the bush. This was a pleasant camp under big trees against a hill, with good water, and close by, a nearly dry water hole where sand grouse flighted in the mornings.

On the naturalistic level the Resolution is the death of the hero, and it is well prepared for in the first sentence of the story: "The marvellous thing is that it's painless," he said, and we know that he is talking about dying when he looks out and sees three buzzards squatting on the plain. But the author has made no provision for the climax of his symbolic action. Our attention is not called to the snow-covered peaks of Kilimanjaro until the end of the story; as a result we do not feel that sense of recognition and inevitability which help to make a *katharsis*.

The passage in which the hero and his pilot confront the mountain is well rendered, from the standpoint of naturalism, but something more than naturalism is needed here. "Compie," turning his head and grinning and pointing, is not an impressive Charon and we are not convinced that he and the hero are going to any country that is different from other countries they have known. The passage lacks elevation of tone and the story itself lacks tonal and symbolic unity (see Appendix A, pp. 632–634). Its three planes of action, the man's intercourse with his wife, his communings with his soul, and the background of Enveloping Action, the mysterious Dark Continent, are never integrated. The story does not make the dramatic impact it would have made had the controlling image operated throughout, tying the several levels of the action together.

Henry James, in "The Art of Fiction," has an explanation for such magnificent failures. He complains that Maupassant omits "one of the items of the problem" when he "simply skipped the whole reflective part of his men and women—that reflective part which governs conduct and produces character." Hemingway's characters reflect, but they do not reflect deeply enough. He, like Maupassant, has limited his field of observation too sharply. Naturalism alone will not sustain the weight of his narrative, and Hemingway, for all his remarkable achievement, remains what James called Maupassant, "a lion in the path."

Ring Lardner

HAICUT

I GOT another barber that comes over from Carterville and helps me out Saturdays, but the rest of the time I can get along all right alone. You can see for yourself that this ain't no New York City and besides that, the most of the boys works all day and don't have no leisure to drop in here and get themselves prettied up.

You're a newcomer, ain't you? I thought I hadn't seen you round before. I hope you like it good enough to stay. As I say, we ain't no New York City or Chicago, but we have pretty good times. Not as good, though, since Jim Kendall got killed. When he was alive, him and Hod Meyers used to keep this town in an uproar. I bet they was more laughin' done here than any town its size in America.

Jim was comical, and Hod was pretty near a match for him. Since Jim's gone, Hod tries to hold his end up just the same as ever, but it's tough goin' when you ain't got nobody to kind of work with.

They used to be plenty fun in here Saturdays. This place is jam-packed Saturdays, from four o'clock on. Jim and Hod would show up right after their supper, round six o'clock. Jim would set himself down in that big chair, nearest the blue spittoon. Whoever had been settin' in that chair, why they'd get up when Jim come in and give it to him.

You'd of thought it was a reserved seat like they have sometimes in a theayter. Hod would generally always stand or walk up and down, or some Saturdays, of course, he'd be settin' in this chair part of the time, gettin' a haircut.

Well, Jim would set there a w'ile without openin' his mouth only to spit, and then finally he'd say to me, "Whitey,"—my right name, that is, my right first name, is Dick, but everybody round here calls me Whitey—Jim would say, "Whitey, your nose looks like a rosebud tonight. You must of been drinkin' some of your aw de cologne."

So I'd say, "No, Jim, but you look like you'd been drinkin' somethin' of that kind or somethin' worse."

Jim would have to laugh at that, but then he'd speak up and say, "No, I ain't had nothin' to drink, but that ain't sayin' I wouldn't like somethin'. I wouldn't even mind if it was wood alcohol."

Then Hod Meyers would say, "Neither would your wife." That would set everybody to laughin' because Jim and his wife wasn't on very good terms. She'd of divorced him only they wasn't no chance to get alimony and she

Reprinted from *The Love Nest and Other Stories* by Ring Lardner, copyright 1926 by Charles Scribner's Sons, and used with the kind permission of the publishers.

didn't have no way to take care of herself and the kids. She couldn't never understand Jim. He *was* kind of rough, but a good fella at heart.

Him and Hod had all kinds of sport with Milt Sheppard. I don't suppose you've seen Milt. Well, he's got an Adam's apple that looks more like a mushmelon. So I'd be shavin' Milt and when I'd start to shave down here on his neck, Hod would holler, "Hey, Whitey, wait a minute! Before you cut into it, let's make up a pool and see who can guess closest to the number of seeds."

And Jim would say, "If Milt hadn't of been so hoggish, he'd of ordered a half a cantaloupe instead of a whole one and it might not of stuck in his throat."

All the boys would roar at this and Milt himself would force a smile, though the joke was on him. Jim certainly was a card!

There's his shavin' mug, settin' on the shelf, right next to Charley Vail's. "Charles M. Vail." That's the druggist. He comes in regular for his shave, three times a week. And Jim's is the cup next to Charley's. "James H. Kendall." Jim won't need no shavin' mug no more, but I'll leave it there just the same for old time's sake. Jim certainly was a character!

Years ago, Jim used to travel for a canned goods concern over in Carterville. They sold canned goods. Jim had the whole northern half of the State and was on the road five days out of every week. He'd drop in here Saturdays and tell his experiences for that week. It was rich.

I guess he paid more attention to playin' jokes than makin' sales. Finally the concern let him out and he come right home here and told everybody he'd been fired instead of sayin' he'd resigned like most fellas would of.

It was a Saturday and the shop was full and Jim got up out of that chair and says, "Gentlemen, I got an important announcement to make. I been fired from my job."

Well, they asked him if he was in earnest and he said he was and nobody could think of nothin' to say till Jim finally broke the ice himself. He says, "I been sellin' canned goods and now I'm canned goods myself."

You see, the concern he'd been workin' for was a factory that made canned goods. Over in Carterville. And now Jim said he was canned himself. He was certainly a card!

Jim had a great trick that he used to play w'ile he was travelin'. For instance, he'd be ridin' on a train and they'd come to some little town like, well, like, we'll say, like Benton. Jim would look out the train window and read the signs on the stores.

For instance, they'd be a sign, "Henry Smith, Dry Goods." Well, Jim would write down the name and the name of the town and when he got to wherever he was goin' he'd mail back a postal card to Henry Smith at Benton and not sign no name to it, but he'd write on the card, well, somethin' like "Ask your wife about that book agent that spent the afternoon last week," or "Ask your Missus who kept her from gettin' lonesome the last time you was in Carterville." And he'd sign the card, "A Friend."

Of course, he never knew what really come of none of these jokes, but he could picture what *probably* happened and that was enough.

Jim didn't work very steady after he lost his position with the Carterville people. What he did earn, doin' odd jobs round town, why he spent pretty near all of it on gin and his family might of starved if the stores hadn't of carried them along. Jim's wife tried her hand at dressmakin', but they ain't nobody goin' to get rich makin' dresses in this town.

As I say, she'd of divorced Jim, only she seen that she couldn't support herself and the kids and she was always hopin' that some day Jim would cut out his habits and give her more than two or three dollars a week.

They was a time when she would go to whoever he was workin' for and ask them to give her his wages, but after she done this once or twice, he beat her to it by borrowin' most of his pay in advance. He told it all round town, how he had outfoxed his Missus. He certainly was a caution!

But he wasn't satisfied with just outwittin' her. He was sore the way she had acted, tryin' to grab off his pay. And he made up his mind he'd get even. Well, he waited till Evans's Circus was advertised to come to town. Then he told his wife and two kiddies that he was goin' to take them to the circus. The day of the circus, he told them he would get the tickets and meet them outside the entrance to the tent.

Well, he didn't have no intentions of bein' there or buyin' tickets or nothin'. He got full of gin and laid round Wright's poolroom all day. His wife and the kids waited and waited and of course he didn't show up. His wife didn't have a dime with her, or nowhere else, I guess. So she finally had to tell the kids it was all off and they cried like they wasn't never goin' to stop.

Well, it seems, w'ile they was cryin', Doc Stair came along and he asked what was the matter, but Mrs. Kendall was stubborn and wouldn't tell him, but the kids told him and he insisted on takin' them and their mother in the show. Jim found this out afterwards and it was one reason why he had it in for Doc Stair.

Doc Stair come here about a year and a half ago. He's a mighty handsome young fella and his clothes always look like he has them made to order. He goes to Detroit two or three times a year and w'ile he's there he must have a tailor take his measure and then make him a suit to order. They cost pretty near twice as much, but they fit a whole lot better than if you just bought them in a store.

For a w'ile everybody was wonderin' why a young doctor like Doc Stair should come to a town like this where we already got old Doc Gamble and Doc Foote that's both been here for years and all the practice in town was always divided between the two of them.

Then they was a story got round that Doc Stair's gal had throwed him over, a gal up in the Northern Peninsula somewheres, and the reason he come here was to hide himself away and forget it. He said himself that he thought they wasn't nothin' like general practice in a place like ours to fit a man to be a good all round doctor. And that's why he'd came.

Anyways, it wasn't long before he was makin' enough to live on, though they tell me that he never dunned nobody for what they owed him, and the folks here certainly has got the owin' habit, even in my business. If I had all that was comin' to me for just shaves alone, I could go to Carterville and put up at the Mercer for a week and see a different picture every night. For instance, they's old George Purdy—but I guess I shouldn't ought to be gossipin'.

Well, last year, our coroner died, died of the flu. Ken Beatty, that was his name. He was the coroner. So they had to choose another man to be coroner in his place and they picked Doc Stair. He laughed at first and said he didn't want it, but they made him take it. It ain't no job that anybody would fight for and what a man makes out of it in a year would just about buy seeds for their garden. Doc's the kind, though, that can't say no to nothin' if you keep at him long enough.

But I was goin' to tell you about a poor boy we got here in town—Paul Dickson. He fell out of a tree when he was about ten years old. Lit on his head and it done somethin' to him and he ain't never been right. No harm in him, but just silly. Jim Kendall used to call him cuckoo; that's a name Jim had for anybody that was off their head, only he called people's head their bean. That was another of his gags, callin' head bean and callin' crazy people cuckoo. Only poor Paul ain't crazy, but just silly.

You can imagine that Jim used to have all kinds of fun with Paul. He'd send him to the White Front Garage for a left-handed monkey wrench. Of course they ain't no such a thing as a left-handed monkey wrench.

And once we had a kind of a fair here and they was a baseball game between the fats and the leans and before the game started Jim called Paul over and sent him way down to Schrader's hardware store to get a key for the pitcher's box.

They wasn't nothin' in the way of gags that Jim couldn't think up, when he put his mind to it.

Poor Paul was always kind of suspicious of people, maybe on account of how Jim had kept foolin' him. Paul wouldn't have much to do with anybody only his own mother and Doc Stair and a girl here in town named Julie Gregg. That is, she ain't a girl no more, but pretty near thirty or over.

When Doc first come to town, Paul seemed to feel like here was a real friend and he hung round Doc's office most of the w'ile; the only time he wasn't there was when he'd go home to eat or sleep or when he seen Julie Gregg doin' her shoppin'.

When he looked out Doc's window and seen her, he'd run downstairs and join her and tag along with her to the different stores. The poor boy was crazy about Julie and she always treated him mighty nice and made him feel like he was welcome, though of course it wasn't nothin' but pity on her side.

Doc done all he could to improve Paul's mind and he told me once that he really thought the boy was gettin' better, that they was times when he was as bright and sensible as anybody else.

But I was goin' to tell you about Julie Gregg. Old Man Gregg was in the lumber business, but got to drinkin' and lost the most of his money and when he died, he didn't leave nothin' but the house and just enough insurance for the girl to skimp along on.

Her mother was a kind of a half invalid and didn't hardly ever leave the house. Julie wanted to sell the place and move somewheres else after the old man died, but the mother said she was born here and would die here. It was tough on Julie, as the young people round this town—well, she's too good for them.

She's been away to school and Chicago and New York and different places and they ain't no subject she can't talk on, where you take the rest of the young folks here and you mention anything to them outside of Gloria Swanson or Tommy Meighan and they think you're delirious. Did you see Gloria in Wages of Virtue? You missed somethin'!

Well, Doc Stair hadn't been here more than a week when he come in one day to get shaved and I recognized who he was as he had been pointed out to me, so I told him about my old lady. She's been ailin' for a couple years and either Doc Gamble or Doc Foote, neither one, seemed to be helpin' her. So he said he would come out and see her, but if she was able to get out herself, it would be better to bring her to his office where he could make a completer examination.

So I took her to his office and w'ile I was waitin' for her in the reception room, in come Julie Gregg. When somebody comes in Doc Stair's office, they's a bell that rings in his inside office so as he can tell they's somebody to see him.

So he left my old lady inside and come out to the front office and that's the first time him and Julie met and I guess it was what they call love at first sight. But it wasn't fifty-fifty. This young fella was the slickest lookin' fella she'd ever seen in this town and she went wild over him. To him she was just a young lady that wanted to see the doctor.

She'd come on about the same business I had. Her mother had been doctorin' for years with Doc Gamble and Doc Foote and without no results. So she'd heard they was a new doc in town and decided to give him a try. He promised to call and see her mother that same day.

I said a minute ago that it was love at first sight on her part. I'm not only judgin' by how she acted afterwards but how she looked at him that first day in his office. I ain't no mind reader, but it was wrote all over her face that she was gone.

Now Jim Kendall, besides bein' a jokesmith and a pretty good drinker, well, Jim was quite a lady-killer. I guess he run pretty wild durin' the time he was on the road for them Carterville people, and besides that, he'd had a couple little affairs of the heart right here in town. As I say, his wife could of divorced him, only she couldn't.

But Jim was like the majority of men, and women, too, I guess. He wanted what he couldn't get. He wanted Julie Gregg and worked his head off tryin' to land her. Only he'd of said bean instead of head.

Well, Jim's habits and his jokes didn't appeal to Julie and of course he was a married man, so he didn't have no more chance than, well, than a rabbit. That's an expression of Jim's himself. When somebody didn't have no chance to get elected or somethin', Jim would always say they didn't have no more chance than a rabbit.

He didn't make no bones about how he felt. Right in here, more than once, in front of the whole crowd, he said he was stuck on Julie and anybody that could get her for him was welcome to his house and his wife and kids included. But she wouldn't have nothin' to do with him; wouldn't even speak to him on the street. He finally seen he wasn't gettin' nowheres with his usual line so he decided to try the rough stuff. He went right up to her house one evenin' and when she opened the door he forced his way in and grabbed her. But she broke loose and before he could stop her, she run in the next room and locked the door and phoned to Joe Barnes. Joe's the marshal. Jim could hear who she was phonin' to and he beat it before Joe got there.

Joe was an old friend of Julie's pa. Joe went to Jim the next day and told him what would happen if he ever done it again.

I don't know how the news of this little affair leaked out. Chances is that Joe Barnes told his wife and she told somebody else's wife and they told their husband. Anyways, it did leak out and Hod Meyers had the nerve to kid Jim about it, right here in this shop. Jim didn't deny nothin' and kind of laughed it off and said for us all to wait; that lots of people had tried to make a monkey out of him, but he always got even.

Meanw'ile everybody in town was wise to Julie's bein' wild mad over the Doc. I don't suppose she had any idear how her face changed when him and her was together; of course she couldn't of, or she'd of kept away from him. And she didn't know that we was all noticin' how many times she made excuses to go up to his office or pass it on the other side of the street and look up in his window to see if he was there. I felt sorry for her and so did most other people.

Hod Meyers kept rubbin' it into Jim about how the Doc had cut him out. Jim didn't pay no attention to the kiddin' and you could see he was plannin' one of his jokes.

One trick Jim had was the knack of changin' his voice. He could make you think he was a girl talkin' and he could mimic any man's voice. To show you how good he was along this line, I'll tell you the joke he played on me once.

You know, in most towns of any size, when a man is dead and needs a shave, why the barber that shaves him soaks him five dollars for the job; that is, he don't soak *him,* but whoever ordered the shave. I just charge three dollars because personally I don't mind much shavin' a dead person. They lay a whole lot stiller than live customers. The only thing is that you don't feel like talkin' to them and you get kind of lonesome.

Well, about the coldest day we ever had here, two years ago last winter, the phone rung at the house w'ile I was home to dinner and I answered the phone and it was a woman's voice and she said she was Mrs. John Scott and her husband was dead and would I come out and shave him.

Old John had always been a good customer of mine. But they live seven miles out in the country, on the Streeter road. Still I didn't see how I could say no.

So I said I would be there, but would have to come in a jitney and it might cost three or four dollars besides the price of the shave. So she, or the voice, it said that was all right, so I got Frank Abbott to drive me out to the place and when I got there, who should open the door but old John himself! He wasn't no more dead than, well, than a rabbit.

It didn't take no private detective to figure out who had played me this little joke. Nobody could of thought it up but Jim Kendall. He certainly was a card!

I tell you this incident just to show you how he could disguise his voice and make you believe it was somebody else talkin'. I'd of swore it was Mrs. Scott had called me. Anyways, some woman.

Well, Jim waited till he had Doc Stair's voice down pat; then he went after revenge.

He called Julie up on a night when he knew Doc was over in Carterville. She never questioned but what it was Doc's voice. Jim said he must see her that night; he couldn't wait no longer to tell her somethin'. She was all excited and told him to come to the house. But he said he was expectin' an important long distance call and wouldn't she please forget her manners for once and come to his office. He said they couldn't nothin' hurt her and nobody would see her and he just *must* talk to her a little w'ile. Well, poor Julie fell for it.

Doc always keeps a night light in his office, so it looked to Julie like they was somebody there.

Meanw'ile Jim Kendall had went to Wright's poolroom, where they was a whole gang amusin' themselves. The most of them had drank plenty of gin, and they was a rough bunch even when sober. They was always strong for Jim's jokes and when he told them to come with him and see some fun they give up their card games and pool games and followed along.

Doc's office is on the second floor. Right outside his door they's a flight of stairs leadin' to the floor above. Jim and his gang hid in the dark behind these stairs.

Well, Julie come up to Doc's door and rung the bell and they was nothin' doin'. She rung it again and she rung it seven or eight times. Then she tried the door and found it locked. Then Jim made some kind of a noise and she heard it and waited a minute, and then she says, "Is that you, Ralph?" Ralph is Doc's first name.

They was no answer and it must of come to her all of a sudden that she'd been bunked. She pretty near fell downstairs and the whole gang after her. They chased her all the way home, hollerin', "Is that you, Ralph?" and "Oh, Ralphie, dear, is that you?" Jim says he couldn't holler it himself, as he was laughin' too hard.

Poor Julie! She didn't show up here on Main Street for a long, long time afterward.

And of course Jim and his gang told everybody in town, everybody but Doc Stair. They was scared to tell him, and he might of never knowed only for Paul Dickson. The poor cuckoo, as Jim called him, he was here in the shop one night when Jim was still gloatin' yet over what he'd done to Julie. And Paul took in as much of it as he could understand and he run to Doc with the story.

It's a cinch Doc went up in the air and swore he'd make Jim suffer. But it was a kind of a delicate thing, because if it got out that he had beat Jim up, Julie was bound to hear of it and then she'd know that Doc knew and of course knowin' that he knew would make it worse for her than ever. He was goin' to do somethin', but it took a lot of figurin'.

Well, it was a couple days later when Jim was here in the shop again, and so was the cuckoo. Jim was goin' duck-shootin' the next day and had come in lookin' for Hod Meyers to go with him. I happened to know that Hod had went over to Carterville and wouldn't be home till the end of the week. So Jim said he hated to go alone and he guessed he would call it off. Then poor Paul spoke up and said if Jim would take him he would go along. Jim thought a w'ile and then he said, well, he guessed a half-wit was better than nothin'.

I suppose he was plottin' to get Paul out in the boat and play some joke on him, like pushin' him in the water. Anyways, he said Paul could go. He asked him had he ever shot a duck and Paul said no, he'd never even had a gun in his hands. So Jim said he could set in the boat and watch him and if he behaved himself, he might lend him his gun for a couple of shots. They made a date to meet in the mornin' and that's the last I seen of Jim alive.

Next mornin', I hadn't been open more than ten minutes when Doc Stair come in. He looked kind of nervous. He asked me had I seen Paul Dickson. I said no, but I knew where he was, out duck-shootin' with Jim Kendall. So Doc says that's what he had heard, and he couldn't understand it because Paul had told him he wouldn't never have no more to do with Jim as long as he lived.

He said Paul had told him about the joke Jim had played on Julie. He said Paul had asked him what he thought of the joke and the Doc had told him that anybody that would do a thing like that ought not to be let live.

I said it had been a kind of a raw thing, but Jim just couldn't resist no kind of a joke, no matter how raw. I said I thought he was all right at heart, but just bubblin' over with mischief. Doc turned and walked out.

At noon he got a phone call from old John Scott. The lake where Jim and Paul had went shootin' is on John's place. Paul had came runnin' up to the house a few minutes before and said they'd been an accident. Jim had shot a few ducks and then give the gun to Paul and told him to try his luck. Paul hadn't never handled a gun and he was nervous. He was shakin' so hard that he couldn't control the gun. He let fire and Jim sunk back in the boat, dead.

Doc Stair, bein' the coroner, jumped in Frank Abbott's flivver and rushed out to Scott's farm. Paul and old John was down on the shore of the lake. Paul had rowed the boat to shore, but they'd left the body in it, waitin' for Doc to come.

Doc examined the body and said they might as well fetch it back to town. They was no use leavin' it there or callin' a jury, as it was a plain case of accidental shootin'.

Personally I wouldn't never leave a person shoot a gun in the same boat I was in unless I was sure they knew somethin' about guns. Jim was a sucker to leave a new beginner have his gun, let alone a half-wit. It probably served Jim right, what he got. But still we miss him round here. He certainly was a card!

Comb it wet or **dry?**

Frank O'Connor

GUESTS OF THE NATION

i

AT DUSK the big Englishman Belcher would shift his long legs out of the ashes and ask, 'Well, chums, what about it?' and Noble or me would say, 'As you please, chum' (for we had picked up some of their curious expressions), and the little Englishman 'Awkins would light the lamp and produce the cards. Sometimes Jeremiah Donovan would come up of an evening and supervise the play, and grow excited over 'Awkins's cards (which he always played badly), and shout at him as if he was one of our own, 'Ach, you divil you, why didn't you play the trey?' But, ordinarily, Jeremiah was a sober and contented poor devil like the big Englishman Belcher, and was looked up to at all only because he was a fair hand at documents, though slow enough at these, I vow. He wore a small cloth hat and big gaiters over his long pants, and seldom did I perceive his hands outside the pockets of that pants. He reddened when you talked to him, tilting from toe to heel and back and looking down all the while at his big farmer's feet. His uncommon broad accent was a great source of jest to me, I being from the town as you may recognise.

I couldn't at the time see the point of me and Noble being with Belcher and 'Awkins at all, for it was and is my fixed belief you could have planted that pair in any untended spot from this to Claregalway and they'd have stayed put and flourished like a native weed. I never seen in my short experience two men that took to the country as they did.

They were handed on to us by the Second Battalion to keep when the search for them became too hot, and Noble and myself, being young, took charge with a natural feeling of responsibility. But little 'Awkins made us look right fools when he displayed he knew the countryside as well as we did and something more. 'You're the bloke they calls Bonaparte?' he said to me. 'Well, Bonaparte, Mary Brigid Ho'Connell was arskin' abaout you and said 'ow you'd a pair of socks belonging to 'er young brother.' For it seemed, as they explained it, that the Second used to have little evenings of their own, and some of the girls of the neighbourhood would turn in, and, seeing they were such decent fellows, our lads couldn't well ignore the two Englishmen, but invited them in and were hail-fellow-well-met with them. 'Awkins told me he learned to dance 'The Walls of Limerick' and 'The Siege of Ennis' and 'The Waves of Tory' in a night or two, though naturally he could not return the compliment, because our lads at that time did not dance foreign dances on principle.

So whatever privileges and favours Belcher and 'Awkins had with the Second they duly took with us, and after the first evening we gave up all pretence of keeping a close eye on their behaviour. Not that they could have got far, for they had a notable accent and wore khaki tunics and overcoats with civilian pants and boots. But it's my belief they never had an idea of escaping and were quite contented with their lot.

Now, it was a treat to see how Belcher got off with the old woman of the house we were staying in. She was a great warrant to scold, and crotchety even with us, but before ever she had a chance of giving our guests, as I may call them, a lick of her tongue, Belcher had made her his friend for life. She was breaking sticks at the time, and Belcher, who hadn't been in the house for more than ten minutes, jumped up out of his seat and went across to her.

'Allow me, madam,' he says, smiling his queer little smile; 'please allow me,' and takes the hatchet from her hand. She was struck too parlatic to speak, and ever after Belcher would be at her heels carrying a bucket, or basket, or load of turf, as the case might be. As Noble wittily remarked, he got into looking before she lept, and hot water or any little thing she wanted Belcher would have it ready before her. For such a huge man (and though I am five foot ten myself I had to look up to him) he had an uncommon shortness— or should I say lack—of speech. It took us some time to get used to him walking in and out like a ghost, without a syllable out of him. Especially because 'Awkins talked enough for a platoon, it was strange to hear big Belcher with his toes in the ashes come out with a solitary 'Excuse me, chum,' or 'That's right, chum.' His one and only abiding passion was cards, and I will say for him he was a good card-player. He could have fleeced me and Noble many a time; only if we lost to him, 'Awkins lost to us, and 'Awkins played with the money Belcher gave him.

'Awkins lost to us because he talked too much, and I think now we lost to Belcher for the same reason. 'Awkins and Noble would spit at one another about religion into the early hours of the morning; the little Englishman as you could see worrying the soul out of young Noble (whose brother was a priest) with a string of questions that would puzzle a cardinal. And to make it worse, even in treating of these holy subjects, 'Awkins had a deplorable tongue; I never in all my career struck across a man who could mix such a variety of cursing and bad language into the simplest topic. Oh, a terrible man was little 'Awkins, and a fright to argue! He never did a stroke of work, and when he had no one else to talk to he fixed his claws into the old woman.

I am glad to say that in her he met his match, for one day when he tried to get her to complain profanely of the drought she gave him a great comedown by blaming the drought upon Jupiter Pluvius (a deity neither 'Awkins nor I had ever even heard of, though Noble said among the pagans he was held to have something to do with rain). And another day the same

'Awkins was swearing at the capitalists for starting the German war, when the old dame laid down her iron, puckered up her little crab's mouth and said, 'Mr. 'Awkins, you can say what you please about the war, thinking to deceive me because I'm an ignorant old woman, but I know well what started the war. It was that Italian count that stole the heathen divinity out of the temple in Japan, for believe me, Mr. 'Awkins, nothing but sorrow and want follows them that disturbs the hidden powers!' Oh, a queer old dame, as you remark!

ii

So one evening we had our tea together, and 'Awkins lit the lamp and we all sat in to cards. Jeremiah Donovan came in too, and sat down and watched us for a while. Though he was a shy man and didn't speak much, it was easy to see he had no great love for the two Englishmen, and I was surprised it hadn't struck me so clearly before. Well, like that in the story, a terrible dispute blew up late in the evening between 'Awkins and Noble, about capitalists and priests and love for your own country.

'The capitalists,' says 'Awkins, with an angry gulp, 'the capitalists pays the priests to tell you all abaout the next world, so's you awon't notice what they do in this!'

'Nonsense, man,' says Noble, losing his temper, 'before ever a capitalist was thought of people believed in the next world.'

'Awkins stood up as if he was preaching a sermon. 'Oh, they did, did they?' he says with a sneer. 'They believed all the things you believe, that's what you mean? And you believe that God created Hadam and Hadam created Shem and Shem created Jehoshophat? You believe all the silly hold fairy-tale abaout Heve and Heden and the happle? Well, listen to me, chum. If you're entitled to 'old to a silly belief like that, I'm entitled to 'old to my own silly belief—which is, that the fust thing your God created was a bleedin' capitalist with mirality and Rolls Royce complete. Am I right, chum?' he says then to Belcher.

'You're right, chum,' says Belcher, with his queer smile, and gets up from the table to stretch his long legs into the fire and stroke his moustache. So, seeing that Jeremiah Donovan was going, and there was no knowing when the conversation about religion would be over, I took my hat and went out with him. We strolled down towards the village together, and then he suddenly stopped, and blushing and mumbling, and shifting, as his way was, from toe to heel, he said I ought to be behind keeping guard on the prisoners. And I, having it put to me so suddenly, asked him what the hell he wanted a guard on the prisoners at all for, and said that so far as Noble and me were concerned we had talked it over and would rather be out with a column. 'What use is that pair to us?' I asked him.

He looked at me for a spell and said, 'I thought you knew we were keeping them as hostages.' 'Hostages—?' says I, not quite understanding. 'The enemy,' he says in his heavy way, 'have prisoners belong' to us, and now they talk of shooting them. If they shoot our prisoners we'll shoot theirs, and serve them right.' 'Shoot them?' said I, the possibility just beginning to dawn on me. 'Shoot them, exactly,' said he. 'Now,' said I, 'wasn't it very unforeseen of you not to tell me and Noble that?' 'How so?' he asks. 'Seeing that we were acting as guards upon them, of course.' 'And hadn't you reason enough to guess that much?' 'We had not, Jeremiah Donovan, we had not. How were we to know when the men were on our hands so long?' 'And what difference does it make? The enemy have our prisoners as long or longer, haven't they?' 'It makes a great difference,' said I. 'How so?' said he sharply; but I couldn't tell him the difference it made, for I was struck too silly to speak. 'And when may we expect to be released from this anyway?' said I. 'You may expect it to-night,' says he. 'Or to-morrow or the next day at latest. So if it's hanging round here that worries you, you'll be free soon enough.'

I cannot explain it even now, how sad I felt, but I went back to the cottage, a miserable man. When I arrived the discussion was still on, 'Awkins holding forth to all and sundry that there was no next world at all and Noble answering in his best canonical style that there was. But I saw 'Awkins was after having the best of it. 'Do you know what, chum?' he was saying, with his saucy smile, 'I think you're jest as big a bleedin' hunbeliever as I am. You say you believe in the next world and you know jest as much abaout the next world as I do, which is sweet damn-all. What's 'Eaven? You dunno. Where's 'Eaven? You dunno. Who's in 'Eaven? You dunno. You know sweet damn-all! I arsk you again, do they wear wings?'

'Very well then,' says Noble, 'they do; is that enough for you? They do wear wings.' 'Where do they get them then? Who makes them? 'Ave they a fact'ry for wings? 'Ave they a sort of store where you 'ands in your chit and tikes your bleedin' wings? Answer me that.'

'Oh, you're an impossible man to argue with,' says Noble. 'Now listen to me—.' And off the pair of them went again.

It was long after midnight when we locked up the Englishmen and went to bed ourselves. As I blew out the candle I told Noble what Jeremiah Donovan had told me. Noble took it very quietly. After we had been in bed about an hour he asked me did I think we ought to tell the Englishmen. I having thought of the same thing myself (among many others) said no, because it was more than likely the English wouldn't shoot our men, and anyhow it wasn't to be supposed the Brigade who were always up and down with the second battalion and knew the Englishmen well would be likely to want them bumped off. 'I think so,' says Noble. 'It would be sort of cruelty to put the wind up them now.' 'It was very unforeseen of Jeremiah Donovan anyhow,' says I, and by Noble's silence I realised he took my meaning.

So I lay there half the night, and thought and thought, and picturing myself and young Noble trying to prevent the Brigade from shooting 'Awkins and Belcher sent a cold sweat out through me. Because there were men on the Brigade you daren't let nor hinder without a gun in your hand, and at any rate, in those days disunion between brothers seemed to me an awful crime. I knew better after.

It was next morning we found it so hard to face Belcher and 'Awkins with a smile. We went about the house all day scarcely saying a word. Belcher didn't mind us much; he was stretched into the ashes as usual with his usual look of waiting in quietness for something unforeseen to happen, but little 'Awkins gave us a bad time with his audacious gibing and questioning. He was disgusted at Noble's not answering him back. 'Why can't you tike your beating like a man, chum?' he says. 'You with your Hadam and Heve! I'm a Communist—or an Anarchist. An Anarchist, that's what I am.' And for hours after he went round the house, mumbling when the fit took him 'Hadam and Heve! Hadam and Heve!'

iii

I don't know clearly how we got over that day, but get over it we did, and a great relief it was when the tea-things were cleared away and Belcher said in his peaceable manner, 'Well, chums, what about it?' So we all sat round the table and 'Awkins produced the cards, and at that moment I heard Jeremiah Donovan's footsteps up the path, and a dark presentiment crossed my mind. I rose quietly from the table and laid my hand on him before he reached the door. 'What do you want?' I asked him. 'I want those two soldier friends of yours,' he says reddening. 'Is that the way it is, Jeremiah Donovan?' I ask. 'That's the way. There were four of our lads went west this morning, one of them a boy of sixteen.' 'That's bad, Jeremiah,' says I.

At that moment Noble came out, and we walked down the path together talking in whispers. Feeney, the local intelligence officer, was standing by the gate. 'What are you going to do about it?' I asked Jeremiah Donovan. 'I want you and Noble to bring them out: you can tell them they're being shifted again; that'll be the quietest way.' 'Leave me out of that,' says Noble suddenly. Jeremiah Donovan looked at him hard for a minute or two. 'All right so,' he said peaceably. 'You and Feeney collect a few tools from the shed and dig a hole by the far end of the bog. Bonaparte and I'll be after you in about twenty minutes. But whatever else you do, don't let anyone see you with the tools. No one must know but the four of ourselves.'

We saw Feeney and Noble go round to the houseen where the tools were kept, and sidled in. Everything if I can so express myself was tottering before my eyes, and I left Jeremiah Donovan to do the explaining as best he could, while I took a seat and said nothing. He told them they were to go back to the Second. 'Awkins let a mouthful of curses out of him at that, and it was plain that Belcher, though he said nothing, was duly perturbed. The old woman was for having them stay in spite of us, and she did not shut her mouth until Jeremiah Donovan lost his temper and said some nasty things to her. Within the house by this time it was pitch dark, but no one thought of lighting the lamp, and in the darkness the two Englishmen fetched their khaki topcoats and said good-bye to the woman of the house. 'Just as a man mikes a 'ome of a bleedin' place,' mumbles 'Awkins shaking her by the hand, 'some bastard at headquarters thinks you're too cushy and shunts you off.' Belcher shakes her hand very hearty. 'A thousand thanks, madam,' he says, 'a thousand thanks for everything . . .' as though he'd made it all up.

We go round to the back of the house and down towards the fatal bog. Then Jeremiah Donovan comes out with what is in his mind. 'There were four of our lads shot by your fellows this morning so now you're to be bumped off.' 'Cut that stuff out,' says 'Awkins flaring up. 'It's bad enough to be mucked about such as we are without you plying at soldiers.' 'It's true,' says Jeremiah Donovan. 'I'm sorry, 'Awkins, but 'tis true,' and comes out with the usual rigmarole about doing our duty and obeying our superiors. 'Cut it out,' says 'Awkins irritably, 'Cut it out!'

Then, when Donovan sees he is not being believed he turns to me. 'Ask Bonaparte here,' he says. 'I don't need to arsk Bonaparte. Me and Bonaparte are chums.' 'Isn't it true, Bonaparte?' says Jeremiah Donovan solemnly to me. 'It is,' I say sadly, 'it is.' 'Awkins stops. 'Now, for Christ's sike. . . .' 'I mean it, chum,' I say. 'You daon't saound as if you mean it. You knaow well you don't mean it.' 'Well, if he don't I do,' says Jeremiah Donovan. 'Why the 'ell sh'd you want to shoot me, Jeremiah Donovan?' 'Why the hell should your people take out four prisoners and shoot them in cold blood upon a barrack square?' I perceive Jeremiah Donovan is trying to encourage himself with hot words.

Anyway, he took little 'Awkins by the arm and dragged him on, but it was impossible to make him understand that we were in earnest. From which you will perceive how difficult it was for me, as I kept feeling my Smith and Wesson and thinking what I would do if they happened to put up a fight or ran for it, and wishing in my heart they would. I knew if only they ran I would never fire on them. 'Was Noble in this?' 'Awkins wanted to know, and we said yes. He laughed. But why should Noble want to shoot him? Why should we want to shoot him? What had he done to us? Weren't we chums (the word lingers painfully in my memory)? Weren't we? Didn't we understand him and didn't he understand us? Did either of us imagine for an instant that he'd shoot us for all the so-and-so brigadiers in the so-and-so British Army? By this time I began to perceive in the dusk the desolate edges of the bog that was to be their last earthly bed, and, so great a sadness overtook my mind, I could not answer him. We walked along the edge of it in the darkness, and every now and then 'Awkins would call a halt and begin again, just as if he was wound up, about us being chums, and I was in despair that nothing but the cold and open grave made ready for his presence would convince him that we meant it all. But all the same, if you can understand, I didn't want him to be bumped off.

iv

At last we saw the unsteady glint of a lantern in the distance and made towards it. Noble was carrying it, and Feeney stood somewhere in the darkness behind, and somehow the picture of the two of them so silent in the boglands was like the pain of death in my heart. Belcher, on recognising Noble, said ' 'Allo, chum' in his usual peaceable way, but 'Awkins flew at the poor boy immediately, and the dispute began all over again, only that Noble hadn't a word to say for himself, and stood there with the swaying lantern between his gaitered legs.

It was Jeremiah Donovan who did the answering. 'Awkins asked for the twentieth time (for it seemed to haunt his mind) if anybody thought he'd shoot Noble. 'You would,' says Jeremiah Donovan shortly. 'I wouldn't, damn you!' 'You would if you knew you'd be shot for not doing it.' 'I wouldn't, not if I was to be shot twenty times over; he's my chum. And Belcher wouldn't—isn't that right, Belcher?' 'That's right, chum,' says Belcher peaceably. 'Damned if I would. Anyway, who says Noble'd be shot if I wasn't bumped off? What d'you think I'd do if I was in Noble's place and we were out in the middle of a blasted bog?' 'What would you do?' 'I'd go with him wherever he was going. I'd share my last bob with him and stick by 'im through thick and thin.'

'We've had enough of this,' says Jeremiah Donovan, cocking his revolver. 'Is there any message you want to send before I fire?' 'No, there isn't but . . .' 'Do you want to say your prayers?' 'Awkins came out with a cold-blooded remark that shocked even me and turned to Noble again. 'Listen to me, Noble,' he said. 'You and me are chums. You won't come over to my side, so I'll come over to your side. Is that fair? Just you give me a rifle and I'll go with you wherever you want.'

Nobody answered him.

'Do you understand?' he said. 'I'm through with it all. I'm a deserter or anything else you like, but from this on I'm one of you. Does that prove to you that I mean what I say?' Noble raised his head, but as Donovan began to speak he lowered it again without answering. 'For the last time have you any messages to send?' says Donovan in a cold and excited voice.

'Ah, shut up, you, Donovan; you don't understand me, but these fellows do. They're my chums; they stand by me and I stand by them. We're not the capitalist tools you seem to think us.'

I alone of the crowd saw Donovan raise his Webley to the back of 'Awkins's neck, and as he did so I shut my eyes and tried to say a prayer. 'Awkins had begun to say something else when Donovan let fly, and, as I opened my eyes at the bang, I saw him stagger at the knees and lie out flat at Noble's feet, slowly, and as quiet as a child, with the lantern-light falling sadly upon his lean legs and bright farmer's boots. We all stood very still for a while watching him settle out in the last agony.

Then Belcher quietly takes out a handkerchief, and begins to tie it about his own eyes (for in our excitement we had forgotten to offer the same to 'Awkins), and, seeing it is not big enough, turns and asks for a loan of mine. I give it to him and as he knots the two together he points with his foot at 'Awkins. ''e's not quite dead,' he says, 'better give 'im another.' Sure enough 'Awkins's left knee as we see it under the lantern is rising again. I bend down and put my gun to his ear; then, recollecting myself and the company of Belcher, I stand up again with a few hasty words. Belcher understands what is in my mind. 'Give 'im 'is first,' he says. 'I don't mind. Poor bastard, we dunno what's 'appening to 'im now.' As by this time I am beyond all feeling I kneel down again and skilfully give 'Awkins the last shot so as to put him for ever out of pain.

Belcher who is fumbling a bit awkwardly with the handkerchief comes out with a laugh when he hears the shot. It is the first time I have heard him laugh, and it sends a shiver down my spine, coming as it does so inappropriately upon the tragic death of his old friend. 'Poor blighter,' he says quietly, 'and last night he was so curious abaout it all. It's very queer, chums, I always think. Naow, 'e knows as much abaout it as they'll ever let 'im know, and last night 'e was all in the dark.'

Donovan helps him to tie the handkerchiefs about his eyes. 'Thanks, chum,' he says. Donovan asks him if there are any messages he would like to send. 'Naow, chum,' he says, 'none for me. If any of you likes to write to 'Awkins's mother you'll find a letter from 'er in 'is pocket. But my missus left me eight years ago. Went away with another fellow and took the kid with her. I likes the feelin' of a 'ome (as you may 'ave noticed) but I couldn't start again after that.'

We stand around like fools now that he can no longer see us. Donovan looks at Noble and Noble shakes his head. Then Donovan raises his Webley again and just at that moment Belcher laughs his queer nervous laugh again. He must think we are talking of him; anyway, Donovan lowers his gun. ''Scuse me, chums,' says Belcher, 'I feel I'm talking the 'ell of a lot . . . and so silly . . . abaout me being so 'andy abaout a 'ouse. But this thing come on me so sudden. You'll forgive me, I'm sure.' 'You don't want to say a prayer?' asks Jeremiah Donovan. 'No, chum,' he replies, 'I don't think that'd 'elp. I'm ready if you want to get it over.' 'You understand,' says Jeremiah Donovan, 'it's not so much our doing. It's our duty, so to speak.' Belcher's head is raised like a real blind man's, so that you can only see his nose and chin in the lamplight. 'I never could make out what duty was myself,' he said, 'but I think you're all good lads, if that's what you mean. I'm not complaining.' Noble, with a look of desperation, signals to Donovan, and in a flash Donovan raises his gun and fires. The big man goes over like a sack of meal, and this time there is no need of a second shot.

I don't remember much about the burying, but that it was worse than all the rest, because we had to carry the warm corpses a few yards before we sunk them in the windy bog. It was all mad lonely, with only a bit of lantern between ourselves and the pitch-blackness, and birds hooting and screeching all round disturbed by the guns. Noble had to search 'Awkins first to get the letter from his mother. Then having smoothed all signs of the grave away, Noble and I collected our tools, said good-bye to the others, and went back along the desolate edge of the treacherous bog without a word. We put the tools in the houseen and went into the house. The kitchen was pitch-black and cold, just as we left it, and the old woman was sitting over the hearth telling her beads. We walked past her into the room, and Noble struck a match to light the lamp. Just then she rose quietly and came to the doorway, being not at all so bold or crabbed as usual.

'What did ye do with them?' she says in a sort of whisper, and Noble took such a mortal start the match quenched in his trembling hand. 'What's that?' he asks without turning round. 'I heard ye,' she said. 'What did you hear?' asks Noble, but sure he wouldn't deceive a child the way he said it. 'I heard ye. Do you think I wasn't listening to ye putting the things back in the houseen?' Noble struck another match and this time the lamp lit for him. 'Was that what ye did with them?' she said, and Noble said nothing— after all what could he say?

So then, by God, she fell on her two knees by the door, and began telling her beads, and after a minute or two Noble went on his knees by the fireplace, so I pushed my way out past her, and stood at the door, watching the stars and listening to the damned shrieking of the birds. It is so strange what you feel at such moments, and not to be written afterwards. Noble says he felt he seen everything ten times as big, perceiving nothing around him but the little patch of black bog with the two Englishmen stiffening into .it; but with me it was the other way, as though the patch of bog where the two Englishmen were was a thousand miles away from me, and even Noble mumbling just behind me and the old woman and the birds and the bloody stars were all far away, and I was somehow very small and very lonely. And anything that ever happened me after I never felt the same about again.

COMMENTARY

The Irish writer Frank O'Connor has been compared to James Joyce. His subject, whether he is writing about the inhabitants of villages or of cities, is the same as Joyce's subject, the soul of the Irish people. He has written half a dozen stories which may be ranked with the stories in *Dubliners,* but his performance is not on a consistently high level. He is not as painstaking a craftsman as Joyce, and he has not got the same kind of literary conscience.

The stories in *Dubliners* cannot be read lightly or even easily. To take hold of them the reader must make an effort which is proportionate to the almost superhuman effort which was required for the writing of them. The result is that one looks back on the stories with somewhat the same feeling that one might have after a hard day's mountain climbing. One never forgets the magnificent view one had from the summit, but the steep climb lingers in the memory, too. O'Connor is more entertaining than Joyce. He possesses in a high degree a literary gift eminently serviceable to a novelist, which Mr. E. M. Forster has labelled "bounce." O'Connor's work is overflowing with vitality. He seems to bounce us along at a great rate of speed and one always has the impression that one is going somewhere, too. A casual reading of his stories may give the student the impression that he is superior to his master. "Here," we might say to ourselves, "is the kind of thing Joyce was doing, only accomplished more easily." But it turns out that O'Connor does not always know where he is going. Many of his stories fail, seem to fall apart in the middle, or present an indecisive Resolution. When his stories fail they fail because of the lack of that painstaking craftsmanship which is dictated by a strict literary conscience. "Bouncing" along at too great a rate of speed, he strikes a rut in the road and proceeds without pausing long enough to discover that his coach has spilled half its passengers. But he has occasionally produced work which is as carefully wrought and as powerful as his master's. "Guests of the Nation" is such a story.

O'Connor has chosen the First Person Narrator (see Appendix A, p. 624) as his authority and employs all the resources which this method makes available. The narrator's easy flow of colloquial speech contributes to the tonal unity (see Appendix A, p. 632), and at the same time each well-placed observation or poignant memory hurries the action to its seemingly inevitable climax.

The Complication (see Appendix A, p. 630) of the action is the growth of brotherly affection between four men, who are of two nations that are at war with each other. The Resolution is the spiritual desolation which comes to the narrator as the result of being forced to kill his "brothers."

O'Connor has spared no pains to strengthen his Complication. The fraternal feeling of the four men is repeatedly emphasized in the first few paragraphs. The Englishmen play cards with their captors and have even learned some of the Irish country dances. The fact that the Irishmen cannot "return the compliment because our lads at that time did not dance foreign dances on principle" prepares the reader for the Englishmen's death at the hands of their jailors. And the narrator's statement that he has never seen two men who "took to the country as they did" prepares us for Hawkins' speech, when, faced with the prospect of death, he asserts that he loves his "chums" better than his country:

> "You won't come over to my side, so I'll come over to your side. Is that fair? Just give me a rifle and I'll go with you wherever you want."

The strong dramatic structure is largely the effect of this interweaving of Complication and Resolution, an interweaving so deft that one seems to grow naturally out of the other.

The character of the big Englishman, Belcher, is revealed progressively and dramatically. He is chivalrously attentive to the old woman of the house, not because he wants to curry favor, but because he "likes the feelin' of a 'ome (as you may have noticed.)" His allusion to his sufferings over the breakup of his own home adds to the pathos of his death. In the end, however, he is a tragic rather than a pathetic figure, for in his death he transcends his individual fate, becoming part of the drama which has been going on since man was first guilty of inhumanity to man.

In this story the Enveloping Action (see Appendix A, p. 631) is the war going on between the two nations. Observed against the background of war, the men's characters have more significance than they would have in ordinary times. The Enveloping Action shares in the swift progression that distinguishes every incident of the story. The old woman plays the part of a Sibyl when she says that "it was the Italian count that stole the heathen divinity out of the temple in Japan" that "started the war"; and again: "Nothing but sorrow and want follow them that disturbs the hidden powers." Her speech sets forth the irrationality of the motives that prompt men to make war and also prophesies the disaster which is to come to at least one of the characters (the narrator) as the result of disobeying the commandment: "Thou shalt not kill."

O'Connor's rhetoric helps to enlarge the theme to tragic proportions. The story is told in a fluent vernacular up to the last paragraph, in which individual cries of anguish alternate with dispassionate pronouncements on the mystery of human life. The passage:

> . . . . so I pushed my way out past her, and stood at the doorway, watching the stars and listening to the *damned* shrieking of the birds.

is followed by:

> It is so strange what you feel at such moments, and not to be written afterwards. Noble says he felt like he seen everything ten times as big, perceiving nothing around him but the little patch of black bog with the two Englishmen stiffening into it; but with me it was the other way, as though the patch of bog where the two Englishmen were was a thousand miles away from me, and even Noble mumbling just behind me and the old woman and the birds and the bloody stars were all far away, and I was somehow very small and lonely.

This speech suddenly introduces another element of action, or rather, brings to the surface the current which has been sweeping the action along. The narrator seems more heroic than he has seemed heretofore. The author has doubled his stature, so to speak, by ascribing to him the sufferings of more than one man, and hence of all humanity.

But the story, in the end, is about what happened to the narrator. It is the First Person who has the last word:

> And anything that ever happened me after I never felt the same about again.

This sentence shows a remarkable compression of dramatic power, together with a pure and elevated, though idiomatic diction. It is perhaps as characteristic of O'Connor at his best as any passage that can be found in his work.

Katherine Anne Porter

OLD MORTALITY

PART I: 1885–1902

S HE WAS a spirited-looking young woman, with dark curly hair cropped and parted on the side, a short oval face with straight eyebrows, and a large curved mouth. A round white collar rose from the neck of her tightly buttoned black basque, and round white cuffs set off lazy hands with dimples in them, lying at ease in the folds of her flounced skirt which gathered around to a bustle. She sat thus, forever in the pose of being photographed, a motionless image in her dark walnut frame with silver oak leaves in the corners, her smiling gray eyes following one about the room. It was a reckless indifferent smile, rather disturbing to her nieces Maria and Miranda. Quite often they wondered why every older person who looked at the picture said, "How lovely"; and why everyone who had known her thought her so beautiful and charming.

There was a kind of faded merriment in the background, with its vase of flowers and draped velvet curtains, the kind of vase and the kind of curtains no one would have any more. The clothes were not even romantic looking, but merely most terribly out of fashion, and the whole affair was associated, in the minds of the little girls, with dead things: the smell of Grandmother's medicated cigarettes and her furniture that smelled of beeswax, and her old-fashioned perfume, Orange Flower. The woman in the picture had been Aunt Amy, but she was only a ghost in a frame, and a sad, pretty story from old times. She had been beautiful, much loved, unhappy, and she had died young.

Maria and Miranda, aged twelve and eight years, knew they were young, though they felt they had lived a long time. They had lived not only their own years; but their memories, it seemed to them, began years before they were born, in the lives of the grown-ups around them, old people above forty, most of them, who had a way of insisting that they too had been young once. It was hard to believe.

Their father was Aunt Amy's brother Harry. She had been his favorite sister. He sometimes glanced at the photograph and said, "It's not very good. Her hair and her smile were her chief beauties, and they aren't shown at all. She was much slimmer than that, too. There were never any fat women in the family, thank God."

When they heard their father say things like that, Maria and Miranda simply wondered, without criticism, what he meant. Their grandmother was thin as a match; the pictures of their mother, long since dead, proved her to have been a candle-wick, almost. Dashing young ladies, who turned out to be, to Miranda's astonishment, merely more of Grandmother's grandchildren, like herself, came visiting from school for the holidays, boasting of their eighteen-inch waists. But how did their father account for great-aunt Eliza, who quite squeezed herself through doors, and who, when seated, was one solid pyramidal monument from floor to neck? What about great-aunt Keziah, in Kentucky? Her husband, great-uncle John Jacob, had refused to allow her to ride his good horses after she had achieved two hundred and twenty pounds. "No," said great-uncle John Jacob, "my sentiments of chivalry are not dead in my bosom; but neither is my common sense, to say nothing of charity to our faithful dumb friends. And the greatest of these is charity." It was suggested to great-uncle John Jacob that charity should forbid him to wound great-aunt Keziah's female vanity by such a comment on her figure. "Female vanity will recover," said great-uncle John Jacob, callously, "but what about my horses' backs? And if she had the proper female vanity in the first place, she would never have got into such shape." Well, great-aunt Keziah was famous for her heft, and wasn't she in the family? But something seemed to happen to their father's memory when he thought of the girls he had known in the family of his youth, and he declared steadfastly they had all been, in every generation without exception, as slim as reeds and graceful as sylphs.

This loyalty of their father's in the face of evidence contrary to his ideal had its springs in family feeling, and a love of legend that he shared with the others. They loved to tell stories, romantic and poetic, or comic with a romantic humor; they did not gild the outward circumstance, it was the feeling that mattered. Their hearts and imaginations were captivated by their past, a past in which worldly considerations had played a very minor role. Their stories were almost always love stories against a bright blank heavenly blue sky.

Photographs, portraits by inept painters who meant earnestly to flatter, and the festival garments folded away in dried herbs and camphor were disappointing when the little girls tried to fit them to the living beings created in their minds by the breathing words of their elders. Grandmother, twice a year compelled in her blood by the change of seasons, would sit nearly all of one day beside old trunks and boxes in the lumber room, unfolding layers of garments and small keepsakes; she spread them out on sheets on the floor around her, crying over certain things, nearly always the same things, looking again at pictures in velvet cases, unwrapping locks of hair and dried flowers, crying gently and easily as if tears were the only pleasure she had left.

If Maria and Miranda were very quiet, and touched nothing until it was offered, they might sit by her at these times, or come and go. There was a tacit understanding that her grief was strictly her own, and must not be noticed or mentioned. The little girls examined the objects, one by one, and did not find them, in themselves, impressive. Such dowdy little wreaths and necklaces, some of them made of pearly shells; such moth-eaten bunches of pink ostrich feathers for the hair; such clumsy big breast pins and bracelets of gold and colored enamel; such silly-looking combs, standing up on tall teeth capped with seed pearls and French paste. Miranda, without knowing why, felt melancholy. It seemed such a pity that these faded things, these yellowed long gloves and misshapen satin slippers, these broad ribbons cracking where they were folded, should have been all those vanished girls had to decorate themselves with. And where were they now, those girls, and the boys in the odd-looking collars? The young men seemed even more unreal than the girls, with their high-buttoned coats, their puffy neckties, their waxed mustaches, their waving thick hair combed carefully over their foreheads. Who could have taken them seriously, looking like that?

No, Maria and Miranda found it impossible to sympathize with those young persons, sitting rather stiffly before the camera, hopelessly out of fashion; but they were drawn and held by the mysterious love of the living, who remembered and cherished these dead. The visible remains were nothing; they were dust, perishable as the flesh; the features stamped on paper and metal were nothing, but their living memory enchanted the little girls. They listened, all ears and eager minds, picking here and there among the floating ends of narrative, patching together as well as they could fragments of tales that were like bits of poetry or music, indeed were associated with the poetry they had heard or read, with music, with the theater.

"Tell me again how Aunt Amy went away when she was married." "She ran into the gray cold and stepped into the carriage and turned and smiled with her face as pale as death, and called out 'Good-by, good-by,' and refused her cloak, and said, 'Give me a glass of wine.' And none of us saw her alive again." "Why wouldn't she wear her cloak, Cousin Cora?" "Because she was not in love, my dear." Ruin hath taught me thus to ruminate, that time will come and take my love away. "Was she really beautiful, Uncle Bill?" "As an angel, my child." There were golden-haired angels with long blue pleated skirts dancing around the throne of the Blessed Virgin. None of them resembled Aunt Amy in the least, nor the type of beauty they had been brought up to admire. There were points of beauty by which one was judged severely. First, a beauty must be tall; whatever color the eyes, the hair must be dark, the darker the better; the skin must be pale and smooth. Lightness and swiftness of movement were important points. A beauty must be a good dancer, superb on horseback, with a serene manner, an amiable gaiety tempered with dignity at all hours. Beautiful teeth and hands, of course, and over and above all this, some mysterious crown of enchantment that attracted and held the heart. It was all very exciting and discouraging.

Miranda persisted through her childhood in believing, in spite of her smallness, thinness, her little snubby nose saddled with freckles, her speckled gray eyes and habitual tantrums, that by some miracle she would grow into a tall, cream-colored brunette, like cousin Isabel; she decided always to wear a trailing white satin gown. Maria, born sensible, had no such illusions. "We are going to take after Mamma's family," she said. "It's no use, we are. We'll never be beautiful, we'll always have freckles. And *you*," she told Miranda, "haven't even a good disposition."

Miranda admitted both truth and justice in this unkindness, but still secretly believed that she would one day suddenly receive beauty, as by inheritance, riches laid suddenly in her hands through no deserts of her own. She believed for quite a while that she would one day be like Aunt Amy, not as she appeared in the photograph, but as she was remembered by those who had seen her.

When Cousin Isabel came out in her tight black riding habit, surrounded by young men, and mounted gracefully, drawing her horse up and around so that he pranced learnedly on one spot while the other riders sprang to their saddles in the same sedate flurry, Miranda's heart would close with such a keen dart of admiration, envy, vicarious pride it was almost painful; but there would always be an elder present to lay a cooling hand upon her emotions. "She rides almost as well as Amy, doesn't she? But Amy had the pure Spanish style, she could bring out paces in a horse no one else knew he had." Young namesake Amy, on her way to a dance, would swish through the hall in ruffled white taffeta, glimmering like a moth in the lamplight, carrying her elbows pointed backward stiffly as wings, sliding along as if she were on rollers, in the fashionable walk of her day. She was considered the best dancer at any party, and Maria, sniffing the wave of perfume that followed Amy, would clasp her hands and say, "Oh, I can't *wait* to be grown up." But the elders would agree that the first Amy had been lighter, more smooth and delicate in her waltzing; young Amy would never equal her. Cousin Molly Parrington, far past her youth, indeed she belonged to the generation before Aunt Amy, was a noted charmer. Men who had known her all her life still gathered about her; now that she was happily widowed for the second time there was no doubt that she would yet marry again. But Amy, said the elders, had the same high spirits and wit without boldness, and you really could not say that Molly had ever been discreet. She dyed her hair, and made jokes about it. She had a way of collecting the men around her in a corner, where she told them stories. She was an unnatural mother to her ugly daughter Eva, an old maid past forty while her mother was still the belle of the ball. "Born when I was fifteen, you remember," Molly would say shamelessly, looking an old beau straight in the eye, both of them remembering that he had been best man at her first wedding when she was past twenty-one. "Everyone said I was like a little girl with her doll."

Eva, shy and chinless, straining her upper lip over two enormous teeth, would sit in corners watching her mother. She looked hungry, her eyes were strained and tired. She wore her mother's old clothes, made over, and taught Latin in a Female Seminary. She believed in votes for women, and had traveled about, making speeches. When her mother was not present, Eva bloomed out a little, danced prettily, smiled, showing all her teeth, and was like a dry little plant set out in a gentle rain. Molly was merry about her ugly duckling. "It's lucky for me my daughter is an old maid. She's not so apt," said Molly naughtily, "to make a grandmother of me." Eva would blush as if she had been slapped.

Eva was a blot, no doubt about it, but the little girls felt she belonged to their everyday world of dull lessons to be learned, stiff shoes to be limbered up, scratchy flannels to be endured in cold weather, measles and disappointed expectations. Their Aunt Amy belonged to the world of poetry. The romance of Uncle Gabriel's long, unrewarded love for her, her early death, was such a story as one found in old books: unworldly books, but true, such as the Vita Nuova, the Sonnets of Shakespeare and the Wedding Song of Spenser; and poems by Edgar Allan Poe. "Her tantalized spirit now blandly reposes, Forgetting or never regretting its roses. . . ." Their father read that to them, and said, "He was our greatest poet," and they knew that "our" meant he was Southern. Aunt Amy was real as the pictures in the old Holbein and Dürer books were real. The little girls lay flat on their stomachs and peered into a world of wonder, turning the shabby leaves that fell apart easily, not surprised at the sight of the Mother of God sitting on a hollow log nursing her Child; not doubting either Death or the Devil riding at the stirrups of the grim knight; not questioning the propriety of the stiffly dressed ladies of Sir Thomas More's household, seated in dignity on the floor, or seeming to be. They missed all the dog and pony shows, and lantern-slide entertainments, but their father took them to see "Hamlet," and "The Taming of the Shrew," and "Richard the Third," and a long sad play with Mary, Queen of Scots, in it. Miranda thought the magnificent lady in black velvet was truly the Queen of Scots, and was pained to learn that the real Queen had died long ago, and not at all on the night she, Miranda, had been present.

The little girls loved the theater, that world of personages taller than human beings, who swept upon the scene and invested it with their presences, their more than human voices, their gestures of gods and goddesses ruling a universe. But there was always a voice recalling other and greater occasions. Grandmother in her youth had heard Jenny Lind, and thought that Nellie Melba was much overrated. Father had seen Bernhardt, and Madame Modjeska was no sort of rival. When Paderewski played for the first time in their city, cousins came from all over the state and went from the grandmother's house to hear him. The little girls were left out of this great occasion. They shared the excitement of the going away, and shared the beautiful moment of return, when cousins stood about in groups, with coffee cups and glasses in their hands, talking in low voices, awed and happy. The little girls, struck with the sense of a great event, hung about in their nightgowns and listened, until someone noticed and hustled them away from the sweet nimbus of all that glory. One old gentleman, however, had heard Rubinstein frequently. He could not but feel that Rubinstein had reached the final height of musical interpretation, and, for him, Paderewski had been something of an anticlimax. The little girls heard him muttering on, holding up one hand, patting the air as if he were calling for silence. The others looked at him, and listened, without any disturbance of their grave tender mood. They had never heard Rubinstein; they had, one hour since, heard Paderewski, and why should anyone need to recall the past? Miranda, dragged away, half understanding the old gentleman, hated him. She felt that she too had heard Paderewski.

There was then a life beyond a life in this world, as well as in the next; such episodes confirmed for the little girls the nobility of human feeling, the divinity of man's vision of the unseen, the importance of life and death, the depths of the human heart, the romantic value of tragedy. Cousin Eva, on a certain visit, trying to interest them in the study of Latin, told them the story of John Wilkes Booth, who, handsomely garbed in a long black cloak, had leaped to the stage after assassinating President Lincoln. "Sic semper tyrannis," he had shouted superbly, in spite of his broken leg. The little girls never doubted that it had happened in just that way, and the moral seemed to be that one should always have Latin, or at least a good classical poetry quotation, to depend upon in great or desperate moments. Cousin Eva reminded them that no one, not even a good Southerner, could possibly approve of John Wilkes Booth's deed. It was murder, after all. They were to remember that. But Miranda, used to tragedy in books and in family legends —two great-uncles had committed suicide and a remote ancestress had gone mad for love—decided that, without the murder, there would have been no point to dressing up and leaping to the stage shouting in Latin. So how could she disapprove of the deed? It was a fine story. She knew a distantly related old gentleman who had been devoted to the art of Booth, had seen him in a great many plays, but not, alas, at his greatest moment. Miranda regretted this; it would have been so pleasant to have the assassination of Lincoln in the family.

Uncle Gabriel, who had loved Aunt Amy so desperately, still lived somewhere, though Miranda and Maria had never seen him. He had gone away, far away, after her death. He still owned racehorses, and ran them at famous tracks all over the country, and Miranda believed there could not possibly be a more brilliant career. He had married again, quite soon, and had written to Grandmother, asking her to accept his new wife as a daughter in place of Amy. Grandmother had written coldly, accepting, inviting them for a visit, but Uncle Gabriel had somehow never brought his bride home. Harry had visited them in New Orleans, and reported that the second wife was a very good-looking well-bred blonde girl who would undoubtedly be a good wife for Gabriel. Still, Uncle Gabriel's heart was broken. Faithfully once a year he wrote a letter to someone of the family, sending money for a wreath for Amy's grave. He had written a poem for her gravestone, and had come home, leaving his second wife in Atlanta, to see that it was carved properly. He could never account for having written this poem; he had certainly never tried to write a single rhyme since leaving school. Yet one day when he had been thinking about Amy, the verse occurred to him, out of the air. Maria and Miranda had seen it, printed in gold on a mourning card. Uncle Gabriel had sent a great number of them to be handed around among the family.

> "She lives again who suffered life,
> Then suffered death, and now set free
> A singing angel, she forgets
> The griefs of old mortality."

"Did she really sing?" Maria asked her father.

"Now what has that to do with it?" he asked. "It's a poem."

"I think it's very pretty," said Miranda, impressed. Uncle Gabriel was second cousin to her father and Aunt Amy. It brought poetry very near.

"Not so bad for tombstone poetry," said their father, "but it should be better."

Uncle Gabriel had waited five years to marry Aunt Amy. She had been ill, her chest was weak; she was engaged twice to other young men and broke her engagements for no reason; and she laughed at the advice of older and kinder-hearted persons who thought it very capricious of her not to return the devotion of such a handsome and romantic young man as Gabriel, her second cousin, too; it was not as if she would be marrying a stranger. Her coldness was said to have driven Gabriel to a wild life and even to drinking. His grandfather was wealthy and Gabriel was his favorite; they had quarreled over the racehorses, and Gabriel had shouted, "By God, I must have *something*." As if he had not everything already: youth, health, good looks, the prospect of riches, and a devoted family circle. His grandfather pointed out to him that he was little better than an ingrate, and showed signs of being a wastrel as well. Gabriel said, "You had racehorses, and made a good thing of them." "I never depended upon them for a livelihood, sir," said his grandfather.

Gabriel wrote letters about this and many other things to Amy from Saratoga and from Kentucky and from New Orleans, sending her presents, and flowers packed in ice, and telegrams. The presents were amusing, such as a huge cage full of small green lovebirds; or, as an ornament for her hair, a full-petaled enameled rose with paste dewdrops, with an enameled butterfly in brillant colors suspended quivering on a gold wire about it; but the telegrams always frightened her mother, and the flowers, after a journey by train and then by stage into the country, were much the worse for wear. He would send roses when the rose garden at home was in full bloom. Amy could not help smiling over it, though her mother insisted it was touching and sweet of Gabriel. It must prove to Amy that she was always in his thoughts.

"That's no place for me," said Amy, but she had a way of speaking, a tone of voice, which made it impossible to discover what she meant by what she said. It was possible always that she might be serious. And she would not answer questions.

"Amy's wedding dress," said the grandmother, unfurling an immense cloak of dove-colored cut velvet, spreading beside it a silvery-gray watered-silk frock, and a small gray velvet toque with a dark red breast of feathers. Cousin Isabel, the beauty, sat with her. They talked to each other, and Miranda could listen if she chose.

"She would not wear white, nor a veil," said Grandmother. "I couldn't oppose her, for I had said my daughters should each have exactly the wedding dress they wanted. But Amy surprised me. 'Now what would I look like in white satin?' she asked. It's true she was pale, but she would have been angelic in it, and all of us told her so. 'I shall wear mourning if I like,' she said, 'it is *my* funeral, you know.' I reminded her that Lou and your mother had worn white with veils and it would please me to have my daughters all alike in that. Amy said, 'Lou and Isabel are not like me,' but I could not persuade her to explain what she meant. One day when she was ill she said, 'Mammy, I'm not long for this world,' but not as if she meant it. I told her, 'You might live as long as anyone, if only you will be sensible.' 'That's the whole trouble,' said Amy. 'I feel sorry for Gabriel,' she told me. 'He doesn't know what he's asking for.'

"I tried to tell her once more," said the grandmother, "that marriage and children would cure her of everything. 'All women of our family are delicate when they are young,' I said. 'Why, when I was your age no one expected me to live a year. It was called greensickness, and everybody knew there was only one cure.' 'If I live for a hundred years and turn green as grass,' said Amy, 'I still shan't want to marry Gabriel.' So I told her very seriously that if she truly felt that way she must never do it, and Gabriel must be told once for all, and sent away. He would get over it. 'I have told him, and I have sent him away,' said Amy. 'He just doesn't listen.' We both laughed at that, and I told her young girls found a hundred ways to deny they wished to be married, and a thousand more to test their power over men, but that she had more than enough of that, and now it was time for her to be entirely sincere and make her decision. As for me," said the grandmother, "I wished with all heart to marry your grandfather, and if he had not asked me, I should have asked him most certainly. Amy insisted that she could not imagine wanting to marry anybody. She would be, she said, a nice old maid like Eva Parrington. For even then it was pretty plain that Eva was an old maid, born. Harry said, 'Oh, Eva—Eva has no chin, that's her trouble. If you had no chin, Amy, you'd be in the same fix as Eva, no doubt.' Your Uncle Bill would say, 'When women haven't anything else, they'll take a vote for consolation. A pretty thin bed-fellow,' said your Uncle Bill. 'What I really need is a good dancing partner to guide me through life,' said Amy, 'that's the match I'm looking for.' It was no good trying to talk to her."

Her brothers remembered her tenderly as a sensible girl. After listening to their comments on her character and ways, Maria decided that they considered her sensible because she asked their advice about her appearance when she was going out to dance. If they found fault in any way, she would change her dress or her hair until they were pleased, and say, "You are an angel not to let your poor sister go out looking like a freak." But she would not listen to her father, nor to Gabriel. If Gabriel praised the frock she was wearing, she was apt to disappear and come back in another. He loved her long black hair, and once, lifting it up from her pillow when she was ill, said, "I love your hair, Amy, the most beautiful hair in the world." When he returned on his next visit, he found her with her hair cropped and curled close to her head. He was horrified, as if she had willfully mutilated herself. She would not let it grow again, not even to please her brothers. The photograph hanging on the wall was one she had made at that time to send to Gabriel, who sent it back without a word. This pleased her, and she framed the photograph. There was a thin inky scrawl low in one corner, "To dear brother Harry, who likes my hair cut."

This was a mischievous reference to a very grave scandal. The little girls used to look at their father, and wonder what would have happened if he had really hit the young man he shot at. The young man was believed to have kissed Aunt Amy, when she was not in the least engaged to him. Uncle Gabriel was supposed to have had a duel with the young man, but Father had got there first. He was a pleasant, everyday sort of father, who held his daughters on his knee if they were prettily dressed and well behaved, and pushed them away if they had not freshly combed hair and nicely scrubbed fingernails. "Go away, you're disgusting," he would say, in a matter-of-fact voice. He noticed if their stocking seams were crooked. He caused them to brush their teeth with a revolting mixture of prepared chalk, powdered charcoal and salt. When they behaved stupidly he could not endure the sight of them. They understood dimly that all this was for their own future good; and when they were snively with colds, he prescribed delicious hot toddy for them, and saw that it was given them. He was always hoping they might not grow up to be so silly as they seemed to him at any given moment, and he had a disconcerting way of inquiring, "How do you *know?*" when they forgot and made dogmatic statements in his presence. It always came out embarrassingly that they did not know at all, but were repeating something they had heard. This made conversation with him difficult, for he laid traps and they fell into them, but it became important to them that their father should not believe them to be fools. Well, this very father had gone to Mexico once and stayed there for nearly a year, because he had shot at a man with whom Aunt Amy had flirted at a dance. It had been very wrong of him, because he should have challenged the man to a duel, as Uncle Gabriel had done. Instead, he just took a shot at him, and this was the lowest sort of manners. It had caused great disturbance in the whole community and had almost broken up the affair between Aunt Amy and Uncle Gabriel for good. Uncle Gabriel insisted that the young man had kissed Aunt Amy, and Aunt Amy insisted that the young man had merely paid her a compliment on her hair.

During the Mardi Gras holidays there was to be a big gay fancy-dress ball. Harry was going as a bull-fighter because his sweetheart, Mariana, had a new black lace mantilla and high comb from Mexico. Maria and Miranda had seen a photograph of their mother in this dress, her lovely face without a trace of coquetry looking gravely out from under a tremendous fall of lace from the peak of the comb, a rose tucked firmly over her ear. Amy copied her costume from a small Dresden-china shepherdess which stood on the mantelpiece in the parlor; a careful copy with ribboned hat, gilded crook, very low-laced bodice, short basket skirts, green slippers and all. She wore it with a black half-mask, but it was no disguise. "You would have known it was Amy at any distance," said Father. Gabriel, six feet three in height as he was, had got himself up to match, and a spectacle he provided in pale blue satin knee breeches and a blond curled wig with a hair ribbon. "He felt a fool, and he looked like one," said Uncle Bill, "and he behaved like one before the evening was over."

Everything went beautifully until the party gathered downstairs to leave for the ball. Amy's father—he must have been born a grandfather, thought Miranda—gave one glance at his daughter, her white ankles shining, bosom deeply exposed, two round spots of paint on her cheeks, and fell into a frenzy of outraged propriety. "It's disgraceful," he pronounced, loudly. "No daughter of mine is going to show herself in such a rig-out. It's bawdy," he thundered. "Bawdy!"

Amy had taken off her mask to smile at him. "Why, Papa," she said very sweetly, "what's wrong with it? Look on the mantelpiece. She's been there all along, and you were never shocked before."

"There's all the difference in the world," said her father, "all the difference, young lady, and you know it. You go upstairs this minute and pin up that waist in front and let down those skirts to a decent length before you leave this house. *And wash your face!*"

"I see nothing wrong with it," said Amy's mother, firmly, "and you shouldn't use such language before innocent young girls." She and Amy sat down with several females of the household to help, and they made short work of the business. In ten minutes Amy returned, face clean, bodice filled in with lace, shepherdess skirt modestly sweeping the carpet behind her.

When Amy appeared from the dressing room for her first dance with Gabriel, the lace was gone from her bodice, her skirts were tucked up more daringly than before, and the spots on her cheeks were like pomegranates. "Now Gabriel, tell me truly, wouldn't it have been a pity to spoil my costume?" Gabriel, delighted that she had asked his opinion, declared it was perfect. They agreed with kindly tolerance that old people were often tiresome, but one need not upset them by open disobedience: their youth was gone, what had they to live for?

Harry, dancing with Mariana who swung a heavy train around her expertly at every turn of the waltz, began to be uneasy about his sister Amy. She was entirely too popular. He saw young men make beelines across the floor, eyes fixed on those white silk ankles. Some of the young men he did not know at all, others he knew too well and could not approve of for his sister Amy. Gabriel, unhappy in his lyric satin and wig, stood about holding his ribboned crook as though it had sprouted thorns. He hardly danced at all with Amy, he did not enjoy dancing with anyone else, and he was having a thoroughly wretched time of it.

There appeared late, alone, got up as Jean Lafitte, a young Creole gentleman who had, two years before, been for a time engaged to Amy. He came straight to her, with the manner of a happy lover, and said, clearly enough for everyone near by to hear him, "I only came because I knew you were to be here. I only want to dance with you and I shall go again." Amy, with a face of delight, cried out, "Raymond!" as if to a lover. She had danced with him four times, and had then disappeared from the floor on his arm.

Harry and Mariana, in conventional disguise of romance, irreproachably betrothed, safe in their happiness, were waltzing slowly to their favorite song, the melancholy farewell of the Moorish King on leaving Granada. They sang in whispers to each other, in their uncertain Spanish, a song of love and parting and that sword's point of grief that makes the heart tender towards all other lost and disinherited creatures: Oh, mansion of love, my earthly paradise . . . that I shall see no more . . . whither flies the poor swallow, weary and homeless, seeking for shelter where no shelter is? I too am far from home without the power to fly. . . . Come to my heart, sweet bird, beloved pilgrim, build your nest near my bed, let me listen to your song, and weep for my lost land of joy. . . .

Into this bliss broke Gabriel. He had thrown away his shepherd's crook and he was carrying his wig. He wanted to speak to Harry at once, and before Mariana knew what was happening she was sitting beside her mother and the two excited young men were gone. Waiting, disturbed and displeased, she smiled at Amy who waltzed past with a young man in Devil costume, including ill-fitting scarlet cloven hoofs. Almost at once, Harry and Gabriel came back, with serious faces, and Harry darted on the dance floor, returning with Amy. The girls and the chaperones were asked to come at once, they must be taken home. It was all mysterious and sudden, and Harry said to Mariana, "I will tell you what is happening, but not now—"

The grandmother remembered of this disgraceful affair only that Gabriel brought Amy home alone and that Harry came in somewhat later. The other members of the party straggled in at various hours, and the story came out piecemeal. Amy was silent and, her mother discovered later, burning with fever. "I saw at once that something was very wrong. 'What happened, Amy?' 'Oh, Harry goes about shooting at people at a party,' she said, sitting down as if she were exhausted. 'It was on your account, Amy,' said Gabriel. 'Oh, no, it was not,' said Amy. 'Don't believe him, Mammy.' So I said, 'Now enough of this. Tell me what happened, Amy.' And Amy said, 'Mammy, this is it. Raymond came in, and you know I like Raymond, and he is a good dancer. So we danced together, too much, maybe. We went on the gallery for a breath of air, and stood there. He said, "How well your hair looks. I like this new shingled style."' She glanced at Gabriel. 'And then another young man came out and said, "I've been looking everywhere. This is our dance, isn't it?" And I went in to dance. And now it seems that Gabriel went out at once and challenged Raymond to a duel about something or other, but Harry doesn't wait for that. Raymond had already gone out to have his horse brought, I suppose one doesn't duel in fancy dress,' she said, looking at Gabriel, who fairly shriveled in his blue satin shepherd's costume, 'and Harry simply went out and shot at him. I don't think that was fair,' said Amy."

Her mother agreed that indeed it was not fair; it was not even decent, and she could not imagine what her son Harry thought he was doing. "It isn't much of a way to defend your sister's honor," she said to him afterward. "I didn't want Gabriel to go fighting duels," said Harry. "That wouldn't have helped much, either."

Gabriel had stood before Amy, leaning over, asking once more the question he had apparently been asking her all the way home. "Did he kiss you, Amy?"

Amy took off her shepherdess hat and pushed her hair back. "Maybe he did," she answered, "and maybe I wished him to."

"Amy, you must not say such things," said her mother. "Answer Gabriel's question."

"He hasn't the right to ask it," said Amy, but without anger.

"Do you love him, Amy?" asked Gabriel, the sweat standing out on his forehead.

"It doesn't matter," answered Amy, leaning back in her chair.

"Oh, it does matter; it matters terribly," said Gabriel. "You must answer me now." He took both of her hands and tried to hold them. She drew her hands away firmly and steadily so that he had to let go.

"Let her alone, Gabriel," said Amy's mother. "You'd better go now. We are all tired. Let's talk about it tomorrow."

She helped Amy to undress, noticing the changed bodice and the shortened skirt. "You shouldn't have done that, Amy. That was not wise of you. It was better the other way."

Amy said, "Mammy, I'm sick of this world. I don't like anything in it. It's so *dull,*" she said, and for a moment she looked as if she might weep. She had never been tearful, even as a child, and her mother was alarmed. It was then she discovered that Amy had fever.

"Gabriel is dull, Mother—he sulks," she said. "I could see him sulking every time I passed. It spoils things," she said. "Oh, I want to go to sleep."

Her mother sat looking at her and wondering how it had happened she had brought such a beautiful child into the world. "Her face," said her mother, "was angelic in sleep."

Some time during that fevered night, the projected duel between Gabriel and Raymond was halted by the offices of friends on both sides. There remained the open question of Harry's impulsive shot, which was not so easily settled. Raymond seemed vindictive about that, it was possible he might choose to make trouble. Harry, taking the advice of Gabriel, his brothers and friends, decided that the best way to avoid further scandal was for him to disappear for a while. This being decided upon, the young men returned about daybreak, saddled Harry's best horse and helped him pack a few things; accompanied by Gabriel and Bill, Harry set out for the border, feeling rather gay and adventurous.

Amy, being wakened by the stirring in the house, found out the plan. Five minutes after they were gone, she came down in her riding dress, had her own horse saddled, and struck out after them. She rode almost every morning; before her parents had time to be uneasy over her prolonged absence, they found her note.

What had threatened to be a tragedy became a rowdy lark. Amy rode to the border, kissed her brother Harry good-by, and rode back again with Bill and Gabriel. It was a three days' journey, and when they arrived Amy had to be lifted from the saddle. She was really ill by now, but in the gayest of humors. Her mother and father had been prepared to be severe with her, but, at sight of her, their feelings changed. They turned on Bill and Gabriel. "Why did you let her do this?" they asked.

"You know we could not stop her," said Gabriel helplessly, "and she did enjoy herself so much!"

Amy laughed. "Mammy, it was splendid, the most delightful trip I ever had. And if I am to be the heroine of this novel, why shouldn't I make the most of it?"

The scandal, Maria and Miranda gathered, had been pretty terrible. Amy simply took to bed and stayed there, and Harry had skipped out blithely to wait until the little affair blew over. The rest of the family had to receive visitors, write letters, go to church, return calls, and bear the whole brunt, as they expressed it. They sat in the twilight of scandal in their little world, holding themselves very rigidly, in a shared tension as if all their nerves began at a common center. This center had received a blow, and family nerves shuddered, even into the farthest reaches of Kentucky. From whence in due time great-great-aunt Sally Rhea addressed a letter to *Mifs Amy Rhea*. In deep brown ink like dried blood, in a spidery hand adept at archaic symbols and abbreviations, great-great-aunt Sally informed Amy that she was fairly convinced that this calamity was only the forerunner of a series shortly to be visited by the Almighty God upon a race already condemned through its own wickedness, a warning that man's time was short, and that they must all prepare for the end of the world. For herself, she had long expected it, she was entirely resigned to the prospect of meeting her Maker; and Amy, no less than her wicked brother Harry, must likewise place herself in God's hands and prepare for the worst. *"Oh, my dear unfortunate young relative,"* twittered great-great-aunt Sally, *"we must in our Extremity join hands and appr before ye Dread Throne of Jdgmnt a United Fmly if One is Mssg from ye Flock, what will Jesus say?"*

Great-great-aunt Sally's religious career had become comic legend. She had forsaken her Catholic rearing for a young man whose family were Cumberland Presbyterians. Unable to accept their opinions, however, she was converted to the Hard-Shell Baptists, a sect as loathsome to her husband's family as the Catholic could possibly be. She had spent a life of vicious self-indulgent martyrdom to her faith; as Harry commented: "Religions put claws on Aunt Sally and gave her a post to whet them on." She had out-argued, out-fought, and out-lived her entire generation, but she did not miss them. She bedeviled the second generation without ceasing, and was beginning hungrily on the third.

Amy, reading this letter, broke into her gay full laugh that always caused everyone around her to laugh too, even before they knew why, and her small green lovebirds in their cage turned and eyed her solemnly. "Imagine drawing a pew in heaven beside Aunt Sally," she said. "What a prospect."

"Don't laugh too soon," said her father. "Heaven was made to order for Aunt Sally. She'll be on her own territory there."

"For my sins," said Amy, "I must go to heaven with Aunt Sally."

During the uncomfortable time of Harry's absence, Amy went on refusing to marry Gabriel. Her mother could hear their voices going on in their endless colloquy, during many long days. One afternoon, Gabriel came out, looking very sober and discouraged. He stood looking down at Amy's mother as she sat sewing, and said, "I think it is all over, I believe now that Amy will never have me." The grandmother always said afterward, "Never have I pitied anyone as I did poor Gabriel at that moment. But I told him, very firmly, 'Let her alone, then, she is ill.'" So Gabriel left, and Amy had no word from him for more than a month.

The day after Gabriel was gone, Amy rose looking extremely well, went hunting with her brothers Bill and Stephen, bought a velvet wrap, had her hair shingled and curled again, and wrote long letters to Harry, who was having a most enjoyable exile in Mexico City.

After dancing all night three times in one week, she woke one morning in a hemorrhage. She seemed frightened and asked for the doctor, promising to do whatever he advised. She was quiet for a few days, reading. She asked for Gabriel. No one knew where he was. "You should write him a letter; his mother will send it on." "Oh, no," she said. "I miss him coming in with his sour face. Letters are no good."

Gabriel did come in, only a few days later, with a very sour face and unpleasant news. His grandfather had died, after a day's illness. On his death bed, in the name of God, being of a sound and disposing mind, he had cut off his favorite grandchild Gabriel with one dollar. "In the name of God, Amy," said Gabriel, "the old devil has ruined me in one sentence."

It was the conduct of his immediate family in the matter that had embittered him, he said. They could hardly conceal their satisfaction. They had known and envied Gabriel's quite just, well-founded expectations. Not one of them offered to make any private settlement. No one even thought of repairing this last-minute act of senile vengeance. Privately they blessed their luck. "I have been cut off with a dollar," said Gabriel, "and they are all glad of it. I think they feel somehow that this justifies every criticism they ever made against me. They were right about me all along. I am a worthless poor relation," said Gabriel. "My God, I wish you could see them."

Amy said, "I wonder how you will ever support a wife, now."

Gabriel said, "Oh, it isn't so bad as that. If you would, Amy—"

Amy said, "Gabriel, if we get married now there'll be just time to be in New Orleans for Mardi Gras. If we wait until after Lent, it may be too late."

"Why, Amy," said Gabriel, "how could it ever be too late?"

"You might change your mind," said Amy. "You know how fickle you are."

There were two letters in the grandmother's many packets of letters that Maria and Miranda read after they were grown. One of them was from Amy. It was dated ten days after her marriage.

"Dear Mammy, New Orleans hasn't changed as much as I have since we saw each other last. I am now a staid old married woman, and Gabriel is very devoted and kind. Footlights won a race for us yesterday, she was the favorite, and it was wonderful. I go to the races every day, and our horses are doing splendidly; I had my choice of Erin Go Bragh or Miss Lucy, and I chose Miss Lucy. She is mine now, she runs like ·a streak. Gabriel says I made a mistake, Erin Go Bragh will stay better. I think Miss Lucy will stay my time.

"We are having a lovely visit. I'm going to put on a domino and take to the streets with Gabriel sometime during Mardi Gras. I'm tired of watching the show from a balcony. Gabriel says it isn't safe. He says he'll take me if I insist, but I doubt it. Mammy, he's very nice. Don't worry about me. I have a beautiful black-and-rose-colored velvet gown for the Proteus Ball. Madame, my new mother-in-law, wanted to know if it wasn't a little dashing. I told her I hoped so or I had been cheated. It is fitted perfectly smooth in the bodice, very low in the shoulders—Papa would not approve— and the skirt is looped with wide silver ribbons between the waist and knees in front, and then it surges around and is looped enormously in the back, with a train just one yard long. I now have an eighteen-inch waist, thanks to Madame Duré. I expect to be so dashing that my mother-in-law will have an attack. She has them quite often. Gabriel sends love. Please take good care of Graylie and Fiddler. I want to ride them again when I come home. We're going to Saratoga, I don't know just when. Give everybody my dear dear love. It rains all the time here, of course. . . .

"P.S. Mammy, as soon as I get a minute to myself I'm going to be terribly homesick. Good-by, my darling Mammy."

The other was from Amy's nurse, dated six weeks after Amy's marriage.

"I cut off the lock of hair because I was sure you would like to have it. And I do not want you to think I was careless, leaving her medicine where she could get it, the doctor has written and explained. It would not have done her any harm except that her heart was weak. She did not know how much she was taking, often she said to me, one more of those little capsules wouldn't do any harm, and so I told her to be careful and not take anything except what I gave her. She begged me for them sometimes but I would not give her more than the doctor said. I slept during the night because she did not seem to be so sick as all that and the doctor did not order me to sit up with her. Please accept my regrets for your great loss and please do not think that anybody was careless with your dear daughter. She suffered a great deal and now she is at rest. She could not get well but she might have lived longer. Yours respectfully. . . ."

The letters and all the strange keepsakes were packed away and forgotten for a great many years. They seemed to have no place in the world.

Part II: 1904

During vacation on their grandmother's farm, Maria and Miranda, who read as naturally and constantly as ponies crop grass, and with much the same kind of pleasure, had by some happy chance laid hold of some forbidden reading matter, brought in and left there with missionary intent, no doubt, by some Protestant cousin. It fell into the right hands if enjoyment had been its end. The reading matter was printed in poor type on spongy paper, and was ornamented with smudgy illustrations all the more exciting to the little girls because they could not make head or tail of them. The stories were about beautiful but unlucky maidens, who for mysterious reasons had been trapped by nuns and priests in dire collusion; they were then "immured" in convents, where they were forced to take the veil—an appalling rite during which the victims shrieked dreadfully—and condemned forever after to most uncomfortable and disorderly existences. They seemed to divide their time between lying chained in dark cells and assisting other nuns to bury throttled infants under stones in moldering rat-infested dungeons.

Immured! It was the word Maria and Miranda had been needing all along to describe their condition at the Convent of the Child Jesus, in New Orleans, where they spent the long winters trying to avoid an education. There were no dungeons at the Child Jesus, and this was only one of numerous marked differences between convent life as Maria and Miranda knew it and the thrilling paper-backed version. It was no good at all trying to fit the stories to life, and they did not even try. They had long since learned to draw the lines between life, which was real and earnest, and the grave was not its goal; poetry, which was true but not real; and stories, or forbidden reading matter, in which things happened as nowhere else, with the most sublime irrelevance and unlikelihood, and one need not turn a hair, because there was not a word of truth in them.

It was true the little girls were hedged and confined, but in a large garden with trees and a grotto; they were locked at night into a long cold dormitory, with all the windows open, and a sister sleeping at either end. Their beds were curtained with muslin, and small night-lamps were so arranged that the sisters could see through the curtains, but the children could not see the sisters. Miranda wondered if they ever slept, or did they sit there all night quietly watching the sleepers through the muslin? She tried to work up a little sinister thrill about this, but she found it impossible to care much what either of the sisters did. They were very dull good-natured women who managed to make the whole dormitory seem dull. All days and all things in the Convent of the Child Jesus were dull, in fact, and Maria and Miranda lived for Saturdays.

No one had even hinted that they should become nuns. On the contrary Miranda felt that the discouraging attitude of Sister Claude and Sister Austin and Sister Ursula towards her expressed ambition to be a nun barely veiled a deeply critical knowledge of her spiritual deficiencies. Still Maria and Miranda had got a fine new word out of their summer reading, and they referred to themselves as "immured." It gave a romantic glint to what was otherwise a very dull life for them, except for blessed Saturday afternoons during the racing season.

If the nuns were able to assure the family that the deportment and scholastic achievements of Maria and Miranda were at least passable, some cousin or other always showed up smiling, in holiday mood, to take them to the races, where they were given a doillar each to bet on any horse they chose. There were black Saturdays now and then, when Maria and Miranda sat ready, hats in hand, curly hair plastered down and slicked behind their ears, their stiffly pleated navy-blue skirts spread out around them, waiting with their hearts going down slowly into their high-topped laced-up black shoes. They never put on their hats until the last minute, for somehow it would have been too horrible to have their hats on, when, after all, Cousin Henry and Cousin Isabel, or Uncle George and Aunt Polly, were not coming to take them to the races. When no one appeared, and Saturday came and went a sickening waste, they were then given to understand that it was a punishment for bad marks during the week. They never knew until it was too late to avoid the disappointment. It was very wearing.

One Saturday they were sent down to wait in the visitors' parlor, and there was their father. He had come all the way from Texas to see them. They leaped at sight of him, and then stopped short, suspiciously. Was he going to take them to the races? If so, they were happy to see him.

"Hello," said father, kissing their cheeks. "Have you been good girls? Your Uncle Gabriel is running a mare at the Crescent City today, so we'll all go and bet on her. Would you like that?"

Maria put on her hat without a word, but Miranda stood and addressed her father sternly. She had suffered many doubts about this day. "*Why* didn't you send word yesterday? I could have been looking forward all this time."

"We didn't know," said father, in his easiest paternal manner, "that you were going to deserve it. Remember Saturday before last?"

Miranda hung her head and put on her hat, with the round elastic under the chin. She remembered too well. She had, in midweek, given way to despair over her arithmetic and had fallen flat on her face on the classroom floor, refusing to rise until she was carried out. The rest of the week had been a series of novel deprivations, and Saturday a day of mourning; secret mourning, for if one mourned too noisily, it simply meant another bad mark against deportment.

"Never mind," said father, as if it were the smallest possible matter, "today you're going. Come along now. We've barely time."

These expeditions were all joy, every time, from the moment they stepped into a closed one-horse cab, a treat in itself with its dark, thick upholstery, soaked with strange perfumes and tobacco smoke, until the thrilling moment when they walked into a restaurant under big lights and were given dinner with things to eat they never had at home, much less at the convent. They felt worldly and grown up, each with her glass of water colored pink with claret.

The great crowd was always exciting as if they had never seen it before, with the beautiful, incredibly dressed ladies, all plumes and flowers and paint, and the elegant gentlemen with yellow gloves. The bands played in turn with thundering drums and brasses, and now and then a wild beautiful horse would career around the track with a tiny, monkey-shaped boy on his back, limbering up for his race.

Miranda had a secret personal interest in all this which she knew better than to confide to anyone, even Maria. Least of all to Maria. In ten minutes the whole family would have known. She had lately decided to be a jockey when she grew up. Her father had said one day that she was going to be a little thing all her life, she would never be tall; and this meant, of course, that she would never be a beauty like Aunt Amy, or Cousin Isabel. Her hope of being a beauty died hard, until the notion of being a jockey came suddenly and filled all her thoughts. Quietly, blissfully, at night before she slept, and too often in the daytime when she should have been studying, she planned her career as jockey. It was dim in detail, but brilliant at the right distance. It seemed too silly to be worried about arithmetic at all, when what she needed for her future was to ride better—much better. "You ought to be ashamed of yourself," said father, after watching her gallop full tilt down the lane at the farm, on Trixie, the mustang mare. "I can see the sun, moon and stars between you and the saddle every jump." Spanish style meant that one sat close to the saddle, and did all kinds of things with the knees and reins. Jockeys bounced lightly, their knees almost level with the horse's back, rising and falling like a rubber ball. Miranda felt she could do that easily. Yes, she would be a jockey, like Tod Sloan, winning every other race at least. Meantime, while she was training, she would keep it a secret, and one day she would ride out, bouncing lightly, with the other jockeys, and win a great race, and surprise everybody, her family most of all.

On that particular Saturday, her idol, the great Tod Sloan, was riding, and he won two races. Miranda longed to bet her dollar on Tod Sloan, but father said, "Not now, honey. Today you must bet on Uncle Gabriel's horse. Save your dollar for the fourth race, and put it on Miss Lucy. You've got a hundred to one shot. Think if she wins."

Miranda knew well enough that a hundred to one shot was no bet at all. She sulked, the crumpled dollar in her hand grew damp and warm. She could have won three dollars already on Tod Sloan. Maria said virtuously, "It wouldn't be nice not to bet on Uncle Gabriel. That way, we keep the money in the family." Miranda put out her under lip at her sister. Maria was too prissy for words. She wrinkled her nose back at Miranda.

They had just turned their dollar over to the bookmaker for the fourth race when a vast bulging man with a red face and immense tan ragged mustaches fading into gray hailed them from a lower level of the grandstand, over the heads of the crowd, "Hey, there, Harry?" Father said, "Bless my soul, there's Gabriel." He motioned to the man, who came pushing his way heavily up the shallow steps. Maria and Miranda stared, first at him, then at each other. "Can that be our Uncle Gabriel?" their eyes asked. "Is that Aunt Amy's handsome romantic beau? Is that the man who wrote the poem about our Aunt Amy?" Oh, what did grown-up people *mean* when they talked, anyway?

He was a shabby fat man with bloodshot blue eyes, sad beaten eyes, and a big melancholy laugh, like a groan. He towered over them shouting to their father, "Well, for God's sake, Harry, it's been a coon's age. You ought to come out and look 'em over. You look just like yourself, Harry, how are you?"

The band struck up "Over the River" and Uncle Gabriel shouted louder. "Come on, let's get out of this. What are you doing up here with the pikers?"

"Can't," shouted Father. "Brought my little girls. Here they are."

Uncle Gabriel's bleared eyes beamed blindly upon them. "Fine looking set, Harry," he bellowed, "pretty as pictures, how old are they?"

"Ten and fourteen now," said Father; "awkward ages. Nest of vipers," he boasted, "perfect batch of serpent's teeth. Can't do a thing with 'em." He fluffed up Miranda's hair, pretending to tousle it.

"Pretty as pictures," bawled Uncle Gabriel, "but rolled into one they don't come up to Amy, do they?"

"No, they don't," admitted their father at the top of his voice, "but they're only half-baked." *Over the river, over the river,* moaned the band, *my sweetheart's waiting for me.*

"I've got to get back now," yelled Uncle Gabriel. The little girls felt quite deaf and confused. "Got the God-damnedest jockey in the world, Harry, just my luck. Ought to tie him on. Fell off Fiddler yesterday, just plain fell off on his tail— Remember Amy's mare, Miss Lucy? Well, this is her namesake, Miss Lucy IV. None of 'em ever came up to the first one, though. Stay right where you are, I'll be back."

Maria spoke up boldly. "Uncle Gabriel, tell Miss Lucy we're betting on her." Uncle Gabriel bent down and it looked as if there were tears in his swollen eyes. "God bless your sweet heart," he bellowed, "I'll tell her." He plunged down through the crowd again, his fat back bowed slightly in his loose clothes, his thick neck rolling over his collar.

Miranda and Maria, disheartened by the odds, by their first sight of their romantic Uncle Gabriel, whose language was so coarse, sat listlessly without watching, their chances missed, their dollars gone, their hearts sore. They didn't even move until their father leaned over and hauled them up. "Watch your horse," he said, in a quick warning voice, "watch Miss Lucy come home."

They stood up, scrambled to their feet on the bench, every vein in them suddenly beating so violently they could hardly focus their eyes, and saw a thin little mahogany-colored streak flash by the judges' stand, only a neck ahead, but their Miss Lucy, oh, their darling, their lovely—oh, Miss Lucy, their Uncle's Gabriel's Miss Lucy, had won, had won. They leaped up and down screaming and clapping their hands, their hats falling back on their shoulders, their hair flying wild. *Whoa, you heifer,* squalled the band with snorting brasses, and the crowd broke into a long roar like the falling of the walls of Jericho.

The little girls sat down, feeling quite dizzy, while their father tried to pull their hats straight, and taking out his handkerchief held it to Miranda's face, saying very gently, "Here, blow your nose," and he dried her eyes while he was about it. He stood up then and shook them out of their daze. He was smiling with deep laughing wrinkles around his eyes, and spoke to them as if they were grown young ladies he was squiring around.

"Let's go out and pay our respects to Miss Lucy," he said. "She's the star of the day."

The horses were coming in, looking as if their hides had been drenched and rubbed with soap, their ribs heaving, their nostrils flaring and closing. The jockeys sat bowed and relaxed, their faces calm, moving a little at the waist with the movement of their horses. Miranda noted this for future use; that was the way you came in from a race, easy and quiet, whether you had won or lost. Miss Lucy came last, and a little handful of winners applauded her and cheered the jockey. He smiled and lifted his whip, his eyes and shriveled brown face perfectly serene. Miss Lucy was bleeding at the nose, two thick red rivulets were stiffening her tender mouth and chin, the round velvet chin that Miranda thought the nicest kind of chin in the world. Her eyes were wild and her knees were trembling, and she snored when she drew her breath.

Miranda stood staring. That was winning, too. Her heart clinched tight; that was winning, for Miss Lucy. So instantly and completely did her heart reject that victory, she did not know when it happened, but she hated it, and was ashamed that she had screamed and shed tears of joy when Miss Lucy, with her bloodied nose and bursting heart, had gone past the judges' stand a neck ahead. She felt empty and sick and held to her father's hand so hard that he shook her off a little impatiently and said, "What is the matter with you? Don't be so fidgety."

Uncle Gabriel was standing there waiting, and he was completely drunk. He watched the mare go in, then leaned against the fence with its white-washed posts and sobbed openly. "She's got the nosebleed, Harry," he said. "Had it since yesterday. We thought we had her all fixed up. But she did it, all right. She's got a heart like a lion. I'm going to breed her, Harry. Her heart's worth a million dollars, by itself, God bless her." Tears ran over his brick-colored face and into his straggling mustaches. "If anything happens to her now I'll blow my brains out. She's my last hope. She saved my life. I've had a run," he said, groaning into a large handkerchief and mopping his face all over, "I've had a run of luck that would break a brass billy goat. God, Harry, let's go somewhere and have a drink."

"I must get the children back to school first, Gabriel," said their father, taking each by a hand.

"No, no, don't go yet," said Uncle Gabriel desperately. "Wait here a minute, I want to see the vet and take a look at Miss Lucy, and I'll be right back. Don't go, Harry, for God's sake. I want to talk to you a few minutes."

Maria and Miranda, watching Uncle Gabriel's lumbering, unsteady back, were thinking that this was the first time they had ever seen a man that they knew to be drunk. They had seen pictures and read descriptions, and had heard descriptions, so they recognized the symptoms at once. Miranda felt it was an important moment in a great many ways.

"Uncle Gabriel's a drunkard, isn't he?" she asked her father, rather proudly.

"Hush, don't say such things," said father, with a heavy frown, "or I'll never bring you here again." He looked worried and unhappy, and, above all, undecided. The little girls stood stiff with resentment against such obvious injustice. They loosed their hands from his and moved away coldly, standing together in silence. Their father did not notice, watching the place where Uncle Gabriel had disappeared. In a few minutes he came back, still wiping his face, as if there were cobwebs on it, carrying his big black hat. He waved at them from a short distance, calling out in a cheerful way, "She's going to be all right, Harry. It's stopped now. Lord, this will be good news for Miss Honey. Come on, Harry, let's all go home and tell Miss Honey. She deserves some good news."

Father said, "I'd better take the children back to school first, then we'll go."

"No, no," said Uncle Gabriel, fondly. "I want her to see the girls. She'll be tickled pink to see them, Harry. Bring 'em along."

"Is it another race horse we're going to see?" whispered Miranda in her sister's ear.

"Don't be silly," said Maria. "It's Uncle Gabriel's second wife."

"Let's find a cab, Harry," said Uncle Gabriel, "and take your little girls out to cheer up Miss Honey. Both of 'em rolled into one look a lot like Amy, I swear they do. I want Miss Honey to see them. She's always liked our family, Harry, though of course she's not what you'd call an expansive kind of woman."

Maria and Miranda sat facing the driver, and Uncle Gabriel squeezed himself in facing them beside their father. The air became at once bitter and sour with his breathing. He looked sad and poor. His necktie was on crooked and his shirt was rumpled. Father said, "You're going to see Uncle Gabriel's second wife, children," exactly as if they had not heard everything; and to Gabriel, "How *is* your wife nowadays? It must be twenty years since I saw her last."

"She's pretty gloomy, and that's a fact," said Uncle Gabriel. "She's been pretty gloomy for years now, and nothing seems to shake her out of it. She never did care for horses, Harry, if you remember; she hasn't been near the track three times since we were married. When I think how Amy wouldn't have missed a race for anything . . . She's very different from Amy, Harry, a very different kind of woman. As fine a woman as ever lived in her own way, but she hates change and moving around, and she just lives in the boy."

"Where is Gabe now?" asked father.

"Finishing college," said Uncle Gabriel; "a smart boy, but awfully like his mother. Awfully like," he said, in a melancholy way. "She hates being away from him. Just wants to sit down in the same town and wait for him to get through with his education. Well, I'm sorry it can't be done if that's what she wants, but God Almighty— And this last run of luck has about got her down. I hope you'll be able to cheer her up a little, Harry, she needs it."

The little girls sat watching the streets grow duller and dingier and narrower, and at last the shabbier and shabbier white people gave way to dressed-up Negroes, and then to shabby Negroes, and after a long way the cab stopped before a desolate-looking little hotel in Elysian Fields. Their father helped Maria and Miranda out, told the cabman to wait, and they followed Uncle Gabriel through a dirty damp-smelling patio, down a long gaslighted hall full of a terrible smell, Miranda couldn't decide what it was made of but it had a bitter taste even, and up a long staircase with a ragged carpet. Uncle Gabriel pushed open a door without warning, saying, "Come in, here we are."

A tall pale-faced woman with faded straw-colored hair and pink-rimmed eyelids rose suddenly from a squeaking rocking chair. She wore a stiff blue-and-white-striped shirtwaist and a stiff black skirt of some hard shiny material. Her large knuckled hands rose to her round, neat pompadour at sight of her visitors.

"Honey," said Uncle Gabriel, with large false heartiness, "you'll never guess who's come to see you." He gave her a clumsy hug. Her face did not change and her eyes rested steadily on the three strangers. "Amy's brother Harry, Honey, you remember, don't you?"

"Of course," said Miss Honey, putting out her hand straight as a paddle, "of course I remember you, Harry." She did not smile.

"And Amy's two little nieces," went on Uncle Gabriel, bringing them forward. They put out their hands limply, and Miss Honey gave each one a slight flip and dropped it. "And we've got good news for you," went on Uncle Gabriel, trying to bolster up the painful situation. "Miss Lucy stepped out and showed 'em today, Honey. We're rich again, old girl, cheer up."

Miss Honey turned her long, despairing face towards her visitors. "Sit down," she said with a heavy sigh, seating herself and motioning towards various rickety chairs. There was a big lumpy bed, with a grayish-white counterpane on it, a marble-topped washstand, grayish coarse lace curtains on strings at the two small windows, a small closed fireplace with a hole in it for a stovepipe, and two trunks, standing at odds as if somebody were just moving in, or just moving out. Everything was dingy and soiled and neat and bare; not a pin out of place.

"We'll move to the St. Charles tomorrow," said Uncle Gabriel, as much to Harry as to his wife. "Get your best dresses together, Honey, the long dry spell is over."

Miss Honey's nostrils pinched together and she rocked slightly, with her arms folded. "I've lived in the St. Charles before, and I've lived here before," she said, in a tight deliberate voice, "and this time I'll just stay where I am, thank you. I prefer it to moving back here in three months. I'm settled now, I feel at home here," she told him, glancing at Harry, her pale eyes kindling with blue fire, a stiff white line around her mouth.

The little girls sat trying not to stare, miserably ill at ease. Their grandmother had pronounced Harry's children to be the most unteachable she had ever seen in her long experience with the young; but they had learned by indirection one thing well—nice people did not carry on quarrels before outsiders. Family quarrels were sacred, to be waged privately in fierce hissing whispers, low choked mutters and growls. If they did yell and stamp, it must be behind closed doors and windows. Uncle Gabriel's second wife was hopping mad and she looked ready to fly out at Uncle Gabriel any second, with him sitting there like a hound when someone shakes a whip at him.

"She loathes and despises everybody in this room," thought Miranda, coolly, "and she's afraid we won't know it. She needn't worry, we knew it when we came in." With all her heart she wanted to go, but her father, though his face was a study, made no move. He seemed to be trying to think of something pleasant to say. Maria, feeling guilty, though she couldn't think why, was calculating rapidly, "Why, she's only Uncle Gabriel's second wife, and Uncle Gabriel was only married before to Aunt Amy, why, she's no kin at all, and I'm glad of it." Sitting back easily, she let her hands fall open in her lap; they would be going in a few minutes, undoubtedly, and they need never come back.

Then father said, "We mustn't be keeping you, we just dropped in for a few minutes. We wanted to see how you are."

Miss Honey said nothing, but she made a little gesture with her hands, from the wrist, as if to say, "Well, you see how I am, and now what next?"

"I must take these young ones back to school," said father, and Uncle Gabriel said stupidly, "Look, Honey, don't you think they resemble Amy a little? Especially around the eyes, especially Maria, don't you think, Harry?"

Their father glanced at them in turn. "I really couldn't say," he decided, and the little girls saw he was more monstrously embarrassed than ever. He turned to Miss Honey, "I hadn't seen Gabriel for so many years," he said, "we thought of getting out for a talk about old times together. You know how it is."

"Yes, I know," said Miss Honey, rocking a little, and all that she knew gleamed forth in a pallid, unquenchable hatred and bitterness that seemed enough to bring her long body straight up out of the chair in a fury, "I know," and she sat staring at the floor. Her mouth shook and straightened. There was a terrible silence, which was broken when the little girls saw their father rise. They got up, too, and it was all they could do to keep from making a dash for the door.

"I must get the young ones back," said their father. "They've had enough excitement for one day. They each won a hundred dollars on Miss Lucy. It was a good race," he said, in complete wretchedness, as if he simply could not extricate himself from the situation. "Wasn't it, Gabriel?"

"It was a grand race," said Gabriel, brokenly, "a grand race."

Miss Honey stood up and moved a step towards the door. "Do you take them to the races, actually?" she asked, and her lids flickered towards them as if they were loathsome insects, Maria felt.

"If I feel they deserve a little treat, yes," said their father, in an easy tone but with wrinkled brow.

"I had rather, much rather," said Miss Honey clearly, "see my son dead at my feet than hanging around a race track."

The next few moments were rather a blank, but at last they were out of it, going down the stairs, across the patio, with Uncle Gabriel seeing them back into the cab. His face was sagging, the features had fallen as if the flesh had slipped from the bones, and his eyelids were puffed and blue. "Good-by, Harry," he said soberly. "How long you expect to be here?"

"Starting back tomorrow," said Harry. "Just dropped in on a little business and to see how the girls were getting along."

"Well," said Uncle Gabriel, "I may be dropping into your part of the country one of these days. Good-by, children," he said, taking their hands one after the other in his big warm paws. "They're nice children, Harry. I'm glad you won on Miss Lucy," he said to the little girls, tenderly. "Don't spend your money foolishly, now. Well, so long, Harry." As the cab jolted away he stood there fat and sagging, holding up his arm and wagging his hand at them.

"Goodness," said Maria, in her most grown-up manner, taking her hat off and hanging it over her knee, "I'm glad that's over."

"What I want to know is," said Miranda, "*is* Uncle Gabriel a real drunkard?"

"Oh, hush," said their father, sharply, "I've got the heartburn."

There was a respectful pause, as before a public monument. When their father had the heartburn it was time to lay low. The cab rumbled on, back to clean gay streets, with the lights coming on in the early February darkness, past shimmering shop windows, smooth pavements, on and on, past beautiful old houses set in deep gardens, on, on back to the dark walls with the heavy-topped trees hanging over them. Miranda sat thinking so hard she forgot and spoke out in her thoughtless way: "I've decided I'm not going to be a jockey, after all." She could as usual have bitten her tongue, but as usual it was too late.

Father cheered up and twinkled at her knowingly, as if that didn't surprise him in the least. "Well, well," said he, "so you aren't going to be a jockey! That's very sensible of you. I think she ought to be a lion-tamer, don't you, Maria? That's a nice, womanly profession."

Miranda, seeing Maria from the height of her fourteen years suddenly joining with their father to laugh at her, made an instant decision and laughed with them at herself. That was better. Everybody laughed and it was such a relief.

"Where's my hundred dollars?" asked Maria, anxiously.

"It's going in the bank," said their father, "and yours too," he told Miranda. "That is your nest-egg."

"Just so they don't buy my stockings with it," said Miranda, who had long resented the use of her Christmas money by their grandmother. "I've got enough stockings to last me a year."

"I'd like to buy a racehorse," said Maria, "but I know it's not enough." The limitations of wealth oppressed her. "*What* could you buy with a hundred dollars?" she asked fretfully.

"Nothing, nothing at all," said their father, "a hundred dollars is just something you put in the bank."

Maria and Miranda lost interest. They had won a hundred dollars on a horse race once. It was already in the far past. They began to chatter about something else.

The lay sister opened the door on a long cord, from behind the grille; Maria and Miranda walked in silently to their familiar world of shining bare floors and insipid wholesome food and cold-water washing and regular prayers; their world of poverty, chastity and obedience, of early to bed and early to rise, of sharp little rules and tittle-tattle. Resignation was in their childish faces as they held them up to be kissed.

"Be good girls," said their father, in the strange serious, rather helpless way he always had when he told them good-by. "Write to your daddy, now, nice long letters," he said, holding their arms firmly for a moment before letting go for good. Then he disappeared, and the sister swung the door closed after him.

Maria and Miranda went upstairs to the dormitory to wash their faces and hands and slick down their hair again before supper.

Miranda was hungry. "We didn't have a thing to eat, after all," she grumbled. "Not even a chocolate nut bar. I think that's mean. We didn't even get a quarter to spend," she said.

"Not a living bite," said Maria. "Not a nickel." She poured out cold water into the bowl and rolled up her sleeves.

Another girl about her own age came in and went to a washbowl near another bed. "Where have you been?" she asked. "Did you have a good time?"

"We went to the races, with our father," said Maria, soaping her hands.

"Our uncle's horse won," said Miranda.

"My goodness," said the other girl, vaguely, "that must have been grand."

Maria looked at Miranda, who was rolling up her own sleeves. She tried to feel martyred, but it wouldn't go. "Immured for another week," she said, her eyes sparkling over the edge of her towel.

Part III: 1912

Miranda followed the porter down the stuffy aisle of the sleeping-car, where the berths were nearly all made down and the dusty green curtains buttoned to a seat at the further end. "Now yo' berth's ready any time, Miss," said the porter.

"But I want to sit up a while," said Miranda. A very thin old lady raised choleric black eyes and fixed upon her a regard of unmixed disapproval. She had two immense front teeth and a receding chin, but she did not lack character. She had piled her luggage around her like a barricade, and she glared at the porter when he picked some of it up to make room for his new passenger. Miranda sat, saying mechanically, "May I?"

"You may, indeed," said the old lady, for she seemed old in spite of a certain brisk, rustling energy. Her taffeta petticoats creaked like hinges every time she stirred. With ferocious sarcasm, after a half second's pause, she added, "You may be so good as to get off my hat!"

Miranda rose instantly in horror, and handed to the old lady a wilted contrivance of black horsehair braid and shattered white poppies. "I'm dreadfully sorry," she stammered, for she had been brought up to treat ferocious old ladies respectfully, and this one seemed capable of spanking her, then and there. "I didn't dream it was your hat."

"And whose hat did you dream it might be?" inquired the old lady, baring her teeth and twirling the hat on a forefinger to restore it.

"I didn't think it was a hat at all," said Miranda with a touch of hysteria.

"Oh, you didn't think it was a hat? Where on earth are your eyes, child?" and she proved the nature and function of the object by placing it on her head at a somewhat tipsy angle, though still it did not much resemble a hat. "Now can you see what it is?"

"Yes, oh, yes," said Miranda, with a meekness she hoped was disarming. She ventured to sit again after a careful inspection of the narrow space she was to occupy.

"Well, well," said the old lady, "let's have the porter remove some of these encumbrances," and she stabbed the bell with a lean sharp forefinger. There followed a flurry of rearrangements, during which they both stood in the aisle, the old lady giving a series of impossible directions to the Negro which he bore philosophically while he disposed of the luggage exactly as he had meant to do. Seated again, the old lady asked in a kindly, authoritative tone, "And what might your name be, child?"

At Miranda's answer, she blinked somewhat, unfolded her spectacles, straddled them across her high nose competently, and took a good long look at the face beside her.

"If I'd had my spectacles on," she said, in an astonishingly changed voice, "I might have known. I'm Cousin Eva Parrington," she said, "Cousin Molly Parrington's daughter, remember? I knew you when you were a little girl. You were a lively little girl," she added as if to console her, "and very opinionated. The last thing I heard about you, you were planning to be a tight-rope walker. You were going to play the violin and walk the tight-rope at the same time."

"I must have seen it at the vaudeville show," said Miranda. "I couldn't have invented it. Now I'd like to be an air pilot!"

"I used to go to dances with your father," said Cousin Eva, busy with her own thoughts, "and to big holiday parties at your grandmother's house, long before you were born. Oh, indeed, yes, a long time before."

Miranda remembered several things at once. Aunt Amy had threatened to be an old maid like Eva. Oh, Eva, the trouble with her is she has no chin. Eva has given up, and is teaching Latin in a Female Seminary. Eva's gone out for votes for women, God help her. The nice thing about an ugly daughter is, she's not apt to make me a grandmother. . . . "They didn't do you much good, those parties, dear Cousin Eva," thought Miranda.

"They didn't do me much good, those parties," said Cousin Eva aloud as if she were a mind-reader, and Miranda's head swam for a moment with fear that she had herself spoken aloud. "Or at least, they didn't serve their purpose, for I never got married; but I enjoyed them, just the same. I had a good time at those parties, even if I wasn't a belle. And so you are Harry's child, and here I was quarreling with you. You do remember me, don't you?"

"Yes," said Miranda, and thinking that even if Cousin Eva had been really an old maid ten years before, still she couldn't be much past fifty now, and she looked so withered and tired, so famished and sunken in the cheeks, so *old,* somehow. Across the abyss separating Cousin Eva from her own youth, Miranda looked with painful premonition. "Oh, must I ever be like that?" She said aloud, "Yes, you used to read Latin to me, and tell me not to bother about the sense, to get the sound in my mind, and it would come easier later."

"Ah, so I did," said Cousin Eva, delighted. "So I did. You don't happen to remember that I once had a beautiful sapphire velvet dress with a train on it?"

"No, I don't remember that dress," said Miranda.

"It was an old dress of my mother's made over and cut down to fit," said Eva, "and it wasn't in the least becoming to me, but it was the only really good dress I ever had, and I remember it as if it were yesterday. Blue was never my color." She sighed with a humorous bitterness. The humor seemed momentary, but the bitterness was a constant state of mind.

Miranda, trying to offer the sympathy of fellow suffering, said, "I know. I've had Maria's dresses made over for me, and they were never right. It was dreadful."

"Well," said Cousin Eva, in the tone of one who did not wish to share her unique disappointments. "How is your father? I always liked him. He was one of the finest-looking young men I ever saw. Vain, too, like all his family. He wouldn't ride any but the best horses he could buy, and I used to say he made them prance and then watched his own shadow. I used to tell this on him at dinner parties, and he hated me for it. I feel pretty certain he hated me." An overtone of complacency in Cousin Eva's voice explained better than words that she had her own method of commanding attention and arousing emotion. "How *is* your father, I asked you, my dear?"

"I haven't seen him for nearly a year," answered Miranda, quickly, before Cousin Eva could get ahead again. "I'm going home now to Uncle Gabriel's funeral; you know, Uncle Gabriel died in Lexington and they have brought him back to be buried beside Aunt Amy."

"So that's how we meet," said Cousin Eva. "Yes, Gabriel drank himself to death at last. I'm going to the funeral, too. I haven't been home since I went to Mother's funeral, it must be, let's see, yes, it will be nine years next

July. I'm going to Gabriel's funeral, though. I wouldn't miss that. Poor fellow, what a life he had. Pretty soon, they'll all be gone."

Miranda said, "We're left, Cousin Eva," meaning those of her own generation, the young, and Cousin Eva said, "Pshaw, you'll live forever, and you won't bother to come to our funerals." She didn't seem to think this was a misfortune, but flung the remark from her like a woman accustomed to saying what she thought.

Miranda sat thinking, "Still, I suppose it would be pleasant if I could say something to make her believe that she and all of them would be lamented, but—but—" With a smile which she hoped would be her denial of Cousin Eva's cynicism about the younger generation, she said, "You were right about the Latin, Cousin Eva, your reading did help when I began with it. I still study," she said. "Latin, too."

"And why shouldn't you?" asked Cousin Eva, sharply, adding at once mildly, "I'm glad you are going to use your mind a little, child. Don't let yourself rust away. Your mind outwears all sorts of things you may set your heart upon; you can enjoy it when all other things are taken away." Miranda was chilled by her melancholy. Cousin Eva went on: "In our part of the country, in my time, we were so provincial—a woman didn't dare to think or act for herself. The whole world was a little that way," she said, "but we were the worst, I believe. I suppose you must know how I fought for votes for women when it almost made a pariah of me—I was turned out of my chair at the Seminary, but I'm glad I did it and I would do it again. You young things don't realize. You'll live in a better world because we worked for it."

Miranda knew something of Cousin Eva's career. She said sincerely, "I think it was brave of you, and I'm glad you did it, too. I loved your courage."

"It wasn't just showing off, mind you," said Cousin Eva, rejecting praise, fretfully. "Any fool can be brave. We were working for something we knew was right, and it turned out that we needed a lot of courage for it. That was all. I didn't expect to go to jail, but I went three times, and I'd go three times three more if it were necessary. We aren't voting yet," she said, "but we will be."

Miranda did not venture any answer, but she felt convinced that indeed women would be voting soon if nothing fatal happened to Cousin Eva. There was something in her manner which said such things could be left safely to her. Miranda was dimly fired for the cause herself; it seemed heroic and worth suffering for, but discouraging, too, to those who came after: Cousin Eva so plainly had swept the field clear of opportunity.

They were silent for a few minutes, while Cousin Eva rummaged in her handbag, bringing up odds and ends: peppermint drops, eye drops, a packet of needles, three handkerchiefs, a little bottle of violet perfume, a book of addresses, two buttons, one black, one white, and, finally, a packet of headache powders.

"Bring me a glass of water, will you, my dear?" she asked Miranda. She poured the headache powder on her tongue, swallowed the water, and put two peppermints in her mouth.

"So now they're going to bury Gabriel near Amy," she said after a while, as if her eased headache had started her on a new train of thought. "Miss Honey would like that, poor dear, if she could know. After listening to stories about Amy for twenty-five years, she must lie alone in her grave in Lexington while Gabriel sneaks off to Texas to make his bed with Amy again. It was a kind of life-long infidelity, Miranda, and now an eternal infidelity on top of that. He ought to be ashamed of himself."

"It was Aunt Amy he loved," said Miranda, wondering what Miss Honey could have been like before her long troubles with Uncle Gabriel. "First, anyway."

"Oh, that Amy," said Cousin Eva, her eyes glittering. "Your Aunt Amy was a devil and a mischief-maker, but I loved her dearly. I used to stand up for Amy when her reputation wasn't worth that." Her fingers snapped like castanets. "She used to say to me, in that gay soft way she had, 'Now, Eva, don't go talking votes for women when the lads ask you to dance. Don't recite Latin poems to 'em,' she would say, 'they got sick of that in school. Dance and say nothing, Eva,' she would say, her eyes perfectly devilish, 'and hold your chin up, Eva.' My chin was my weak point, you see. 'You'll never catch a husband if you don't look out,' she would say. Then she would laugh and fly away, and where did she fly to?" demanded Cousin Eva, her sharp eyes pinning Miranda down to the bitter facts of the case, "To scandal and to death, nowhere else."

"She was joking, Cousin Eva," said Miranda, innocently, "and everybody loved her."

"Not everybody, by a long shot," said Cousin Eva in triumph. "She had enemies. If she knew, she pretended she didn't. If she cared, she never said. You couldn't make her quarrel. She was sweet as a honeycomb to everybody. *Everybody*," she added, "that was the trouble. She went through life like a spoiled darling, doing as she pleased and letting other people suffer for it, and pick up the pieces after her. I never believed for one moment," said Cousin Eva, putting her mouth close to Miranda's ear and breathing peppermint hotly into it, "that Amy was an impure woman. Never! But let me tell you, there were plenty who did believe it. There were plenty to pity poor Gabriel for being so completely blinded by her. A great many persons were not surprised when they heard that Gabriel was perfectly miserable all the time, on their honeymoon, in New Orleans. Jealousy. And why not? But I used to say to such persons that, no matter what the appearances were, I had faith in Amy's virtue. Wild, I said, indiscreet, I said, heartless, I said, but *virtuous* I feel certain. But you could hardly blame anyone for being mystified. The way she rose up suddenly from death's door to marry Gabriel Breaux, after refusing him and treating him like a dog for years, looked odd, to say the least. To say the very least," she added, after a moment, "odd is a mild word for it. And there was something very mysterious about her death, only six weeks after marriage."

Miranda roused herself. She felt she knew this part of the story and could set Cousin Eva right about one thing. "She died of a hemorrhage from the lungs," said Miranda. "She had been ill for five years, don't you remember?"

Cousin Eva was ready for that. "Ha, that was the story, indeed. The official account, you might say. Oh, yes, I heard that often enough. But did you ever hear about that fellow Raymond somebody-or-other from Calcasieu Parish, almost a stranger, who persuaded Amy to elope with him from a dance one night, and she just ran out into the darkness without even stopping for her cloak, and your poor dear nice father Harry—you weren't even thought of then—had to run him down to earth and shoot him?"

Miranda leaned back from the advancing flood of speech. "Cousin Eva, my father shot *at* him, don't you remember? He didn't hit him. . . ."

"Well, that's a pity."

". . . and they had only gone out for a breath of air between dances. It was Uncle Gabriel's jealousy. And my father shot at the man because he thought that was better than letting Uncle Gabriel fight a duel about Aunt Amy. There was *nothing* in the whole affair except Uncle Gabriel's jealousy."

"You poor baby," said Cousin Eva, and pity gave a light like daggers to her eyes, "you dear innocent, you—do you believe that? How old are you, anyway?"

"Just past eighteen," said Miranda.

"If you don't understand what I tell you," said Cousin Eva portentously, "you will later. Knowledge can't hurt you. You mustn't live in a romantic haze about life. You'll understand when you're married, at any rate."

"I'm married now, Cousin Eva," said Miranda, feeling for almost the first time that it might be an advantage, "nearly a year. I eloped from school." It seemed very unreal even as she said it, and seemed to have nothing at all to do with the future; still, it was important, it must be declared, it was a situation in life which people seemed to be most exacting about, and the only feeling she could rouse in herself about it was an immense weariness as if it were an illness that she might one day hope to recover from.

"Shameful, shameful," cried Cousin Eva, genuinely repelled. "If you had been my child I should have brought you home and spanked you."

Miranda laughed out. Cousin Eva seemed to believe things could be arranged like that. She was so solemn and fierce, so comic and baffled.

"And you must know I should have just gone straight out again, through the nearest window," she taunted her. "If I went the first time, why not the second?"

"Yes, I suppose so," said Cousin Eva. "I hope you married rich."

"Not so very," said Miranda. "Enough." As if anyone could have stopped to think of such a thing!

Cousin Eva adjusted her spectacles and sized up Miranda's dress, her luggage, examined her engagement ring and wedding ring, with her nostrils fairly quivering as if she might smell out wealth on her.

"Well, that's better than nothing," said Cousin Eva. "I thank God every day of my life that I have a small income. It's a Rock of Ages. What would have become of me if I hadn't a cent of my own? Well, you'll be able now to do something for your family."

Miranda remembered what she had always heard about the Parringtons. They were money-hungry, they loved money and nothing else, and when they had got some they kept it. Blood was thinner than water between the Parringtons where money was concerned.

"We're pretty poor," said Miranda, stubbornly allying herself with her father's family instead of her husband's, "but a rich marriage is no way out," she said, with the snobbishness of poverty. She was thinking, "You don't know my branch of the family, dear Cousin Eva, if you think it is."

"Your branch of the family," said Cousin Eva, with that terrifying habit she had of lifting phrases out of one's mind, "has no more practical sense than so many children. Everything for love," she said, with a face of positive nausea, "that was it. Gabriel would have been rich if his grandfather had not disinherited him, but would Amy be sensible and marry him and make him settle down so the old man would have been pleased with him? No. And what could Gabriel do without money? I wish you could have seen the life he led Miss Honey, one day buying her Paris gowns and the next day pawning her earrings. It just depended on how the horses ran, and they ran worse and worse, and Gabriel drank more and more."

Miranda did not say, "I saw a little of it." She was trying to imagine Miss Honey in a Paris gown. She said, "But Uncle Gabriel was so mad about Aunt Amy, there was no question of her not marrying him at last, money or no money."

Cousin Eva strained her lips tightly over her teeth, let them fly again and leaned over, gripping Miranda's arm. "What I ask myself, what I ask myself over and over again," she whispered, "is, what connection did this man Raymond from Calcasieu have with Amy's sudden marriage to Gabriel, and *what* did Amy do to make away with herself so soon afterward? For mark my words, child, Amy wasn't so ill as all that. She'd been flying around for years after the doctors said her lungs were weak. Amy did away with herself to escape some disgrace, some exposure that she faced."

The beady black eyes glinted; Cousin Eva's face was quite frightening, so near and so intent. Miranda wanted to say, "Stop. Let her rest. What harm did she ever do you?" but she was timid and unnerved, and deep in her was a horrid fascination with the terrors and the darkness Cousin Eva had conjured up. What was the end of this story?

"She was a bad, wild girl, but I was fond of her to the last," said Cousin Eva. "She got into trouble somehow, and she couldn't get out again, and I have every reason to believe she killed herself with the drug they gave her to keep her quiet after a hemorrhage. If she didn't, what happened, what happened?"

"I don't know," said Miranda. "How should I know? She was very beautiful," she said, as if this explained everything. "Everybody said she was very beautiful."

"Not everybody," said Cousin Eva, firmly, shaking her head. "I for one never thought so. They made entirely too much fuss over her. She was good-looking enough, but why did they think she was beautiful? I cannot understand it. She was too thin when she was young, and later I always thought she was too fat, and again in her last year she was altogether too thin. She always got herself up to be looked at, and so people looked, of course. She rode too hard, and she danced too freely, and she talked too much, and you'd have to be blind, deaf and dumb not to notice her. I don't mean she was loud or vulgar, she wasn't, but she was *too free*," said Cousin Eva. She stopped for breath and put a peppermint in her mouth. Miranda could see Cousin Eva on the platform, making her speeches, stopping to take a peppermint. But why did she hate Aunt Amy so, when Aunt Amy was dead and she alive? Wasn't being alive enough?

"And her illness wasn't romantic either," said Cousin Eva, "though to hear them tell it she faded like a lily. Well, she coughed blood, if that's romantic. If they had made her take proper care of herself, if she had been nursed sensibly, she might have been alive today. But no, nothing of the kind. She lay wrapped in beautiful shawls on a sofa with flowers around her, eating as she liked or not eating, getting up after a hemorrhage and going out to ride or dance, sleeping with the windows closed; with crowds coming in and out laughing and talking at all hours, and Amy sitting up so her hair wouldn't get out of curl. And why wouldn't that sort of thing kill a well person in time? I have almost died twice in my life," said Cousin Eva, "and both times I was sent to a hospital where I belonged and left there until I came out. And I came out," she said, her voice deepening to a bugle note, "and I went to work again."

"Beauty goes, character stays," said the small voice of axiomatic morality in Miranda's ear. It was a dreary prospect; why was a strong character so deforming? Miranda felt she truly wanted to be strong, but how could she face it, seeing what it did to one?

"She had a lovely complexion," said Cousin Eva, "perfectly transparent with a flush on each cheekbone. But it was tuberculosis, and is disease beautiful? And she brought it on herself by drinking lemon and salt to stop her periods when she wanted to go to dances. There was a superstition among young girls about that. They fancied that young men could tell what ailed them by touching their hands, or even by looking at them. As if it mattered? But they were terribly self-conscious and they had immense respect for man's worldly wisdom in those days. My own notion is that a man couldn't— but anyway, the whole thing was stupid."

"I should have thought they'd have stayed at home if they couldn't manage better than that," said Miranda, feeling very knowledgeable and modern.

"They didn't dare. Those parties and dances were their market, a girl couldn't afford to miss out, there were always rivals waiting to cut the ground from under her. The rivalry—" said Cousin Eva, and her head lifted, she arched like a cavalry horse getting a whiff of the battlefield— "you can't imagine what the rivalry was like. The way those girls treated each other— nothing was too mean, nothing too false—"

Cousin Eva wrung her hands. "It was just sex," she said in despair; "their minds dwelt on nothing else. They didn't call it that, it was all smothered under pretty names, but that's all it was, sex." She looked out of the window into the darkness, her sunken cheek near Miranda flushed deeply. She turned back. "I took to the soap box and the platform when I was called upon," she said proudly, "and I went to jail when it was necessary, and my condition didn't make any difference. I was booed and jeered and shoved around just as if I had been in perfect health. But it was part of our philosophy not to let our physical handicaps make any difference to our work. You know what I mean," she said, as if until now it was all mystery. "Well, Amy carried herself with more spirit than the others, and she didn't seem to be making any sort of fight, but she was simply sex-ridden, like the rest. She behaved as if she hadn't a rival on earth, and she pretended not to know what marriage was about, but I know better. None of them had, and they didn't want to have, anything else to think about, and they didn't really know anything about that, so they simply festered inside—they festered—"

Miranda found herself deliberately watching a long procession of living corpses, festering women stepping gaily towards the charnel house, their corruption concealed under laces and flowers, their dead faces lifted smiling, and thought quite coldly, "Of course it was not like that. This is no more true than what I was told before, it's every bit as romantic," and she realized that she was tired of her intense Cousin Eva, she wanted to go to sleep, she wanted to be at home, she wished it were tomorrow and she could see her father and her sister, who were so alive and solid; who would mention her freckles and ask her if she wanted something to eat.

"My mother was not like that," she said, childishly. "My mother was a perfectly natural woman who liked to cook. I have seen some of her sewing," she said. "I have read her diary."

"Your mother was a saint," said Cousin Eva, automatically.

Miranda sat silent, outraged. "My mother was nothing of the sort," she wanted to fling in Cousin Eva's big front teeth. But Cousin Eva had been gathering bitterness until more speech came of it.

" 'Hold your chin up, Eva,' Amy used to tell me," she began, doubling up both her fists and shaking them a little. "All my life the whole family bedeviled me about my chin. My entire girlhood was spoiled by it. Can you imagine," she asked, with a ferocity that seemed much too deep for this one cause, "people who call themselves civilized spoiling life for a young girl because she had one unlucky feature? Of course, you understand perfectly it was all in the very best humor, everybody was very amusing about it, no harm meant—oh, no, no harm at all. That is the hellish thing about it. It is that I can't forgive," she cried out, and she twisted her hands together as if they were rags. "Ah, the family," she said, releasing her breath and sitting back quietly, "the whole hideous institution should be wiped from the face of the earth. It is the root of all human wrongs," she ended, and relaxed, and her face became calm. She was trembling. Miranda reached out and took Cousin Eva's hand and held it. The hand fluttered and lay still, and Cousin Eva said, "You've not the faintest idea what some of us went through, but I wanted you to hear the other side of the story. And I'm keeping you up when you need your beauty sleep," she said grimly, stirring herself with an immense rustle of petticoats.

Miranda pulled herself together, feeling limp, and stood up. Cousin Eva put out her hand again, and drew Miranda down to her. "Good night, you dear child," she said, "to think you're grown up." Miranda hesitated, then quite suddenly kissed her Cousin Eva on the cheek. The black eyes shown brightly through water for an instant, and Cousin Eva said with a warm note in her sharp clear orator's voice, "Tomorrow we'll be at home again. I'm looking forward to it, aren't you? Good night."

Miranda fell asleep while she was getting off her clothes. Instantly it was morning again. She was still trying to close her suitcase when the train pulled into the small station, and there on the platform she saw her father, looking tired and anxious, his hat pulled over his eyes. She rapped on the window to catch his attention, then ran out and threw herself upon him. He said, "Well, here's my big girl," as if she were still seven, but his hands on her arms held her off, the tone was forced. There was no welcome for her, and there had not been since she had run away. She could not persuade herself to remember how it would be; between one home-coming and the next her mind refused to accept its own knowledge. Her father looked over her head and said, without surprise, "Why, hello, Eva, I'm glad somebody sent you a telegram." Miranda, rebuffed again, let her arms fall away again, with the same painful dull jerk of the heart.

"No one in my family," said Eva, her face framed in the thin black veil she reserved, evidently, for family funerals, "ever sent me a telegram in my life. I had the news from young Keziah who had it from young Gabriel. I suppose Gabe is here?"

"Everybody seems to be here," said Father. "The house is getting full."

"I'll go to the hotel if you like," said Cousin Eva.

"Damnation, no," said Father. "I didn't mean that. You'll come with us where you belong."

Skid, the handy man, grabbed the suitcases and started down the rocky village street. "We've got the car," said Father. He took Miranda by the hand, then dropped it again, and reached for Cousin Eva's elbow.

"I'm perfectly able, thank you," said Cousin Eva, shying away.

"If you're so independent now," said Father, "God help us when you get that vote."

Cousin Eva pushed back her veil. She was smiling merrily. She liked Harry, she always had liked him, he could tease as much as he liked. She slipped her arm through his. "So it's all over with poor Gabriel, isn't it?"

"Oh, yes," said Father, "it's all over, all right. They're pegging out pretty regularly now. It will be our turn next, Eva?"

"I don't know, and I don't care," said Eva, recklessly. "It's good to be back now and then, Harry, even if it is only for funerals. I feel sinfully cheerful."

"Oh, Gabriel wouldn't mind, he'd like seeing you cheerful. Gabriel was the cheerfullest cuss I ever saw, when we were young. Life for Gabriel," said Father, "was just one perpetual picnic."

"Poor fellow," said Cousin Eva.

"Poor old Gabriel," said Father, heavily.

Miranda walked along beside her father, feeling homeless, but not sorry for it. He had not forgiven her, she knew that. When would he? She could not guess, but she felt it would come of itself, without words and without acknowledgment on either side, for by the time it arrived neither of them would need to remember what had caused their division, nor why it had seemed so important. Surely old people cannot hold their grudges forever because the young want to live, too, she thought, in her arrogance, her pride. I will make my own mistakes, not yours; I cannot depend upon you beyond a certain point, why depend at all? There was something more beyond, but this was a first step to take, and she took it, walking in silence beside her elders who were no longer Cousin Eva and Father, since they had forgotten her presence, but had become Eva and Harry, who knew each other well, who were comfortable with each other, being contemporaries on equal terms, who occupied by right their place in this world, at the time of life to which they had arrived by paths familiar to them both. They need not play their roles of daughter, of son, to aged persons who did not understand them; nor of father and elderly female cousin to young persons whom they did not understand. They were precisely themselves; their eyes cleared, their voices relaxed into perfect naturalness, they need not weigh their words or calculate the effect of their manner. "It is I who have no place," thought Miranda. "Where are my own people and my own time?" She resented, slowly and deeply and in profound silence, the presence of these aliens who lectured and admonished her, who loved her with bitterness and denied her the right to look at the world with her own eyes, who demanded that she accept their version of life and yet could not tell her the truth, not in the smallest thing. "I hate them both," her most inner and secret mind said plainly, *"I will be free of them, I shall not even remember them."*

She sat in the front seat with Skid, the Negro boy. "Come back with us,

Miranda," said Cousin Eva, with the sharp little note of elderly command, "there is plenty of room."

"No, thank you," said Miranda, in a firm cold voice. "I'm quite comfortable. Don't disturb yourself."

Neither of them noticed her voice or her manner. They sat back and went on talking steadily in their friendly family voices, talking about their dead, their living, their affairs, their prospects, their common memories, interrupting each other, catching each other up on small points of dispute, laughing with a gaiety and freshness Miranda had not known they were capable of, going over old stories and finding new points of interest in them.

Miranda could not hear the stories above the noisy motor, but she felt she knew them well, or stories like them. She knew too many stories like them, she wanted something new of her own. The language was familiar to them, but not to her, not any more. The house, her father had said, was full. It would be full of cousins, many of them strangers. Would there be any young cousins there, to whom she could talk about things they both knew? She felt a vague distaste for seeing cousins. There were too many of them and her blood rebelled against the ties of blood. She was sick to death of cousins. She did not want any more ties with this house, she was going to leave it, and she was not going back to her husband's family either. She would have no more bonds that smothered her in love and hatred. She knew now why she had run away to marriage, and she knew that she was going to run away from marriage, and she was not going to stay in any place, with anyone, that threatened to forbid her making her own discoveries, that said "No" to her. She hoped no one had taken her old room, she would like to sleep there once more, she would say good-by there where she had loved sleeping once, sleeping and waking and waiting to be grown, to begin to live. Oh, what is life, she asked herself in desperate seriousness, in those childish unanswerable words, and what shall I do with it? It is something of my own, she thought in a fury of jealous possessiveness, what shall I make of it? She did not know that she asked herself this because all her earliest training had argued that life was a substance, a material to be used, it took shape and direction and meaning only as the possessor guided and worked it; living was a progress of continuous and varied acts of the will directed towards a definite end. She had been assured that there were good and evil ones, one must make a choice. But what was good, and what was evil? I hate love, she thought, as if this were the answer, I hate loving and being loved, I hate it. And her disturbed and seething mind received a shock of comfort from this sudden collapse of an old painful structure of distorted images and misconceptions. "You don't know anything about it," said Miranda to herself, with extraordinary clearness as if she were an elder admonishing some younger misguided creature. "You have to find out about it." But nothing in her prompted her to decide, "I will now do this, I will be that, I will go yonder, I will take a certain road to a certain end." There are questions to be asked first, she thought, but who will answer them? No one, or there will be too many answers, none of them right. What is the truth, she asked herself as intently as if the question had never been asked, the truth, even about the smallest, the least important of all the things I must find out? and where shall I begin to look for it? Her mind closed stubbornly against remembering, not the past but the legend of the past, other people's memory of the past, at which she had spent her life peering in wonder like a child at a magic-lantern show. Ah, but there is my own life to come yet, she thought, my own life now and beyond. I don't want any promises, I won't have false hopes, I won't be romantic about myself. I can't live in their world any longer, she told herself, listening to the voices back of her. Let them tell their stories to each other. Let them go on explaining how things happened. I don't care. At least I can know the truth about what happens to me, she assured herself silently, making a promise to herself, in her hopefulness, her ignorance.

Elizabeth Bowen

THE DEMON LOVER

TOWARDS the end of her day in London Mrs. Drover went round to her shut-up house to look for several things she wanted to take away. Some belonged to herself, some to her family, who were by now used to their country life. It was late August; it had been a steamy, showery day: at the moment the trees down the pavement glittered in an escape of humid yellow afternoon sun. Against the next batch of clouds, already piling up ink-dark, broken chimneys and parapets stood out. In her once familiar street, as in any unused channel, an unfamiliar queerness had silted up; a cat wove itself in and out of railings, but no human eye watched Mrs. Drover's return. Shifting some parcels under her arm, she slowly forced round her latchkey in an unwilling lock, then gave the door, which had warped, a push with her knee. Dead air came out to meet her as she went in.

The staircase window having been boarded up, no light came down into the hall. But one door, she could just see, stood ajar, so she went quickly through into the room and unshuttered the big window in there. Now the prosaic woman, looking about her, was more perplexed than she knew by everything that she saw, by traces of her long former habit of life—the yellow smoke-stain up the white marble mantelpiece, the ring left by a vase on the top of the escritoire; the bruise in the wallpaper where, on the door being thrown open widely, the china handle had always hit the wall. The piano, having gone away to be stored, had left what looked like claw-marks on its part of the parquet. Though not much dust had seeped in, each object wore a film of another kind; and, the only ventilation being the chimney, the whole drawing-room smelled of the cold hearth. Mrs. Drover put down her parcels on the escritoire and left the room to proceed upstairs; the things she wanted were in a bedroom chest.

She had been anxious to see how the house was—the part-time caretaker she shared with some neighbours was away this week on his holiday, known to be not yet back. At the best of times he did not look in often, and she was never sure that she trusted him. There were some cracks in the structure, left by the last bombing, on which she was anxious to keep an eye. Not that one could do anything—

A shaft of refracted daylight now lay across the hall. She stopped dead and stared at the hall table—on this lay a letter addressed to her.

She thought first—then the caretaker *must* be back. All the same,

Reprinted from *Ivy Gripped the Steps* by Elizabeth Bowen, by permission of Alfred A. Knopf, Inc. Copyright 1941, 1946 by Elizabeth Bowen.

who, seeing the house shuttered, would have dropped a letter in at the box?
It was not a circular, it was not a bill. And the post office redirected, to the
address in the country, everything for her that came through the post. The
caretaker (even if he *were* back) did not know she was due in London
to-day—her call here had been planned to be a surprise—so his negligence
in the manner of this letter, leaving it to wait in the dusk and the dust,
annoyed her. Annoyed, she picked up the letter, which bore no stamp. But it
cannot be important, or they would know . . . She took the letter rapidly
upstairs with her, without a stop to look at the writing till she reached what
had been her bedroom, where she let in light. The room looked over the
garden and other gardens: the sun had gone in; as the clouds sharpened
and lowered, the trees and rank lawns seemed already to smoke with dark.
Her reluctance to look again at the letter came from the fact that she felt
intruded upon—and by someone contemptuous of her ways. However, in the
tenseness preceding the fall of rain she read it: it was a few lines.

DEAR KATHLEEN,
    You will not have forgotten that to-day is our anniversary, and the
day we said. The years have gone by at once slowly and fast. In view of
the fact that nothing has changed, I shall rely upon you to keep your
promise. I was sorry to see you leave London, but was satisfied that you
would be back in time. You may expect me, therefore, at the hour
arranged.
Until then . . .
K.

Mrs. Drover looked for the date: it was to-day's. She dropped the letter on to
the bed-springs, then picked it up to see the writing again—her lips, beneath
the remains of lipstick, beginning to go white. She felt so much the change
in her own face that she went to the mirror, polished a clear patch in it and
looked at once urgently and stealthily in. She was confronted by a woman of
forty-four, with eyes starting out under a hat-brim that had been rather carelessly pulled down. She had not put on any more powder since she left the
shop where she ate her solitary tea. The pearls her husband had given her on
their marriage hung loose round her now rather thinner throat, slipping into
the V of the pink wool jumper her sister knitted last autumn as they sat
round the fire. Mrs. Drover's most normal expression was one of controlled
worry, but of assent. Since the birth of the third of her little boys, attended
by a quite serious illness, she had had an intermittent muscular flicker to the
left of her mouth, but in spite of this she could always sustain a manner that
was at once energetic and calm.
    Turning from her own face as precipitately as she had gone to meet it,
she went to the chest where the things were, unlocked it, threw up the lid
and knelt to search. But as rain began to come crashing down she could not
keep from looking over her shoulder at the stripped bed on which the letter
lay. Behind the blanket of rain the clock of the church that still stood struck

six—with rapidly heightening apprehension she counted each of the slow strokes. "The hour arranged . . . My God," she said, "*what* hour? How should I . . . ? After twenty-five years. . . ."

The young girl talking to the soldier in the garden had not ever completely seen his face. It was dark; they were saying good-bye under a tree. Now and then—for it felt, from not seeing him at this intense moment, as though she had never seen him at all—she verified his presence for these few moments longer by putting out a hand, which he each time pressed, without very much kindness, and painfully, on to one of the breast buttons of his uniform. That cut of the button on the palm of her hand was, principally, what she was to carry away. This was so near the end of a leave from France that she could only wish him already gone. It was August 1916. Being not kissed, being drawn away from and looked at intimidated Kathleen till she imagined spectral glitters in the place of his eyes. Turning away and looking back up the lawn she saw, through branches of trees, the drawing-room window alight: she caught a breath for the moment when she could go running back there into the safe arms of her mother and sister, and cry: "What shall I do, what shall I do? He has gone."

Hearing her catch her breath, her fiancé said, without feeling: "Cold?"

"You're going away such a long way."

"Not so far as you think."

"I don't understand?"

"You don't have to," he said. "You will. You know what we said."

"But that was—suppose you—I mean, suppose."

"I shall be with you," he said, "sooner or later. You won't forget that. You need do nothing but wait."

Only a little more than a minute later she was free to run up the silent lawn. Looking in through the window at her mother and sister, who did not for the moment perceive her, she already felt that unnatural promise drive down between her and the rest of all human kind. No other way of having given herself could have made her feel so apart, lost and foresworn. She could not have plighted a more sinister troth.

Kathleen behaved well when, some months later, her fiancé was reported missing, presumed killed. Her family not only supported her but were able to praise her courage without stint because they could not regret, as a husband for her, the man they knew almost nothing about. They hoped she would, in a year or two, console herself—and had it been only a question of consolation things might have gone much straighter ahead. But her trouble, behind just a little grief, was a complete dislocation from everything. She did not reject other lovers, for these failed to appear: for years she failed to attract men—and with the approach of her thirties she became natural enough to share her family's anxiousness on this score. She began to put herself out, to wonder; and at thirty-two she was very greatly relieved to find herself being courted by William Drover. She married him, and the two of them settled down in this quiet, arboreal part of Kensington: in this house the years piled up, her children were born and they all lived till they were driven out by the bombs of the next war. Her movements as Mrs. Drover were circumscribed, and she dismissed any idea that they were still watched.

As things were—dead or living the letter-writer sent her only a threat. Unable, for some minutes, to go on kneeling with her back exposed to the empty room, Mrs. Drover rose from the chest to sit on an upright chair whose back was firmly against the wall. The desuetude of her former bed-room, her married London home's whole air of being a cracked cup from which memory, with its reassuring power, had either evaporated or leaked away, made a crisis—and at just this crisis the letter-writer had, knowl-edgeably, struck. The hollowness of the house this evening cancelled years on years of voices, habits and steps. Through the shut windows she only heard rain fall on the roofs around. To rally herself, she said she was in a mood—and, for two or three seconds shutting her eyes, told herself that she had imagined the letter. But she opened them—there it lay on the bed.

On the supernatural side of the letter's entrance she was not permitting her mind to dwell. Who, in London, knew she meant to call at the house to-day? Evidently, however, this had been known. The caretaker, *had* he come back, had had no cause to expect her: he would have taken the letter in his pocket, to forward it, at his own time, through the post. There was no other sign that the caretaker had been in—but, if not? Letters dropped in at doors of deserted houses do not fly or walk to tables in halls. They do not sit on the dust of empty tables with the air of certainty that they will be found. There is needed some human hand—but nobody but the caretaker had a key. Under circumstances she did not care to consider, a house can be entered without a key. It was possible that she was not alone now. She might be being waited for, downstairs. Waited for—until when? Until "the hour arranged." At least that was not six o'clock: six has struck.

She rose from the chair and went over and locked the door.

The thing was, to get out. To fly? No, not that: she had to catch her train. As a woman whose utter dependability was the keystone of her family life she was not willing to return to the country, to her husband, her little boys and her sister, without the objects she had come up to fetch. Resuming work at the chest she set about making up a number of parcels in a rapid, fumbling-decisive way. These, with her shopping parcels, would be too much to carry; these meant a taxi—at the thought of the taxi her heart went up and her normal breathing resumed. I will ring up the taxi now; the taxi cannot come too soon: I shall hear the taxi out there running its engine, till I walk calmly down to it through the hall. I'll ring up— But no: the tele-phone is cut off . . . She tugged at a knot she had tied wrong.

The idea of flight . . . He was never kind to me, not really. I don't remember him kind at all. Mother said he never considered me. He was set on me, that was what it was—not love. Not love, not meaning a person well.

What did he do, to make me promise like that? I can't remember— But she found that she could.

She remembered with such dreadful acuteness that the twenty-five years since then dissolved like smoke and she instinctively looked for the weal left by the button on the palm of her hand. She remembered not only all that he said and did but the complete suspension of *her* existence during that August week. I was not myself—they all told me so at the time. She remembered—but with one white burning blank as where acid has dropped on a photograph: *under no conditions* could she remember his face.

So, wherever he may be waiting, I shall not know him. You have no time to run from a face you do not expect.

The thing was to get to the taxi before any clock struck what could be the hour. She would slip down the street and round the side of the square to where the square gave on the main road. She would return in the taxi, safe, to her own door, and bring the solid driver into the house with her to pick up the parcels from room to room. The idea of the taxi driver made her decisive, bold: she unlocked her door, went to the top of the staircase and listened down.

She heard nothing—but while she was hearing nothing the *passé* air of the staircase was disturbed by a draught that travelled up to her face. It emanated from the basement: down there a door or window was being opened by someone who chose this moment to leave the house.

The rain had stopped; the pavements steamily shone as Mrs. Drover let herself out by inches from her own front door into the empty street. The unoccupied houses opposite continued to meet her look with their damaged stare. Making towards the thoroughfare and the taxi, she tried not to keep looking behind. Indeed, the silence was so intense—one of those creeks of London silence exaggerated this summer by the damage of war—that no tread could have gained on hers unheard. Where her street debouched on the square where people went on living she grew conscious of and checked her unnatural pace. Across the open end of the square two buses impassively passed each other; women, a perambulator, cyclists, a man wheeling a barrow signalized, once again, the ordinary flow of life. At the square's most populous corner should be—and was—the short taxi rank. This evening, only one taxi—but this, although it presented its blank rump, appeared already to be alertly waiting for her. Indeed, without looking round the driver started his engine as she panted up from behind and put her hand on the door. As she did so, the clock struck seven. The taxi faced the main road: to make the trip back to her house it would have to turn—she had settled back on the seat and the taxi *had* turned before she, surprised by its knowing movement, recollected that she had not "said where." She leaned forward to scratch at the glass panel that divided the driver's head from her own.

The driver braked to what was almost a stop, turned round and slid the glass panel back: the jolt of this flung Mrs. Drover forward till her face was almost into the glass. Through the aperture driver and passenger, not six inches between them, remained for an eternity eye to eye. Mrs. Drover's mouth hung open for some seconds before she could issue her first scream. After that she continued to scream freely and to beat with her gloved hands on the glass all round as the taxi, accelerating without mercy, made off with her into the hinterland of deserted streets.

William Faulkner

SPOTTED HORSES

i

A LITTLE while before sundown the men lounging about the gallery of the store saw, coming up the road from the south, a covered wagon drawn by mules and followed by a considerable string of obviously alive objects which in the levelling sun resembled vari-sized and -colored tatters torn at random from large billboards—circus posters, say—attached to the rear of the wagon and inherent with its own separate and collective motion, like the tail of a kite.

"What in the hell is that?" one said.

"It's a circus," Quick said. They began to rise, watching the wagon. Now they could see that the animals behind the wagon were horses. Two men rode in the wagon.

"Hell fire," the first man—his name was Freeman—said. "It's Flem Snopes." They were all standing when the wagon came up and stopped and Snopes got down and approached the steps. He might have departed only this morning. He wore the same cloth cap, the minute bow tie against the white shirt, the same gray trousers. He mounted the steps.

"Howdy, Flem," Quick said. The other looked briefly at all of them and none of them, mounting the steps. "Starting you a circus?"

"Gentlemen," he said. He crossed the gallery; they made way for him. Then they descended the steps and approached the wagon, at the tail of which the horses stood in a restive clump, larger than rabbits and gaudy as parrots and shackled to one another and to the wagon itself with sections of barbed wire. Calico-coated, small-bodied, with delicate legs and pink faces in which their mismatched eyes rolled wild and subdued, they huddled, gaudy, motionless, and alert, wild as deer, deadly as rattlesnakes, quiet as doves. The men stood at a respectful distance, looking at them. At that moment Jody Varner came through the group, shouldering himself to the front of it.

"Watch yourself, doc," a voice said from the rear. But it was already too late. The nearest animal rose on its hind legs with lightning rapidity and struck twice with its forefeet at Varner's face, faster than a boxer, the movement of its surge against the wire which held it travelling backward among the rest of the band in a wave of thuds and lunges. "Hup, you broom-

tailed, hay-burning sidewinders," the same voice said. This was the second
man who had arrived in the wagon. He was a stranger. He wore a heavy,
densely black moustache, a wide pale hat. When he thrust himself through
and turned to herd them back from the horses they saw, thrust into the hip
pockets of his tight jeans pants, the butt of a heavy pearl-handled pistol and
a florid carton such as small cakes come in. "Keep away from them, boys," he
said. "They've got kind of skittish, they ain't been rode in so long."

"Since when have they been rode?" Quick said. The stranger looked at
Quick. He had a broad, quite cold, wind-gnawed face and bleak, cold eyes.
His belly fitted neat and smooth as a peg into the tight trousers.

"I reckon that was when they were rode on the ferry to get across the
Mississippi River," Varner said. The stranger looked at him. "My name's
Varner," Jody said.

"Hipps," the other said. "Call me Buck." Across the left side of his head,
obliterating the tip of that ear, was a savage and recent gash gummed over
with a blackish substance like axle-grease. They looked at the scar. Then
they watched him remove the carton from his pocket and tilt a gingersnap
into his hand and put the gingersnap into his mouth, beneath the moustache.

"You and Flem have some trouble back yonder?" Quick said. The
stranger ceased chewing. When he looked directly at anyone, his eyes became
like two pieces of flint turned suddenly up in dug earth.

"Back where?" he said.

"Your nigh ear," Quick said.

"Oh," the other said. "That." He touched his ear. "That was my mistake.
I was absent-minded one night when I was staking them out. Studying about
something else and forgot how long the wire was." He chewed. They looked
at his ear. "Happen to any man careless around a horse. Put a little axel-dope
on it and you won't notice it tomorrow though. They're pretty lively now,
lazing along all day doing nothing. It'll work out of them in a couple of
days." He put another gingershap into his mouth, chewing, "Don't you believe they'll gentle?" No one answered. They looked at the ponies, grave
and noncommittal. Jody turned and went back into the store. "Them's good,
gentle ponies," the stranger said. "Watch now." He put the carton back into
his pocket and approached the horses, his hand extended. The nearest one
was standing on three legs now. It appeared to be asleep. Its eyelid drooped
over the cerulean eye; its head was shaped like an ironing-board. Without
even raising the eyelid it flicked its head, the yellow teeth cropped. For an
instant it and the man appeared to be inextricable in one violence. Then
they became motionless, the stranger's high heels dug into the earth, one
hand gripping the animal's nostrils, holding the horse's head wrenched half
around while it breathed in hoarse, smothered groans. "See?" the stranger
said in a panting voice, the veins standing white and rigid in his neck and
along his jaw. "See? All you got to do is handle them a little and work hell
out of them for a couple of days. Now look out. Give me room back there."
They gave back a little. The stranger gathered himself then sprang away. As

he did so, a second horse slashed at his back, severing his vest from collar to hem down the back exactly as the trick swordsman severs a floating veil with one stroke.

"Sho now," Quick said. "But suppose a man don't happen to own a vest."

At that moment Jody Varner, followed by the blacksmith, thrust through them again. "All right, Buck," he said. "Better get them on into the lot. Eck here will help you." The stranger, the severed halves of the vest swinging from either shoulder, mounted to the wagon seat, the blacksmith following.

"Get up, you transmogrified hallucinations of Job and Jezebel," the stranger said. The wagon moved on, the tethered ponies coming gaudily into motion behind it, behind which in turn the men followed at a respectful distance, on up the road and into the lane and so to the lot gate behind Mrs. Littlejohn's. Eck got down and opened the gate. The wagon passed through but when the ponies saw the fence the herd surged backward against the wire which attached it to the wagon, standing on its collective hind legs and then trying to turn within itself, so that the wagon moved backward for a few feet until the Texan, cursing, managed to saw the mules about and so lock the wheels. The men following had already fallen rapidly back. "Here, Eck," the Texan said. "Get up here and take the reins." The blacksmith got back in the wagon and took the reins. Then they watched the Texan descend, carrying a looped-up blacksnake whip, and go around to the rear of the herd and drive it through the gate, the whip snaking about the harlequin rumps in methodical and pistol-like reports. Then the watchers hurried across Mrs. Littlejohn's yard and mounted to the veranda, one end of which overlooked the lot.

"How do you reckon he ever got them tied together?" Freeman said.

"I'd a heap rather watch how he aims to turn them loose," Quick said. The Texan had climbed back into the halted wagon. Presently he and Eck both appeared at the rear end of the open hood. The Texan grasped the wire and began to draw the first horse up to the wagon, the animal plunging and surging back against the wire as though trying to hang itself, the contagion passing back through the herd from animal to animal until they were rearing and plunging again against the wire.

"Come on, grab a holt," the Texan said. Eck grasped the wire also. The horses laid back against it, the pink faces tossing above the back-surging mass. "Pull him up, pull him up," the Texan said sharply. "They couldn't get up here in the wagon even if they wanted to." The wagon moved gradually backward until the head of the first horse was snubbed up to the tailgate. The Texan took a turn of the wire quickly about on the wagon stakes. "Keep the slack out of it," he said. He vanished and reappeared, almost in the same second, with a pair of heavy wire-cutters. "Hold them like that," he said, and leaped. He vanished, broad hat, flapping vest, wire-cutters and all, into a kaleidoscopic maelstrom of long teeth and wild eyes and slashing feet, from which presently the horses began to burst one by one like partridges flushing, each wearing a necklace of barbed wire. The first one crossed the lot at top speed, on a straight line. It galloped into the fence without any diminution whatever. The wire gave, recovered, and slammed the horse to earth where it lay for a moment, glaring, its legs still galloping in air. It scrambled up without having ceased to gallop and crossed the lot and galloped into the opposite fence and was slammed again to earth. The others were now freed. They whipped and whirled about the lot like dizzy fish in a bowl. It had seemed like a big lot until now, but now the very idea that all that fury and motion should be transpiring inside any one fence was something to be repudiated with contempt, like a mirror trick. From the ultimate dust the stranger, carrying the wire-cutters and his vest completely gone now, emerged. He was not running, he merely moved with a light-poised and watchful celerity, weaving among the calico rushes of the animals, feinting and dodging like a boxer until he reached the gate and crossed the yard and mounted to the veranda. One sleeve of his shirt hung only at one point from his shoulder. He ripped it off and wiped his face with it and threw it away and took out the paper carton and shook a gingersnap into his hand. He was breathing only a little heavily. "Pretty lively now," he said. "But it'll work out of them in a couple of days." The ponies still streaked back and forth through the growing dusk like hysterical fish, but not so violently now.

"What'll you give a man to reduce them odds a little for you?" Quick said. The Texan looked at him, the eyes bleak, pleasant and hard above the chewing jaw, the heavy moustache. "To take one of them off your hands?" Quick said.

At that moment the little periwinkle-eyed boy came along the veranda, saying, "Papa, papa; where's papa?"

"Who you looking for, sonny?" one said.

"It's Eck's boy," Quick said. "He's still out yonder in the wagon. Helping Mr. Buck here." The boy went on to the end of the veranda, in diminutive overalls—a miniature replica of the men themselves.

"Papa," he said. "Papa." The blacksmith was still leaning from the rear of the wagon, still holding the end of the severed wire. The ponies, bunched for the moment, now slid past the wagon, flowing, stringing out again so that they appeared to have doubled in number, rushing on; the hard, rapid, light patter of unshod hooves came out of the dust. "Mamma says to come on to supper," the boy said.

The moon was almost full then. When supper was over and they had gathered again along the veranda, the alteration was hardly one of visibility even. It was merely a translation from the lapidary-dimensional of day to the treacherous and silver receptivity in which the horses huddled in mazy camouflage, or singly or in pairs rushed, fluid, phantom, and unceasing, to huddle again in mirage-like clumps from which came high, abrupt squeals and the vicious thudding of hooves.

Ratliff was among them now. He had returned just before supper. He had not dared to take his team into the lot at all. They were now in Book-wright's stable a half mile from the store. "So Flem has come home again," he said. "Well, well, well. Will Varner paid to get him to Texas, so I reckon it ain't no more than fair for you fellows to pay the freight on him back." From the lot there came a high, thin squeal. One of the animals emerged. It seemed not to gallop but to flow, bodiless, without dimension. Yet there was the rapid light beat of hard hooves on the packed earth.

"He ain't said they was his yet," Quick said.

"He ain't said they ain't neither," Freeman said.

"I see," Ratliff said. "That's what you are holding back on. Until he tells you whether they are his or not. Or maybe you can wait until the auction's over and split up and some can follow Flem and some can follow that Texas fellow and watch to see which one spends the money. But then, when a man's done got trimmed, I don't reckon he cares who's got the money."

"Maybe if Ratliff would leave here tonight, they wouldn't make him buy one of them ponies tomorrow," a third said.

"That's fact," Ratliff said. "A fellow can dodge a Snopes if he just starts lively enough. In fact, I don't believe he would have to pass more than two folks before he would have another victim intervened betwixt them. You folks ain't going to buy them things sho enough, are you?" Nobody answered. They sat on the steps, their backs against the veranda posts, or on the railing itself. Only Ratliff and Quick sat in chairs, so that to them the others were black silhouettes against the dreaming lambence of the moon-light beyond the veranda. The pear tree across the road opposite was now in full and frosty bloom, the twigs and branches springing not outward from the limbs but standing motionless and perpendicular above the horizontal boughs like the separate and upstreaming hair of a drowned woman sleep-ing upon the uttermost floor of the windless and tideless sea.

"Anse McCallum brought two of them horses back from Texas once," one of the men on the steps said. He did not move to speak. He was not speaking to anyone. "It was a good team. A little light. He worked it for ten years. Light work, it was."

"I mind it," another said. "Anse claimed he traded fourteen rifle car-tridges for both of them, didn't he?"

"It was the rifle too, I heard," a third said.

"No, it was just the shells," the first said. "The fellow wanted to swap him four more for the rifle too, but Anse said he never needed them. Cost too much to get six of them back to Mississippi."

"Sho," the second said. "When a man don't have to invest so much into a horse or a team, he don't need to expect so much from it." The three of them were not talking any louder, they were merely talking among them-selves, to one another, as if they sat there alone. Ratliff, invisible in the shadow against the wall, made a sound, harsh, sardonic, not loud.

"Ratliff's laughing," a fourth said.

"Don't mind me," Ratliff said. The three speakers had not moved. They did not move now, yet there seemed to gather about the three silhouettes something stubborn, convinced, and passive, like children who have been chidden. A bird, a shadow, fleet and dark and swift, curved across the moonlight, upward into the pear tree and began to sing; a mockingbird.

"First one I've noticed this year," Freeman said.

"You can hear them along Whiteleaf every night," the first man said. "I heard one in February. In that snow. Singing in a gum."

"Gum is the first tree to put out," the third said. "That was why. It made it feel like singing, fixing to put out that way. That was why it taken a gum."

"Gum first to put out?" Quick said. "What about willow?"

"Willow ain't a tree," Freeman said. "It's a weed."

"Well, I don't know what it is," the fourth said. "But it ain't no weed. Because you can grub up a weed and you are done with it. I been grubbing up a clump of willows outen my spring pasture for fifteen years. They are the same size every year. Only difference is, it's just two or three more trees every time."

"And if I was you," Ratliff said, "that's just exactly where I would be come sunup tomorrow. Which of course you ain't going to do. I reckon there ain't nothing under the sun or in Frenchman's Bend neither that can keep you folks from giving Flem Snopes and that Texas man your money. But I'd sholy like to know just exactly who I was giving my money to. Seems like Eck here would tell you. Seems like he'd do that for his neighbors, don't it? Besides being Flem's cousin, him and that boy of his, Wallstreet, helped that Texas man tote water for them tonight and Eck's going to help him feed them in the morning too. Why, maybe Eck will be the one that will catch them and lead them up one at a time for you folks to bid on them. Ain't that right, Eck?"

The other man sitting on the steps with his back against the post was the blacksmith. "I don't know," he said.

"Boys," Ratliff said, "Eck knows all about them horses. Flem's told him, how much they cost and how much him and that Texas man aim to get for them, make off of them. Come on, Eck. Tell us." The other did not move, sitting on the top step, not quite facing them, sitting there beneath the successive layers of their quiet and intent concentrated listening and waiting.

"I don't know," he said. Ratliff began to laugh. He sat in the chair, laughing while the others sat or lounged upon the steps and the railing, sitting beneath his laughing as Eck had sat beneath their listening and waiting. Ratliff ceased laughing. He rose. He yawned quite loud.

"All right. You folks can buy them critters if you want to. But me, I'd just as soon buy a tiger or a rattlesnake. And if Flem Snopes offered me either one of them, I would be afraid to touch it for fear it would turn out to be a painted dog or a piece of garden hose when I went up to take possession of it. I bid you one and all goodnight." He entered the house. They did not look after him, though after a while they all shifted a little and looked down into the lot, upon the splotchy, sporadic surge and flow of the horses, from among which from time to time came an abrupt squeal, a thudding blow. In the pear tree the mockingbird's idiot reiteration pulsed and purled.

"Anse McCallum made a good team outen them two of hisn," the first man said. "They was a little light. That was all."

When the sun rose the next morning a wagon and three saddled mules stood in Mrs. Littlejohn's lane and six men and Eck Snopes' son were already leaning on the fence, looking at the horses which huddled in a quiet clump before the barn door, watching the men in their turn. A second wagon came up the road and into the lane and stopped, and then there were eight men beside the boy standing at the fence, beyond which the horses stood, their blue-and-brown eyeballs rolling alertly in their gaudy faces. "So this here is the Snopes circus, is it?" one of the newcomers said. He glanced at the faces, then he went to the end of the row and stood beside the blacksmith and the little boy. "Are them Flem's horses?" he said to the blacksmith.

"Eck don't know who them horses belong to any more than we do," one of the others said. "He knows that Flem come here on the same wagon with them, because he saw him. But that's all."

"And all he will know," a second said. "His own kin will be the last man in the world to find out anything about Flem Snopes' business."

"No," the first said. "He wouldn't even be that. The first man Flem would tell his business to would be the man that was left after the last man died. Flem Snopes don't even tell himself what he is up to. Not if he was laying in bed with himself in a empty house in the dark of the moon."

"That's a fact," a third said. "Flem would trim Eck or any other of his kin quick as he would us. Ain't that right, Eck?"

"I don't know," Eck said. They were watching the horses, which at that moment broke into a high-eared, stiff-kneed swirl and flowed in a patchwork wave across the lot and brought up again, facing the men along the fence, so they did not hear the Texan until he was among them. He wore a new shirt and another vest a little too small for him and he was putting the paper carton back into his hip pocket.

"Morning, morning," he said. "Come to get an early pick, have you? Want to make me an offer for one or two before the bidding starts and runs the prices up?" They had not looked at the stranger long. They were not looking at him now, but at the horses in the lot, which had lowered their heads, snuffing into the dust.

"I reckon we'll look a while first," one said.

"You are in time to look at them eating breakfast, anyhow," the Texan said. "Which is more than they done without they staid up all night." He opened the gate and entered it. At once the horses jerked their heads up, watching him. "Here, Eck," the Texan said over his shoulder, "two or three of you boys help me drive them into the barn." After a moment Eck and two others approached the gate, the little boy at his father's heels, though the other did not see him until he turned to shut the gate.

"You stay out of here," Eck said. "One of them things will snap your head off same as a acorn before you even know it." He shut the gate and went on after the others, whom the Texan had now waved fanwise outward as he approached the horses which now drew into a restive huddle, beginning to mill slightly, watching the men. Mrs. Littlejohn came out of the kitchen and crossed the yard to the woodpile, watching the lot. She picked up two or three sticks of wood and paused, watching the lot again. Now there were two more men standing at the fence.

"Come on, come on," the Texan said. "They won't hurt you. They just ain't never been in under a roof before."

"I just as lief let them stay out here, if that's what they want to do," Eck said.

"Get yourself a stick—there's a bunch of wagon stakes against the fence yonder—and when one of them tries to rush you, bust him over the head so he will understand what you mean." One of the men went to the fence and got three of the stakes and returned and distributed them. Mrs. Littlejohn, her armful of wood complete now, paused again halfway back to the house, looking into the lot. The little boy was directly behind his father again, though this time the father had not discovered him yet. The men advanced toward the horses, the huddle of which began to break into gaudy units turning inward upon themselves. The Texan was cursing them in a loud steady cheerful voice. "Get in there, you banjo-faced jack rabbits. Don't hurry them, now. Let them take their time. Hi! Get in there. What do you think that barn is—a law court maybe? Or maybe a church and somebody is going to take up a collection on you?" The animals fell slowly back. Now and then one feinted to break from the huddle, the Texan driving it back each time with skillfully thrown bits of dirt. Then one at the rear saw the barn door just behind it but before the herd could break the Texan snatched the wagon stake from Eck and, followed by one of the other men, rushed at the horses and began to lay about the heads and shoulders, choosing by unerring instinct the point animal and striking it first square in the face then on the withers as it turned and then on the rump as it turned further, so that when the break came it was reversed and the entire herd rushed into the long open hallway and brought up against the further wall with a hollow, thunderous sound like that of a collapsing mine-shaft. "Seems to have held all right," the Texan said. He and the other man slammed the half-length doors and looked over them into the tunnel of the barn, at the far end of which the ponies were now a splotchy, phantom moiling punctuated by crackings of wooden partitions and the dry reports of hooves which gradually died away. "Yep, it held all right," the Texan said. The other two came to the doors and looked over them. The little boy came up beside his father now, trying to see through a crack, and Eck saw him.

"Didn't I tell you to stay out of here?" Eck said. "Don't you know them things will kill you quicker than you can say scat? You go and get outside of that fence and stay there."

"Why don't you get your paw to buy you one of them, Wall?" one of the men said.

"Me buy one of them things?" Eck said. "When I can go to the river anytime and catch me a snapping turtle or a moccasin for nothing? You go on, now. Get out of here and stay out." The Texan had entered the barn. One of the men closed the doors after him and put the bar up again and over the top of the doors they watched the Texan go on down the hallway, toward the ponies which now huddled like gaudy phantoms in the gloom, quiet now and already beginning to snuff experimentally into the long lipworn trough fastened against the rear wall. The little boy had merely gone around behind his father, to the other side, where he stood peering now through a knot-hole in a plank. The Texan opened a smaller door in the wall and entered it, though almost immediately he reappeared.

"I don't see nothing but shelled corn in here," he said. "Snopes said he would send some hay up here last night."

"Won't they eat corn either?" one of the men said.

"I don't know," the Texan said. "They ain't never seen any that I know of. We'll find out in a minute though." He disappeared, though they could still hear him in the crib. Then he emerged once more, carrying a big double-ended feed-basket, and retreated into the gloom where the parti-colored rumps of the horses were now ranged quietly along the feeding-trough. Mrs. Littlejohn appeared once more, on the veranda this time, carrying a big brass dinner bell. She raised it to make the first stroke. A small commotion set up among the ponies as the Texan approached but he began to speak to them at once, in a brisk loud unemphatic mixture of cursing and cajolery, disappearing among them. The men at the door heard the dry rattling of the corn-pellets into the trough, a sound broken by a single snort of amazed horror. A plank cracked with a loud report; before their eyes the depths of the hallway dissolved in loud fury, and while they stared over the doors, unable yet to begin to move, the entire interior exploded into mad tossing shapes like a downrush of flames.

"Hell fire," one of them said. "Jump!" he shouted. The three turned and ran frantically for the wagon, Eck last. Several voices from the fence were now shouting something but Eck did not even hear them until, in the act of scrambling madly at the tail-gate, he looked behind him and saw the little boy still leaning to the knot-hole in the door which in the next instant vanished into matchwood, the knot-hole itself exploding from his eye and leaving him, motionless in the diminutive overalls and still leaning forward a little until he vanished utterly beneath the towering parti-colored wave full of feet and glaring eyes and wild teeth which, overtopping, burst into scattering units, revealing at last the gaping orifice and the little boy still standing in it, unscratched, his eye still leaned to the vanished knot-hole.

"Wall!" Eck roared. The little boy turned and ran for the wagon. The

horses were whipping back and forth across the lot, as if while in the barn
they had once more doubled their number; two of them rushed up quarter-
ing and galloped all over the boy again without touching him as he ran,
earnest and diminutive and seemingly without progress, though he reached
the wagon at last, from which Eck, his sunburned skin now a sickly white,
reached down and snatched the boy into the wagon by the straps of his
overalls and slammed him face down across his knees and caught up a coiled
hitching-rope from the bed of the wagon.

"Didn't I tell you to get out of here?" Eck said in a shaking voice.
"Didn't I tell you?"

"If you're going to whip him, you better whip the rest of us too and
then one of us can frail hell out of you," one of the others said.

"Or better still, take the rope and hang that durn fellow yonder," the
second said. The Texan was now standing in the wrecked door of the barn,
taking the gingersnap carton from his hip pocket. "Before he kills the rest
of Frenchman's Bend too."

"You mean Flem Snopes," the first said. The Texan tilted the carton
above his other open palm. The horses still rushed and swirled back and
forth but they were beginning to slow now, trotting on high, stiff legs,
although their eyes were still rolling whitely and various.

"I misdoubted that damn shell corn all along," the Texan said. "But at
least they have seen what it looks like. They can't claim they ain't got
nothing out of this trip." He shook the carton over his open hand. Nothing
came out of it. Mrs. Littlejohn on the veranda made the first stroke with the
dinner bell; at the sound the horses rushed again, the earth of the lot becoming vibrant with the light dry clatter of hooves. The Texan crumpled
the carton and threw it aside. "Chuck wagon," he said. There were three
more wagons in the lane now and there were twenty or more men at the
fence when the Texan, followed by his three assistants and the little boy,
passed through the gate. The bright cloudless early sun gleamed upon the
pearl butt of the pistol in his hip pocket and upon the bell which Mrs.
Littlejohn still rang, peremptory, strong, and loud.

When the Texan, picking his teeth with a splintered kitchen match,
emerged from the house twenty minutes later, the tethered wagons and
riding horses and mules extended from the lot gate to Varner's store, and
there were more than fifty men now standing along the fence beside the
gate, watching him quietly, a little covertly, as he approached, rolling a
little, slightly bowlegged, the high heels of his carved boots printing neatly
into the dust. "Morning, gents," he said. "Here, Bud," he said to the little
boy, who stood slightly behind him, looking at the protruding butt of the
pistol. He took a coin from his pocket and gave it to the boy. "Run to the
store and get me a box of gingersnaps." He looked about at the quiet faces,
protuberant, sucking his teeth. He rolled the match from one side of his
mouth to the other without touching it. "You boys done made your picks,
have you? Ready to start her off, hah?" They did not answer. They were

not looking at him now. That is, he began to have the feeling that each face had stopped looking at him the second before his gaze reached it. After a moment Freeman said:

"Ain't you going to wait for Flem?"

"Why?" the Texan said. Then Freeman stopped looking at him too. There was nothing in Freeman's face either. There was nothing, no alteration, in the Texan's voice. "Eck, you done already picked out yours. So we can start her off when you are ready."

"I reckon not," Eck said. "I wouldn't buy nothing I was afraid to walk up and touch."

"Them little ponies?" the Texan said. "You helped water and feed them. I bet that boy of yours could walk up to any one of them."

"He better not let me catch him," Eck said. The Texan looked about at the quiet faces, his gaze at once abstract and alert, with an impenetrable surface quality like flint, as though the surface were impervious or perhaps there was nothing behind it.

"Them ponies is gentle as a dove, boys. The man that buys them will get the best piece of horseflesh he ever forked or druv for the money. Naturally they got spirit; I ain't selling crowbait. Besides, who'd want Texas crowbait anyway, with Mississippi full of it?" His stare was still absent and unwinking; there was no mirth or humor in his voice and there was neither mirth nor humor in the single guffaw which came from the rear of the group. Two wagons were now drawing out of the road at the same time, up to the fence. The men got down from them and tied them to the fence and approached. "Come up, boys," the Texan said. "You're just in time to buy a good gentle horse cheap."

"How about that one that cut your vest off last night?" a voice said. This time three or four guffawed. The Texan looked toward the sound, bleak and unwinking.

"What about it?" he said. The laughter, if it had been laughter, ceased. The Texan turned to the nearest gatepost and climbed to the top of it, his alternate thighs deliberate and bulging in the tight trousers, the butt of the pistol catching and losing the sun in pearly gleams. Sitting on the post, he looked down at the faces along the fence which were attentive, grave, reserved and not looking at him. "All right," he said. "Who's going to start her off with a bid? Step right up; take your pick and make your bid, and when the last one is sold, walk in that lot and put your rope on the best piece of horseflesh you ever forked or druv for the money. There ain't a pony there that ain't worth fifteen dollars. Young, sound, good for saddle or work stock, guaranteed to outlast four ordinary horses; you couldn't kill one of them with a axle-tree—" There was a small violent commotion at the rear of the group. The little boy appeared, burrowing among the motionless overalls. He approached the post, the new and unbroken paper carton lifted. The Texan leaned down and took it and tore the end from it and shook three or four of the cakes into the boy's hand, a hand as small and almost as black as that of a coon. He held the carton in his hand while he talked, pointing out the horses with it as he indicated them. "Look at that one with the three stocking-feet and the frost-bit ear; watch him now when they pass again. Look at that shoulder-action; that horse is worth twenty dollars of any man's money. Who'll make me a bid on him to start her off?" His voice was harsh, ready, forensic. Along the fence below him the men stood with, buttoned close in their overalls, the tobacco-sacks and worn purses the sparse silver and frayed bills hoarded a coin at a time in the cracks of chimneys or chinked into the logs of walls. From time to time the horses broke and rushed with purposeless violence and huddled again, watching the faces along the fence with wild mismatched eyes. The lane was full of wagons now. As the others arrived they would have to stop in the road beyond it and the occupants came up the lane on foot. Mrs. Littlejohn came out of her kitchen. She crossed the yard, looking toward the lot gate. There was a blackened wash pot set on four bricks in the corner of the yard. She built a fire beneath the pot and came to the fence and stood there for a time, her hands on her hips and the smoke from the fire drifting blue and slow behind her. Then she turned and went back into the house. "Come on, boys," the Texan said. "Who'll make me a bid?"

"Four bits," a voice said. The Texan did not even glance toward it.

"Or, if he don't suit you, how about that fiddle-head horse without no mane to speak of? For a saddle pony, I'd rather have him than that stocking-foot. I heard somebody say fifty cents just now. I reckon he meant five dollars, didn't he? Do I hear five dollars?"

"Four bits for the lot," the same voice said. This time there were no guffaws. It was the Texan who laughed, harshly, with only his lower face, as if he were reciting a multiplication table.

"Fifty cents for the dried mud offen them, he means," he said. "Who'll give a dollar more for the genuine Texas cockle-burrs?" Mrs. Littlejohn came out of the kitchen, carrying the sawn half of a wooden hogshead which she set on a stump beside the smoking pot, and stood with her hands on her hips, looking into the lot for a while without coming to the fence this time. Then she went back into the house. "What's the matter with you boys?" the Texan said. "Here, Eck, you been helping me and you know them horses. How about making me a bid on that wall-eyed one you picked out last night? Here. Wait a minute." He thrust the paper carton into his other hip pocket and swung his feet inward and dropped, cat-light, into the lot. The ponies, huddled, watched him. Then they broke before him and slid stiffly along the fence. He turned them and they whirled and rushed back across the lot; whereupon, as though he had been waiting his chance when they should have turned their backs on him, the Texan began to run too, so that when they reached the opposite side of the lot and turned, slowing to huddle again, he was almost upon them. The earth became thunderous; dust arose, out of which the animals began to burst like flushed quail and into which, with that apparently unflagging faith in his own invulnerability, the Texan rushed. For an instant the watchers could see them in the dust—the pony backed into the angle of the fence and the stable, the man facing it, reaching toward his hip. Then the beast rushed at him in a sort of fatal and hopeless desperation and he struck it between the eyes with the pistol-butt and felled it and leaped onto its prone head. The pony recovered almost at once and pawed itself to its knees and heaved at its prisoned head and fought itself up, dragging the man with it; for an instant in the dust the watchers saw the man free of the earth and in violent lateral motion like a rag attached to the horse's head. Then the Texan's feet came back to earth and the dust blew aside and revealed them, motionless, the Texan's sharp heels braced into the ground, one hand gripping the pony's forelock and the other its nostrils, the long evil muzzle wrung backward over its scarred shoulder while it breathed in labored and hollow groans. Mrs. Littlejohn was in the yard again. No one had seen her emerge this time. She carried an armful of clothing and a metal-ridged washboard and she was standing motionless at the kitchen steps, looking into the lot. Then she moved across the yard, still looking into the lot, and dumped the garments into the tub, still looking into the lot. "Look him over, boys," the Texan panted, turning his own suffused face and the protuberant glare of his eyes toward the fence. "Look him over quick. Them shoulders and—" He had relaxed for an instant apparently. The animal exploded again; again for an instant the Texan was free of the earth, though he was still talking: "—and legs you whoa I'll tear your face right look him over quick boys worth fifteen dollars of let me get a holt of who'll make me a bid whoa you blare-eyed jack rabbit, whoa!" They were moving now—a kaleidoscope of inextricable and incredible violence on the periphery of which the metal clasps of the Texan's suspenders sun-glinted in ceaseless orbit, with terrific slowness across the lot. Then the broad clay-colored hat soared deliberately outward; an instant later the Texan followed it, though still on his feet, and the pony shot free in mad, staglike bounds. The Texan picked up the hat and struck the dust from it against his leg, and returned to the fence and mounted the post again. He was breathing heavily. Still the faces did not look at him as he took the carton from his hip and shook a cake from it and put the cake into his mouth, chewing, breathing harshly. Mrs. Littlejohn turned away and began to bail water from the pot into the tub, though after each bucketful she turned her head and looked into the lot again. "Now, boys," the Texan said. "Who says that pony ain't worth fifteen dollars? You couldn't buy that much dynamite for just fifteen dollars. There ain't one of them can't do a mile in three minutes; turn them into pasture and they will board themselves; work them like hell all day and every time you think about it, lay them over the head with a single-tree and after a couple of days every jack rabbit one of them will be so tame you will have to put them out of the house at night like a cat." He shook another cake from the carton and ate it. "Come on, Eck," he said. "Start her off. How about ten dollars for that horse, Eck?"

"What need I got for a horse I would need a bear-trap to catch?" Eck said.

"Didn't you just see me catch him?"

"I seen you," Eck said. "And I don't want nothing as big as a horse if I got to wrastle with it every time it finds me on the same side of a fence it's on."

"All right," the Texan said. He was still breathing harshly, but now there was nothing of fatigue or breathlessness in it. He shook another cake into his palm and inserted it beneath his moustache. "All right. I want to get this auction started. I ain't come here to live, no matter how good a country you folks claim you got. I'm going to give you that horse." For a moment there was no sound, not even that of breathing except the Texan's.

"You going to give it to me?" Eck said.

"Yes. Provided you will start the bidding on the next one." Again there was no sound save the Texan's breathing, and then the clash of Mrs. Little-john's pail against the rim of the pot.

"I just start the bidding," Eck said. "I don't have to buy it lessen I ain't over-topped." Another wagon had come up the lane. It was battered and paintless. One wheel had been repaired by crossed planks bound to the spokes with baling wire and the two underfed mules wore a battered harness patched with bits of cotton rope; the reins were ordinary cotton plowlines, not new. It contained a woman in a shapeless gray garment and a faded sunbonnet, and a man in faded and patched though clean overalls. There was not room for the wagon to draw out of the lane so the man left it stand-ing where it was and got down and came forward—a thin man, not large, with something about his eyes, something strained and washed-out, at once vague and intense, who shoved into the crowd at the rear, saying,

"What? What's that? Did he give him that horse?"

"All right," the Texan said. "That wall-eyed horse with the scarred neck belongs to you. Now. That one that looks like he's had his head in a flour barrel. What do you say? Ten dollars?"

"Did he give him that horse?" the newcomer said.

"A dollar," Eck said. The Texan's mouth was still open for speech; for an instant his face died so behind the hard eyes.

"A dollar?" he said. "One dollar? Did I actually hear that?"

"Durn it," Eck said. "Two dollars then. But I ain't——"

"Wait," the newcomer said. "You, up there on the post." The Texan looked at him. When the others turned, they saw that the woman had left the wagon too, though they had not known she was there since they had not seen the wagon drive up. She came among them behind the man, gaunt in the gray shapeless garment and the sunbonnet, wearing stained canvas gym-nasium shoes. She overtook the man but she did not touch him, standing just behind him, her hands rolled before her into the gray dress.

"Henry," she said in a flat voice. The man looked over his shoulder.

"Get back to that wagon," he said.

"Here, missus," the Texan said. "Henry's going to get the bargain of his life in about a minute. Here, boys, let the missus come up close where she can see. Henry's going to pick out that saddle-horse the missus has been wanting. Who says ten——"

"Henry," the woman said. She did not raise her voice. She had not once looked at the Texan. She touched the man's arm. He turned and struck her hand down.

"Get back to that wagon like I told you." The woman stood behind him, her hands rolled again into her dress. She was not looking at anything, speaking to anyone.

"He ain't no more despair than to buy one of them things," she said. "And us not but five dollars away from the poorhouse, he ain't no more despair." The man turned upon her with that curious air of leashed, of dreamlike fury. The others lounged along the fence in attitudes gravely inattentive, almost oblivious. Mrs. Littlejohn had been washing for some time now, pumping rhythmically up and down above the washboard in the sud-foamed tub. She now stood erect again, her soap-raw hands on her hips, looking into the lot.

"Shut your mouth and get back in that wagon," the man said. "Do you want me to take a wagon stake to you?" He turned and looked up at the Texan. "Did you give him that horse?" he said. The Texan was looking at the woman. Then he looked at the man; still watching him, he tilted the paper carton over his open palm. A single cake came out of it.

"Yes," he said.

"Is the fellow that bids in this next horse going to get that first one too?"

"No," the Texan said.

"All right," the other said. "Are you going to give a horse to the man that makes the first bid on the next one?"

"No," the Texan said.

"Then if you were just starting the auction off by giving away a horse, why didn't you wait till we were all here?" The Texan stopped looking at the other. He raised the empty carton and squinted carefully into it, as if it might contain a precious jewel or perhaps a deadly insect. Then he crumpled it and dropped it carefully beside the post on which he sat.

"Eck bids two dollars," he said. "I believe he still thinks he's bidding on them scraps of bob-wire they come here in instead of on one of the horses. But I got to accept it. But are you boys——"

"So Eck's going to get two horses at a dollar a head," the newcomer said. "Three dollars." The woman touched him again. He flung her hand off without turning and she stood again, her hands rolled into her dress across her flat stomach, not looking at anything.

"Misters," she said, "we got chaps in the house that never had shoes last winter. We ain't got corn to feed the stock. We got five dollars I earned weaving by firelight after dark. And he ain't no more despair."

"Henry bids three dollars," the Texan said. "Raise him a dollar, Eck, and the horse is yours." Beyond the fence the horses rushed suddenly and for no reason and as suddenly stopped, staring at the faces along the fence.

"Henry," the woman said. The man was watching Eck. His stained and broken teeth showed a little beneath his lip. His wrists dangled into fists below the faded sleeves of his shirt too short from many washings.

"Four dollars," Eck said.

"Five dollars!" the husband said raising one clenched hand. He shouldered himself forward toward the gatepost. The woman did not follow him. She now looked at the Texan for the first time. Her eyes were a washed gray also, as though they had faded too like the dress and the sunbonnet.

"Mister," she said, "if you take that five dollars I earned my chaps a-weaving for one of them things, it'll be a curse on you and yours during all the time of man."

"Five dollars!" the husband shouted. He thrust himself up to the post, his clenched hand on a level with the Texan's knees. He opened it upon a wad of frayed banknotes and silver. "Five dollars! And the man that raises it will have to beat my head off or I'll beat hisn."

"All right," the Texan said. "Five dollars is bid. But don't you shake your hand at me."

At five o'clock that afternoon the Texan crumpled the third paper carton and dropped it to the earth beneath him. In the copper slant of the levelling sun which fell also upon the line of limp garments in Mrs. Littlejohn's backyard and which cast his shadow and that of the post on which he sat long across the lot where now and then the ponies still rushed in purposeless and tireless surges, the Texan straightened his leg and thrust his hand into his pocket and took out a coin and leaned down to the little boy. His voice was now hoarse, spent. "Here, bud," he said. "Run to the store and get me a box of gingersnaps." The men still stood along the fence, tireless, in their overalls and faded shirts. Flem Snopes was there now, appeared suddenly from nowhere, standing beside the fence with a space the width of three or four men on either side of him, standing there in his small yet definite isolation, chewing tobacco, in the same gray trousers and minute bow tie in which he had departed last summer but in a new cap, gray too like the other, but new, and overlaid with a bright golfer's plaid, looking also at the horses in the lot. All of them save two had been sold for sums ranging from three dollars and a half to eleven and twelve dollars. The purchasers, as they had bid them in, had gathered as though by instinct into a separate group on the other side of the gate, where they stood with their hands lying upon the top strand of the fence, watching with a still more sober intensity the animals which some of them had owned for seven and eight hours now but had not yet laid hands upon. The husband, Henry, stood beside the post on which the Texan sat. The wife had gone back to the wagon, where she sat gray in the gray garment, motionless, looking at nothing, still, she might have been something inanimate which he had loaded into the wagon to move it somewhere, waiting now in the wagon until he should be ready to go on again, patient, insensate, timeless.

"I bought a horse and I paid cash for it," he said. His voice was harsh and spent too, the mad look in his eyes had a quality glazed now and even sightless. "And yet you expect me to stand around here till they are all sold before I can get my horse. Well, you can do all the expecting you want. I'm going to take my horse out of there and go home." The Texan looked down at him. The Texan's shirt was blotched with sweat. His big face was cold and still, his voice level.

"Take your horse then." After a moment Henry looked away. He stood with his head bent a little, swallowing from time to time.

"Ain't you going to catch him for me?"

"It ain't my horse," the Texan said in that flat still voice. After a while Henry raised his head. He did not look at the Texan.

"Who'll help me catch my horse?" he said. Nobody answered. They stood along the fence, looking quietly into the lot where the ponies huddled, already beginning to fade a little where the long shadow of the house lay upon them, deepening. From Mrs. Littlejohn's kitchen the smell of frying ham came. A noisy cloud of sparrows swept across the lot and into a china-berry tree beside the house, and in the high soft vague blue swallows stooped and whirled in erratic indecision, their cries like strings plucked at random. Without looking back, Henry raised his voice: "Bring that ere plowline." After a time the wife moved. She got down from the wagon and took a coil of new cotton rope from it and approached. The husband took the rope from her and moved toward the gate. The Texan began to descend from the post, stiffly, as Henry put his hand on the latch. "Come on here," he said. The wife had stopped when he took the rope from her. She moved again, obediently, her hands rolled into the dress across her stomach, passing the Texan without looking at him.

"Don't go in there, missus," he said. She stopped, not looking at him, not looking at anything. The husband opened the gate and entered the lot and turned, holding the gate open but without raising his eyes.

"Come on here," he said.

"Don't you go in there, missus," the Texan said. The wife stood motionless between them, her face almost concealed by the sunbonnet, her hands folded across her stomach.

"I reckon I better," she said. The other men did not look at her at all, at her or Henry either. They stood along the fence, grave and quiet and inattentive, almost bemused. Then the wife passed through the gate; the husband shut it behind them and turned and began to move toward the huddled ponies, the wife following in the gray and shapeless garment within which she moved without inference of locomotion, like something on a moving platform, a float. The horses were watching them. They clotted and blended and shifted among themselves, on the point of breaking though not breaking yet. The husband shouted at them. He began to curse them, advancing, the wife following. Then the huddle broke, the animals moving with high, stiff knees, circling the two people who turned and followed again as the herd flowed and huddled again at the opposite side of the lot.

"There he is," the husband said. "Get him into that corner." The herd divided; the horse which the husband had bought jolted on stiff legs. The wife shouted at it; it spun and poised, plunging, then the husband struck it across the face with the coiled rope, and it whirled and slammed into the corner of the fence. "Keep him there now," the husband said. He shook out the rope, advancing. The horse watched him with wild, glaring eyes; it rushed again, straight toward the wife. She shouted at it and waved her arms but it soared past her in a long bound and rushed again into the huddle of its fellows. They followed and hemmed it again into another corner; again the wife failed to stop its rush for freedom and the husband turned and struck her with the coiled rope. "Why didn't you head him?" he said. "Why didn't you?" He struck her again; she did not move, not even to fend the rope with a raised arm. The men along the fence stood quietly, their faces lowered as though brooding upon the earth at their feet. Only Flem Snopes was still watching—if he ever had been looking into the lot at all, standing in his little island of isolation, chewing with his characteristic faint sidewise thrust beneath the new plaid cap.

The Texan said something, not loud, harsh and short. He entered the lot and went to the husband and jerked the uplifted rope from his hand. The husband whirled as though he were about to spring at the Texan, crouched slightly, his knees bent and his arms held slightly away from his sides, though his gaze never mounted higher than the Texan's carved and dusty boots. Then the Texan took the husband by the arm and led him back toward the gate, the wife following, and through the gate which he held open for the woman and then closed. He took a wad of banknotes from his trousers and removed a bill from it and put it into the woman's hand. "Get him into the wagon and get him on home," he said.

"What's that for?" Flem Snopes said. He had approached. He now stood beside the post on which the Texan had been sitting. The Texan did not look at him.

"Thinks he bought one of them ponies," the Texan said. He spoke in a flat still voice, like that of a man after a sharp run. "Get him on away, missus."

"Give him back that money," the husband said, in his lifeless, spent tone. "I bought that horse and I aim to have him if I got to shoot him before I can put a rope on him." The Texan did not even look at him.

"Get him on away from here, missus," he said.

"You take your money and I take my horse," the husband said. He was shaking slowly and steadily now, as though he were cold. His hands open and shut below the frayed cuffs of his shirt. "Give it back to him," he said.

"You don't own no horse of mine," the Texan said. "Get him on home, missus." The husband raised his spent face, his mad glazed eyes. He reached out his hand. The woman held the banknote in her folded hands across her stomach. For a while the husband's shaking hand merely fumbled at it. Then he drew the banknote free.

"It's my horse," he said. "I bought it. These fellows saw me. I paid for it. It's my horse. Here." He turned and extended the banknote toward Snopes. "You got something to do with these horses. I bought one. Here's the money for it. I bought one. Ask him." Snopes took the banknote. The others stood, gravely inattentive, in relaxed attitudes along the fence. The sun had gone now; there was nothing save violet shadow upon them and upon the lot where once more and for no reason the ponies rushed and flowed. At that moment the little boy came up, tireless and indefatigable still, with the new paper carton. The Texan took it, though he did not open it at once. He had dropped the rope and now the husband stooped for it, fumbling at it for some time before he lifted it from the ground. Then he stood with his head bent, his knuckles whitening on the rope. The woman had not moved. Twilight was coming fast now; there was a last mazy swirl of swallows against the high and changing azure. Then the Texan tore the end from the carton and tilted one of the cakes into his hand; he seemed to be watching the hand as it shut slowly upon the cake until a fine powder of snuff-colored dust began to rain from his fingers. He rubbed the hand carefully on his thigh and raised his head and glanced about until he saw the little boy and handed the carton back to him.

"Here, Bud," he said. Then he looked at the woman, his voice flat, quiet again. "Mr. Snopes will have your money for you tomorrow. Better get him in the wagon and get him on home. He don't own no horse. You can get your money tomorrow from Mr. Snopes." The wife turned and went back to the wagon and got into it. No one watched her, nor the husband who still stood, his head bent, passing the rope from one hand to the other. They leaned along the fence, grave and quiet, as though the fence were in another land, another time.

"How many you got left?" Snopes said. The Texan roused; they all seemed to rouse then, returning, listening again.

"Got three now," the Texan said. "Swap all three of them for a buggy or a——"

"It's out in the road," Snopes said, a little shortly, a little quickly, turning away. "Get your mules." He went on up the lane. They watched the Texan enter the lot and cross it, the horses flowing before him but without the old irrational violence, as if they too were spent, vitiated with the long day, and enter the barn and then emerge, leading the two harnessed mules. The wagon had been backed under the shed beside the barn. The Texan entered this and came out a moment later, carrying a bedding-roll and his coat, and led the mules back toward the gate, the ponies huddled again and watching him with their various unmatching eyes, quietly now, as if they too realized there was not only an armistice between them at last but that they would never look upon each other again in both their lives. Someone opened the gate. The Texan led the mules through it and they followed in a body, leaving the husband standing beside the closed gate, his head still bent and the coiled rope in his hand. They passed the wagon in which the wife sat, her gray garment fading into the dusk, almost the same color and as still, looking at nothing; they passed the clothesline with its limp and unwinded drying garments, walking through the hot vivid smell of ham from Mrs. Littlejohn's kitchen. When they reached the end of the lane they could see the moon, almost full, tremendous and pale and still lightless in the sky from which day had not quite gone. Snopes was standing at the end of the lane beside an empty buggy. It was the one with the glittering wheels and the fringed parasol top in which he and Will Varner had used to drive. The Texan was motionless too, looking at it.

"Well well well," he said. "So this is it."

"If it don't suit you, you can ride one of the mules back to Texas," Snopes said.

"You bet," the Texan said. "Only I ought to have a powder puff or at least a mandolin to ride it with." He backed the mules onto the tongue and lifted the breastyoke. Two of them came forward and fastened the traces for him. Then they watched him get into the buggy and raise the reins.

"Where you heading for?" one said. "Back to Texas?"

"In this?" the Texan said. "I wouldn't get past the first Texas saloon without starting the vigilance committee. Besides, I ain't going to waste all this here lace-trimmed top and these spindle wheels just on Texas. Long as I am this far, I reckon I'll go on a day or two and look-see them Northern towns. Washington and New York and Baltimore. What's the short way to New York from here?" They didn't know. But they told him how to reach Jefferson.

"You're already headed right," Freeman said. "Just keep right on up the road past the schoolhouse."

"All right," the Texan said. "Well, remember about busting them ponies over the head now and then until they get used to you. You won't have any trouble with them then." He lifted the reins again. As he did so Snopes stepped forward and got into the buggy.

"I'll ride as far as Varner's with you," he said.

"I didn't know I was going past Varner's," the Texan said.

"You can go to town that way," Snopes said. "Drive on." The Texan shook the reins. Then he said,

"Whoa." He straightened his leg and put his hand into his pocket. "Here, Bud," he said to the little boy, "run to the store and— Never mind. I'll stop and get it myself, long as I am going back that way. Well, boys," he said. "Take care of yourselves." He swung the team around. The buggy went on. They looked after it.

"I reckon he aims to kind of come up on Jefferson from behind," Quick said.

"He'll be lighter when he gets there," Freeman said. "He can come up to it easy from any side he wants."

"Yes," Bookwright said. "His pockets won't rattle." They went back to the lot; they passed on through the narrow way between the two lines of patient and motionless wagons, which at the end was completely closed by the one in which the woman sat. The husband was still standing beside the gate with his coiled rope, and now night had completely come. The light itself had not changed so much; if anything, it was brighter but with that other-worldly quality of moonlight, so that when they stood once more looking into the lot, the splotchy bodies of the ponies had a distinctness, almost a brilliance, but without individual shape and without depth—no longer horses, no longer flesh and bone directed by a principle capable of calculated violence, no longer inherent with the capacity to hurt and harm.

"Well, what are we waiting for?" Freeman said. "For them to go to roost?"

"We better all get our ropes first," Quick said. "Get your ropes, everybody." Some of them did not have ropes. When they left home that morning, they had not heard about the horses, the auction. They had merely happened through the village by chance and learned of it and stopped.

"Go to the store and get some then," Freeman said.

"The store will be closed now," Quick said.

"No it won't," Freeman said, "If it was closed, Lump Snopes would a been up here." So while the ones who had come prepared got their ropes from the wagons, the others went down to the store. The clerk was just closing it.

"You all ain't started catching them yet, have you?" he said. "Good; I was afraid I wouldn't get there in time." He opened the door again and amid the old strong sunless smells of cheese and leather and molasses he measured and cut off sections of plow-line for them and in a body and the clerk in the center and still talking, voluble and unlistened to, they returned up the road. The pear tree before Mrs. Littlejohn's was like drowned silver now in the moon. The mockingbird of last night, or another one, was already singing in it, and they now saw, tied to the fence, Ratliff's buckboard and team.

"I thought something was wrong all day," one said. "Ratliff wasn't there to give nobody advice." When they passed down the lane, Mrs. Littlejohn was in her backyard, gathering the garments from the clothesline; they could still smell the ham. The others were waiting at the gate, beyond which the ponies, huddled again, were like phantom fish, suspended apparently without legs now in the brilliant treachery of the moon.

"I reckon the best way will be for us all to take and catch them one at a time," Freeman said.

"One at a time," the husband, Henry, said. Apparently he had not moved since the Texan had led his mules through the gate, save to lift his hands to the top of the gate, one of them still clutching the coiled rope. "One at a time," he said. He began to curse in a harsh, spent monotone. "After I've stood around here all day, waiting for that—" He cursed. He began to jerk at the gate, shaking it with spent violence until one of the others slid the latch back and it swung open and Henry entered it, the others following, the little boy pressing close behind his father until Eck became aware of him and turned.

"Here," he said. "Give me that rope. You stay out of here."

"Aw, paw," the boy said.

"No sir. Them things will kill you. They almost done it this morning. You stay out of here."

"But we got two to catch." For a moment Eck stood looking down at the boy.

"That's right," he said. "We got two. But you stay close to me now. And when I holler run, you run. You hear me?"

"Spread out, boys," Freeman said. "Keep them in front of us." They began to advance across the lot in a ragged crescent-shaped line, each one with his rope. The ponies were now at the far side of the lot. One of them snorted; the mass shifted within itself but without breaking. Freeman, glancing back, saw the little boy. "Get that boy out of here," he said.

"I reckon you better," Eck said to the boy. "You go and get in the wagon yonder. You can see us catch them from there." The little boy turned and trotted toward the shed beneath which the wagon stood. The line of men advanced, Henry a little in front.

"Watch them close now," Freeman said. "Maybe we better try to get them into the barn first—" At that moment the huddle broke. It parted and flowed in both directions along the fence. The men at the ends of the line began to run, waving their arms and shouting. "Head them," Freeman said tensely. "Turn them back." They turned them, driving them back upon themselves again; the animals merged and spun in short, huddling rushes, phantom and inextricable. "Hold them now," Freeman said. "Don't let them get by us." The line advanced again. Eck turned; he did not know why— whether a sound, what. The little boy was just behind him again.

"Didn't I tell you to get in that wagon and stay there?" Eck said.

"Watch out, paw!" the boy said. "There he is! There's ourn!" It was the one the Texan had given Eck. "Catch him, paw!"

"Get out of my way," Eck said. "Get back to that wagon." The line was still advancing. The ponies milled, clotting, forced gradually backward toward the open door of the barn. Henry was still slightly in front, crouched slightly, his thin figure, even in the mazy moonlight, emanating something of that spent fury. The splotchy huddle of animals seemed to be moving before the advancing line of men like a snowball which they might have been pushing before them by some invisible means, gradually nearer and nearer to the black yawn of the barn door. Later it was obvious that the ponies were so intent upon the men that they did not realize the barn was even behind them until they backed into the shadow of it. Then an indescribable sound, a movement desperate and despairing arose among them; for an instant of static horror men and animals faced one another, then the men whirled and ran before a gaudy vomit of long wild faces and splotched chests which overtook and scattered them and flung them sprawling aside and completely obliterated from sight Henry and the little boy, neither of whom had moved though Henry had flung up both arms, still holding his coiled rope, the herd sweeping on across the lot, to crash through the gate which the last man through it had neglected to close, leaving it slightly ajar, carrying all of the gate save the upright to which the hinges were nailed with them, and so among the teams and wagons which choked the lane, the teams springing and lunging too, snapping hitch-reins and tongues. Then the whole inextricable mass crashed among the wagons and eddied and divided about the one in which the woman sat, and rushed on down the lane and into the road, dividing, one half going one way and one half the other.

The men in the lot, except Henry, got to their feet and ran toward the gate. The little boy once more had not been touched, not even thrown off his feet; for a while his father held him clear of the ground in one hand, shaking him like a rag doll. "Didn't I tell you to stay in that wagon?" Eck cried. "Didn't I tell you?"

"Look out, paw!" the boy chattered out of the violent shaking, "there's ourn! There he goes!" It was the horse the Texan had given them again. It was as if they owned no other, the other one did not exist; as if by some absolute and instantaneous rapport of blood they had relegated to oblivion the one for which they had paid money. They ran to the gate and down the lane where the other men had disappeared. They saw the horse the Texan had given them whirl and dash back and rush through the gate into Mrs. Littlejohn's yard and run up the front steps and crash once on the wooden veranda and vanish through the front door. Eck and the boy ran up onto the veranda. A lamp sat on a table just inside the door. In its mellow light they saw the horse fill the long hallway like a pinwheel, gaudy, furious and thunderous. A little further down the hall there was a varnished yellow melodeon. The horse crashed into it; it produced a single note, almost a chord, in bass, resonant and grave, of deep and sober astonishment; the horse with its monstrous and antic shadow whirled again and vanished through another door. It was a bedroom; Ratliff, in his underclothes and one sock and with the other sock in his hand and his back to the door, was leaning out the open window facing the lane, the lot. He looked back over his shoulder. For an instant he and the horse glared at one another. Then he sprang through the window as the horse backed out of the room and into the hall again and whirled and saw Eck and the little boy just entering the front door, Eck still carrying his rope. It whirled again and rushed on down the hall and onto the back porch just as Mrs. Littlejohn, carrying an armful of clothes from the line and the washboard, mounted the steps.

"Get out of here, you son of a bitch," she said. She struck with the wash-board; it divided neatly on the long mad face and the horse whirled and rushed back up the hall, where Eck and the boy now stood.

"Get to hell out of here, Wall!" Eck roared. He dropped to the floor, covering his head with his arms. The boy did not move, and for the third time the horse soared above the unwinking eyes and the unbowed and untouched head and onto the front veranda again just as Ratliff, still carry-ing the sock, ran around the corner of the house and up the steps. The horse whirled without breaking or pausing. It galloped to the end of the veranda and took the railing and soared outward, hobgoblin and floating, in the moon. It landed in the lot still running and crossed the lot and galloped through the wrecked gate and among the overturned wagons and the still intact one in which Henry's wife still sat, and on down the lane and into the road.

A quarter of a mile further on, the road gashed pallid and moony be-tween the moony shadows of the bordering trees, the horse still galloping, galloping its shadow into the dust, the road descending now toward the creek and the bridge. It was of wood, just wide enough for a single vehicle. When the horse reached it, it was occupied by a wagon coming from the opposite direction and drawn by two mules already asleep in the harness and the soporific motion. On the seat was Tull and his wife, in splint chairs in the wagon behind them sat their four daughters, all returning belated from an all-day visit with some of Mrs. Tull's kin. The horse neither checked nor swerved. It crashed once on the wooden bridge and rushed between the two mules which waked lunging in opposite directions in the traces, the horse now apparently scrambling along the wagon-tongue itself like a mad squirrel and scrabbling at the end-gate of the wagon with its forefeet as if it intended to climb into the wagon while Tull shouted at it and struck at its face with his whip. The mules were now trying to turn the wagon around in the middle of the bridge. It slewed and tilted, the bridge-rail cracked with a sharp report above the shrieks of the women; the horse scrambled at last across the back of one of the mules and Tull stood up in the wagon and kicked at its face. Then the front end of the wagon rose, flinging Tull, the reins now wrapped several times about his wrist, backward into the wagon bed among the overturned chairs and the exposed stockings and undergar-ments of his women. The pony scrambled free and crashed again on the wooden planking, galloping again. The wagon lurched again; the mules had finally turned it on the bridge where there was not room for it to turn and were now kicking themselves free of the traces. When they came free, they snatched Tull bodily out of the wagon. He struck the bridge on his face and was dragged for several feet before the wrist-wrapped reins broke. Far up the road now, distancing the frantic mules, the pony faded on. While the five women still shrieked above Tull's unconscious body, Eck and the little boy came up, trotting, Eck still carrying his rope. He was panting. "Which way'd he go?" he said.

In the now empty and moon-drenched lot, his wife and Mrs. Littlejohn and Ratliff and Lump Snopes, the clerk, and three other men raised Henry out of the trampled dust and carried him into Mrs. Littlejohn's back yard. His face was blanched and stony, his eyes were closed, the weight of his head tautened his throat across the protruding larynx; his teeth glinted dully beneath his lifted lip. They carried him on toward the house, through the dappled shade of the chinaberry trees. Across the dreaming and silver night a faint sound like remote thunder came and ceased. "There's one of them on the creek bridge," one of the men said.

"It's that one of Eck Snopes'," another said. "The one that was in the house." Mrs. Littlejohn had preceded them into the hall. When they entered with Henry, she had already taken the lamp from the table and she stood beside an open door, holding the lamp high.

"Bring him in here," she said. She entered the room first and set the lamp on the dresser. They followed with clumsy scufflings and pantings and laid Henry on the bed and Mrs. Littlejohn came to the bed and stood looking down at Henry's peaceful and bloodless face. "I'll declare," she said. "You men." They had drawn back a little, clumped, shifting from one foot to another, not looking at her nor at his wife either, who stood at the foot of the bed, motionless, her hands folded into her dress. "You all get out of here, V. K.," she said to Ratliff. "Go outside. See if you can't find something else to play with that will kill some more of you."

"All right," Ratliff said. "Come on, boys. Ain't no more horses to catch in here." They followed him toward the door, on tiptoe, their shoes scuffling, their shadows monstrous on the wall.

"Go get Will Varner," Mrs. Littlejohn said. "I reckon you can tell him it's still a mule." They went out; they didn't look back. They tiptoed up the hall and crossed the veranda and descended into the moonlight. Now that they could pay attention to it, the silver air seemed to be filled with faint and sourceless sounds—shouts, thin and distant, again a brief thunder of hooves on a wooden bridge, more shouts faint and thin and earnest and clear as bells; once they even distinguished the words: "Whooey. Head him."

"He went through that house quick," Ratliff said. "He must have found another woman at home." Then Henry screamed in the house behind them. They looked back into the dark hall where a square of light fell through the bedroom door, listening while the scream sank into a harsh respiration: "Ah. Ah. Ah" on a rising note about to become screaming again. "Come on," Ratliff said. "We better get Varner." They went up the road in a body, treading the moon-blanched dust in the tremulous April night murmurous with the moving of sap and the wet bursting of burgeoning leaf and bud and constant with the thin and urgent cries and the brief and fading bursts of galloping hooves. Varner's house was dark, blank and without depth in the moonlight. They stood, clumped darkly in the silver yard and called up at the blank windows until suddenly someone was standing in one of them. It was Flem Snopes' wife. She was in a white garment; the heavy braided club of her hair looked almost black against it. She did not lean out, she merely stood there, full in the moon, apparently blank-eyed or certainly not looking downward at them—the heavy gold hair, the mask not tragic and perhaps not even doomed: just damned, the strong faint lift of breasts beneath marblelike fall of the garment; to those below what Brunhilde, what Rhinemaiden on what spurious river-rock of papier-mache, what Helen returned to what topless and shoddy Argos, waiting for no one. "Evening, Mrs. Snopes," Ratliff said. "We want Uncle Will. Henry Armstid is hurt at Mrs. Littlejohn's." She vanished from the window. They waited in the moonlight, listening to the faint remote shouts and cries, until Varner emerged, sooner than they had actually expected, hunching into his coat and buttoning his trousers over the tail of his nightshirt, his suspenders still dangling in twin loops below the coat. He was carrying the battered bag which contained the plumber-like tools with which he drenched and wormed and blistered and floated or drew the teeth of horses and mules; he came down the steps, lean and loosejointed, his shrewd ruthless head cocked a little as he listened also to the faint bell-like cries and shouts with which the silver air was full.

"Are they still trying to catch them rabbits?" he said.

"All of them except Henry Armstid," Ratliff said. "He caught his."

"Hah," Varner said. "That you, V. K.? How many did you buy?"

"I was too late," Ratliff said. "I never got back in time."

"Hah," Varner said. They moved on to the gate and into the road again. "Well, it's a good bright cool night for running them." The moon was now high overhead, a pearled and mazy yawn in the soft sky, the ultimate ends of which rolled onward, whorl on whorl, beyond the pale stars and by pale stars surrounded. They walked in a close clump, tramping their shadows into the road's mild dust, blotting the shadows of the burgeoning trees which soared, trunk branch and twig against the pale sky, delicate and finely thinned. They passed the dark store. Then the pear tree came in sight. It rose in mazed and silver immobility like exploding snow; the mockingbird still sang in it. "Look at that tree," Varner said. "It ought to make this year, sho."

"Corn'll make this year too," one said.

"A moon like this is good for every growing thing outen earth," Varner said. "I mind when me and Mrs. Varner was expecting Eula. Already had a mess of children and maybe we ought to quit then. But I wanted some more gals. Others had done married and moved away, and a passel of boys, soon as they get big enough to be worth anything, they ain't got time to work. Got to set around the store and talk. But a gal will stay home and work until she does get married. So there was a old woman told my mammy once that if a woman showed her belly to the full moon after she had done caught, it would be a gal. So Mrs. Varner taken and laid every night with the moon on her nekid belly, until it fulled and after. I could lay my ear to her belly and hear Eula kicking and scrouging like all get-out, feeling the moon."

"You mean it actually worked sho enough, Uncle Will?" the other said.

"Hah," Varner said. "You might try it. You get enough women showing their nekid bellies to the moon or the sun either or even just to your hand fumbling around often enough and more than likely after a while there will be something in it you can lay your ear and listen to, provided something come up and you ain't got away by that time. Hah, V. K.?" Someone guffawed.

"Don't ask me," Ratliff said. "I can't even get nowhere in time to buy a cheap horse." Two or three guffawed this time. Then they began to hear Henry's respirations from the house: "Ah. Ah. Ah." and they ceased abruptly, as if they had not been aware of their closeness to it. Varner walked on in front, lean, shambling, yet moving quite rapidly, though his head was still slanted with listening as the faint, urgent, indomitable cries murmured in the silver lambence, sourceless, at times almost musical, like fading bell-notes; again there was a brief rapid thunder of hooves on wooden planking.

"There's another one on the creek bridge," one said.

"They are going to come out even on them things, after all," Varner said. "They'll get the money back in exercise and relaxation. You take a man that ain't got no other relaxation all year long except dodging mule-dung up and down a field furrow. And a night like this one, when a man ain't old enough yet to lay still and sleep, and yet he ain't young enough anymore to be tomcatting in and out of other folks' back windows, something like this is good for him. It'll make him sleep tomorrow night anyhow, provided he gets back home by then. If we had just knowed about this in time, we could have trained up a pack of horse-dogs. Then we could have held one of these field trials."

"That's one way to look at it, I reckon," Ratliff said. "In fact, it might be a considerable comfort to Bookwright and Quick and Freeman and Eck Snopes and them other new horse-owners if that side of it could be brought to their attention, because the chances are ain't none of them thought to look at it in that light yet. Probably there ain't a one of them that believes now there's any cure a tall for that Texas disease Flem Snopes and that Dead-eye Dick brought here."

"Hah," Varner said. He opened Mrs. Littlejohn's gate. The dim light still fell outward across the hall from the bedroom door; beyond it, Armstid was saying "Ah. Ah. Ah" steadily. "There's a pill for every ill but the last one."

"Even if there was always time to take it," Ratliff said.

"Hah," Varner said again. He glanced back at Ratliff for an instant, pausing. But the little hard bright eyes were invisible now; it was only the bushy overhang of the brows which seemed to concentrate downward toward him in writhen immobility, not frowning but with a sort of fierce risibility. "Even if there was time to take it. Breathing is a sight-draft dated yesterday."

ii

At nine o'clock on the second morning after that, five men were sitting or squatting along the gallery of the store. The sixth was Ratliff. He was standing up, and talking: "Maybe there wasn't but one of them things in Mrs. Littlejohn's house that night, like Eck says. But it was the biggest drove of just one horse I ever seen. It was in my rooms and it was on the front porch and I could hear Mrs. Littlejohn hitting it over the head with that washboard in the back yard all at the same time. And still it was missing everybody everytime. I reckon that's what that Texas man meant by calling them bargains: that a man would need to be powerful unlucky to ever get close enough to one of them to get hurt." They laughed, all except Eck himself. He and the little boy were eating. When they mounted the steps, Eck had gone on into the store and emerged with a paper sack, from which he took a segment of cheese and with his pocket knife divided it carefully into two exact halves and gave one to the boy and took a handful of crackers from the sack and gave them to the boy, and now they squatted against the wall, side by side and, save for the difference in size, identical, eating.

"I wonder what that horse thought Ratliff was," one said. He held a spray of peach bloom between his teeth. It bore four blossoms like miniature ballet skirts of pink tulle. "Jumping out windows and running indoors in his shirt-tail? I wonder how many Ratliffs that horse thought he saw."

"I don't know," Ratliff said. "But if he saw just half as many of me as I saw of him, he was sholy surrounded. Everytime I turned my head, that thing was just running over me or just swirling to run back over that boy again. And that boy there, he stayed right under it one time to my certain knowledge for a full one-and-one-half minutes without ducking his head or even batting his eyes. Yes sir, when I looked around and seen that varmint in the door behind me blaring its eyes at me, I'd a made sho Flem Snopes had brought a tiger back from Texas except I knowed that couldn't no just one tiger completely fill a entire room." They laughed again, quietly. Lump Snopes, the clerk, sitting in the only chair tilted back against the door-facing and partly blocking the entrance, cackled suddenly.

"If Flem had knowed how quick you fellows was going to snap them horses up, he'd a probably brought some tigers," he said. "Monkeys too."

"So they was Flem's horses," Ratliff said. The laughter stopped. The other three had open knives in their hands, with which they had been trimming idly at chips and slivers of wood. Now they sat apparently absorbed in the delicate and almost tedious movements of the knife-blades. The clerk had looked quickly up and found Ratliff watching him. His constant expression of incorrigible and mirthful disbelief had left him now; only the empty wrinkles of it remained about his mouth and eyes.

"Has Flem ever said they was?" he said. "But you town fellows are

smarter than us country folks. Likely you done already read Flem's mind."
But Ratliff was not looking at him now.

"And I reckon we'd a bought them," he said. He stood above them
again, easy, intelligent, perhaps a little sombre but still perfectly impenetrable. "Eck here, for instance. With a wife and family to support. He owns
two of them, though to be sho he never had to pay money for but one. I
heard folks chasing them things up until midnight last night, but Eck and
that boy ain't been home at all in two days." They laughed again, except
Eck. He pared off a bit of cheese and speared it on the knife-point and put
it into his mouth.

"Eck caught one of hisn," the second man said.

"That so?" Ratliff said. "Which one was it, Eck? The one he give you
or the one you bought?"

"The one he give me," Eck said, chewing.

"Well, well," Ratliff said. "I hadn't heard about that. But Eck's still one
horse short. And the one he had to pay money for. Which is pure proof
enough that them horses wasn't Flem's because wouldn't no man even give
his own blood kin something he couldn't even catch." They laughed again,
but they stopped when the clerk spoke. There was no mirth in his voice
at all.

"Listen," he said. "All right. We done all admitted you are too smart
for anybody to get ahead of. You never bought no horse from Flem or
nobody else, so maybe it ain't none of your business and maybe you better
just leave it at that."

"Sholy," Ratliff said. "It's done already been left at that two nights ago.
The fellow that forgot to shut that lot gate done that. With the exception
of Eck's horse. And we know that wasn't Flem's, because that horse was
give to Eck for nothing."

"There's others besides Eck that ain't got back home yet," the man with
the peach spray said. "Bookwright and Quick are still chasing theirs. They
was reported three miles west of Burtsboro Old Town at eight o'clock last
night. They ain't got close enough to it yet to tell which one it belongs to."

"Sholy," Ratliff said. "The only new horse-owner in this country that
could a been found without bloodhounds since whoever it was left that gate
open two nights ago, is Henry Armstid. He's laying right there in Mrs.
Littlejohn's bedroom where he can watch the lot so that any time the one
he bought happens to run back into it, all he's got to do is to holler at his
wife to run out with the rope and catch it—" He ceased, though he said,
"Morning, Flem," so immediately afterward and with no change whatever
in tone, that the pause was not even discernible. With the exception of the
clerk, who sprang up, vacated the chair with a sort of servile alacrity, and
Eck and the little boy who continued to eat, they watched above their stilled
hands as Snopes in the gray trousers and the minute tie and the new cap
with its bright overplaid mounted the steps. He was chewing; he already
carried a piece of white pine board; he jerked his head at them, looking at

nobody, and took the vacated chair and opened his knife and began to whittle. The clerk now leaned in the opposite side of the door, rubbing his back against the facing. The expression of merry and invincible disbelief had returned to his face, with a quality watchful and secret.

"You're just in time," he said. "Ratliff here seems to be in a considerable sweat about who actually owned them horses." Snopes drew his knife-blade neatly along the board, the neat, surgeon-like sliver curling before it. The others were whittling again, looking carefully at nothing, except Eck and the boy, who were still eating, and the clerk rubbing his back against the door-facing and watching Snopes with that secret and alert intensity. "Maybe you could put his mind at rest." Snopes turned his head slightly and spat, across the gallery and the steps and into the dust beyond them. He drew the knife back and began another curling sliver.

"He was there too," Snopes said. "He knows as much as anybody else." This time the clerk guffawed, chortling, his features gathering toward the center of his face as though plucked there by a hand. He slapped his leg, cackling.

"You might as well to quit," he said. "You can't beat him."

"I reckon not," Ratliff said. He stood above them, not looking at any of them, his gaze fixed apparently on the empty road beyond Mrs. Little-john's house, impenetrable, brooding even. A hulking, half-grown boy in overalls too small for him, appeared suddenly from nowhere in particular. He stood for a while in the road, just beyond spitting-range of the gallery, with the air of having come from nowhere in particular and of not knowing where he would go next when he should move again and of not being troubled by that fact. He was looking at nothing, certainly not toward the gallery, and no one on the gallery so much as looked at him except the little boy, who now watched the boy in the road, his periwinkle eyes grave and steady above the bitten cracker in his halted hand. The boy in the road moved on, thickly undulant in the tight overalls, and vanished beyond the corner of the store, the round head and the unwinking eyes of the little boy on the gallery turning steadily to watch him out of sight. Then the little boy bit the cracker again, chewing. "Of course there's Mrs. Tull," Ratliff said. "But that's Eck she's going to sue for damaging Tull against that bridge. And as for Henry Armstid——"

"If a man ain't got gumption enough to protect himself, it's his own look-out," the clerk said.

"Sholy," Ratliff said, still in that dreamy, abstracted tone, actually speaking over his shoulder even. "And Henry Armstid, that's all right because from what I hear of the conversation that taken place, Henry had already stopped owning that horse he thought was his before that Texas man left. And as for that broke leg, that won't put him out none because his wife can make his crop." The clerk had ceased to rub his back against the door. He watched the back of Ratliff's head, unwinking too, sober and intent; he glanced at Snopes who, chewing, was watching another sliver curl away from the advancing knife-blade, then he watched the back of Ratliff's head again.

"It won't be the first time she has made their crop," the man with the peach spray said. Ratliff glanced at him.

"You ought to know. This won't be the first time I ever saw you in their field, doing plowing Henry never got around to. How many days have you already given them this year?" The man with the peach spray removed it and spat carefully and put the spray back between his teeth.

"She can run a furrow straight as I can," the second said.

"They're unlucky," the third said. "When you are unlucky, it don't matter much what you do."

"Sholy," Ratliff said. "I've heard laziness called bad luck so much that maybe it is."

"He ain't lazy," the third said. "When their mule died three or four years ago, him and her broke their land working time about in the traces with the other mule. They ain't lazy."

"So that's all right," Ratliff said, gazing up the empty road again. "Likely she will begin right away to finish the plowing; that oldest gal is pretty near big enough to work with a mule, ain't she? or at least to hold the plow steady while Mrs. Armstid helps the mule?" He glanced again toward the man with the peach spray as though for an answer, but he was not looking at the other and he went on talking without any pause. The clerk stood with his rump and back pressed against the door-facing as if he had paused in the act of scratching, watching Ratliff quite hard now, unwinking. If Ratliff had looked at Flem Snopes, he would have seen nothing below the down-slanted peak of the cap save the steady motion of his jaws. Another sliver was curling with neat deliberation before the moving knife. "Plenty of time now because all she's got to do after she finishes washing Mrs. Littlejohn's dishes and sweeping out the house to pay hers and Henry's board, is to go out home and milk and cook up enough vittles to last the children until tomorrow and feed them and get the littlest ones to sleep and wait outside the door until that biggest gal gets the bar up and gets into bed herself with the axe——"

"The axe?" the man with the peach spray said.

"She takes it to bed with her. She's just twelve, and what with this country still more or less full of them uncaught horses that never belonged to Flem Snopes, likely she feels maybe she can't swing a mere washboard like Mrs. Littlejohn can—and then come back and wash up the supper dishes. And after that, not nothing to do until morning except to stay close enough where Henry can call her until it's light enough to chop the wood to cook breakfast and then help Mrs. Littlejohn wash the dishes and make the beds and sweep while watching the road. Because likely any time now Flem Snopes will get back from wherever he has been since the auction, which of course is to town naturally to see about his cousin that's got into a little legal trouble, and so get that five dollars. 'Only maybe he won't give it back to me,' she says, and maybe that's what Mrs. Littlejohn thought too, because she never said nothing. I could hear her——"

"And where did you happen to be during all this?" the clerk said.

"Listening," Ratliff said. He glanced back at the clerk, then he was looking away again, almost standing with his back to them. "—could hear her dumping the dishes into the pan like she was throwing them at it. 'Do you reckon he will give it back to me?' Mrs. Armstid says. 'That Texas man give it to him and said he would. All the folks there saw him give Mr. Snopes the money and heard him say I could get it from Mr. Snopes tomorrow.' Mrs. Littlejohn was washing the dishes now, washing them like a man would, like they was made out of iron. 'No,' she says. 'But asking him won't do no hurt.'—'If he wouldn't give it back, it ain't no use to ask,' Mrs. Armstid says.—'Suit yourself,' Mrs. Littlejohn says. 'It's your money.' Then I couldn't hear nothing but the dishes for a while. 'Do you reckon he might give it back to me?' Mrs. Armstid says. 'That Texas man said he would. They all heard him say it.'—'Then go and ask him for it,' Mrs. Littlejohn says. Then I couldn't hear nothing but the dishes again. 'He won't give it back to me,' Mrs. Armstid says.—'All right,' Mrs. Littlejohn says. 'Don't ask him, then.' Then I just heard the dishes. They would have two pans, both washing. 'You don't reckon he would, do you?' Mrs. Armstid says. Mrs. Littlejohn never said nothing. It sounded like she was throwing the dishes at one another. 'Maybe I better go and talk to Henry,' Mrs. Armstid says.—'I would,' Mrs. Littlejohn says. And I be dog if it didn't sound exactly like she had two plates in her hands, beating them together like these here brass bucket-lids in a band. 'Then Henry can buy another five-dollar horse with it. Maybe he'll buy one next time that will out and out kill him. If I just thought he would, I'd give him back that money, myself.'—'I reckon I better talk to him first,' Mrs. Armstid says. And then it sounded just like Mrs. Littlejohn taken up the dishes and pans and all and throwed the whole business at the cookstove—" Ratliff ceased. Behind him the clerk was hissing "Psst! Psst! Flem. Flem!" Then he stopped, and all of them watched Mrs. Armstid approach and mount the steps, gaunt in the shapeless gray garment, the stained tennis shoes hissing faintly on the boards. She came among them and stood, facing Snopes but not looking at anyone, her hands rolled into her apron.

"He said that day he wouldn't sell Henry that horse," she said in a flat toneless voice. "He said you had the money and I could get it from you." Snopes raised his head and turned it slightly again and spat neatly past the woman, across the gallery and into the road.

"He took all the money with him when he left," he said. Motionless, the gray garment hanging in rigid, almost formal folds like drapery in bronze, Mrs. Armstid appeared to be watching something near Snopes' feet, as though she had not heard him, or as if she had quitted her body as soon as she finished speaking and although her body, hearing, had received the words, they would have no life nor meaning until she returned. The clerk was rubbing his back steadily against the door-facing again, watching her. The little boy was watching her too with his unwinking ineffable gaze, but nobody else was. The man with the peach spray removed it and spat and put the twig back into his mouth.

"He said Henry hadn't bought no horse," she said. "He said I could get the money from you."

"I reckon he forgot it," Snopes said. "He took all the money away with him when he left." He watched her a moment longer, then he trimmed again at the stick. The clerk rubbed his back gently against the door, watching her. After a time Mrs. Armstid raised her head and looked up the road where it went on, mild with spring dust, past Mrs. Littlejohn's, beginning to rise, on past the not-yet-bloomed (that would be in June) locust grove across the way, on past the schoolhouse, the weathered roof of which, rising beyond an orchard of peach and pear trees, resembled a hive swarmed about by a cloud of pink-and-white bees, ascending, mounting toward the crest of the hill where the church stood among its sparse gleam of marble headstones in the sombre cedar grove where during the long afternoons of summer the constant mourning doves called back and forth. She moved; once more the rubber soles hissed on the gnawed boards.

"I reckon it's about time to get dinner started," she said.

"How's Henry this morning, Mrs. Armstid?" Ratliff said. She looked at him, pausing, the blank eyes waking for an instant.

"He's resting, I thank you kindly," she said. Then the eyes died again and she moved again. Snopes rose from the chair, closing his knife with his thumb and brushing a litter of minute shavings from his lap.

"Wait a minute," he said. Mrs. Armstid paused again, half-turning, though still not looking at Snopes nor at any of them. Because she can't possibly actually believe it, Ratliff told himself, any more than I do. Snopes entered the store, the clerk, motionless again, his back and rump pressed against the door-facing as though waiting to start rubbing again, watched him enter, his head turning as the other passed him like the head of an owl, the little eyes blinking rapidly now. Jody Varner came up the road on his horse. He did not pass but instead turned in beside the store, toward the mulberry tree behind it where he was in the habit of hitching his horse. A wagon came up the road, creaking past. The man driving it lifted his hand; one or two of the men on the gallery lifted theirs in response. The wagon went on. Mrs. Armstid looked after it. Snopes came out of the door, carrying a small striped paper bag and approached Mrs. Armstid. "Here," he said. Her hand turned just enough to receive it. "A little sweetening for the chaps," he said. His other hand was already in his pocket, and as he turned back to the chair, he drew something from his pocket and handed it to the clerk, who took it. It was a five-cent piece. He sat down in the chair and tilted it back against the door again. He now had the knife in his hand again, already open. He turned his head slightly and spat again, neatly past the gray garment, into the road. The little boy was watching the sack in Mrs. Armstid's hand. Then she seemed to discover it also, rousing.

"You're right kind," she said. She rolled the sack into the apron, the little boy's unwinking gaze fixed upon the lump her hands made beneath the cloth. She moved again. "I reckon I better get on and help with dinner," she said. She descended the steps, though as soon as she reached the level earth and began to retreat, the gray folds of the garment once more lost all inference and intimation of locomotion, so that she seemed to progress without motion like a figure on a retreating and diminishing float; a gray and blasted tree-trunk moving, somehow intact and upright, upon an un-hurried flood. The clerk in the doorway cackled suddenly, explosively, chortling. He slapped his thigh.

"By God," he said. "You can't beat him."

Jody Varner, entering the store from the rear, paused in midstride like a pointing bird-dog. Then, on tiptoe, in complete silence and with aston-ishing speed, he darted behind the counter and sped up the gloomy tunnel, at the end of which a hulking, bear-shaped figure stooped, its entire head and shoulders wedged into the glass case which contained the needles and thread and snuff and tobacco and the stale gaudy candy. He snatched the boy savagely and viciously out; the boy gave a choked cry and struggled flabbily, cramming a final handful of something into his mouth, chewing. But he ceased to struggle almost at once and became slack and inert save for his jaws. Varner dragged him around the counter as the clerk entered, seemed to bounce suddenly into the store with a sort of alert concern. "You, Saint Elmo!" he said.

"Ain't I told you and told you to keep him out of here?" Varner de-manded, shaking the boy. "He's damn near eaten that candy-case clean. Stand up!" The boy hung like a half-filled sack from Varner's hand, chewing with a kind of fatalistic desperation, the eyes shut tight in the vast flaccid colorless face, the ears moving steadily and faintly to the chewing. Save for the jaw and the ears, he appeared to have gone to sleep chewing.

"You, Saint Elmo!" the clerk said. "Stand up!" The boy assumed his own weight, though he did not open his eyes yet nor cease to chew. Varner released him. "Git on home," the clerk said. The boy turned obediently to re-enter the store. Varner jerked him about again.

"Not that way," he said. The boy crossed the gallery and descended the steps, the tight overalls undulant and reluctant across his flabby thighs. Before he reached the ground, his hand rose from his pocket to his mouth; again his ears moved faintly to the motion of chewing.

"He's worse than a rat, ain't he?" the clerk said.

"Rat, hell," Varner said, breathing harshly. "He's worse than a goat. First thing I know, he'll graze on back and work through that lace leather and them hame-strings and lap-links and ring-bolts and eat me and you and him all three clean out the back door. And then be damned if I wouldn't be afraid to turn my back for fear he would cross the road and start in on the gin and the blacksmith shop. Now you mind what I say. If I catch him hanging around here one more time, I'm going to set a bear-trap for him."

He went out onto the gallery, the clerk following. "Well, Eck," he said, "I hear you caught one of your horses."

"That's right," Eck said. He and the little boy had finished the crackers and cheese and he had sat for some time now, holding the empty bag.

"It was the one he give you, wasn't it?" Varner said.

"That's right," Eck said.

"Give the other one to me, paw," the little boy said.

"What happened?" Varner said.

"He broke his neck," Eck said.

"I know," Varner said. "But how?" Eck did not move. Watching him, they could almost see him visibly gathering and arranging words, speech. Varner, looking down at him, began to laugh steadily and harshly, sucking his teeth. "I'll tell you what happened. Eck and that boy finally run it into that blind lane of Freeman's, after a chase of about twenty-four hours. They figured it couldn't possibly climb them eight-foot fences of Freeman's so him and the boy tied their rope across the end of the lane, about three feet off the ground. And sho enough, soon as the horse come to the end of the lane and seen Freeman's barn, it whirled just like Eck figured it would and come helling back up that lane like a scared hen-hawk. It probably never even seen the rope at all. Mrs. Freeman was watching from where she had run up onto the porch. She said that when it hit that rope, it looked just like one of these here great big Christmas pinwheels. But the one you bought got clean away, didn't it?"

"That's right," Eck said. "I never had time to see which way the other one went."

"Give him to me, paw," the little boy said.

"You wait till we catch him," Eck said. "We'll see about it then."

iii

The two actions of Armstid pl. vs. Snopes, and Tull pl. vs. Eckrum Snopes (and anyone else named Snopes or Varner either which Tull's irate wife could contrive to involve, as the village well knew) were accorded a change of venue by mutual agreement and arrangement among the litigants. Three of the parties did, that is, because Flem Snopes flatly refused to recognise the existence of the suit against himself, stating once and without heat and first turning his head slightly aside to spit. "They wasn't none of my horses," then fell to whittling again while the baffled and helpless bailiff stood before the tilted chair with the papers he was trying to serve.

So the Varner surrey was not among the wagons, the buggies, and the saddled horses and mules which moved out of the village on that May Saturday morning, to converge upon Whiteleaf store eight miles away, coming not only from Frenchman's Bend but from other directions too, since by that time what Ratliff had called 'that Texas sickness,' that spotted corruption of frantic and uncatchable horses, had spread as far as twenty and thirty miles. By the time the Frenchman's Bend people began to arrive, there were two dozen wagons, the teams reversed and eased of harness and tied to the rear wheels in order to pass the day, and twice that many saddled animals already standing about the locust grove beside the store and the site of the hearing had already been transferred from the store to an adjacent shed where in the fall cotton would be stored. But by nine o'clock it was seen that even the shed would not hold them all, so the palladium was moved again, from the shed to the grove itself. The horses and mules and wagons were cleared from it; the single chair, the gnawed table bearing a thick Bible which had the appearance of loving and constant use of a piece of old and perfectly-kept machinery and an almanac and a copy of Mississippi Reports dated 1881 and bearing along its opening edge a single thread-thin line of soilure, as if during all the time of his possession its owner (or user) had opened it at only one page though that quite often, were fetched from the shed to the grove; a wagon and four men were dispatched and returned presently from the church a mile away with four wooden pews for the litigants and their clansmen and witnesses; behind these in turn the spectators stood—the men, the women, the children, sober, attentive, and neat, not in their Sunday clothes to be sure, but in the clean working garments donned that morning for the Saturday's diversion of sitting about the country stores or trips into the county seat, and in which they would return to the field on Monday morning and would wear all that week until Friday night came round again.

The Justice of the Peace was a neat, small, plump old man resembling a tender caricature of all grandfathers who ever breathed, in a beautifully laundered though collarless white shirt with immaculate starch-gleaming cuffs and bosom, and steel-framed spectacles and neat, faintly curling white hair. He sat behind the table and looked at them—at the gray woman in the gray sunbonnet and dress, her clasped and motionless hands on her lap resembling a gnarl of pallid and drowned roots from a drained swamp; at Tull in his faded but absolutely clean shirt and the overalls which his womenfolks not only kept immaculately washed but starched and ironed also, and not creased through the legs but flat across them from seam to seam, so that on each Saturday morning they resembled the short pants of a small boy, and the sedate and innocent blue of his eyes above the month-old corn-silk beard which concealed most of his abraded face and which gave him an air of incredible and paradoxical dissoluteness, not as though at last and without warning he had appeared in the sight of his fellowmen in his true character, but as if an old Italian portrait of a child saint had been defaced by a vicious and idle boy; at Mrs. Tull, a strong, full-bosomed though slightly dumpy woman with an expression of grim and seething outrage which the elapsed four weeks had apparently neither increased nor diminished but had merely set, an outrage which curiously and almost at

once began to give the impression of being directed not at any Snopes or
at any other man in particular but at all men, all males, and of which Tull
himself was not at all the victim but the subject, who sat on one side of her
husband while the biggest of the four daughters sat on the other as if they
(or Mrs. Tull at least) were not so much convinced that Tull might leap
up and flee, as determined that he would not; and at Eck and the little boy,
identical save for size, and Lump, the clerk, in a gray cap which someone
actually recognized as being the one which Flem Snopes had worn when
he went to Texas last year, who between spells of rapid blinking would sit
staring at the Justice with the lidless intensity of a rat—and into the lens-
distorted and irisless old-man's eyes of the Justice there grew an expression
not only of amazement and bewilderment but, as in Ratliff's eyes while he
stood on the store gallery four weeks ago, something very like terror.

"This—" he said. "I didn't expect—I didn't look to see—. I'm going to
pray," he said. "I ain't going to pray aloud. But I hope—" He looked at
them. "I wish. . . . Maybe some of you all anyway had better do the same."
He bowed his head. They watched him, quiet and grave, while he sat
motionless behind the table, the light morning wind moving faintly in his
thin hair and the shadow-stipple of windy leaves gliding and flowing across
the starched bulge of bosom and the gleaming bone-buttoned cuffs, as rigid
and almost as large as sections of six-inch stovepipe, at his joined hands. He
raised his head. "Armstid against Snopes," he said. Mrs. Armstid spoke.
She did not move, she looked at nothing, her hands clasped in her lap,
speaking in that flat, toneless and hopeless voice:

"That Texan man said——"

"Wait," the Justice said. He looked about at the faces, the blurred eyes
fleeing behind the thick lenses. "Where is the defendant? I don't see
him."

"He wouldn't come," the bailiff said.

"Wouldn't come?" the Justice said. "Didn't you serve the papers on
him?"

"He wouldn't take them," the bailiff said. "He said——"

"Then he is in contempt!" the Justice cried.

"What for?" Lump Snopes said. "Ain't nobody proved yet they was his
horses." The Justice looked at him.

"Are you representing the defendant?" he said. Snopes blinked at him
for a moment.

"What's that mean?" he said. "That you aim for me to pay whatever
fine you think you can clap onto him?"

"So he refuses to defend himself," the Justice said. "Don't he know that
I can find against him for that reason, even if pure justice and decency ain't
enough?"

"It'll be pure something," Snopes said. "It don't take no mind-reader
to see how your mind is——"

"Shut up, Snopes," the bailiff said. "If you ain't in this case, you keep out of it." He turned back to the Justice. "What you want me to do: go over to the Bend and fetch Snopes here anyway? I reckon I can do it."

"No," the Justice said. "Wait." He looked about at the sober faces again with that bafflement, that dread. "Does anybody here know for sho who them horses belonged to? Anybody?" They looked back at him, sober, attentive— at the neat immaculate old man sitting with his hands locked together on the table before him to still the trembling. "All right, Mrs. Armstid," he said. "Tell the court what happened." She told it, unmoving, in the flat, inflectionless voice, looking at nothing, while they listened quietly, coming to the end and ceasing without even any fall of voice, as though the tale mattered nothing and came to nothing. The Justice was looking down at his hands. When she ceased, he looked up at her. "But you haven't showed yet that Snopes owned the horses. The one you want to sue is that Texas man. And he's gone. If you got a judgment against him, you couldn't collect the money. Don't you see?"

"Mr. Snopes brought him here," Mrs. Armstid said. "Likely that Texas man wouldn't have knowed where Frenchman's Bend was if Mr. Snopes hadn't showed him."

"But it was the Texas man that sold the horses and collected the money for them." The Justice looked about again at the faces. "Is that right? You, Bookwright, is that what happened?"

"Yes," Bookwright said. The Justice looked at Mrs. Armstid again, with that pity and grief. As the morning increased the wind had risen, so that from time to time gusts of it ran through the branches overhead, bringing a faint snow of petals, prematurely bloomed as the spring itself had condensed with spendthrift speed after the hard winter, and the heavy and drowsing scent of them, about the motionless heads.

"He give Mr. Snopes Henry's money. He said Henry hadn't bought no horse. He said I could get the money from Mr. Snopes tomorrow."

"And you have witnesses that saw and heard him?"

"Yes, sir. The other men that was there saw him give Mr. Snopes the money and say that I could get it——"

"And you asked Snopes for the money?"

"Yes, sir. He said that Texas man taken it away with him when he left. But I would. . . ." She ceased again, perhaps looking down at her hands also. Certainly she was not looking at anyone.

"Yes?" the Justice said. "You would what?"

"I would know them five dollars. I earned them myself, weaving at night after Henry and the chaps was asleep. Some of the ladies in Jefferson would save up string and such and give it to me and I would weave things and sell them. I earned that money a little at a time and I would know it when I saw it because I would take the can outen the chimney and count it now and then while it was making up to enough to buy my chaps some shoes for next winter. I would know it if I was to see it again. If Mr. Snopes would just let——"

"Suppose there was somebody seen Flem give that money back to that Texas fellow," Lump Snopes said suddenly.

"Did anybody here see that?" the Justice said.

"Yes," Snopes said, harshly and violently. "Eck here did." He looked at Eck. "Go on. Tell him." The Justice looked at Eck; the four Tull girls turned their heads as one head and looked at him, and Mrs. Tull leaned forward to look past her husband, her face cold, furious, and contemptuous, and those standing shifted to look past one another's heads at Eck sitting motionless on the bench.

"Did you see Snopes give Armstid's money back to the Texas man, Eck?" the Justice said. Still Eck did not answer nor move, Lump Snopes made a gross violent sound through the side of his mouth.

"By God, I ain't afraid to say it if Eck is. I seen him do it."

"Will you swear that as testimony?" Snopes looked at the Justice. He did not blink now.

"So you won't take my word," he said.

"I want the truth," the Justice said. "If I can't find that, I got to have sworn evidence of what I will have to accept as truth." He lifted the Bible from the two other books.

"All right," the bailiff said. "Step up here." Snopes rose from the bench and approached. They watched him, though now there was no shifting nor craning, no movement at all among the faces, the still eyes. Snopes at the table looked back at them once, his gaze traversing swiftly the crescent-shaped rank; he looked at the Justice again. The bailiff grasped the Bible; though the Justice did not release it yet.

"You are ready to swear you saw Snopes give that Texas man back the money he took from Henry Armstid for that horse?" he said.

"I said I was, didn't I?" Snopes said. The Justice released the Bible.

"Swear him," he said.

"Put your left hand on the Book raise your right hand you solemnly swear and affirm—" the bailiff said rapidly. But Snopes had already done so, his left hand clapped onto the extended Bible and the other hand raised and his head turned away as once more his gaze went rapidly along the circle of expressionless and intent faces, saying in that harsh and snarling voice:

"Yes. I saw Flem Snopes give back to that Texas man whatever money Henry Armstid or anybody else thinks Henry Armstid or anybody else paid Flem for any of them horses. Does that suit you?"

"Yes," the Justice said. Then there was no movement, no sound anywhere among them. The bailiff placed the Bible quietly on the table beside the Justice's locked hands, and there was no movement save the flow and recover of the windy shadows and the drift of the locust petals. Then Mrs. Armstid rose; she stood once more (or still) looking at nothing, her hands clasped across her middle.

"I reckon I can go now, can't I?" she said.

"Yes," the Justice said, rousing. "Unless you would like——"

"I better get started," she said. "It's a right far piece." She had not come in the wagon, but on one of the gaunt and underfed mules. One of the men followed her across the grove and untied the mule for her and led it up to a wagon, from one hub of which she mounted. Then they looked at the Justice again. He sat behind the table, his hands still joined before him, though his head was not bowed now. Yet he did not move until the bailiff leaned and spoke to him, when he roused, came suddenly awake without starting, as an old man wakes from an old man's light sleep. He removed his hands from the table and, looking down, he spoke exactly as if he were reading from a paper:

"Tull against Snopes. Assault and——"

"Yes!" Mrs. Tull said. "I'm going to say a word before you start." She leaned, looking past Tull at Lump Snopes again. "If you think you are going to lie and perjure Flem and Eck Snopes out of——"

"Now, mamma," Tull said. Now she spoke to Tull, without changing her position or her tone or even any break or pause in her speech:

"Don't you say hush to me! You'll let Eck Snopes or Flem Snopes or that whole Varner tribe snatch you out of the wagon and beat you half to death against a wooden bridge. But when it comes to suing them for your just rights and a punishment, oh no. Because that wouldn't be neighborly. What's neighborly got to do with you lying flat on your back in the middle of planting time while we pick splinters out of your face?" By this time the bailiff was shouting.

"Order! Order! This here's a law court!" Mrs. Tull ceased. She sat back, breathing hard, staring at the Justice, who sat and spoke again as if he were reading aloud:

"——assault and battery on the person of Vernon Tull, through the agency and instrument of one horse, unnamed, belonging to Eckrum Snopes. Evidence of physical detriment and suffering, defendant himself. Witnesses, Mrs. Tull and daughters——"

"Eck Snopes saw it too," Mrs. Tull said, though with less violence now. "He was there. He got there in plenty of time to see it. Let him deny it. Let him look me in the face and deny it if he——"

"If you please, ma'am," the Justice said. He said it so quietly that Mrs. Tull hushed and became quite calm, almost a rational and composed being. "The injury to your husband ain't disputed. And the agency of the horse ain't disputed. The law says that when a man owns a creature which he knows to be dangerous and if that creature is restrained and restricted from the public commons by a pen or enclosure capable of restraining and restricting it, if a man enter that pen or enclosure, whether he knows the creature in it is dangerous or not dangerous, then that man has committed trespass and the owner of that creature is not liable. But if that creature known to him to be dangerous ceases to be restrained by that suitable pen or enclosure, either by accident or design and either with or without the owner's knowledge, then that owner is liable. That's the law. All necessary now is to establish first, the ownership of the horse, and second, that the horse was a dangerous creature within the definition of the law as provided."

"Hah," Mrs. Tull said. She said it exactly as Bookwright would have. "Dangerous. Ask Vernon Tull. Ask Henry Armstid if them things was pets."

"If you please, ma'am," the Justice said. He was looking at Eck. "What is the defendant's position? Denial of ownership?"

"What?" Eck said.

"Was that your horse that ran over Mr. Tull?"

"Yes," Eck said. "It was mine. How much do I have to p——"

"Hah," Mrs. Tull said again. "Denial of ownership. When there were at least forty men—fools too, or they wouldn't have been there. But even a fool's word is good about what he saw and heard—at least forty men heard that Texas murderer give that horse to Eck Snopes. Not sell it to him, mind; give it to him."

"What?" the Justice said. "Gave it to him?"

"Yes," Eck said. "He give it to me. I'm sorry Tull happened to be using that bridge too at the same time. How much do I——"

"Wait," the Justice said. "What did you give him? a note? a swap of some kind?"

"No," Eck said. "He just pointed to it in the lot and told me it belonged to me."

"And he didn't give you a bill of sale or a deed or anything in writing?"

"I reckon he never had time," Eck said. "And after Lon Quick forgot and left that gate open, never nobody had time to do no writing even if we had a thought of it."

"What's all this?" Mrs. Tull said. "Eck Snopes has just told you he owned that horse. And if you won't take his word, there were forty men standing at that gate all day long doing nothing, that heard that murdering card-playing whiskey-drinking anti-christ—" This time the Justice raised one hand, in its enormous pristine cuff, toward her. He did not look at her.

"Wait," he said. "Then what did he do?" he said to Eck. "Just lead the horse up and put the rope in your hand?"

"No," Eck said. "Him nor nobody else never got no ropes on none of them. He just pointed to the horse in the lot and said it was mine and auctioned off the rest of them and got into the buggy and said good-bye and druv off. And we got our ropes and went into the lot, only Lon Quick forgot to shut the gate. I'm sorry it made Tull's mules snatch him outen the wagon. How much do I owe him?" Then he stopped, because the Justice was no longer looking at him and, as he realized a moment later, no longer listening either. Instead, he was sitting back in the chair, actually leaning back in it for the first time, his head bent slightly and his hands resting on the table before him, the fingers lightly overlapped. They watched him quietly for almost a half-minute before anyone realized that he was looking quietly and steadily as Mrs. Tull.

"Well, Mrs. Tull," he said, "by your own testimony, Eck never owned that horse."

"What?" Mrs. Tull said. It was not loud at all. "What did you say?"

"In the law, ownership can't be conferred or invested by word-of-mouth. It must be established either by recorded or authentic document, or by possession or occupation. By your testimony and his both, he never gave that Texan anything in exchange for that horse, and by his testimony the Texas man never gave him any paper to prove he owned it, and by his testimony and by what I know myself from these last four weeks, nobody yet has ever laid hand or rope either on any one of them. So that horse never came into Eck's possession at all. That Texas man could have given that same horse to a dozen other men standing around that gate that day, without even needing to tell Eck he had done it; and Eck himself could have transferred all his title and equity in it to Mr. Tull right there while Mr. Tull was lying unconscious on that bridge just by thinking it to himself, and Mr. Tull's title would be just as legal as Eck's."

"So I get nothing," Mrs. Tull said. Her voice was still calm, quiet, though probably no one but Tull realized that it was too calm and quiet. "My team is made to run away by a wild spotted mad dog, my wagon is wrecked; my husband is jerked out of it and knocked unconscious and unable to work for a whole week with less than half of our seed in the ground, and I get nothing."

"Wait," the Justice said. "The law——"

"The law," Mrs. Tull said. She stood suddenly up—a short, broad, strong woman, balanced on the balls of her planted feet.

"Now, mamma," Tull said.

"Yes, ma'am," the Justice said. "Your damages are fixed by statute. The law says that when a suit for damages is brought against the owner of an animal which has committed damage or injury, if the owner of the animal either can't or won't assume liability, the injured or damaged party shall find recompense in the body of the animal. And since Eck Snopes never owned that horse at all, and since you just heard a case here this morning that failed to prove that Flem Snopes had any equity in any of them, that horse still belongs to that Texas man. Or did belong. Because now that horse that made your team run away and snatch your husband out of the wagon, belongs to you and Mr. Tull."

"Now, mamma!" Tull said. He rose quickly. But Mrs. Tull was still quiet, only quite rigid and breathing hard, until Tull spoke. Then she turned on him, not screaming: shouting; presently the bailiff was banging the table-top with his hand-polished hickory cane and roaring "Order! Order!" while the neat old man, thrust backward in his chair as though about to dodge and trembling with an old man's palsy, looked on with amazed unbelief.

"The horse!" Mrs. Tull shouted. "We see it for five seconds, while it is climbing into the wagon with us and then out again. Then it's gone, God don't know where and thank the Lord He don't! And the mules gone with it and the wagon wrecked and you laying there on the bridge with your face full of kindling-wood and bleeding like a hog and dead for all we knew. And he gives us the horse! Don't hush me! Get on to that wagon, fool that would sit there behind a pair of young mules with the reins tied around his wrist! Get on to that wagon, all of you!"

"I can't stand no more!" the old Justice cried. "I won't! This court's adjourned! Adjourned!"

COMMENTARY

William Faulkner's "Spotted Horses" will bear comparison with Flaubert's story, "A Simple Heart." It does not come as near formal perfection—there is a flaw in its structure—but it is a question whether it is not, on the whole, a more significant story. The action takes place on a larger stage and at the same time attains the same high degree of objectivity which Flaubert attained, and the same dramatic and symbolic unity. The unity of both stories is achieved through the powerful operation of a controlling symbol (see Appendix A, p. 633), in one case God, in the other the Devil. Both stories are accounts of a simple heart in relation to supernatural forces. Félicité, in "A Simple Heart," loves God all her life and when she nears death is rewarded by a vision of Heaven. Faulkner's Simple Heart—that of Mrs. Henry Armstid—is shown in conflict with the Devil and his allies, and the Devil wins.

Faulkner's viewpoint throughout is that of the Omniscient Narrator (see Appendix A, p. 623), with two exceptions when the viewpoint is suddenly shifted for a breathing space. The first shift occurs when the men are sitting on the gallery after supper and "Only Ratliff and Quick sat in chairs, so that to them the others were black silhouettes against the dreaming lambence of the moonlight." And again, the Texan, about to start the bidding for the horses, "began to have the feeling that each face had stopped looking at him the second before his gaze reached it." At no other time are we privy to what is going on in the mind of either Ratliff or the Texan. The two shifts remind us of a similar rapid shift of viewpoint in Flaubert, when Emma Bovary conceives the idea of solving her difficulties by committing suicide, and "in an ecstasy of heroism" runs to the chemist's shop. She taps on the window and the little servant, Justin, looks out at her, astonished, and "She seemed to him extraordinary beautiful and majestic as a phantom." In all three cases the rapid shift of viewpoint (really an almost instantaneous use of the Effaced Narrator [Appendix A, p. 624] method) serves not so much to reveal what is going on in the minds of the persons as to bring the whole scene into sharper focus.

With the two exceptions just mentioned, Faulkner's story is told from the viewpoint of the Omniscient Narrator. Only a master is able to achieve immediacy by the use of this method, and many a master has come to grief in the attempt. Balzac's story, "The Executioner," is unforgettable but not satisfying. One believes that the members of the family of the Marquis de Leganes met death with extraordinary composure, but one is not convinced that their heads were cut off. Clara's white neck seems "to appeal to the blade to fall," but when the blade falls no blood seems to flow. Balzac, who always moved ponderously, is not close enough to his scene.

In "Spotted Horses" Faulkner inclines to Flaubert's method rather than to that of James. The omniscient narrator is himself so passionate and meticulous an observer that he does not need to view the scene through the eyes of any of the characters. The Texan, backing a pony into a corner, hammering its head with his pistol butt or grasping its forelock with one hand, its nostrils with the other and wringing "the long, evil muzzle back over its shoulder," is repeating desperate, unerring motions that men have watched for generations. A Southern tenant farmer (if he were not "bemused" by Faulkner's rhetoric!) could find no flaw in his knowledge of country ways. Henry Armstid's wagon wheel is repaired exactly the way a man of his kind and condition would repair a wagon wheel, "with crossed planks, bound to the spokes with baling wire." Mrs. Armstid's garments are grey and shapeless from age, work stains and frequent washings. Her stained canvas gymnasium shoes strike a slightly ridiculous note; even her despair is not allowed its due dignity.

This kind of mastery comes as the result of a lifelong devotion to a particular scene. The writer has to contemplate the objects or persons described over a period of years, at all times of year, in all kinds of weather before he can unerringly select the detail which will convey their essence. Flaubert was eminently successful at this as long as he stayed on his—to him so detestable—home ground. Every blade of grass, every cobblestone in "A Simple Heart" has an air of reality. He used the same method of attack in "Herodias" but the incidents do not carry the same conviction. He was not himself convinced of the brute fact that Saint John the Baptist's head had ever lain on a salver and so could not wholly convince us.

Faulkner, writing, with a tact that is rare in our age, about scenes he has known from childhood, is able to carry Flaubert's method a step farther, to do, in fact, the thing that Flaubert himself longed to do: to unite concrete historical detail with lyricism. His temperament and his heredity—for his style is a sort of distillation of the eloquence of old-fashioned Southern oratory—incline him to poetic images and rhetorical flights, but the "underpinnings" of his story are usually substantial enough to sustain them. The reader has subscribed at every turn to the illusion, and the narrator, freed from the constant obligation to convince, can, as it were, pause for comment. There is no novelty for us in the notion of Mrs. Armstid as "a grey and blasted tree trunk, moving, somehow intact and upright, upon an unhurried flood." This vision of her has been prepared for the reader's mind from his first sight of her. Faulkner's comment frees it, sets it in motion. He thus adds another *activity* to the whole story, giving to the observed detail a symbolic dimension that Flaubert was able to give his story only at the end.

The speech of the characters contributes powerfully to the effect of verisimilitude. The Texan's dramatic under-statements—"Seems to have held all right," or "I misdoubted that shelled corn all along"—and his eyes, which when he looked at any one "became like two pieces of flint turned up suddenly in dug earth," reveal the shattered spirit behind the brittle, as yet impenetrable surface. Mrs. Armstid voices hopelessness: "He ain't no more despair than to buy one of them things . . ." The men, sitting on the porch after supper, talk of other Western horses they have known: "Anse McCollum made a good team outen them two of hisn. They was a little light. That was all . . . When a man don't have to invest so much into a horse or team he don't need so much from them." The cadences announce their "stubborn, convinced and passive advance" into the trap Flem Snopes has set for him.

Ratliff, the sewing machine agent, and Mrs. Littlejohn, the boarding house keeper, represent the Enveloping Action (see Appendix A, p. 631) of the story. They serve as foils to each other, reminding us that it is possible for human beings to think intelligently and act wisely. Mrs. Littlejohn turns her head away when the spectacle of the men's folly becomes too much for her but keeps her head when she herself confronts one of the horses in her house. The long speech in which Ratliff recounts what goes on between Mrs. Littlejohn and Mrs. Armstid, when Mrs. Littlejohn finds out that Snopes won't give the money back, is the least successful passage in the story, the one place where Faulkner has failed to solve the problem of Authority (see Appendix A, p. 621). Ratliff is here trying to convey the emotions of other persons, Mrs. Littlejohn, Mrs. Armstid and Mrs. Littlejohn's daughter. The passage is not equal to the weight the narrative puts upon it, but for the most part Ratliff enacts successfully the rôle of a Greek chorus to the madmen's antics.

The Enveloping Action is twofold, however. The Devil also makes his comments. "Well, it's a good bright cool night for running them," Old Jody Varner, Flem Snopes' father-in-law, remarks as the madmen swarm over the countryside in pursuit of the spotted ponies. He explains that such madness is salutary: "A night like this one, when a man ain't old enough to lay still and sleep, and yet he ain't young enough to go tomcatting in and out of other folks' back windows, something like this is good for him." His own daughter, Eula, Flem's wife, was begotten on such a night and is, therefore, a creature of the same moon: "Mrs. Varner taken and laid every night with the moon on her nekid belly . . . I . . . could hear Eula kicking and scrouging like all get out, feeling the moon."

The passage in which this Helen, "returning to what topless and shoddy Argos," stands blank-eyed at the window in her long white garment, "not doomed, just damned," is poorly written—a flight that failed—but the passage serves the story structurally. Flem Snopes, who is in league with the Prince of Darkness (though the Devil is somewhat puzzled to know what to do with him when he goes to Hell in another story), must have a moon woman for wife.

This is a skillful use of the device which James called undercutting (see Appendix B, p. 636). As a mountain peak is defined by its valleys, Snopes' character is portrayed through its effect on others and through emanations from his adherents. The few remarks Snopes makes are ritualistic: "Gentlemen," when he joins the other men on the porch; or factual: "Them ain't my horses." His facial expression is mask-like. And yet we must see him plain at some time if his deviltry is to have the proper effect upon us. He reveals himself most fully through the mouth of one of his followers. After his talk about the moon Old Jody Varner looks out from under his slanting brows and gives way—as a lesser disciple, Lump Snopes, the clerk, has given way at intervals during the action—to Mephistophelean mirth over human credulity.

Faulkner rounds out the picture of Flem Snopes by a skillful use of "psychic distance." This is symbolized often by actual physical space. When Flem stands at the fence to watch the horses, nobody stands directly beside him; there is always a little space cleared about him. The omniscient narrator does not lead the reader inside this magic circle. Flem leaves the story as he entered it, a man of mystery. But the triumph of evil is complete. The Texan is ruined, adrift in the world. Henry Armstid's leg is broken, his wife has lost the heart that might have enabled her to make the crop he cannot make. Tull has lost two young mules. Everybody who has had anything to do with the horses has suffered—except the Devil's disciples— and in the end, Justice itself raises its hands to Heaven.

"I can't stand no more!" the old judge cries. "I won't! This court's adjourned. Adjourned!"

Sean O'Faolain

THE BOMBSHOP

AT FIRST it was easy to work steadily in the Bombshop, all day long and into the night too. They found all the pleasure they needed in making the bombs and there was a special malicious pleasure in knowing that while they made them there were the markets, so fussy, so noisy, beneath their windows, too busily engaged selling their fish and their vegetables and their old clothes to suspect anything. The three would chuckle when they thought of it and say to one another with a wink, "If they only knew!" and return with vigour to their deadly tasks. There was never any question, then, of going out into the streets, not even after dark or in the early dawn, or if they thought of it they were ashamed to mention it. Even when the work began to pall on them, when they began to halt in the middle of it to lounge and smoke in the front room, or to peep through the drawn blinds at the streets, they returned shamefaced with a joke about the Freedom of the City that would one day be conferred on them. And when they did at last confess to one another that they would like to go out into the streets it was a long time before they talked of it as something that might possibly be done. When they did they found that only two things prevented them—the danger to themselves and the danger to the Bombshop; they might easily be recognized by a spy and arrested, or, worse still and more likely, they might not be arrested at once but watched as they went back to their lair. So they abandoned the idea, only to return to it again, and abandon it again, and return to it and abandon it, until the very thought of the streets tormented them. In this way they discovered something that nobody else could have taught them—that it is easy to do anything at first, no matter how difficult or dangerous, but the inevitable desires of the heart swell and burst in the end like a well gathering beneath the surface of the earth.

They came to fear special hours of the day, and the nights tormented them. They feared especially the early cock-crow when the market-life began and their sleep ended, the dark hours of the morning when the carts went rumbling in beneath their windows from the fields and the seashore. Leo, the youngest of the three and who should have slept better than any of them, was the first to admit that he often rose on his elbow to watch the loads go by, the cabbage glistening, the fish crates brown, the domes of hay darkened by the rain falling on them so heavily from the great leaking sieve of a sky that the fish almost swam in their boxes and the cabbage-heads cupped the water and splashed it on the fishwives who unloaded

Reprinted from *Midsummer Night Madness* by Sean O'Faolain, copyright 1932 by The Viking Press, Inc., reprinted with the kind permission of The Viking Press, Inc.

them from their places in the carts. Once he saw a drenched carter look enviously up at his window and angrily flick his horse's glistening rump with his whiplash. "If he only knew!" said the boy, with a bitter self-pity, and leaned back wearily in his bed wishing he could sleep again. Their work would not begin until the angelus bells began to chime, here, there, everywhere, over the city, and from that on the roar of the spirit-lamps and the rattle of the pestle in the mortar, and the hiss of the sifters kept the city sounds at bay, except alone the cries of the fish-woman outside that they could not stifle—the "Here's the herrings, here's the herrings, here's the herrings" in a torrent of words, or the wail of "Fine cod a' hake, oh, fine cod a' hake"; but at lunch-hour the lamps would fall silent and all the city enter through the windows, and from that on they toiled as best they might through the long afternoon. Then the markets would gradually be dissipated and the dark fall, and they too cease work, and old memories and old habits recur.

On wet nights—almost every night that is for the two months since they came—they sat before their fire in the sitting-room while the rain dripped musically on the tin roof in the yard, and Shandon tower struck out the hours from the wet dark above their heads. They could see it through the window in the landing if they chose to look, a tapering mass, dark against the wet luminous sky, its golden weather-fish swimming endlessly through the aqueous air. They sat there, almost always in silence, playing chess, or reading, or writing long letters until Norah—their courier and housekeeper—returned with dispatches, and the dispatches almost always taunted them to hurry, to get finished, saying that everything and everybody was ready for the attack but the Bombshop. Or if there were no dispatches, one of them wishing to be alone would go to his room till the following morning (as Leo did more often than any of them) or another down into the yard to sit on the ash-bin, to smoke and look up at their square of sky, returning with his hair wet with points of mist like dew.

On the few fine nights there were, they could see, by peeping carefully through the front windows, the lane children racing and shouting under the lit lamps, or hear a group of girls circling arm in arm about the markets, singing as they went the mournful harmony of old sentimental numbers—those songs from the Edwardian music-halls that are remembered in the provinces long after they are forgotten elsewhere:

> "Come over the garden wall,
>   Little girl to me.
> I've been lonely a long, long time,
> And the wall isn't hard to climb.
> Just jump up and then jump down,
>   I won't let you fall.
> We'll play at sweethearts
> And then we'll be married, so,
> Come over the garden wall."

Or they would sing something from the *Prince of Pilsen* or *Florodora*; and Sean, with his great awkward body, would leap up and imitate the girls of the chorus with their fleshy, pink-tighted thighs that popped in and popped out like the mechanical men on circus roundabouts, and the others would laugh at him and at them. But hearing the voices come from the distance and vanish into it as the girls went round and round the squares the three bomb-makers would hum in turn after them,

> "I've been lonely a long, long time,
>   Little girl of mine. . . ."

Or they would read the evening paper over and over again, sharing it between them until it became a wrinkled ball. Then Norah would come and draw the tiny envelopes from her bosom and they receive them still warm from her flesh—and, reading them, forget her.

Sometimes, indeed, they were merry, if there were many dispatches from Norah. Or if she brought much news they would gossip for hours on end. Or they would be coaxed from their silence on the rare nights when they were visited by Mother Dale. She was the owner of the house, the only other woman who knew of the Bombshop; she kept the old-clothes shop beneath them, and lived between them and it.

She rarely troubled them—as if she knew that they did not want her old woman's talk, but now and again of nights the door would open and there she would stand under the lintel, tall in the gloom like a slender statue from a Middle Ages porch, a spear carved into womanshape. She was a wonderful old woman; even Sean and Caesar, rough fellows as they were, could find no other word for her but that, and as she peered down at them, with child-soft eyes and inclined brow, unbuttoning her little mouth, that was wrinkled like cloth, into a smooth gentle smile they would wink at her or smile foolishly, not knowing whether to believe those open mother's eyes or her torture-tightened lips.

One wet night she came, early in the night, not going out that one night of all her nights to pray in the chapels for them, and as they looked up at her wet spangled bonnet, Norah ran and gently removed it from the lowered pate before her, pretending to be exasperated that she should have been out in such weather. But she only removed her wet cloak, and smiling at them said:

"Sure the best night of all to be out is the wet night when there's nobody to follow me. If it was a fine night I'd be rounding the markets for an hour before I'd come to my own doorbell, and all for fear of a fellow that warn't watching me at all, but only out for a drink after hours. But a night like this there's none abroad but the lost cats and the night police. And how is Leo?" turning to the boy amongst them.

He grinned back to her.

"I went out to pray for ye," she continued, "and to pray for the good work, but I got a pain in my side and I came home. And what need is there to pray for ye or the work when God is always on the watch over the boys of Ireland. Look what I brought ye, Sean."

It was a bottle of invalid's wine. Out went his great hand, and back she snatched it in her bony one.

"Oh," he wailed in mock despair, "and I that haven't been in a pub for two months."

"Ye'll get none of this then."

"Oh, oh," from Sean as if he were the most crestfallen man in the world.

"Not a drop! If I was to let you put your big mouth to it the bottle would be empty in a flash."

Then she laughed at him.

"Ah, no. Sure no! I don't mean that at all. Take it, Norah. It's for all of ye. I pray for yeer souls and I bring wine for yeer bodies. Norah understands me, doesn't she? Norah?"

"Yes I do, Mother Dale," from Norah, her prominent teeth bared, her soft lips spread.

"Mind yeerselves though, boys," she said, as she rose and turned to go. "They say the city is full of spies."

She laid an envelope of new records on the table for Sean's gramophone. "I nearly forgot them. Good night, Sean."

He raised his big paw.

"Good night, mother."

"Caesar?"

"Good night, mother."

"Leo?"

"Good night, mother."

"Good night, Norah."

"Cheerio, mother," said Norah, who always had a special "good night" to herself, the last of all. The old woman had to stoop her lofty head to leave the room. Down she went to her own room below, and they opened the wine and sipped the weak juice in a returning silence while Norah went out quietly for her nightly batch of messages. Even as she closed the hall-door behind her she could hear the opening bars of the "Turkish Patrol" ("As played by the band of the Highland Light Infantry") come blaring from the great brass-horned gramophone. She was glad that Sean had something to occupy him for the night, but as she thought again of the great maw of the gramophone, pasted all over inside and out with postage stamps, and of the rusted needles, and the cracked sound-box, she strode gladly away, into the drizzling rain, crunching savagely over cabbage stumps and the heads of decapitated fish. But the wind over the bridges blew her umbrella inside out and the rain seeped into her shoes and her body became chilled in the cold womb of the chapel, where she exchanged dispatches with the Headquarters courier, and on her way home she felt so miserable that she almost thought of the Bombshop as "home." Once inside the door, however, there was the "Turkish Patrol" still blaring away as if they had all gone out and forgotten to shut off the record and it had ever since been repeating and repeating itself while the needle wore to a stump. She raced up the stairs in a rage and found Caesar hanging over a chess problem and Leo staring mournfully and without interest at the gramophone. By this a new record had been set in the machine and as she entered the room Sean caught her up in his great hands and set her down right before it—he had the hands and body of a navvy and the concave profile of a prize-fighter, and as she glared at him he laughed at her, and winked behind Caesar's back. Before she could speak a nasal whine of song scraped and whined in the horn.

"It's just one line," roared Sean, "one line we can't make out. It's called— 'Where the old horse died.' "

> "In the lag behind the hollow,
> Where the grath ith golden red,"

cried a deep basso from the depths of the gramophone.

"Now," cried Sean.

"And the coopoo goonoo moonoo nuroon," said the basso.

"What do you make of it?" roared Sean, the gramophone whining on and on.

"There we sometimes hear the churchbells," roared the basso.

> "There no more we hear them now,
> In the place where the old horse died."

"Well?" repeated Sean.

"Not a word of it," said Norah, wearily removing her hat and damp coat, while the chess-player groaned and Leo shook his head and sighed.

"Slowly now this time," said Sean, and as for a moment he held the needle from the record to adjust the regulator, they could hear the rain drip before the wind on the tin roof outside and Shandon booming out the quarter. Then the rite began once more.

> "In the lag behind the hollow,
> Where the grath ith golden red,"

sang the basso for the hundredth time in the house that night, now with the slowness of a dead-march.

"Now," roared Sean towering over her.

"And the coopoo goonoo moonoo nuroon," said the basso once again.

"No," said Norah, and she shook her head.

"We think," he said, "that it's either 'and the grey grass blooms upon the lawn,' or 'and the churchbells boom through the dawn.' But wait. Twice as slow this time."

The silent chess-player looked up and in a low voice of bitterness he said: "Stop it!"

Caesar was quite different from the prize-fighter—a long slim figure with the eyes of an ascetic or a fanatic, one of them slightly askew so that he always had an impenetrable look; but it was his pendulous nose and his hollowed cheeks and his elongated neck that had christened him.

"Ah! Caesar!" mocked Sean at him. "One more little bouteen now. One more now. All listen with the utmost attention and devotion, and in all moments of temptation danger and affliction—" he quoted blasphemously from the Catechism as the rite began again and the chess player leaped to his feet and thrust out his hand to the machine.

At once broken-nose grew dark-faced and stood up to him.

"For God's sake give it a rest," said Caesar.

"Why should I?" cried Sean. "What else have we here to occupy our minds?"

"Sean!" implored the girl, while Leo sat still and looked gloomily at the three of them. This was what life had been like in the Bombshop for a month now.

"Let it alone!" cried Sean.

"In-the-lag-behind-the-hollow," wailed the dying basso.

"Stop it or I'll smash it," said Caesar, and with his fist he smashed the whirling black circle, and the rain dripped audibly on the corrugated roof. The prize-fighter was furious. He thrust his fist into his hip-pocket and the nickel of a revolver flashed. Norah was between them in a second but as they struggled two deafening shots rang and the air was hot-flavoured with the smell of powder. At once they all grew quiet, looking at one another to see if anyone was hurt, and then they returned to their places. Caesar fingered his chessmen; by the fire Sean ejected the empty shells, and dropped the broken record bit by bit into the fire, frowning as each morsel shot up in acrid flame. Secretly we were all listening for some sign that the shots had been heard in the street. Norah removed her shoes and felt her damp feet, and to fill the uneasy silence she turned to the boy.

"Not a single dispatch tonight," she said. "But I met Frank Boland."

"Where has he been?"

"He's been in the mountains, and in Dublin and Kildare, too."

"My home counties," said Leo. "Where was he? Clane or Sallins or Celbridge? Has he any news?"

"He said it was very wet weather there."

"Yet the beech would be out by now," said Leo.

"He said something was out. He watches things like that."

"He does."

"Maybe it was the beech, he mentioned," she said. "But he preferred the mountains for all that they were cold and harsh. He said every road there is a bog and the torrents pouring down the mountain-cliffs like snow."

They could see that Caesar was listening, and Sean held a piece of broken record poised on his fingers.

"Out here," said Leo wistfully, "every pool is a big lake."

"And every pub," said Sean, "is a filled room."

He was thinking of the frieze-coated peasants, with their pints before them and the smell of the bogs and the byres from their clothes and their twisted bits of ash-plants scraping the spittle into shapes on the sawdust floor. Leo turned to him.

"Wouldn't you scoff a frothy pint now, Sean?" he mocked timidly.

"It's not the pint I want," he said, and he rose and went to bed.

When he was gone they looked at one another as people might who have heard a strange sound and wonder if their companions can explain it. And as none of them had anything to say Norah leaped up and went down to Mother Dale. They knew she would be wondering what had happened, frightened by those sudden shots. The two heard Norah's steps go down the stairs, the old woman's door open, and then a brief silence.

"I was once in Sallins," Caesar was saying, when they heard scream after scream ring through the silent house. They heard Norah pounding up the stairs and when she stood panting before them her face was as pale as her bosom. She pointed through the floor and as they looked stupidly down at it they saw two neat little holes drilled there by the passage of Sean's bullets.

They found the old woman seated as if asleep in her armchair, not a rib of hair askew, her arms lying on the arm-rests, her body as erect as a Caryatid supporting a great weight on its head, but as Leo laid his hand on the back of her neck his fingers grew wet and sticky with blood, and her blood was warm still though the flesh was already rough with the chill of death. There they left her, for all that Norah could say, with tears of pity and rage, half-mad with both, protesting against Caesar's orders that he gave through his tight fanatic's lips. Not a priest nor a doctor would he have; she was dead, cold as a stone already; priests and doctors could do her no good. He stood and looked coldly while Norah applied a mirror to her lips to see if there was any life at all, and then as the glass came away untarnished he looked at the girl and shrugged his shoulders as if to say, "I told you so."

"Let us kneel and pray for her," he said, perhaps with some thought of easing the girl's pain, perhaps to think quietly while we prayed. But at any rate he could not lead our prayers but stumbled and stuttered at them, and Norah rose and pleaded again.

"The work must go on at all costs," said Caesar. "Unless she can be removed secretly she stays where she is. Lead the Rosary for her, Norah."

But Norah cursed him and all of us for a pack of cowards, while Caesar placed a crucifix between the dead woman's fingers and laid a cloth over her face, and as they went up to bed Norah followed them step by step taunting them as she went.

All night long Leo heard her turning uneasily on her pallet and in the morning she was heavy-lidded and her hands trembled. That day they were so long in beginning work that before the lamps began to boom the country carts were long trundled away and the parallelograms of sunlight disappeared from the tiles of the kitchen floor. Then Sean discovered that a jar of his acid was cracked behind its straw and had leaked empty and there was nothing for him to do but fall idle for the day.

Those idle hours finished him. He wandered aimlessly about the house, and they even heard him enter the dead woman's room. He came to Norah where she sat in the kitchen cutting the cotton-wool in long strips for the incendiaries and tried to gossip with her about his children, and when she would not he went poking in the old disused front room. When she followed, after listening for a long time for any sound from him, she found him at the window watching the children playing in the sun; there, she at one side of the window, he at the other, they stood watching them, delighted, until the musty air began to choke her and she fled to her work. It was an old lumber-room, crowded to the door with boxes, trunks, and packing-cases, in which and on which every kind of useless but cherished household god was living—or rather dying, malodorously. To her, too young to care about anybody's past, these sea-shells stuck on velvet, those rows of cracked decanters, the fox under the glass dome (with a special hole cut for his long tail), all those long-cherished useless things commemorated the breaking one by one of the heart-strings of the dead woman. Mother Dale, she knew, had kept them—and all women keep them—because they hope that as long as they look at them their past is not yet dead, their lives not yet spent. During the long ennui of those empty days passed in hiding in whatever house opened its "front drawing-room" to her, she had become artful, and hated herself for being so artful, in smelling out the faintest must of those private and particular gods of her women friends—the chinaware shoe (from Youghal), the filigree plate (from the Royal Oriental Exhibition), the tarnished silver teapot presented at marriage or retirement, the specially-bound prize book (from Sister Joanna to dear May), the *Cabinet of Literature* never cut, the *History of all Time* never read, memories all, mortuaries of the dead past. When she would be older, she well knew, she too would have her monuments and love them as old men love antiquity that is musty like their hearts and she would look fondly at them and carefully preserve the photograph of her marriage-day and the marble clock with the tarnished brass-plate commemorating the first step in the ending of her youth.

"Sean," she called in to him, "come out of that bloody charnel-house."

But he had found a red velvet-covered, brass-bound, gilt-latched photograph album, with a musical-box buried in it so that as one looked at the pictures of one's antecedents it ping-ponged out its sad meowing tune:

"Oh, there's, no, place, like, home; oh, no, place, like home." Guffawing at it, he opened it again and again, and would not come to her.

As if to mock her and tempt him the sun burst on the city at noon, and the damp of three months rose in curling exhalations from the pavements. Feeling the sun she returned to peep into the streets and found them filled with points of light that leaped from the scales of the mackerel, the white bosoms of the women, their arms diving among the flat fish and the sprats and the slender plaice. She looked up and the seagulls turned their white breasts to her and the vegetables below shone like polished ware; she looked up into the sky where the clouds were lifted slowly up through the blue air like flock for gods to lie on, and below the onion-girls and the lane children were crying louder than ever, screaming as they ran, the one for customers, the others as for pure joy in the sudden parturition of the year. Even the wail of "Fine cod a' hake" became faster and more joyous, and even this dim blind-drawn room filled with warmth and light, the great sun glowing through it like fiery bronze. But in the gloom of one corner behind her the musical-box iterated its dozen notes, and Sean, in his fine baritone voice, sang the same few notes over and over again:

> "Mid pleasures and palaces,
> No matter where we roam,
> Be it never so humble,
> There's no place like home."

She turned and swore at him. "For Christ's sake, stop it, Sean."

He only laughed at her, and the others, hearing them, left their work to join in the fun. Before them Sean donned a bonnet and a wrap.

"But I haven't the wasp waist," he roared at them, "nor the puffed shoulders. If I had the waist it would only be after a month of pulling and hauling on the laces with the maid cocking her leg on the side of the bed for leverage."

"No, you haven't the waist," said Leo, imitating his capers.

"The corset wasn't made that would circle your belly," said Caesar more coarsely than he had ever before spoken in that house.

"To be sure women have narrower waists than men," said Leo, and then he blushed; he saw Norah bite her soft big lips with her prominent teeth, and look up at him through her hair that had fallen forward over her bowed head. In his confusion he spoke foolishly.

"Who do you think, now," he said, "wore them things last?"

They broke up at that, silently, like men parting in a church or at a funeral—one going one way, another that, overcome by the thought of the passing away of something they had loved.

The sun moved downward so slowly and so brightly that they noticed without difficulty the lengthening of the day. They talked of the spring while they worked, Leo speaking often of the beechwoods of Kildare, Norah of the smell of the furze and the bracken hot and damp in the mountains. When the dusk fell Sean was still in the old lumber-room watching the scattering of the markets, and when the dark came he packed his bag and despite Caesar's furious taunts he left the house. Norah accompanied him, hoping it might be safer for him, and Caesar and Leo spent the night examining their secret dump under the stairs to see how little they had yet done. There was yet not a third of the amount required, and Caesar, rather than receive another taunting note from the quartermasters when Norah should return, went in despair to his room and Leo sat alone before the empty grate, watching vacantly where a yellow slug, tempted by the sudden heat, drew his silver trail inch by inch to the open window.

It was not the market-people who awoke them the following morning but the milkman thundering on the door. After he had made the whole street resound they saw him stand back from the door and survey the house and then whip up his pony in wonderment, looking back many times as he went. For the first time they realized the risks they were taking. The old woman had few friends, but one of the few might come at any time to visit her, and be astonished at the shutters on the shop-windows and the closed door. At once Caesar went rummaging in the dead-room for a specimen of the old woman's script—finally breaking open a tin safe where she kept her money and her private papers. He winked at Leo with his impenetrable eye and smiled at his own cunning as he copied her hand in a notice for the shop-door: *Gone to the country for a fortnight, May Dale.* If they could now get a man to replace Sean, get a new jar of acid, and arrange to remove the body of the old woman they might bring their work to a successful end. But there was no longer any excuse now for bringing a packing-case or a trunk to the shop as they formerly did whenever they needed raw material, and headquarters complained that it would be even more difficult to get a new man for them than to get a case in or a coffin out. But Caesar threw their taunts back at them in a long dispatch that Norah carried out that night, and he made extreme plans and preparations like a successful general who has received an unexpected defeat. Norah was not to leave now until quite late at night; he would have the Scouts extinguish the lamps near him in the markets so as to give additional darkness; they would rise earlier and finish later. He overflowed with a rash self-confidence and he always said afterwards that he would have won through if the unexpected had not happened. For his plans did not get very far. Norah actually went out the following night quite late, and the Boy Scouts extinguished every light in the markets—that was Thursday, the third night after her death—by shooting every bulb to pieces with their revolvers; they thereby attracted the attention of the patrols for the first time to the markets and attracted to themselves Caesar's rage, for he sent their Master a long profane dispatch pleading for a "less spectacular method of hastening the gentle night." He need not have been so sarcastic with the boys. Even while they were making cockshots of the market-lights there occurred, at the very gateway of the police headquarters over the river, an ambush in which three Tans and two soldiers were killed, and as a punishment an instant curfew was imposed to the very boundaries of the city, and every man and woman was ordered to be within doors from five o'clock in the afternoon until five o'clock on the following morning, and so nightly "until further notice." *Until further notice* read to Caesar like—*For Ever*.

The first afternoon of curfew the foot-patrols were doubled and armoured-cars roared through the deserted streets, leaving as they went from earshot a silence as of death in their wake. In the Bombshop they feared to continue working after the silence of curfew fell and they peeped through the blinds at the bare markets where the only live thing was a cat quietly washing its face in the warm sun, and a dog crunching a fish-head. Beyond the end of the square a section of main street stood empty as if it were early dawn instead of an hour before sundown, and the naked tram rails in the distance and the closed warehouses made it appear as if every clock in the city had stopped and all Cork had forgotten to rise.

Then night came and there was no moon, and in the markets not a lamp was lit; everything was impenetrable shadow out to the farthest end of the distant street and the cold light of a street-lamp. Once towards ten o'clock a lorry roared into the square and a searchlight flooded the place with a sudden blaze as of protracted lightning. The cats stood still and glared into the light, the cabbage-stumps and the fish-crates leaped out of their black shadows as if they were alive. Then the light swooped and the lorry moved slowly to another street. As they returned to sit by the empty grate they thought to themselves that it would be like that now for weeks to come. They looked at Caesar questioningly, and Caesar shrugged his shoulders and returned to peep again out of the lumber-room; in their hearts they felt defeat gradually approaching. As they listened to the strange quietness they felt themselves islanded in an empty sea.

It was plain to Caesar that he was in the position of an outpost whose communications had been cut, and so, at eleven, promising to return if the luck were with him, he gave his revolver to Sean, put a battered hat on his head—it was his only disguise—slipped a half-filled whisky bottle in his pocket, first taking a dram to fume his breath. Then he stole quietly out of the house and the door was closed to behind him. When he and Leo met again, months afterwards, in the mountains, he merely said that immediately he sat down that night in his own house, unnerved by the danger of the journey, he saw at once "how impossible it all was." Leo asked him if he attempted to return, but he shook his head and looked at Leo out of his impenetrable eye, and Leo nodded, and they spoke of other things.

But that night in the Bombshop they waited patiently, certain that Caesar would return. Shandon tower alone struck, and struck the hope from their hearts. It was their first night sitting awake in that house and as the hours came and went into eternity they remembered that another beside themselves was sitting, waiting also, below them. To distract the girl, Leo talked and talked of the beauty of the driving clouds and said that it was many a month and more, it seemed like many a year, since he had the peace of mind to look up at the sky at night and marvel at its beauty, while she said passionately that he seemed not to care whether Caesar returned, and called them cowards again, and wished Ireland were better served than by such soldiers.

"Caesar will return in a few hours," said Leo, almost glad to see her angry because it kept her mind free of thinking on other things. Oh, yes, Caesar would come back, he was a fine fellow, he was sure to return if it could possibly be done. Last night when there was a moon he wished they had been alone. There were four squares of moonlight under the lobby window and they were good to look at, better to stand on, he in one square, she in another.

"There must be beauty in a thing to make it worth fighting for," he said, trying to make her argue. "A man won't die for a mere abstraction. Keats said Truth was Beauty. I say Freedom is Beauty. Christ was not really the Son of the God of Love, he was the Son of the God of Freedom. He freed men because He knew that in Freedom all beauty has its source. Shelley was wiser than Keats, more human, more true. If Keats had not been a poet, a sensuous youth, he would have been an abstract rationalist. With his "truth is beauty"! A Manichean, a bloody Manichean he'd have been, like all abstract thinkers—like Augustine. *Gaudium de veritate,* your eyebrow! I say *Gaudium de libertate.* The whole Irish church is on the Augustine tack. They herd us in, they circumscribe us, they herd us up the gangway to Heaven, they take us by the scruff of the neck and shove us into Heaven whether we like it or not. They always did it, so overcome by the fear of Hell-fire that they have no time for the love of the Christ-light. Scholastics without the scholastic brains, medievalists without the medievalists' sense of beauty. If man could only be free, truly free, if he could only be as God made him. . . ."

But Norah could have hit him in the face. And she left him because she could not hold her temper in, going upstairs, with that strange attractive waddle she had, to lean recklessly with arms akimbo on the moonlit windowsill, thinking that the dead woman sitting below was happiest of all, wishing to the dead Christ—she swore in her rage and despair—that she was lying on her hands and face on the green fields she could see across the city in the light of the rising moon. As she leaned there the quarters and the halves struck, and she listened to them with a sinking heart, thinking of the men on the hills, seeing the quartermaster trudging through the boglands to his dumps, marking up his smudgy note-book by the light of a farm-house fire—so few incendiary bombs, so few cartridges for the grenades and cursing them and everyone else that they could do no better with the lives of men depending on their efforts, and the success of a great cause in the balance. She went wearily to bed, feeling so lonely as she lay, that before she slept she sobbed at the darkness and the emptiness of the house like a little child.

It was only by pure will-power that she rose from bed that Sunday morning. On looking at her watch she found it was only half-past five, and suddenly hearing the first chapel-bell toll faintly across the streets she decided she must go out to Mass. The dawn was so dark that she had to light a candle and it reminded her of Christmas time when one lights the lights over the Christmas dinner, even in the daytime. She stole down past Leo's door, and as she glanced at it she noticed that it was open. Peeping through the slit of the hinges she saw the bed was empty and she could hear no breathing. She opened the door cautiously and found the room deserted. She tried every other room—she even opened the dead woman's door and peeped through. There in the dim light of the curtained room sat the corpse, still and statuesque as they left it. Fright overcame her and she fled thundering down the stairs and out into the markets, and not daring to think of her or of Leo or of anything, she hurried across the intervening streets to the monks' chapel. It lay at the end of a great sweep of grazing land; on the grass a soft mist like frost, and through the morning dusk the little Gothic windows of the chapel glowed yellow like the windows of a toy house. When she reached it a stream of people was passing in from the Incurables hospital across the road, the blind, the crippled, the stumbling, the maimed—people whose disease was hidden from the eye. Nobody spoke as they hurried in to Mass—all cold and silent but for their feet on the damp gravel-path, around them the city lying quietly asleep. They were like a meeting of the dumb and sleepless ones of Cork hurrying to a gift of peace that sleep had denied them, hurrying as if to snatch that gift beefore the morning should come, for overhead the sky was still dark and the larger stars were shining and the night-wind swept through the higher regions of the air.

The chapel was full when she entered, and as if Death were never to be avoided a coffin on trestles stood under a black and silver shroud in the centre of the flags. She sat on a bench that faced the pall, peeping nervously around, half afraid for having ventured out, beginning to wonder where she should go when Mass had finished. Two young people attracted her for a long time, a young man and a young woman who prayed so seriously, for their youthful looks, that she wondered at them in her heart. They seemed as if they had only recently been married, or not married for very long, but they were here at the earliest Mass in Cork, on a cold April morning, kneeling shoulder to shoulder and praying to what Leo once called a problematical God with an earnestness that frightened her. It was not beautiful to see in the body such young people so fanatically pious—it made her fear God. Meanwhile the ceremony went on, the priest genuflecting as he passed the tabernacle, the acolyte tapping the low-booming bell at the consecration of the Host. Then there was a general scurry as people rose to approach the altar rails. There, as she looked at them, she saw among the crowd the youthful face of Leo; he knelt, he waited for the priest to come with the Host, he raised his head, and the age-old ceremony was fulfilled. Christ the God, the God of Love or the God of Freedom—which she thought was Leo thinking of?—descended on earth to lie on the boy's tongue. She hid her face as he passed back and the next thing she heard was the organ playing tremulously and the priest saying, "Your prayers are requested for the repose of the soul of Brother Senan who has died at the age of twenty-one." The congregation murmured pityingly in reply, "May God have mercy on his soul and the souls of all the faithful departed, Amen." She rose and slipped out, and when she stepped on the gravel path the sky was bright and the east was red and all the stars were gone. She hurried back to the Bombshop, looking over her shoulder many times, to see if Leo were in sight, and then to her room where she lay on her bed fully dressed, listening for his return, listening to the city wakening by degrees from its night's slumber, to the bells of the city churches, to the occasional footsteps returning from or going to the early Mass.

At last he came, and when she descended he was already at work, and as she fried the rashers for their breakfast the tang of the potassium rose in the air. She entered the workshop smiling to call him to breakfast, but immediately she looked at him she noticed a change. The Mass that had filled her heart with peace, a serene and happy peace, had filled his with far other feelings. He would not talk to her; and when she ventured a question or two—as whether the incendiaries would be finished in time—he replied with a short No.

"Why not?" she asked.

How could they? Anyway, why should he care? What a small business they were engaged in! A dirty business. Bombs? Incendiaries? He would do the grenade cartridges. He would do that. Others would have to do the bombs. And when, because she did not understand what he was driving at (and woman-like seized the practical objection first), she protested that he had never done the grenade cartridges which were always Caesar's job, he flared up and his tongue loosened, and he became argumentative.

"Can't do them? I'll tell you how to do them. Empty the old Mausers first of all. Now listen!"

As he spoke he jabbed his greasy fork in the air, so that she had to draw back from his whirling hands. Afterwards when she realized that the well had merely burst through his clay also, she was sorry for him, but now as he argued she had neither sympathy nor patience left.

"Weigh out the grains," he cried, "with the utmost care. I know what I'm talking about. Clean the old cartridges with dilute nitric, and when they're ready cut them down and file them down. Then the cardboard wads. And the cotton wads. Then after that you just coax the little grains carefully, one by one, a single one might make twenty yards of difference in the cast, and ram the wads tight, and the paper wads, and close the lot with your tweezers."

"But, Leo, what is it all for? What do you want to change for?"

"Now, let me finish. I'll show you if I know."

"But even if you do know, Leo?"

"Now, the cap. Shellac for that. And a trick to dry them is to put them on a hot plate over a Bunsen. Yes, well, now, the caps. The caps. Oh, yes! They must be impressed. Tight. And that's not all. . . ."

She looked at him, and he saw she was looking at him as one looks at somebody one has known for a long time and trusted for a long time and suddenly begun to doubt or suspect. He fell silent, and returned her look in kind. There they sat, all about them the monuments of their hopes, the bags of chemicals, the roughly-fashioned ovens and heating trays, the books of instructions, the jars of acid. Beneath them the silent statue in her chair. Outside the awakening city and the climbing sun; there at least was peace, or the appearance of peace, with the shadows slanting from the houses, the bells falling into silence.

Knock, knock, knock-knock! Like cringing curs their tongues sank down in their throats and they swallowed hard with fear, staring at one another and listening for the next bold knocking on the door below. Knock! And after it a series of running knocks in the rhythm of the cry of "Here's the herrings, here's the herrings, here's the herrings." So they had come for her? Or was it a raid? If so this was the end. For some reason Norah wondered why the old woman did not rise up and go down to that insistent knocking and say, "Here I am, and long enough I waited for you." A long silence was followed by a single knock. They stole on tiptoe to the lumber-room window and peeped out, half-expecting to see scattered figures in uniform thrown in a half circle before the house, rifles at the ready. All they saw was a man passing by on the opposite side of the square look across in the direction of the door. Nobody came forward to look up at the house, but after a while steps moved away from the door beneath them and they returned and sat as before. Then Leo jumped to his feet.

"This puts a finish to it," he said.

"I don't see that," persisted Norah, flinging her hair back from her brow.

"Are we to wait to be taken? Who was that at the door?"

"They're gone."

"Do you think they won't return? Do you think she has no relations or friends who don't know she never went 'to the country' like that before? Let's clear out. Come on quick."

Panic had seized him. He caught up the sweeping brush with some wild notion of leaving the house tidy as they found it, the death below left unexplained.

"You are afraid," she taunted.

"Sean and Caesar were right to leave you," he retorted, "with your bickering tongue."

"How soft the men leave their posts! Wait till the story spreads on you. Leo, Leo! Aren't you thinking of the men on the hills waiting for the stuff? They must have something to fight with."

"For God's sake. . . ."

She laid her hand gently on his shoulder. He could not bear that—after all he was only a boy.

"Leo," she pleaded, "I know you dearly love Ireland. . . ."

"Oh, vomit on Ireland," he cried. "Vomit on her."

He began to sweep the workroom, the silver powder and the grey powder and the red, the curls of cotton-wool, the brass-filings, and she began to work on the incendiary cartridges at the bench by the window. But he followed her, packing away the things she needed, brushing the dust around her feet, he even knocked the brush-end deliberately against her ankles. He put the matches in his pocket, saying they were his, and when she went to the kitchen for more he snapped them up, saying he believed they were his also. When she changed her place over to the other window, he followed her and flung open the shutters and chanted some song out to the backyards that had never heard a man's voice in that house as long as the oldest resident could remember. At that she turned on him in a rage, and he in a rage turned to face her. She gripped the shutter to close it; he held it to keep it wide. They could see a woman looking across at them in amazement from the window of a slum-house opposite. Tears came to the girl's eyes, and her flaxen hair fell around her shoulders so that the sun made an aureole of it about her trembling features, and looking at her the boy released his grasp and blushing with shame he left the room.

As she began to work on the little caps, dropping warm shellac one by one into each, she could hear in the distance a group of merry-makers leaving the city for the day in cars, the sound of the horses' hoofs and the sound of their concertina playing gaily, and those happy, indifferent sounds dispirited her. The room now grew warm, and she felt the sweat gather on her brow, and the sky darkened until presently her spirit lamp was throwing leaping shadows on the benches, and her hands as they moved were shadowed on the ceiling. Between the room and the murmurs of the city there seemed to hang a heavy curtain dulling all sound, and what light came through the chinks of the shutter was livid. One by one she filled the caps, arranging them when filled in a neat little row before her. Once the lamp threw a strange shadow high in front of her and she leaped around in terror to see who was in the room, and from that on she kept glancing right and left, listening to know where Sean was, looking over her shoulder at the door, looking down at the floor as if she thought she heard some noise below her. At last she seemed to hear something clearly, and she rose and faced the door; she had heard the heavy steps come slowly up the stairs, step by step, to each landing, to the last landing, to the very handle of the door.

"Leo! Leo!" she screamed. "She's coming. She's coming!"

"What is it? What is it?" he cried and ran in to her.

"Look at her! Look! Look!"

A frightful rattle of thunder crashed over the room as if mighty billiard-balls were cannoning in the sky. He clasped her to him and she clung to him—she could see the fish-head eyes of the corpse staring at her through the linen cloth. Then the soft rain outside changed into a downpour so that they heard it on the iron roof in the yard. Leo flung open the shutters again so that they could see the sun shining through the falling water, and as she continued to tremble he kissed her right on the lips. She did not try to prevent him. She heard him whispering that this was the best end of all, and she did not try to deny it, for as he whispered she grew calmer and knew that an end there must be.

So they spent that morning cleaning the house, packing everything away in the secret dump, ready to be removed if the chance should offer. Last of all they unlocked her door and dusted and tidied her room, and they set a great fire going in front of her, and they poured fresh milk into her glass and put their own food in her cupboard. The last thing they did before they left was to remove the linen cloth from her face. Then they walked boldly out into the markets and the city streets just a little before curfew when everybody was hastening home. They spent the night in a country house on the hills that lay just outside the city to the south-west, sitting silently together as soon as they could be alone, hand in hand. Norah flung her shoes from off her feet, and to please Leo she let her hair down about her shoulders.

"I am afraid, darling," she said to him, "there are streaks of grey in it."

"I cannot see them," he said gallantly.

"I shan't search for them," she said gaily, holding his hand tighter than ever.

If they wished to raise their eyes from under the glow of the old reading-lamp they could see through the open window the fireflies of the city far below them, a thin row of footlights to the night, but where they could smell the country smells of budding-time they had no wish to look down into that dark hollow with its thousand blinking eyes. No city should they see if they looked, but a house in the centre of the markets, vegetable and fish refuse around it, dogs barking in the yards behind it, and the one occupant they left there waiting for her burial to come, seated before the warm fire and staring fixedly into its flames—her eyes big with Death.

Andrew Lytle

THE GUIDE

THE big car rolled smoothly into the night. The sharp bright smudge of the headlights slid under the darkness with mathematical exactitude. Dressed in his hunting clothes, the boy sat beside his uncle and watched the road. He sat rather stiffly. His new boots, greased by his mother, prodded the boxes of shells piled carelessly onto the floor of the car. He was not comfortable. The shells gave him no easy rest for his feet, his clothes were strange in their bulk, and he could not make up his mind how to act with his Uncle Bomar. This was to him at the moment the most serious matter in the world. He tied himself into knots thinking about it. He rather felt that the childish deference to an elder was out of place now that they were going hunting together, and not merely hunting but to the Lake for ducks. The invitation was plainly Bomar's way of accepting him as a man. Bomar did not take boys duck shooting. Quail or dove hunting, but never duck. He had begged too often not to know. The boy felt that at last he was ready for a man's pleasures and responsibilities. This thought made him all the more anxious to behave as he should. This and the way his mother had seen them off.

But how was he to behave? Nobody had told him, just as nobody had told him what it meant to put on long pants. His mother had cried, his father had asked the cost, his grandfather had spouted Latin about the *toga virilis*. And his Brother Bob, all he had said was, "Keep it buttoned up, kid." "Of course I'll keep buttoned up," he had answered with shame and petulance, thinking only of the technical handling of the clothes. He knew at once he had made a mistake, even before he saw the smirk on his brother's face. Suddenly the long months of expectation, at last realized, turned bitter under his tongue and he did not know rightly why. Vaguely and with confusion it came to him how narrow had been his understanding of what he had wanted. His wish had been little more than to masquerade in grown-up clothes. But the fact was another thing. Changing clothes had changed him. He felt the same and yet he was not the same. For days it puzzled him how this could be, then he gave it up as he grew accustomed to his new condition, but for a while longer he carried about him a feeling of unease. This made him sensitive and timid, so that he would cross over to the other side of the street rather than speak to someone he had known all his life.

The car took a curve. From the darkness a large stock barn with white

Reprinted from *The Sewanee Review* and used with the kind permission of the author, Andrew Lytle.

doors appeared, disappeared. A board fence made a slapping noise as they passed down its narrow lane. He watched the posts go down like piles. The air sucked in, the fence was gone, and he knew they were entering poorer country.

"Tommy phoned me the big flights were coming in," Bomar said. "Had been for two days."

The boy stiffened in his seat, thinking desperately hard what reply a sportsman would make to such an important statement. The moment of his indecision dragged interminably, so that he blurted out, "You reckon they'll still be there?" His cheeks burned with shame at the over-eager, inadequate words.

"If the weather holds," Bomar replied in his slow, unexcitable voice. "It's got to be cold enough for the streams and back water to freeze over before the ducks come on to the Lake in any number. It's pretty cold. I expect they'll be there."

The boy leaned back in his seat. His uncle had answered him seriously. His question no longer seemed to him childish and ineffective. He even recovered from the humiliation of the leave-taking, his mother following them to the car, pulling his scarf about his neck, telling him not to get shot, not to take cold and to promise her, if his feet got wet, to tell the man to row him in, a few ducks is not worth pneumonia. . . . Great God, Effie, the boy's going duck shooting, not the North Pole. He had been grateful for Bomar's words then. He was more grateful now. They had not meant regret for asking him to come along. Maybe Bomar, too, knew what it was to be hindered by the solicitude of women.

The older man reached up and turned on the car's spot. He played it about the countryside, objects in the rough fields, then set it to the center of the road. The headlights swelled to a new fullness and the car took up speed. "A spot is a good thing to have in the country," Bomar said, as if his gesture needed some explanation.

"It sure is," the boy replied.

His uncle had turned as he spoke, turned easily, almost lazily, and yet all his movements showed perfect coördination. The boy felt a slight shock of surprise. His uncle was not so old a man as he had always thought, or rather he had never thought about his age at all. He had been Uncle Bomar, his mother's younger brother, sometimes whispered about in the family, but one of the opposition nevertheless who stood for authority, dullness, and obstacles to freedom. Except that he had never been so dull as the others. He had threatened older boys with Bomar's name and he would always let you go along to pick up doves. And Bomar had taken time to teach him how to shoot. He looked at the older man's eyes as if for the first time. They wore a look of furious haste which seemed out of keeping with his fleshy cheeks. As the boy looked more closely, it seemed to him that the fury had grown cold and the haste had set like the film over the racer's pupils as he is being led from the track, blinded to the shouting in the stands, to winning and losing, to all but the burning strain of the race and the gorged heart.

Bomar said, "You had better take that heavy coat off. You won't feel it in the morning. It gets cold as hell out on that Lake."

Hastily the boy took off the coat, for the second time thinking bitterly of his mother, whom he had allowed in his ignorance to dress him as she had once done for parties and Sunday school, as if the whole affair were no more than a fashion parade. His uncle wore his good clothes. Hunters changed for the Lake after they got there.

"How do you think you will like it, kid?"

"Oh, fine," he said hastily. "I've always wanted to go. Old Jake used to tell me about grandfather Laus going there. He said he went in a wagon and it took him two weeks to go, and he always stayed two or three weeks hunting and fishing. Jake said he was a little boy, and they took him along to gather up fat pine and keep the fires."

"It's quite a difference these days," the older man said.

"Oh, yes, sir. When will we get there?"

"Well, we could make it tonight, but I think we'll stop off and sleep at Center. There's a good hotel there. The quarters at Hornbec are pretty rugged. And the guides keep you up drinking your whiskey."

"Oh," the boy said. He kept silent a moment, then resumed eagerly. "Jake said there were all kinds of hunting, and on one trip grandfather Laus brought back a live bear."

"The old boy must have been quite a sport."

"Oh, he was. Sometimes he would sleep under the trees, by a spring or creek. Jake said when he put up with people along the way, he would copy the design of a quilt he liked and have his wife make it when he got back home."

Bomar looked curiously at the boy at his side. "You seem to know a lot about that old guy. Which one was he?"

"He's the one that hangs to the right of the mantel in the living room."

"Let's see. That's the . . ."

"He hangs in the mahogany frame."

"Yeah. He was the one that was such a rounder."

"But he reformed. Mother says he received the mantle of grace when the Methodists held their great revival and built a Church for his slaves."

"When the hell was that?"

"Oh, a long time ago. I don't know rightly."

"You might know it would be a long time. The United Daughters like'm dead."

The boy regarded his uncle with a puzzled expression. "You mean the United Daughters of the Confederacy, sir?"

"I mean all united daughters. The club don't make any difference. In union is strength. That's their battle cry. But hell, boy, you don't know what I'm talking about," Bomar said with impatience. "What I mean is the only man they'll have any truck with is a dead one. After a certain age, that is. The deader the better, if he's buried deep enough so he don't stink."

The boy nodded knowingly, although his head was awhirl. He had heard his father and his father's friends occasionally refer to women in disparaging terms. One spoke of women and preachers, he discovered, in the same tone of voice. It apparently was a thing one did to relieve certain difficult situations, but there was never a particular woman, or a particular preacher, named. The reference was invariably general. And his grandfather —only with him it was religion. He never spoke impolitely of ladies, but he could fling himself into a passion about the Church, especially at the dinner table when the conversation fell off. And his grandmother gave always the same reproving speech, in the same falsely affronted manner, "Don't blaspheme before these young men, Mr. Hancock." And Mr. Hancock would reply with righteous vehemence, "The truth, Madam, cannot blaspheme." None of this banter had he taken to mean anything, but with his Uncle Bomar he felt a difference. Bomar had actual women in mind and a grievance which seemed, however mysterious, real and vaguely threatening. He could not help but be disturbed the more he thought about Bomar's remark. Did he mean his own mother? She talked a great deal about her family, living and dead. The truth heretofore hidden in things familiar confronted him: most of the people she talked about were dead.

After a while, in the silence which had fallen between the man and boy, Bomar said, "Forget it, kid." And the boy knew it was hard for him to speak, that inadvertently he had allowed talk which he considered unseemly to pass between them.

But he could not forget so easily. Considerations too disturbing to be summarily dismissed had been set loose in his head. Was it true that ladies of his mother's years thought only of the dead, or thought of them to the disfavor of the living? He was sure it could not be so with his mother. The tales she told never called to mind the dead but only the very dearest of kin who perhaps lived too far away to visit. Above all was this true of grandfather Laus, whom she set him for example. "Hold your head up and step lightly," she would say and he knew who it was she had in mind. Or, "Always be able to look any man in the eye." And again, "Think what you please but never speak loosely and you'll have nothing to take back." These admonitions he was conscious of but never in the forepart of his mind. They underlay and gave firm texture to all he found delightful in his great-grandfather's life, and he somehow knew that had they been lacking the stories which won his heart would have seemed less true. But now that he thought of things in a way he never had thought before, all which touched him dearly lay bright and clear before his vision, the beginning, the middle, and the end clarified in a burst of illumination, where the parts were the whole and the whole defined the parts. And so it came to him that from his mother he got most of the admonitions but the stories he had from his grandfather or from Jake.

The near duel with General Jackson he liked best of all, for the two friends were parted over a horse race. This seemed to him right and fitting, for only some such great occasion was proper cause to break the bonds between two "gentlemen who held each other in the highest esteem." The story as it was told, without directly accusing the General, was told to his discredit. Large sums had been placed on the race. In the last half mile the General's horse was gaining, when his grandfather Laus's horse threw his rider and crossed the finishing line several lengths ahead of his rival. Proud of himself, he turned to the stand where his master sat, and whinnied. At this point in the story his grandfather would pause dramatically. "The spectators to a man rose and cheered the gallant animal." But of course no riderless horse could win a race. Words passed, just what words he was never told, a challenge was given and taken, but the night before the morning of the duel friends intervened and the matter was disposed of to the honor of both parties. "Else," his grandfather would say, "Else," he would repeat, looking significantly about him, "the history of our nation had been played out in different fashion."

Tall, gallant, and forever young, this was the man whose image he carried, not that of the picture in the mahogany frame. That never made him think of grandfather Laus. It looked like the dead or would have so looked if the straight-glancing eyes had been closed. But they narrowed too sharply out of some great reserve, above the stiff neck and stock and the black broadcloth coat. He could never imagine the man in the picture lying under the trees, wrapped in a bear skin, with the shine of the camp fire on his face and the sound of the hobbled horses grazing in the dark. The grandfather who was hunter was the man he liked to think about. Now he was going over the same road he had taken and to the Lake where he had had such great sport with all kinds of game. The road was changed, there was no more a forest, but the Lake at least would still be wild and the guides simple, noble men.

"Wake up, kid, we're here."

He opened wide his eyes, but for a moment his senses delayed. Startled, he thought the car was drawing up before the hotel in Center under its large neon sign glowing evilly red in the darkness. Here the night before they had stepped out of the frosty air into the shabby newness of the lobby, had been shown to their room by a grey-haired elevator boy. It had seemed to him that he had scarcely closed his eyes before his uncle was shaking him awake. Behind the desk the proprietor greeted them. He was dressed in hunting clothes. His eyes were bright as a bird's and he jerked about like a mechancal toy as he cocked his head to one side and talked glibly of the shooting, but what he wanted to find out was whether they would be back that night. "Bastard," Bomar said as they turned away.

It was still dark as they passed a second time under the neon sign. The car was white and glistened in the dark. The exhaust made a loud noise in the deserted street. In the distance he had heard an ash can clattering. . . .

"Well, here we are," Bomar said and got out of the car with a motion which was quick for a man his size. He called into the darkness, "Anybody seen Tommy?"

A voice answered, "He stepped up to his house. He'll be on down in a little."

"Are we really here?" the boy asked. He noticed that he had lowered his voice. His uncle had spoken right out.

"This is Hornbec. There's the Lake over there."

The boy glanced towards a rough pier, but it was all dark beyond and he could see nothing of the water. They walked up the narrow street which bordered the Lake. Lights from the windows and door of a plain two-storey building glared from its porch and threw a milky shadow onto the steps. But the light did not penetrate, although he could see his uncle's face and the half-solid forms of men stirring busily around him. He was wide awake now, with the cold wind from the Lake blowing his face, but he felt as if he were acting in a dream, where all was topsy-turvy yet all seemed natural. It was this very naturalness of things which made him feel as he did: people going about their business, talking in a normal voice, but all in the dead of night.

"Let's go in the hotel," Bomar said.

Inside it was warm and bright. Some dozen men dressed in their hunting clothes, several of them in hip boots, sat around a pot-bellied stove. It was red hot about its middle. He shivered and walked over to warm himself.

"How about a little breakfast, Nelly?" Bomar called out and walked into the long dining room.

The walls were plain and unfinished. Most of the tables were in disarray and he could see that the guests of the hotel had already eaten. Where he sat, there were crumbs on the cloth and somebody had spilled catsup. The woman Nelly came in with fried eggs shining white with grease, thick bacon, large thick biscuits, and coffee in heavy china cups. She flung her head and shoulders about as she walked. The boy thought he had never seen less sense in a face, but he could see the hunters liked her or at least that she thought the hunters liked her.

"Good old Nelly. She won't let us starve," Bomar called out with too loud a heartiness and grabbed playfully at her waist. She tossed her head and flung herself out of the way, but her wide bright eyes grew brighter.

"Quit, now-wah," she said.

The brazen stupidity in her dare that was not a dare chilled his spirits. The eggs were cold, but he ate the bacon and poured a lot of milk and sugar in his coffee and drank it. The coffee was steaming hot.

"Paul's wife may come up with him today," Bomar said to the girl.

"I hope she does."

"Do you now?"

"Why not. I ain't got nothing to hide."

"No. Nothing to hide. Nothing at all."

"That's right."

"Who did I see kissing you?"

"He was jest being jolly."

"Yeah. Jolly. Good old jolly Paul."

"That's right," she said. "Jolly and friendly. You all want lunches?"

"Sure. You want us to go hungry on that Lake?"

"I didn't know. I thought maybe you'd brought lunches with you."

Bomar turned to his nephew. "This hotel thinks it's got a monopoly."

"We don't care where you stay." Her head came up. A light flush at the cheek bones rushed to her eyes. For the first time the woman seemed real to the boy. His mother had told him that plain people were quick to take offense but it was her show of pride which gave her being, and he understood that it was a thing she held in common with those around her as she shared a speech which his mother called country.

"Well, will you be here tonight?" she continued.

Bomar paused. "Yeah. The kid and I'll be here."

"I jest wanted to know. I have to plan about supper."

She left the dining room, and the man and boy ate hurriedly and in silence. From the other room they heard spurts of talk. None of it flowed easily, as happens with men who are idling. It jabbed at the silence, a silence enclosing a time of waiting upon action, when the mind grows fearful lest its edge grow dull from images. The boy was trying to catch the drift of the talk. He had not heard the soft steps approaching. He heard only the words, "Now if you ain't a pretty bastard."

He stiffened and waited for the blow which Bomar in all honor must give. He waited a second. There was no stirring of the chair. He raised his eyes upon his uncle's smiling, placid features.

Bomar's lips were moving. "You ain't no handsome son-of-a-bitch yourself," they said.

"Getting in here this time of day. You drive all night?"

"Hell, no. We stopped off at Center to get a few hours' sleep."

"What you think you are, a goddam tourist?"

"You got an interest in this hotel?"

"Hell, no. It's just the company you keep. When I want to sleep in a whore house, I don't want no pimp to show me my bed. That mealy-mouthed bastard dressing up like a hunter to catch the suckers like you, only I didn't know you was a sucker before. And they'll steal there, too."

"Hell, Applegate."

"Hell they don't. Last week a man from Indiana lost his purse with ninety-seven dollars in it."

"You're just afraid he'll take away your business."

"Hell. None of the guides around here will go up there. And we don't let him down here."

Bomar turned to his nephew. "Kid, shake hands with Tommy Applegate."

The boy rose and gave the small heavy-set man his hand. He was a little dazed. Bastard and son-of-a-bitch were fighting words, not friendly greetings. He didn't understand. He knew his uncle had fought for less, much less. And he well knew that no such greeting would have passed between grandfather Laus and his lean, weathered guide, when they met again at the return of the hunting season. But of course there were no professional guides in those days. The people who lived about the Lake at that time hunted or trapped for a living. They might go along with a friend out of pure courtesy, or for companionship, but he was sure they took no money for it. But it was not money either. It was the greeting which shocked and puzzled him. For a second his hand gripped the guide's hand. He felt the inert calloused flesh, and the strength within, near the bone, but there was no response to his clasp. The man was not being unfriendly, but as he drew away the boy felt he had been rebuffed. Later he remembered the eyes. They were brown, which he did not expect. And there was something else, something wrong about them. They lacked the sharpness of a hunter's eyes.

"We are about ready to shove off, kid," Bomar interrupted. "We're going to the first pocket. Tommy got you a good guide. Watch him, though, or he'll shoot up too many of your shells. And you give him this at the end of the day."

The boy looked at the money. "All of this, Uncle Bomar?"

"Yeah, I know. It's too damn much, but it's what they charge."

Outside the darkness was thinning. The Lake spread out for a way like a black floor. The boy hesitated on the edge of the porch. His clothes were slick from the cold, but the blood charged through his body. It seemed a trivial thing that he had worried at not finding the place and the people what he had expected, for the surroundings are nothing. The only thing that mattered was the shoot. Hunters passed him on the steps, all with a common purpose, the same thoughts, the same sense of excitement and expectation. He could feel it as they went by. One or two looked curiously at him. He knew he must go on or they would think him strange, but still he delayed to savor the full measure of the experience before it was played out by the act. All this stir, the time of day, the learning of the guides, the rich men who hunted, who came from places where their word was law, others who came out of some urgent need they did not rightly understand—all of them now and in his great-grandfather's day, were guided, were governed by the instincts of a bird. Bomar half turned. "Where are you?" he called sharply.

"Coming," the boy answered and hurried down the steps. He noticed that Bomar's bulky clothes spreading out over his hips enlarged them. He looked from the rear like his mother.

At the water's edge two boats were drawn close into the bank. Tommy was standing in one. Bomar was handing him his gear.

"Your gun unloaded?" Tommy asked.

"You know I wouldn't hand you any loaded gun," Bomar replied.

"Be God-damned sure. I don't want you to blow my ass off."

"Don't put it where it'll get wet."

"If it gets wet, you'll get wet. Hand me that sack of charcoal."

"Your arm's not broke. Pick it up."

"What's the matter with your back? Been riding it too much?"

"My back's all right. This is Jack Daniel's number seven. Catch it."

"Three's my lucky number."

"Well, this will more than double your luck. Won't it, Goosetree?"

A man looked up from blowing the charcoal burner in the adjoining boat. The light from the charcoal showed a pair of flat eyes, with sharp points at their centers. Even in the steady red glow his features seemed pale. He said dryly, "He'll double your drinks."

"This is the kid, Goosetree, that's going with you," Bomar said.

The man nodded. "They'll make the noise, sonny," he said. "We'll bring in the meat."

"Hell," Tommy said with heavy scorn.

"I've got the gun will do it," Goosetree added. "And this boy looks like he can shoot."

"You may get a mud hen or two."

"I'm going to hole up at the point. We'll bring'm in."

"Bring in my ass," Tommy said.

"Now that ud be a right heavy load."

The boy no longer felt ill at ease with these people. At first he had been repelled by their obscenities. The words had struck him with all the force of their literal meaning. And in his disgust there had been fear, not so much of the men and the place, as of his own sensations. All things he had found different from his imaginings. Bomar's unintended remarks in the car had begun it. He had got in beside his uncle, never doubting that things could ever be otherwise than as they seemed. He had found that even a fact about which there could not be the slightest uncertainty, such as Bomar's eyes, was not a fact at all. Almost without attending it, so fast did it happen, one certainty after another had slipped away from him until he felt exposed in all his privacy. Now this in some way had changed. He had scarcely listened to the guides talk. He watched them get the boats set for the shoot. What they did went quickly, but there was no haste to their movements, and their banter was spoken with as little attention to the meaning as the congregation repeating the doxology on Sunday.

Goosetree straightened up. His movement was unmistakable. There came a pause and Bomar turned hastily. "Now, kid," he said, "you got to lead these duck."

"Like doves?"

"Yeah. Maybe further. I can't tell you exactly. You'll have to judge. But when they come flying in at you, shoot at their bills." He stepped into the boat. "All ready, me lads?"

"We been ready," Goosetree replied.

The boy sat forward in the boat, astraddle the charcoal burner. There was barely room for his legs and he had to watch to see that his boots didn't burn. They pushed off and he thought surely the ice must chew up the bottom of the boat. The going got better after a while, but every now and then the guide had to strike the ice several times before he could set the oars to water. The darkness thinned and the cold began to bite into him. It had a different quality over water. He felt weight as well as chill. He wore two wool shirts, a heavy wool coat and next to his body close-knit woolen underwear, but it went through all these garments like air through a sack in a broken window light. He got to wondering if he could stand it all day and leaned forward to rub his hands over the open mouth of the burner.

His teeth began to chatter and he drew down his chin so it wouldn't be seen. He could hear Bomar and Tommy. Their voices had the flat clear sound of coming from a distance and yet they were not far away. And then he looked up. . . . Dawn had swamped the sky. There was no light and yet he could see. He was first conscious of a wonderful ease to his eyes. Wide open, without a thread's strain, they saw everywhere through the colorless haze. Never had he been able to see so clearly and so far. He thought it must be like this with animal eyes at night or whenever they hunt, to see and not know they are seeing, when the vision and prey are made one for the spring. A wonderfully fresh strength streamed through his body. All things seemed at a beginning. It was the world on the first day.

The boat struck a snag. He looked more closely about. Black slick tree trunks stuck up out of the water like the splintered piles of a pier which has rotted away. Occasionally they passed a stump that was still alive, but its stunted growth only made the desolate surroundings more forbidding. And the Lake, he saw, was forbidding. Miles upon miles of saw grass, more grass than water, and everywhere the illusion of solid ground. Slimy ooze, even quicksand, was its floor. His first elation drained away. He told himself the place was not meant for man. It was more foreign and distant to his experience than the most outlandish reaches of human habitation. Over him came a great and terrible loneliness.

The boats entered an open pocket of frozen water. His boat began to rock and he grasped the sides.

"Give with the boat," Goosetree commanded.

"What's the matter, Mr. Goosetree?"

"Nothing's the matter. I'm breaking the ice."

"What for?"

"To throw out the blocks." Goosetree's voice made him feel the depth of his ignorance.

The ice broke up in sheets and the boat sloshed it out of the way. Into the open water the guide began to throw his decoys. He unwound the string, glanced at the water with quick precision and then threw out the painted block. In no time the false birds rode their anchors in front of the blind. Goosetree now drove the boat into the edge of the grass. He handed the boy a pole. "When I pull, you push on that," he said and stepped into the water. His hip boots sank down and he said, "All right." At each push the boat slid further into the blind. Empty shells and cigarette butts soiled the flattened tufts of grass. One cigarette, scarcely smoked, touched the water, its damp brown insides spilling and staining the paper. A smear of lipstick gashed its upper end. Instinctively the boy averted his gaze. A blot formed in the blue-gray haze, hung for a moment to the air, desperately, noiselessly fluttering its wings, and turned and disappeared. Motionless, he watched the spot where it had been, feeling he could almost have touched the duck, if duck it was, for how could its wings beat so and not make a sound?

"I reckon it's hid," Goosetree said.

"No, it just melted away," the boy replied.

Goosetree's eyes came on guard. The boy said hastily. "Oh, the boat. Yes, sir, it looks hid."

"What'd you think I meant?"

"I didn't hear you well."

He felt that his guide was studying him, trying to make up his mind whether he was responsible enough to risk in the close quarters they must keep. At last Goosetree pulled himself out of the water and began to prepare the boat for action. He set the burner between them, changed the seats so that they faced each other, set his lunch beside him, his water bottle to the rear. He took bunches of grass from both sides and tied them together over the boat. Carefully he loaded his gun and set it down pointing into the grass. He loaded the boy's and handed it to him. "Point it that way," he said, "and always keep the safety on until you get up to shoot. And don't get up until I tell you."

"Where are Uncle Bomar and Tommy gone?" he asked.

The guide was dropping charcoal into the burner. "They went to the other side of the pocket." He leaned over to blow the coals. The boy noticed that his hands were black and his face sooty from handling the coal. When the fire suited him, he dropped a tomato can over the low tin chimney, then rose in the boat. He stood with his body half bent and with a short jerk of the head looked up. A shadow passed over his eyes as he flicked them across the arc of the sky.

"See anything?" the boy asked.

"They'll be in," he replied.

Then they sat in silence, leaning towards each other over the burner.

Around the boat, out of the grass, the cold boiled up through a slimy mist. Now that they were settled and waiting the boy felt his body relax and his head grow dull. He was wondering how he could get up from his cramped quarters in time to shoot. He did not see the guide rise. He heard the shot and looked up, his heart fluttering, in time to see the red feet draw up under the white belly, see the inert body slanting to the Lake.

"When they hit the ice, they don't git up no more," Goosetree said. He added, "I seen him too late to call you."

His first feeling was chagrin and resentment. A guide should give others a chance to shoot. But in his heart he knew he had been a bad hunter. Too much excitement had worn him out. He must learn how to wait, be idle and still wound up, like a spring. That was it. Like a spring.

"There they come," Goosetree hissed.

"Where?" he breathed.

"A Susie. In front of you."

Almost over head and to the left he saw the duck. The spring in him snapped. He heard the report of his gun, saw the bird falter, fly for a hundred yards and then go down. He shot at another passing to his front, missed, shot and missed again. He tried to aim but his eyes felt frozen and wide open. His gun and Goosetree's went off together. The bird stopped short in flight and fell straight down. For the first time Goosetree smiled.

"I missed the second shot," the boy said and his voice was trembling and his throat dry.

"You didn't lead him enough. The air from your load fanned his tail."

"We both shot at the same time. Think we both got him. I expect you got him."

"It was a teal," Goosetree said, glancing swiftly around. The sky seemed to open out of his eyes.

It seemed a long time before the next ducks flew over. At last he heard, "There!" He grabbed his gun, half rose. "Git down," the guide ordered and hastily put his hands to his mouth and called, the reedy imitation of the duck's cry rasping the air. The call seemed too urgent to the boy, faster than a bird would make. The birds dipped and turned, then flew away.

"No use aiming. Whenever they see you, it's too late."

"Did they see me?"

"Hell, yes. Never get up until you're ready to shoot."

The nasal call to death and the sound of guns travelled from different parts of the Lake, gradually drifted into silence until the whole world grew as still as the painted ducks riding their anchors in the pool of rotten ice. He and the guide were close enough to touch. The intimacy which was not intimacy began to close in on him. He felt that he ought to say something. He said, "Is your son going to follow in your footsteps, Mr. Goosetree?"

"Hell, no. There's no money in guiding. Soon's he's old enough I'm going to send him to college."

"I would think this was a wonderful life," the boy said in surprise, "being able to hunt or fish every day and get paid for it."

"It gits stale, up before day freezing your balls off sloshing around in this ice."

The guide picked up a jug of milky water and poured it into a pan and set the pan on the open mouth of the burner. "I'll make us some coffee," he said. "And we can eat." The ducks won't be back until about eleven o'clock. I've noticed that's the time they been coming in."

He measured the coffee and dumped it into the water, took a dirty rag and carefully wiped out two cups and put them beside him. Then he took a spoon and began to stir the coffee and blow the coals. "No," he said, "it's hard on you. I'm going to quit it soon. I bought me the finest summer house ever built around this Lake. Old man Simpkins built it, a rich lumber man from Mississippi. He spent eight thousand dollars on it. Built it of pine and not a knot in it, plumbing, lights, frigidaire, and good water. I heard his widow wanted to sell and I let her know by the woman who looks after it that I might, might mind you, try to buy it. So old lady Simpkins called me long distance. And I asked her what she wanted for it and she commenced telling me how much she'd put in it. I cut her off. I said I'll give you two thousand cash for it. She couldn't listen to any such figure, it was giving it away. Two thousand's my offer. Take it or leave it. She hung up on me. But a week later I got a letter from her son saying his mother couldn't bear to come up here no more since her old man had went away and that they'd close the deal." Goosetree poured a cup of coffee and handed it to the boy. "I'd of give twenty-five hundred as easy I give two thousand." He unwrapped a sandwich. "I'm going to build two cabins, put a toilet and shower in em, they's eight rooms to the house, and rent by the week or month. A man and his wife can come up and fish. They come sometime with women they claim to be their wives. There'll be money in it."

"How many'd you get?" a voice from the Lake asked.

It was Bomar and Tommy. Goosetree rose. "Aw, we got'm, boys. How many'd you knock down?"

"None," Tommy said. His face was grave and averted, as though still turned from the incomprehensible workings of Fate.

"We shot twice, but they were too high," Bomar added apologetically.

Tommy began throwing out his decoys.

"Don't throw them blocks out here," Goosetree said.

Tommy rowed about, continuing to throw them out. He asked, "Don't we work together?"

"Hell. The quarters is too close."

Bomar said in his slow, soothing voice, "Goosetree, I believe you are afraid we'll outshoot you."

"Who's got the duck?"

"Well, how many did you get?"

"Three," Goosetree said, his voice less belligerent.

"I really got one, Uncle Bomar. On the nose."

"Fine, kid."

"Yes, sir, this boy's gonna knock'm," Goosetree said. The boy felt a glow of pleasure. He was beginning to think more of his guide.

Tommy masked his boat in the grass behind the others.

"You want some coffee?" Goosetree asked.

"We got something better'n coffee," Tommy replied.

"Here, take a drink," Bomar said.

Tommy turned up the bottle. His Adam's apple worked like a piston as the bright brown liquid flowed down his throat. He wiped the mouth of the bottle on his sleeve and returned it casually. "Warms you better than any charcoal," he said matter-of-factly.

From where he reclined in the boat Bomar took a drink. The boy noticed it was much less than Tommy took. "How about it, Goosetree?"

"I got ulcers. Drinking too much in Arkansas," Goosetree replied. "Hod, but that stuff lightened you as it went down. Set your tail on fire."

"Kid?"

"No, thank you, sir." The boy knew by the way the whiskey was offered that he was supposed to refuse, but he mightily wanted to taste it. He drank his coffee instead and took a bite out of a ham sandwich. There was too much bread for the meat and he threw away the top slice.

"My daddy tole me to stay out'n Arkansas," Goosetree continued.

"Ain't nothing there," Tommy added sourly.

"I went over there to a duck-calling contest oncet. I called as purty as ever you please." Goosetree added bitterly, "They give the prize to a eleven-year-old boy."

"Ain't nothing for nobody in Arkansas," Tommy said.

The boy tried another sandwich, peanut butter and jelly spread together on the bread. It tasted good. At least it wasn't so dry. He finished his coffee and felt better for the food.

"Tommy, where are these duck you called me about?"

Tommy looked shocked at the question and glanced over the Lake towards the woods. "They're roosting on the reserve," he said.

"Government birds, eh?" Bomar said. "Well, they'll sit on their fat asses until we starve to death."

Tommy looked even more serious. "They'll come out after a while,"

"...a rumor, Applegate. You wouldn't recognize it, though. It bore no reference to fornication."

Bomar drank again and passed the whiskey to his guide. Tommy took it and turned it up in one motion. He swallowed like a thirsty man drinking water. "That's seven times seven," he said. "What does it make?"

"You drunk," Bomar replied.

"It'll make you holler." He opened his mouth and his voice rang lustily over the Lake.

Bomar examined his companion's face for a moment. "Applegate," he said, "if you had rings in your ears, you'd look like a damn pirate."

Tommy shouted again. "Hi-yo!"

The boy thought he did look like a pirate, anyway like a foreigner, the way his eyes didn't suit his rough, swarthy features but looked both boldly and evasively at the same time. With Mr. Goosetree it was different. He looked like a guide ought to look, although he was a little small and didn't think much of guiding, which was a disappointment the boy didn't explore but which lay uneasily in the back of his head. But Tommy at least was human and it was somehow because of his eyes. Watching the sky, they absorbed it like a blotter. Maybe it was this which made him seem always on guard. When Mr. Goosetree looked at the sky, he skinned it.

"Hi-yo!" Tommy shouted again. As if suddenly spent by the shouting, he said, "My daddy was a Jew and my mother an Indian. Now ain't that a hell of a combination?"

He had half turned away. Bomar looked at him but said nothing. Tommy continued in a conversational tone. "He used to trade up and down this country. I reckon he made a pretty good living until he took to drinking. When I was a shirt-tail boy, he'd come in on Satday nights and run all of us out of the house. I sort of liked it in summer, like a kid will. My mother would bed us down in the leaves and moss. It didn't seem to worry her much. I reckon Indians are sort of used to the woods. There was generally plenty to eat. She made a good truck patch. She'd take the littlest one and go out in the corn when it was tosselling and sing to it. Homesick kind of a singing. As I got older, I didn't like it so much. Looked like he didn't do so well trading. He'd come in during the week drunk and beat her up. She never hollered, but if he tried to take his scantling to one of us young-uns, she'd scratch and bite him like a cat.

"I was about eleven, I guess. We still had plenty to eat, well not a plenty but enough. She always managed to keep us in victuals, but we was all ragged. It takes money to buy clothes. He wasn't doing no trading at all, except he'd take her corn and swap it for licker. Well, he come a night of the worst blizzard that ever you saw, mean drunk and dirty. He looked like he's been laying out for a week. He commenced cussin' and stumbling around and hollered, 'Clear all these half breeds outer here.' I said, 'Daddy, I don't aim to go out in no blizzard.' His red eyes kind o̶f̶ ̶ He picked a old table leg that was laying around and c̶a̶r̶ raised the gun. He still kept coming. I let him have it r̶i̶g̶h̶t̶ ̶i̶n̶ ̶t̶h̶e̶ belly." Tommy's voice ceased. He said after a while, "Sober, he wasn't no mean-natured kind of a man."

Without saying anything Bomar passed the whiskey over to Tommy. Nobody spoke again for a long while. Goosetree had covered himself up and gone to sleep. Bomar lay back, reclining in the boat. The day had advanced but there was no sun to relieve the cold. The frozen clouds stretched tight across the sky. After a while the boy became conscious of Bomar's soothing voice. It flowed too smoothly. It was getting confidential. He recognized the signs. Miserable from the cold and the long, trying wait, he felt the shoot would be a failure. Nobody would watch for the ducks, maybe there wouldn't be any more to come in. He felt the need to stand up. It was a little less cold up in the air. There was not a duck in the sky. He looked down and his blood danced. Three were playing in the water before a jutting strip of the grass. "Look, Tommy," he cried.

"Mud hens," Tommy said and sat back down.

Bomar had turned where he lay. His eyes were gay. "What," he asked, "would the old boy, what's his name, Menelaus, say if he knew his grandson had taken a mud hen for a duck. The pious Menelaus, our noble ancestor, unequalled in the arts of field and stream and Ovid's pupil. What would he say, kid?"

He was too surprised to say anything—Bomar wondering about grandfather Laus, too, for it was plain that he only pretended to recollect his name. . . .

"Never, oh, never, would that nonpareil, that prince among men, that cock of the walk, have mistaken a mud hen for a duck. Or so we're told. What I like, Applegate, about this revered ancestor of mine and the kid's, was his timing. Now I know that timing is everything, but damn if I can bring it off. But this guy Menelaus did. When he was young, he went the rounds. When it came time to settle down, he didn't settle, but nobody held it against him, least of all his large female connection. He hunted when he wanted to, he had plenty of money, he played the races and was a family man all at the same time. He was a genius, Applegate. And while he stepped high, wide and handsome, his Helen stayed at home making quilts and raising his young. That's the way to do it, Applegate. Be fruitful and multiply. And don't forget the quilts. He didn't. He made it a point to keep her in fresh patterns, just in case. . . . And then when he had dropped all the grains of corn from one jar to the other and it was time to change'm back, he saw the light. At a camp meeting at Walnut Grove the dove, not the kind you're thinking about, Applegate, but the blessed, the miraculous dove, came bearing the twig of salvation." He paused. His voice had grown harder as he spoke. "Don't take it hard, kid, you're not the first to take a wooden nickel."

He couldn't make heads or tails of what his uncle was saying. What did a wooden nickel have to do with it? It was very important. He could tell by Bomar's voice. Before he could try to figure it out, Tommy interrupted.

"There was a lady here fishing once named Helen," Tommy said. "She come here with a doctor from Chicago. They claimed they was married, but I been rowing a long time. These two didn't much care whether they caught anything or not. She wasn't having much luck and I said,—I wasn't thinking anything—'diddle on this side.' I meant her hook of course, and she said, "What? Right there?" and giggled. You know, it was the way she giggled. And the doctor, he laughed too. They did a sight of loose laughing.

Tommy leaned over and stirred the charcoal in the burner. "When I first took up guiding people, didn't no women come here to hunt or fish."

Bomar raised his bottle, "Here's to Argive Helen and all her kin."

The boy felt the boat move. Goosetree was awake and staring at Bomar's large, well-wrapped body. "Look at him," he said, "laying over there like a fattening hog."

Far away, over near the island a lone gun shot once. It made no more noise than a popgun but the men in the two boats grew very quiet. Then all rose to their feet. Goosetree took out his watch. "Eleven twenty," he said.

The importunate duck calls, still at a distance, now buzzed like insects. More guns went off over by the reserve. The firing was scattered. Then somebody said, "Get down." The boy didn't see anything and he got panicky. "Coming over you." "Where, where?" he asked in a tight voice. And then all four of them were shooting furiously. He thought he hit one but he wasn't sure. Two of the ducks turned and flew over a blind across the channel. The hunters there shot up a lot of shells but the ducks went on their way. Goosetree called out, "You want my gun?" His voice was taunting and cheerful. "You can have my gun if you want it."

"How about that for shooting, Applegate?" Bomar asked. His voice was even and full.

"Boy, you stopped him."

"Didn't I stop him, though?"

"Did you? A mallard, too."

"Purty good shooting," Goosetree said. "But look over here in the water."

"Here's where to look," Tommy called back. "Them ducks jest killed theyselves, but we had to shoot to bring'm down."

"Hell."

"We're hitting them, ain't we?" Bomar said.

"Watch it, boys," Goosetree snapped.

Down in the boat Tommy was calling. The hunters across the channel called. The boy crouched and watched the bird, the bending wings, the red feet drawn in. . . . The duck dipped and dove toward the water. The world vanished. There was nothing but space, a streak in space. The moving bolt was all. His ears crashed, the thud against his shoulder, another crash, the red feet gashed the white breast. The dead body dropped and the world was.

"Not bad, kid."

"I think you got him, Uncle Bomar."

"Hard to say. We shot together."

The two of them, the boy and his uncle, were alone in the boat. They watched the guides row from place to place, gathering in the ducks. At last the long full day was over. Behind the island the darkness crouched. As if sensing the hunters could no longer shoot, the ducks now lighted everywhere around them. "God, God . . . Bomar whispered. Then the guides turned their boat about. It sped toward the hunters. Quietly the water parted about the prow, quietly closed behind the rippling wake. No sign of passage marred its surface—waiting to receive the falling night.

"It's been a good shoot," Bomar said evenly. "But it's over."

The boy turned towards his uncle. What he saw made him raise his hand, as though for support. Bomar stood erect and waiting. His eyes were regarding the boy: they were the eyes in the mahogany frame.

Robert Penn Warren

WHEN THE LIGHT GETS GREEN

MY GRANDFATHER had a long white beard and sat under the cedar tree. The beard, as a matter of fact, was not very long and not white, only gray, but when I was a child and was away from him at school during the winter, I would think of him, not seeing him in my mind's eye, and say: He has a long white beard. Therefore, it was a shock to me, on the first morning back home, to watch him lean over the dresser toward the wavy green mirror, which in his always shadowy room reflected things like deep water riffled by a little wind, and clip his gray beard to a point. It is gray and pointed, I would say then, remembering what I had thought before.

He turned his face to the green wavy glass, first one side and then the other in quarter profile, and lifted the long shears, which trembled a little, to cut the beard. His face being turned like that, with his good nose and pointed gray beard, he looked like General Robert E. Lee, without any white horse to ride. My grandfather had been a soldier, too, but now he wore blue-jean pants and when he leaned over like that toward the mirror, I couldn't help but notice how small his hips and backsides were. Only they weren't just small, they were shrunken. I noticed how the blue jeans hung loose from his suspenders and loose off his legs and down around his shoes. And in the morning when I noticed all this about his legs and backsides, I felt a tight feeling in my stomach like when you walk behind a woman and see the high heel of her shoe is worn and twisted and jerks her ankle every time she takes a step.

Always before my grandfather had finished clipping his beard, my Uncle Kirby came to the door and beat on it for breakfast. "I'll be down in just a minute, thank you, sir," my grandfather said. My uncle called him Mr. Barden. "Mr. Barden, breakfast is ready." It was because my Uncle Kirby was not my real uncle, having married my Aunt Lucy, who lived with my grandfather. Then my grandfather put on a black vest and put his gold watch and chain in the vest and picked up his cob pipe from the dresser top, and he and I went down to breakfast, after Uncle Kirby was already downstairs.

When he came into the dining room, Aunt Lucy was sitting at the foot of the table with the iron coffee pot on a plate beside her. She said, "Good morning, Papa."

"Good morning, Lucy," he said, and sat down at the head of the table, taking one more big puff off his pipe before laying it beside his plate.

"You've brought that old pipe down to breakfast again," my aunt said, while she poured the bright-looking coffee into the cups.

"Don't it stink," he always said.

My uncle never talked at breakfast, but when my grandfather said that, my uncle always opened his lips to grin like a dog panting, and showed his hooked teeth. His teeth were yellow because he chewed tobacco, which my grandfather didn't do, although his beard was yellow around the mouth from smoking. Aunt Lucy didn't like my uncle to chew, that was the whole trouble. So she rode my grandfather for bringing his pipe down, all in fun at first before she got serious about it. But he always brought it down just the same, and said to her, "Don't it stink."

After we ate, my uncle got up and said, "I got to get going," and went out through the kitchen where the cook was knocking and sloshing around. If it had rained right and was a good tobacco-setting season, my grandfather went off with me down to the stable to get his mare, for he had to see the setting. We saddled up the mare and went across the lot, where limestone bunched out of the ground and cedar trees and blue grass grew out of the split rock. A branch of cold water with minnows in it went through the lot between rocks and under the cedar trees; it was where I used to play before I got big enough to go to the river with the niggers to swim.

My grandfather rode across the lot and over the rise back of the house. He sat up pretty straight for an old man, holding the bridle in his left hand, and in his right hand a long hickory tobacco stick whittled down to make a walking cane. I walked behind him and watched the big straw hat he wore waggle a little above his narrow neck, or how he held the stick in the middle, firm and straight up like something carried in a parade, or how smooth and slow the muscles in the mare's flanks worked as she put each hoof down in the ground, going up hill. Sassafras bushes and blackberry bushes grew thick along the lane over the rise. In summer, tufts of hay would catch and hang on the dry bushes and showed that the hay wagons had been that way; but when we went that way in setting time, just after breakfast, the blackberry blooms were hardly gone, only a few rusty patches of white left, and the sassafras leaves showed still wet with dew or maybe the rain.

From the rise we could look back on the house. The shingles were black with damp, and the whitewash grayish, except in spots where the sun already struck it and it was drying. The tops of the cedar trees, too, were below us, very dark green and quiet. When we crossed the rise, there were the fields going down toward the river, all checked off and ready for setting, very even, only for the gullies where brush was piled to stop the washing. The fields were reddish from the wet, not yet steaming. Across them, the green woods and the sycamores showing white far off told where the river was.

The hands were standing at the edge of the field under the trees when we got there. The little niggers were filling their baskets with the wet plants to drop, and I got me a basket and filled it. My Uncle Kirby gave me fifty cents for dropping plants, but he didn't give the little niggers that much, I remember. The hands and women stood around waiting a minute, watching Uncle Kirby, who always fumed around, waving his dibble, his blue shirt already sticking to his arms with sweat. "Get the lead out," he said. The little niggers filled faster, grinning with their teeth at him. "Goddam, get the lead out!" My grandfather sat on his mare under the trees, still holding the walking cane, and said, "Why don't you start 'em, sir?"

Then, all of a sudden, they all moved out into the field, scattering out down the rows, the droppers first, and after a minute the setters, who lurched along, never straightening up, down the rows toward the river. I walked down my row, separating out the plants and dropping them at the hills, while it got hotter and the ground steamed. The sun broke out now and then, making my shadow on the ground, then the cloud would come again, and I could see its shadow drifting at me on the red field.

My grandfather rode very slow along the edge of the field to watch the setting, or stayed still under the trees. After a while, maybe about ten o'clock, he would leave and go home. I could see him riding the mare up the rise and then go over the rise; or if I was working the other way toward the river, when I turned round at the end, the lane would be empty and nothing on top the rise, with the cloudy, blue-gray sky low behind it.

The tobacco was all he cared about, now we didn't have any horses that were any real good. He had some silver cups, only one real silver one though, that his horses won at fairs, but all that was before I was born. The real silver one, the one he kept on his dresser and kept string and old minnie balls and pins and things in, had *1859* on it because his horse won it then before the War, when he was a young man. Uncle Kirby said horses were foolishness, and Grandfather said, yes, he reckoned horses were foolishness, all right. So what he cared about now was the tobacco. One time he was a tobacco-buyer for three years, but after he bought a lot of tobacco and had it in his sheds, the sheds burned up on him. He didn't have enough insurance to do any good and he was a ruined man. After that all his children, he had all girls and his money was gone, said about him, "Papa's just visionary, he tried to be a tobacco-buyer but he's too visionary and not practical." But he always said, "All tobacco-buyers are sons-of-bitches, and three years is enough of a man's life for him to be a son-of-a-bitch, I reckon." Now he was old, the corn could get the rust or the hay get rained on for all he cared, it was Uncle Kirby's worry, but all summer, off and on, he had to go down to the tobacco field to watch them sucker or plow or worm, and sometimes he pulled a few suckers himself. And when a cloud would blow up black in summer, he got nervous as a cat, not knowing whether it was the rain they needed or maybe a hail storm coming that would cut the tobacco up bad.

Mornings he didn't go down to the field, he went out under the cedar tree where his chair was. Most of the time he took a book with him along with his pipe, for he was an inveterate reader. His being an inveterate reader was one of the things made his children say he was visionary. He read a lot until his eyes went bad the summer before he had his stroke, then after that, I read to him some, but not as much as I ought. He used to read out loud some from Macaulay's *History of England* or Gibbon's *Decline and Fall,* about Flodden Field or about how the Janizaries took Constantinople amid great slaughter and how the Turk surveyed the carnage and quoted from the Persian poet about the lizard keeping the courts of the mighty. My grandfather knew some poetry, too, and he said it to himself when he didn't have anything else to do. I lay on my back on the ground, feeling the grass cool and tickly on the back of my neck, and looked upside down into the cedar tree where the limbs were tangled and black-green like big hairy fern fronds with the sky blue all around, while he said some poetry. Like the "Isles of Greece, the Isles of Greece, where burning Sappho loved and sung." Or like "Roll on, thou deep and dark blue ocean, roll."

But he never read poetry, he just said what he already knew. He only read history and *Napoleon and His Marshals,* having been a soldier and fought in the War himself. He rode off and joined the cavalry, but he never told me whether he took the horse that won the real silver cup or not. He was with Forrest before Forrest was a general. He said Forrest was a great general, and if they had done what Forrest wanted and cleaned the country ahead of the Yankees, like the Russians beat Napoleon, they'd whipped the Yankees sure. He told me about Fort Donelson, how they fought in the winter woods, and how they got away with Forrest at night, splashing through the cold water. And how the dead men looked in the river bottoms in winter, and I lay on my back on the grass, looking up in the thick cedar limbs, and thought how it was to be dead.

After Shiloh was fought and they pushed the Yankees down in the river, my grandfather was a captain, for he raised a cavalry company of his own out of West Tennessee. He was a captain, but he never got promoted after the War; when I was a little boy everybody still called him Captain Barden, though they called lots of other people in our section Colonel and Major. One time I said to him: "Grandpa, did you ever kill any Yankees?" He said: "God-a-mighty, how do I know?" So, being little, I thought he was just a captain because he never killed anybody, and I was ashamed. He talked about how they took Fort Pillow, and the drunk niggers under the bluff. And one time he said niggers couldn't stand a charge or stand the cold steel, so I thought maybe he killed some of them. But then I thought, Niggers don't count, maybe.

He only talked much in the morning. Almost every afternoon right after dinner, he went to sleep in his chair, with his hands curled up in his lap, one of them holding the pipe that still sent up a little smoke in the shadow, and his head propped back on the tree trunk. His mouth hung open, and under the hairs of his mustache, all yellow with nicotine, you could see his black teeth and his lips that were wet and pink like a baby's. Usually I remember him that way, asleep.

I remember him that way, or else trampling up and down the front porch, nervous as a cat, while a cloud blew up and the trees began to rustle. He tapped his walking cane on the boards and whistled through his teeth with his breath and kept looking off at the sky where the cloud and some-times the lightning was. Then of a sudden it came, and if it was rain he used to go up to his room and lie down; but if it came hail on the tobacco, he stayed on the front porch, not trampling any more, and watched the hail rattle off the roof and bounce soft on the grass. "God-a-Mighty," he always said, "bigger'n minnie balls," even when it wasn't so big.

In 1914, just before the war began, it was a hot summer with the tobacco mighty good but needing rain. And when the dry spell broke and a cloud blew up, my grandfather came out on the front porch, watching it like that. It was mighty still, with lightning way off, so far you couldn't hardly hear the thunder. Then the leaves began to ruffle like they do when the light gets green, and my grandfather said to me, "Son, it's gonna hail." And he stood still. Down in the pasture, that far off, you could see the cattle bunching up and the white horse charging across the pasture, looking bright, for the sun was shining bright before the cloud struck it all at once. "It's gonna hail," my grandfather said. It was dark, with jagged lightning and the thunder high and steady. And there the hail was.

He just turned around and went in the house. I watched the hail bounc-ing, then I heard a noise and my aunt yelled. I ran back in the dining room where the noise was, and my grandfather was lying on the floor with the old silver pitcher he dropped and a broken glass. We tried to drag him, but he was too heavy; then my Uncle Kirby came up wet from the stable and we carried my grandfather upstairs and put him on his bed. My aunt tried to call the doctor even if the lightning might hit the telephone. I stayed back in the dining room and picked up the broken glass and the pitcher and wiped up the floor with a rag. After a while Dr. Blake came from town; then he went away.

When Dr. Blake was gone, I went upstairs to see my grandfather. I shut the door and went in his room, which was almost dark, like always, and quiet because the hail didn't beat on the roof any more. He was lying on his back in the feather-bed, with a sheet pulled up over him, lying there in the dark. He had his hands curled loose on his stomach, like when he went to sleep in his chair holding the pipe. I sat on a split-bottom chair by the bed and looked at him: he had his eyes shut and his mouth hung loose, but you couldn't hear his breathing. Then I quit looking at him and looked round the room, my eyes getting used to the shadow. I could see his pants on the floor, and the silver cup on the dresser by the mirror, which was green and wavy like water.

When he said something, I almost jumped out of my skin, hearing his voice like that. He said, "Son, I'm gonna die." I tried to say something, but I couldn't. And he waited, then he said, "I'm on borrowed time, it's time to die." I said, "No!" so sudden and loud I jumped. He waited a long time and said, "It's time to die. Nobody loves me." I tried to say, "Grandpa, I love you." And then I did say it all right, feeling like it hadn't been me said it, and knowing all of a sudden it was a lie, because I didn't feel anything. He just lay there; and I went downstairs.

It was sunshiny in the yard, the clouds gone, but the grass was wet. I walked down toward the gate, rubbing my bare feet over the slick cold grass. A hen was in the yard and she kept trying to peck up a piece of hail, like a fool chicken will do after it hails; but every time she pecked, it bounced away from her over the green grass. I leaned against the gate, noticing the ground on one side the posts, close up, was still dry and dusty. I wondered if the tobacco was cut up bad, because Uncle Kirby had gone to see. And while I looked through the gate down across the pasture where everything in the sun was green and shiny with wet and the cattle grazed, I thought about my grandfather, not feeling anything. But I said out loud anyway, "Grandpa, I love you."

My grandfather lived four more years. The year after his stroke they sold the farm and moved away, so I didn't stay with them any more. My grandfather died in 1918, just before the news came that my Uncle Kirby was killed in France, and my aunt had to go to work in a store. I got the letter about my grandfather, who died of flu, but I thought about four years back, and it didn't matter much.

Eudora Welty

WHY I LIVE AT THE P.O.

I WAS getting along fine with Mama, Papa-Daddy and Uncle Rondo until my sister Stella-Rondo just separated from her husband and came back home again. Mr. Whitaker! Of course I went with Mr. Whitaker first, when he first appeared here in China Grove, taking "Pose Yourself" photos, and Stella-Rondo broke us up. Told him I was one-sided. Bigger on one side than the other, which is a deliberate, calculated falsehood: I'm the same. Stella-Rondo is exactly twelve months to the day younger than I am and for that reason she's spoiled.

She's always had anything in the world she wanted and then she'd throw it away. Papa-Daddy gave her this gorgeous Add-a-Pearl necklace when she was eight years old and she threw it away playing baseball when she was nine, with only two pearls.

So as soon as she got married and moved away from home the first thing she did was separate! From Mr. Whitaker! This photographer with the popeyes she said she trusted. Came home from one of those towns up in Illinois and to our complete surprise brought this child of two.

Mama said she like to make her drop dead for a second. "Here you had this marvelous blonde child and never so much as wrote your mother a word about it," says Mama. "I'm thoroughly ashamed of you." But of course she wasn't.

Stella-Rondo just calmly takes off this *hat,* I wish you could see it. She says, "Why, Mama, Shirley-T.'s adopted, I can prove it."

"How?" says Mama, but all I says was, "H'm!" There I was over the hot stove, trying to stretch two chickens over five people and a completely unexpected child into the bargain, without one moment's notice.

"What do you mean—'H'm!'?" says Stella-Rondo, and Mama says, "I heard that, Sister."

I said that oh, I didn't mean a thing, only that whoever Shirley-T. was, she was the spit-image of Papa-Daddy if he'd cut off his beard, which of course he'd never do in the world. Papa-Daddy's Mama's papa and sulks.

Stella-Rondo got furious! She said, "Sister, I don't need to tell you you got a lot of nerve and always did have and I'll thank you to make no future reference to my adopted child whatsoever."

"Very well," I said. "Very well, very well. Of course I noticed at once she looks like Mr. Whitaker's side too. That frown. She looks like a cross between Mr. Whitaker and Papa-Daddy."

"Well, all I can say is she isn't."

"She looks exactly like Shirley Temple to me," says Mama, but Shirley-T. just ran away from her.

So the first thing Stella-Rondo did at the table was turn Papa-Daddy against me.

"Papa-Daddy," she says. He was trying to cut up his meat. "Papa-Daddy!" I was taken completely by surprise. Papa-Daddy is about a million years old and's got this long-long beard. "Papa-Daddy, Sister says she fails to understand why you don't cut off your beard."

So Papa-Daddy l-a-y-s down his knife and fork! He's real rich. Mama says he is, he says he isn't. So he says, "Have I heard correctly? You don't understand why I don't cut off my beard?"

"Why," I says, "Papa-Daddy, of course I understand, I did not say any such of a thing, the idea!"

He says, "Hussy!"

I says, "Papa-Daddy, you know I wouldn't any more want you to cut off your beard than the man in the moon. It was the farthest thing from my mind! Stella-Rondo sat there and made that up while she was eating breast of chicken."

But he says, "So the postmistress fails to understand why I don't cut off my beard. Which job I got you through my influence with the government. 'Bird's nest'—is that what you call it?"

Not that it isn't the next to smallest P.O. in the entire state of Mississippi.

I says, "Oh, Papa-Daddy," I says, "I didn't say any such of a thing, I never dreamed it was a bird's nest, I have always been grateful though this is the next to smallest P.O. in the state of Mississippi, and I do not enjoy being referred to as a hussy by my own grandfather."

But Stella-Rondo says, "Yes, you did say it too. Anybody in the world could of heard you, that had ears."

"Stop right there," says Mama, looking at *me*.

So I pulled my napkin straight back through the napkin ring and left the table.

As soon as I was out of the room Mama says, "Call her back, or she'll starve to death," but Papa-Daddy says, "This is the beard I started growing on the Coast when I was fifteen years old." He would of gone on till nightfall if Shirley-T. hadn't lost the Milky Way she ate in Cairo.

So Papa-Daddy says, "I am going out and lie in the hammock, and you can all sit here and remember my words: I'll never cut off my beard as long as I live, even one inch, and I don't appreciate it in you at all." Passed right by me in the hall and went straight out and got in the hammock.

It would be a holiday. It wasn't five minutes before Uncle Rondo suddenly appeared in the hall in one of Stella-Rondo's flesh-colored kimonos, all cut on the bias, like something Mr. Whitaker probably thought was gorgeous.

"Uncle Rondo!" I says. "I didn't know who that was! Where are you going?"

"Sister," he says, "get out of my way, I'm poisoned."

"If you're poisoned stay away from Papa-Daddy," I says. "Keep out of the hammock, Papa-Daddy will certainly beat you on the head if you come within forty miles of him. He thinks I deliberately said he ought to cut off his beard after he got me the P.O., and I've told him and told him and told him, and he acts like he just don't hear me. Papa-Daddy must of gone stone deaf."

"He picked a fine day to do it then," says Uncle Rondo, and before you could say "Jack Robinson" flew out in the yard.

What he'd really done, he'd drunk another bottle of that prescription. He does it every single Fourth of July as sure as shooting, and it's horribly expensive. Then he falls over in the hammock and snores. So he insisted on zigzagging right on out to the hammock, looking like a half-wit.

Papa-Daddy woke up with this horrible yell and right there without moving an inch he tried to turn Uncle Rondo against me. I heard every word he said. Oh, he told Uncle Rondo I didn't learn to read till I was eight years old and he didn't see how in the world I ever got the mail put up at the P.O., much less read it all, and he said if Uncle Rondo could only fathom the lengths he had gone to to get me that job! And he said on the other hand he thought Stella-Rondo had a brilliant mind and deserved credit for getting out of town. All the time he was just lying there swinging as pretty as you please and looping out his beard, and poor Uncle Rondo was *pleading* with him to slow down the hammock, it was making him as dizzy as a witch to watch it. But that's what Papa-Daddy likes about a hammock. So Uncle Rondo was too dizzy to get turned against me for the time being. He's Mama's only brother and is a good case of a one-track mind. Ask anybody. A certified pharmacist.

Just then I heard Stella-Rondo raising the upstairs window. While she was married she got this peculiar idea that it's cooler with the windows shut and locked. So she has to raise the window before she can make a soul hear her outdoors.

So she raises the window and says, *"Oh!"* You would have thought she was mortally wounded.

Uncle Rondo and Papa-Daddy didn't even look up, but kept right on with what they were doing. I had to laugh.

I flew up the stairs and threw the door open! I says, "What in the wide world's the matter, Stella-Rondo? You mortally wounded?"

"No," she says, "I'm not mortally wounded but I wish you would do me the favor of looking out that window there and telling me what you see."

So I shade my eyes and look out the window.

"I see the front yard," I says.

"Don't you see any human beings?" she says.

"I see Uncle Rondo trying to run Papa-Daddy out of the hammock," I says. "Nothing more. Naturally, it's so suffocating-hot in the house, with all the windows shut and locked, everybody who cares to stay in their right mind will have to go out and get in the hammock before the Fourth of July is over."

"Don't you notice anything different about Uncle Rondo?" asks Stella-Rondo.

"Why, no, except he's got on some terrible-looking flesh-colored contraption I wouldn't be found dead in, is all I can see," I says.

"Never mind, you won't be found dead in it, because it happens to be part of my trousseau, and Mr. Whitaker took several dozen photographs of me in it," says Stella-Rondo. "What on earth could Uncle Rondo *mean* by wearing part of my trousseau out in the broad open daylight without saying so much as 'Kiss my foot,' *knowing* I only got home this morning after my separation and hung my negligee up on the bathroom door, just as nervous as I could be?"

"I'm sure I don't know, and what do you expect me to do about it?" I says. "Jump out the window?"

"No, I expect nothing of the kind. I simply declare that Uncle Rondo looks like a fool in it, that's all," she says. "It makes me sick to my stomach."

"Well, he looks as good as he can," I says. "As good as anybody in reason could." I stood up for Uncle Rondo, please remember. And I said to Stella-Rondo, "I think I would do well not to criticize so freely if I were you and came home with a two-year-old child I had never said a word about, and no explanation whatever about my separation."

"I asked you the instant I entered this house not to refer one more time to my adopted child, and you gave me your word of honor you would not," was all Stella-Rondo would say, and started pulling out every one of her eyebrows with some cheap Kress tweezers.

So I merely slammed the door behind me and went down and made some green-tomato pickle. Somebody had to do it. Of course Mama had turned both the niggers loose; she always said no earthly power could hold one anyway on the Fourth of July, so she wouldn't even try. It turned out that Jaypan fell in the lake and came within a very narrow limit of drowning.

So Mama trots in. Lifts up the lid and says, "H'm! Not very good for your Uncle Rondo in his precarious condition, I must say. Or poor little adopted Shirley-T. Shame on you!"

That made me tired. I says, "Well, Stella-Rondo had better thank her lucky stars it was her instead of me came trotting in with that very peculiar-looking child. Now if it had been me that trotted in from Illinois and brought a peculiar-looking child of two, I shudder to think of the reception I'd of got, much less controlled the diet of an entire family."

"But you must remember, Sister, that you were never married to Mr. Whitaker in the first place and didn't go up to Illinois to live," says Mama, shaking a spoon in my face. "If you had I would of been just as overjoyed to see you and your little adopted girl as I was to see Stella-Rondo, when you wound up with your separation and came on back home."

"You would not," I says.

"Don't contradict me, I would," says Mama.

But I said she couldn't convince me though she talked till she was blue in the face. Then I said, "Besides, you know as well as I do that that child is not adopted."

"She most certainly is adopted," says Mama, stiff as a poker.

I says, "Why, Mama, Stella-Rondo had her just as sure as anything in this world, and just too stuck up to admit it."

"Why, Sister," said Mama. "Here I thought we were going to have a pleasant Fourth of July, and you start right out not believing a word your own baby sister tells you!"

"Just like Cousin Annie Flo. Went to her grave denying the facts of life," I remind Mama.

"I told you if you ever mentioned Annie Flo's name I'd slap your face," says Mama, and slaps my face.

"All right, you wait and see," I says.

"I," says Mama, "*I* prefer to take my children's word for anything when it's humanly possible." You ought to see Mama, she weighs two hundred pounds and has real tiny feet.

Just then something perfectly horrible occurred to me.

"Mama," I says, "can that child talk?" I simply had to whisper! "Mama, I wonder if that child can be—you know—in any way? Do you realize," I says, "that she hasn't spoken one single, solitary word to a human being up to this minute? This is the way she looks," I says, and I looked like this.

Well, Mama and I just stood there and stared at each other. It was horrible!

"I remember well that Joe Whitaker frequently drank like a fish," says Mama. "I believed to my soul he drank *chemicals*." And without another word she marches to the foot of the stairs and calls Stella-Rondo.

"Stella-Rondo? O-o-o-o-o! Stella-Rondo!"

"What?" says Stella-Rondo from upstairs. Not even the grace to get up off the bed.

"Can that child of yours talk?" asks Mama.

Stella-Rondo says, "Can she what?"

"Talk! Talk!" says Mama. "Burdyburdyburdyburdy!"

So Stella-Rondo yells back, "Who says she can't talk?"

"Sister says so," says Mama.

"You didn't have to tell me, I know whose word of honor don't mean a thing in this house," says Stella-Rondo.

And in a minute the loudest Yankee voice I ever heard in my life yells out, "OE'm Pop-OE the Sailor-r-r Ma-a-an!" and then somebody jumps up and down in the upstairs hall. In another second the house would of fallen down.

"Not only talks, she can tap-dance!" calls Stella-Rondo. "Which is more than some people I won't name can do."

"Why, the little precious darling thing!" Mama says, so surprised. "Just as smart as she can be!" Starts talking baby talk right there. Then she turns on me. "Sister, you ought to be thoroughly ashamed! Run upstairs this instant and apologize to Stella-Rondo and Shirley-T."

"Apologize for what?" I says. "I merely wondered if the child was normal, that's all. Now that she's proved she is, why, I have nothing further to say."

But Mama just turned on her heel and flew out, furious. She ran right upstairs and hugged the baby. She believed it was adopted. Stella-Rondo hadn't done a thing but turn her against me from upstairs while I stood there helpless over the hot stove. So that made Mama, Papa-Daddy and the baby all on Stella-Rondo's side.

Next, Uncle Rondo.

I must say that Uncle Rondo has been marvelous to me at various times in the past and I was completely unprepared to be made to jump out of my skin, the way it turned out. Once Stella-Rondo did something perfectly horrible to him—broke a chain letter from Flanders Field—and he took the radio back he had given her and gave it to me. Stella-Rondo was furious! For six months we all had to call her Stella instead of Stella-Rondo, or she wouldn't answer. I always thought Uncle Rondo had all the brains of the entire family. Another time he sent me to Mammoth Cave, with all expenses paid.

But this would be the day he was drinking that prescription, the Fourth of July.

So at supper Stella-Rondo speaks up and says she thinks Uncle Rondo ought to try to eat a little something. So finally Uncle Rondo said he would try a little cold biscuits and ketchup, but that was all. So *she* brought it to him.

"Do you think it wise to disport with ketchup in Stella-Rondo's flesh-colored kimono?" I says. Trying to be considerate! If Stella-Rondo couldn't watch out for her trousseau, somebody had to.

"Any objections?" asks Uncle Rondo, just about to pour out all the ketchup.

"Don't mind what she says, Uncle Rondo," says Stella-Rondo. "Sister has been devoting this solid afternoon to sneering out my bedroom window at the way you look."

"What's that?" says Uncle Rondo. Uncle Rondo has got the most terrible temper in the world. Anything is liable to make him tear the house down if it comes at the wrong time.

So Stella-Rondo says, "Sister says, 'Uncle Rondo certainly does look like a fool in that pink kimono!'"

Do you remember who it was really said that?

Uncle Rondo spills out all the ketchup and jumps out of his chair and tears off the kimono and throws it down on the dirty floor and puts his foot on it. It had to be sent all the way to Jackson to the cleaners and re-pleated.

"So that's your opinion of your Uncle Rondo, is it?" he says. "I look like a fool, do I? Well, that's the last straw. A whole day in this house with nothing to do, and then to hear you come out with a remark like that behind my back!"

"I didn't say any such of a thing, Uncle Rondo," I says, "and I'm not saying who did, either. Why, I think you look all right. Just try to take care of yourself and not talk and eat at the same time," I says. "I think you better go lie down."

"Lie down my foot," says Uncle Rondo. I ought to of known by that he was fixing to do something perfectly horrible.

So he didn't do anything that night in the precarious state he was in— just played Casino with Mama and Stella-Rondo and Shirley-T. and gave Shirley-T. a nickel with a head on both sides. It tickled her nearly to death, and she called him "Papa." But at 6:30 A.M. the next morning, he threw a whole five-cent package of some unsold one-inch firecrackers from the store as hard as he could into my bedroom and they every one went off. Not one bad one in the string. Anybody else, there 'd be one that wouldn't go off.

Well, I'm just terribly susceptible to noise of any kind, the doctor has always told me I was the most sensitive person he had ever seen in his whole life, and I was simply prostrated. I couldn't eat! People tell me they heard it as far as the cemetery, and old Aunt Jep Patterson, that had been holding her own so good, thought it was Judgment Day and she was going to meet her whole family. It's usually so quiet here.

And I'll tell you it didn't take me any longer than a minute to make up my mind what to do. There I was with the whole entire house on Stella-Rondo's side and turned against me. If I have anything at all I have pride.

So I just decided I'd go straight down to the P.O. There's plenty of room there in the back, I says to myself.

Well! I made no bones about letting the family catch on to what I was up to. I didn't try to conceal it.

The first thing they knew, I marched in where they were all playing Old Maid and pulled the electric oscillating fan out by the plug, and everything got real hot. Next I snatched the pillow I'd done the needlepoint on right off the davenport from behind Papa-Daddy. He went "Ugh!" I beat Stella-Rondo up the stairs and finally found my charm bracelet in her bureau drawer under a picture of Nelson Eddy.

"So that's the way the land lies," says Uncle Rondo. There he was, piecing on the ham. "Well, Sister, I'll be glad to donate my army cot if you got any place to set it up, providing you'll leave right this minute and let me get some peace." Uncle Rondo was in France.

"Thank you kindly for the cot and 'peace' is hardly the word I would select if I had to resort to firecrackers at 6:30 A.M. in a young girl's bedroom," I says back to him. "And as to where I intend to go, you seem to forget my position as postmistress of China Grove, Mississippi," I says. "I've always got the P.O."

Well, that made them all sit up and take notice.

I went out front and started digging up some four-o'clocks to plant around the P.O.

"Ah-ah-ah!" says Mama, raising the window. "Those happen to be my four-o'clocks. Everything planted in that star is mine. I've never known you to make anything grow in your life."

"Very well," I says. "But I take the fern. Even you, Mama, can't stand there and deny that I'm the one watered that fern. And I happen to know where I can send in a box top and get a packet of one thousand mixed seeds, no two the same kind, free."

"Oh, where?" Mama wants to know.

But I says, "Too late. You 'tend to your house, and I'll 'tend to mine. You hear things like that all the time if you know how to listen to the radio. Perfectly marvelous offers. Get anything you want free."

So I hope to tell you I marched in and got that radio, and they could of all bit a nail in two, especially Stella-Rondo, that it used to belong to, and she well knew she couldn't get it back, I'd sue for it like a shot. And I very politely took the sewing-machine motor I helped pay the most on to give Mama for Christmas back in 1929, and a good big calendar, with the first-aid remedies on it. The thermometer and the Hawaiian ukulele certainly were rightfully mine, and I stood on the step-ladder and got all my watermelon-rind preserves and every fruit and vegetable I'd put up, every jar. Then I began to pull the tacks out of the bluebird wall vases on the archway to the dining room.

"Who told you you could have those, Miss Priss?" says Mama, fanning as hard as she could.

"I bought 'em and I'll keep track of 'em," I says. "I'll tack 'em up one on each side the post-office window, and you can see 'em when you come to ask me for your mail, if you're so dead to see 'em."

"Not I! I'll never darken the door to that post office again if I live to be a hundred," Mama says. "Ungrateful child! After all the money we spent on you at the Normal."

"Me either," says Stella-Rondo. "You can just let my mail lie there and *rot*, for all I care. I'll never come and relieve you of a single, solitary piece."

"I should worry," I says. "And who you think's going to sit down and write you all those big fat letters and postcards, by the way? Mr. Whitaker? Just because he was the only man ever dropped down in China Grove and you got him—unfairly—is he going to sit down and write you a lengthy correspondence after you come home giving no rhyme nor reason whatsoever for your separation and no explanation for the presence of that child? I may not have your brilliant mind, but I fail to see it."

So Mama says, "Sister, I've told you a thousand times that Stella-Rondo simply got homesick, and this child is far too big to be hers," and she says, "Now, why don't you all just sit down and play Casino?"

Then Shirley-T. sticks out her tongue at me in this perfectly horrible way. She has no more manners than the man in the moon. I told her she was going to cross her eyes like that some day and they'd stick.

"It's too late to stop me now," I says. "You should have tried that yesterday. I'm going to the P.O. and the only way you can possibly see me is to visit me there."

So Papa-Daddy says, "You'll never catch me setting foot in that post office, even if I should take a notion into my head to write a letter some place." He says, "I won't have you reachin' out of that little old window with a pair of shears and cuttin' off any beard of mine. I'm too smart for you!"

"We all are," says Stella-Rondo.

But I said, "If you're so smart, where's Mr. Whitaker?"

So then Uncle Rondo says, "I'll thank you from now on to stop reading all the orders I get on postcards and telling everybody in China Grove what you think is the matter with them," but I says, "I draw my own conclusions and will continue in the future to draw them." I says, "If people want to write their inmost secrets on penny postcards, there's nothing in the wide world you can do about it, Uncle Rondo."

"And if you think we'll ever *write* another postcard you're sadly mistaken," says Mama.

"Cutting off your nose to spite your face then," I says. "But if you're all determined to have no more to do with the U. S. mail, think of this: What will Stella-Rondo do now, if she wants to tell Mr. Whitaker to come after her?"

"Wah!" says Stella-Rondo. I knew she'd cry. She had a conniption fit right there in the kitchen.

"It will be interesting to see how long she holds out," I says. "And now— I am leaving."

"Good-bye," says Uncle Rondo.

"Oh, I declare," says Mama, "to think that a family of mine should quarrel on the Fourth of July, or the day after, over Stella-Rondo leaving old Mr. Whitaker and having the sweetest little adopted child! It looks like we'd all be glad!"

"Wah!" says Stella-Rondo, and has a fresh conniption fit.

"*He* left *her*—you mark my words," I says. "That's Mr. Whitaker. I know Mr. Whitaker. After all, I knew him first. I said from the beginning he'd up and leave her. I foretold every single thing that's happened."

"Where did he go?" asks Mama.

"Probably to the North Pole, if he knows what's good for him," I says.

But Stella-Rondo just bawled and wouldn't say another word. She flew to her room and slammed the door.

"Now look what you've gone and done, Sister," says Mama. "You go apologize."

"I haven't got time, I'm leaving," I says.

"Well, what are you waiting around for?" asks Uncle Rondo.

So I just picked up the kitchen clock and marched off, without saying "Kiss my foot" or anything, and never did tell Stella-Rondo good-bye.

There was a nigger girl going along on a little wagon right in front.

"Nigger girl," I says, "come help me haul these things down the hill, I'm going to live in the post office."

Took her nine trips in her express wagon. Uncle Rondo came out on the porch and threw her a nickel.

And that's the last I've laid eyes on any of my family or my family laid eyes on me for five solid days and nights. Stella-Rondo may be telling the most horrible tales in the world about Mr. Whitaker, but I haven't heard them. As I tell everybody, I draw my own conclusions.

But oh, I like it here. It's ideal, as I've been saying. You see, I've got everything cater-cornered, the way I like it. Hear the radio? All the war news. Radio, sewing machine, book ends, ironing board and that great big piano lamp—peace, that's what I like. Butter-bean vines planted all along the front where the strings are.

Of course, there's not much mail. My family are naturally the main people in China Grove, and if they prefer to vanish from the face of the earth, for all the mail they get or the mail they write, why, I'm not going to open my mouth. Some of the folks here in town are taking up for me and some turned against me. I know which is which. There are always people who will quit buying stamps just to get on the right side of Papa-Daddy.

But here I am, and here I'll stay. I want the world to know I'm happy.

And if Stella-Rondo should come to me this minute, on bended knees, and *attempt* to explain the incidents of her life with Mr. Whitaker, I'd simply put my fingers in both my ears and refuse to listen.

J. F. Powers

LIONS, HARTS, LEAPING DOES

‛‛ ‛THIRTY-NINTH POPE. Anastasius, a Roman, appointed that while the Gospel was reading they should stand and not sit. He exempted from the ministry those that were lame, impotent, or diseased persons, and slept with his forefathers in peace, being a confessor.' "

"Anno?"

" 'Anno 404.' "

They sat there in the late afternoon, the two old men grown gray in the brown robes of the Order. Angular winter daylight forsook the small room, almost a cell in the primitive sense, and passed through the window into the outside world. The distant horizon, which it sought to join, was still bright and strong against approaching night. The old Franciscans, one priest, one brother, were left among the shadows in the room.

"Can you see to read one more, Titus?" the priest Didymus asked. "Number fourteen." He did not cease staring out the window at day becoming night on the horizon. The thirty-ninth pope said Titus might not be a priest. Did Titus, reading, understand? He could never really tell about Titus, who said nothing now. There was only silence, then a dry whispering of pages turning. "Number fourteen," Didymus said. "That's Zephyrinus. I always like the old heretic on that one, Titus."

According to one bibliographer, Bishop Bale's *Pageant of Popes Contayninge the Lyves of all the Bishops of Rome, from the Beginninge of them to the Year of Grace 1555* was a denunciation of every pope from Peter to Paul IV. However inviting to readers that might sound, it was in sober fact a lie. The first popes, persecuted and mostly martyred, wholly escaped the author's remarkable spleen and even enjoyed his crusty approbation. Father Didymus, his aged appetite for biography jaded by the orthodox lives, found the work fascinating. He usually referred to it as "Bishop Bale's funny book" and to the Bishop as a heretic.

Titus squinted at the yellowed page. He snapped a glance at the light hovering at the window. Then he closed his eyes and with great feeling recited:

" 'O how joyous and how delectable is it to see religious men devout and fervent in the love of God, well-mannered—' "

"Titus," Didymus interrupted softly.

" '—and well taught in ghostly learning.' "

"Titus, read." Didymus placed the words in their context. The First Book of *The Imitation* and Chapter, if he was not mistaken, XXV. The trick was no longer in finding the source of Titus's quotations; it was putting them in their exact context. It had become an unconfessed contest between them, and it gratified Didymus to think he had been able to place the fragment. Titus knew two books by heart, *The Imitation* and *The Little Flowers of St. Francis.* Lately, unfortunately, he had begun to learn another. He was more and more quoting from Bishop Bale. Didymus reminded himself he must not let Titus read past the point where the martyred popes left off. What Bale had to say about Peter's later successors sounded incongruous— "unmete" in the old heretic's own phrase—coming from a Franciscan brother. Two fathers had already inquired of Didymus concerning Titus. One had noted the antique style of his words and had ventured to wonder if Brother Titus, Christ preserve us, might be slightly possessed. He cited the case of the illiterate Missouri farmer who cursed the Church in a forgotten Aramaic tongue.

"Read, Titus."

Titus squinted at the page once more and read in his fine dead voice.

" 'Fourteenth pope, Zephyrinus. Zephyrinus was a Roman born, a man as writers do testify, more addicted with all endeavor to the service of God than to the cure of any worldly affairs. Whereas before his time the wine in the celebrating the communion was ministered in a cup of wood, he first did alter that, and instead thereof brought in cups or chalices of glass. And yet he did not this upon any superstition, as thinking wood to be unlawful, or glass to be more holy for that use, but because the one is more comely and seemly, as by experience it appeareth than the other. And yet some wooden dolts do dream that the wooden cups were changed by him because that part of the wine, or as they thought, the royal blood of Christ, did soak into the wood, and so it can not be in glass. Surely sooner may wine soak into any wood than any wit into those winey heads that thus both deceive themselves and slander this Godly martyr.' "

"Anno?"

Titus squinted at the page again. " 'Anno 222,' " he read.

They were quiet for a moment which ended with the clock in the tower booming once for the half hour. Didymus got up and stood so close to the window his breath became visible. Noticing it, he inhaled deeply and then, exhaling, he sent a gust of smoke churning against the freezing pane, clouding it. Some old unmelted snow in tree crotches lay dirty and white in the gathering dark.

"It's cold out today," Didymus said.

He steps away from the window and over to Titus, whose face was relaxed in open-eyed sleep. He took Bishop Bale's funny book unnoticed from Titus's hands.

"Thank you, Titus," he said.

Titus blinked his eyes slowly once, then several times quickly. His body gave a shudder, as if coming to life.

"Yes, Father?" he was asking.

"I said thanks for reading. You are a great friend to me."

"Yes, Father."

"I know you'd rather read other authors." Didymus moved to the window, stood there gazing through the tops of trees, their limbs black and bleak against the sky. He rubbed his hands. "I'm going for a walk before vespers. Is it too cold for you, Titus?"

" 'A good religious man that is fervent in his religion taketh all things well, and doth gladly all that he is commanded to do.' "

Didymus, walking across the room, stopped and looked at Titus just in time to see him open his eyes. He was quoting again: *The Imitation* and still in Chapter XXV. Why had he said that? To himself Didymus repeated the words and decided Titus, his mind moving intelligently but so pathetically largo, was documenting the act of reading Bishop Bale when there were other books he preferred.

"I'm going out for a walk," Didymus said.

Titus rose and pulled down the full sleeves of his brown robe in anticipation of the cold.

"I think it is too cold for you, Titus," Didymus said.

Titus faced him undaunted, arms folded and hands muffled in his sleeves, eyes twinkling incredulously. He was ready to go. Didymus got the idea Titus knew himself to be the healthier of the two. Didymus was vaguely annoyed at this manifestation of the truth. *Vanitas.*

"Won't they need you in the kitchen now?" he inquired.

Immediately he regretted having said that. And the way he had said it, with some malice, as though labor *per se* were important and the intention not so. *Vanitas* in a friar, and at his age, too. Confronting Titus with a distinction his simple mind could never master and which, if it could, his great soul would never recognize. Titus only knew all that was necessary, that a friar did what he was best at in the community. And no matter the nature of his toil, the variety of the means at hand, the end was the same for all friars. Or indeed for all men, if they cared to know. Titus worked in the kitchen and garden. Was Didymus wrong in teaching geometry out of personal preference and perhaps—if this was so he was—out of pride? Had the spiritual worth of his labor been vitiated because of that? He did not think so, no. No, he taught geometry because it was useful and eternally true, like his theology, and though of a lower order of truth it escaped the common fate of theology and the humanities, perverted through the ages in the mouths of dunderheads and fools. From that point of view, his work came to the same thing as Titus's. The vineyard was everywhere; they were in it, and that was essential.

Didymus, consciously humble, held open the door for Titus. Sandals scraping familiarly, they passed through dark corridors until they came to the stairway. Lights from floors above and below spangled through the carven apertures of the winding stair and fell in confusion upon the worn oaken steps.

At the outside door they were ambushed. An old friar stepped out of the shadows to intercept them. Standing with Didymus and Titus, however, made him appear younger. Or possibly it was the tenseness of him.

"Good evening, Father," he said to Didymus. "And Titus."

Didymus nodded in salutation and Titus said deliberately, as though he were the first one ever to put words in such conjunction:

"Good evening, Father Rector."

The Rector watched Didymus expectantly. Didymus studied the man's face. It told him nothing but curiosity—a luxury which could verge on vice in the cloister. Didymus frowned his incomprehension. He was about to speak. He decided against it, turning to Titus:

"Come on, Titus, we've got a walk to take before vespers."

The Rector was left standing.

They began to circle the monastery grounds. Away from the buildings it was brighter. With a sudden shudder, Didymus felt the freezing air bite into his body all over. Instinctively he drew up his cowl. That was a little better. Not much. It was too cold for him to relax, breathe deeply, and stride freely. It had not looked this cold from his window. He fell into Titus's gait. The steps were longer, but there was an illusion of warmth about moving in unison. Bit by bit he found himself duplicating every aspect of Titus in motion. Heads down, eyes just ahead of the next step, undeviating, they seemed peripatetic figures in a Gothic frieze. The stones of the walk were trampled over with frozen footsteps. Titus's feet were gray and bare in their open sandals. Pieces of ice, the thin edges of ruts, cracked off under foot, skittering sharply away. A crystal fragment lit between Titus's toes and did not melt there. He did not seem to notice it. This made Didymus lift his eyes.

A fine Franciscan! Didymus snorted, causing a flurry of vapors. He had the despicable caution of the comfortable who move mountains, if need be, to stay that way. Here he was, cowl up and heavy woolen socks on, and regretting the weather because it exceeded his anticipations. Painfully he stubbed his toe on purpose and at once accused himself of exhibitionism. Then he damned the expression for its modernity. He asked himself wherein lay the renunciation of the world, the flesh and the devil, the whole point of following after St. Francis today. Poverty, Chastity, Obedience—the three vows. There was nothing of suffering in the poverty of the friar nowadays: he was penniless, but materially rich compared to—what was the phrase he used to hear?—"one third of the nation." A beggar, a homeless mendicant by very definition, he knew nothing—except as it affected others "less fortunate" —of the miseries of begging in the streets. Verily, it was no heavy cross, this vow of Poverty, so construed and practiced, in the modern world. Begging had become unfashionable. Somewhere along the line the meaning had been lost; they had become too "fortunate." Official agencies, to whom it was a nasty but necessary business, dispensed Charity without mercy or grace. He recalled with wry amusement Frederick Barbarossa's appeal to fellow princes when opposed by the might of the medieval Church: "We have a clean conscience, and it tells us that God is with us. Ever have we striven to bring back priests and, in especial, those of the topmost rank, to the condition of the first Christian Church. In those days the clergy raised their eyes to the angels, shone through miracles, made whole the sick, raised the dead, made Kings and Princes subject to them, not with arms but with their holiness. But now they are smothered in delights. To withdraw from them the harmful riches which burden them to their own undoing is a labor of love in which all Princes should eagerly participate."

And Chastity, what of that? Well, that was all over for him—a battle he had fought and won many years ago. A sin whose temptations had prevailed undiminished through the centuries, but withal for him, an old man, a dead issue, a young man's trial. Only Obedience remained, and that, too, was no longer difficult for him. There was something—much as he disliked the term —to be said for "conditioning." He had to smile at himself: why should he bristle so at using the word? It was only contemporary slang for a theory the Church had always known. "Psychiatry," so called, and all the ghastly superstition that attended its practice, the deification of its high priests in the secular schools, made him ill. But it would pass. Just look how alchemy had flourished, and where was it today?

Clearly an abecedarian observance of the vows did not promise perfection. Stemmed in divine wisdom, they were branches meant to flower forth, but requiring of the friar the water and sunlight of sacrifice. The letter led nowhere. It was the spirit of the vows which opened the way and revealed to the soul, no matter the flux of circumstance, the means of salvation.

He had picked his way through the welter of familiar factors again— again to the same bitter conclusion. He had come to the key and core of his trouble anew. When he received the letter from Seraphin asking him to come to St. Louis, saying his years prohibited unnecessary travel and endowed his request with a certain prerogative—No, he had written back, it's simply impossible, not saying why. God help him, as a natural man, he had the desire, perhaps the inordinate desire, to see his brother again. He should not have to prove that. One of them must die soon. But as a friar, he remembered: "Unless a man be clearly delivered from the love of all creatures, he may not fully tend to his Creator." Therein, he thought, the keeping of the vows having become an easy habit for him, was his opportunity—he thought! It was plain and there was sacrifice and it would be hard. So he had not gone.

Now it was plain that he had been all wrong. Seraphin was an old man with little left to warm him in the world. Didymus asked himself—recoiling at the answer before the question was out—if his had been the only sacrifice. Rather, had he not been too intent on denying himself at the time to notice that he was denying Seraphin also? Harshly Didymus told himself he had used his brother for a hair shirt. This must be the truth, he thought; it hurts so.

The flesh just above the knees felt frozen. They were drawing near the entrance again. His face, too, felt the same way, like a slab of pasteboard, stiffest at the tip of his nose. When he wrinkled his brow and puffed out his cheeks to blow hot air up to his nose, his skin seemed to crackle like old parchment. His eyes watered from the wind. He pressed a hand, warm from his sleeve, to his exposed neck. Frozen, like his face. It would be chapped tomorrow.

Titus, white hair awry in the wind, looked just the same.

They entered the monastery door. The Rector stopped them. It was almost as before, except that Didymus was occupied with feeling his face and patting it back to life.

"Ah, Didymus! It must be cold indeed!" The Rector smiled at Titus and returned his gaze to Didymus. He made it appear that they were allied in being amused at Didymus's face. Didymus touched his nose tenderly. Assured it would stand the operation, he blew it lustily. He stuffed the handkerchief up his sleeve. The Rector, misinterpreting all this ceremony, obviously was afraid of being ignored.

"The telegram, Didymus. I'm sorry; I thought it might have been important."

"I received no telegram."

They faced each other, waiting, experiencing a hanging moment of uneasiness.

Then, having employed the deductive method, they both looked at Titus. Although he had not been listening, rather had been studying the naked toes in his sandals, he sensed their eyes questioning him.

"Yes, Father Rector?" he answered.

"The telegram for Father Didymus, Titus?" the Rector demanded. "Where is it?" Titus started momentarily out of willingness to be of service, but ended, his mind refusing to click, impassive before them. The Rector shook his head in faint exasperation and reached his hand down into the folds of Titus's cowl. He brought forth two envelopes. One, the telegram, he gave to Didymus. The other, a letter, he handed back to Titus.

"I gave you this letter this morning, Titus. It's for Father Anthony." Intently Titus stared unremembering at the letter. "I wish you would see that Father Anthony gets it right away, Titus. I think it's a bill."

Titus held the envelope tightly to his breast and said, "Father Anthony."

Then his eyes were attracted by the sound of Didymus tearing open the telegram. While Didymus read the telegram, Titus's expression showed he at last understood his failure to deliver it. He was perturbed, mounting inner distress moving his lips silently.

Didymus looked up from the telegram. He saw the grief in Titus's face and said, astonished, "How did you know, Titus?"

Titus's eyes were both fixed and lowered in sorrow. It seemed to Didymus that Titus knew the meaning of the telegram. Didymus was suddenly weak, as before a miracle. His eyes went to the Rector to see how he was taking it. Then it occurred to him the Rector could not know what had happened.

As though nothing much had, the Rector laid an absolving hand lightly upon Titus's shoulder.

"Didymus, he can't forgive himself for not delivering the telegram now that he remembers it. That's all."

Didymus was relieved. Seeing the telegram in his hand, he folded it quickly and stuffed it back in the envelope. He handed it to the Rector. Calmly, in a voice quite drained of feeling, he said, "My brother, Father Seraphin, died last night in St. Louis."

"Father Seraphin *from Rome?*"

"Yes," Didymus said, "in St. Louis. He was my brother. Appointed a confessor in Rome, a privilege for a foreigner. He was ninety-two."

"I know that, Didymus, an honor for the Order. I had no idea he was in this country. Ninety-two! God rest his soul!"

"I had a letter from him only recently."

"You did?"

"He wanted me to come to St. Louis. I hadn't seen him for twenty-five years at least."

"Twenty-five years?"

"It was impossible for me to visit him."

"But if he was in this country, Didymus . . ."

The Rector waited for Didymus to explain.

Didymus opened his mouth to speak, heard the clock in the tower sound the quarter hour, and said nothing, listening, lips parted, to the last of the strokes die away.

"Why, Didymus, it could easily have been arranged," the Rector persisted.

Didymus turned abruptly to Titus, who, standing in a dream, had been inattentive since the clock struck.

"Come, Titus, we'll be late."

He hastened down the corridor with Titus. "No," he said in agitation, causing Titus to look at him in surprise. "I told him no. It was simply impossible." He was conscious of Titus's attention. "To visit him, Seraphin, who is dead." That had come naturally enough, for being the first time in his thoughts that Seraphin was dead. Was there not some merit in his dispassionate acceptance of the fact?

They entered the chapel for vespers and knelt down.

The clock struck. One, two . . . two. Two? No, there must have been one or two strokes before. He had gone to sleep. It was three. At least three, probably four. Or five. He waited. It could not be two: he remembered the brothers filing darkly into the chapel at that hour. Disturbing the shadows

for matins and lauds. If it was five—he listened for faint noises in the building—it would only be a few minutes. They would come in, the earliest birds,
to say their Masses. There were no noises. He looked toward the windows
on the St. Joseph side of the chapel. He might be able to see a light from a
room across the court. That was not certain even if it was five. It would have
to come through the stained glass. Was that possible? It was still night.
Was there a moon? He looked round the chapel. If there was, it might shine
on a window. There was no moon. Or it was overhead. Or powerless against
the glass. He yawned. It could not be five. His knees were numb from
kneeling. He shifted on them. His back ached. Straightening it, he gasped
for breath. He saw the sanctuary light. The only light, red. Then it came
back to him. Seraphin was dead. He tried to pray. No words. Why words?
Meditation in the Presence. The perfect prayer. He fell asleep . . .

. . . Spiraling brown coil on coil under the golden sun the river slithered across the blue and flower-flecked land. On an eminence they held
identical hands over their eyes for visors and mistook it with pleasure for
an endless murmuring serpent. They considered unafraid the prospect of
its turning in its course and standing on tail to swallow them gurgling alive.
They sensed it was in them to command this also by a wish. Their visor
hands vanished before their eyes and became instead the symbol of brotherhood clasped between them. This they wished. Smiling the same smile back
and forth they began laughing: "Jonah!" And were walking murkily up and
down the brown belly of the river in mock distress. Above them, foolishly
triumphant, rippling in contentment, mewed the waves. Below swam an
occasional large fish, absorbed in ignoring them, and the mass of crustacea,
eagerly seething, too numerous on the bottom to pretend exclusiveness.
"Jonah indeed!" the brothers said, surprised to see the bubbles they birthed.
They strolled then for hours this way. The novelty wearing off (without
regret, else they would have wished themselves elsewhere), they began to
talk and say ordinary things. Their mother had died, their father too, and
how old did that make them? It was the afternoon of the funerals, which
they had managed, transcending time, to have held jointly. She had seemed
older and for some reason he otherwise. How, they wondered, should it be
with them, *memento mori* clicking simultaneously within them, lackaday.
The sound of dirt descending six feet to clatter on the coffins was memorable
but unmentionable. Their own lives, well . . . only half curious (something
to do) they halted to kick testingly a waterlogged rowboat resting on the
bottom, the crustacea complaining and olive-green silt rising to speckle the
surface with dark stars . . . well, what *had* they been doing? A crayfish
pursued them, clad in sable armor, dearly desiring to do battle, brandishing
hinged swords. Well, for one thing, working for the canonization of Fra
Bartolomeo, had got two cardinals interested, was hot after those remaining
who were at all possible, a slow business. Yes, one would judge so in the light
of past canonizations, though being stationed in Rome had its advantages.
Me, the same old grind, teaching, pounding away, giving Pythagoras no rest

in his grave . . . They made an irresolute pass at the crayfish, who had caught up with them. More about Fra Bartolomeo, what else is there? Except, you will laugh or have me excommunicated for wanton presumption, though it's only faith in a faithless age, making a vow not to die until he's made a saint, recognized rather—he is one, convinced of it, Didymus (never can get used to calling you that), a saint sure as I'm alive, having known him, no doubt of it, something wrong with your knee? Knees then? The crayfish, he's got hold of you there, another at your back. If you like, we'll leave —only I do like it here. Well, go ahead then, you never did like St. Louis, isn't that what you used to say? Alone, in pain, he rose to the surface, parting the silt stars. The sun like molten gold squirted him in the eye. Numb now, unable to remember, and too blind to refurnish his memory by observation, he waited for this limbo to clear away. . . .

Awake now, he was face to face with a flame, blinding him. He avoided it. A dead weight bore him down, his aching back. Slowly, like ink in a blotter, his consciousness spread. The supports beneath him were kneeling limbs, his, the veined hands, bracing him, pressing flat, his own. His body, it seemed, left off there; the rest was something else, floor. He raised his head to the flame again and tried to determine what kept it suspended even with his face. He shook his head, blinking dumbly, a four-legged beast. He could see nothing, only his knees and hands, which he felt rather, and the flame floating unaccountably in the darkness. That part alone was a mystery. And then there came a pressure and pull on his shoulders, urging him up. Fingers, a hand, a rustling related to its action, then the rustling in rhythm with the folds of a brown curtain, a robe naturally, ergo a friar, holding a candle, trying to raise him up, Titus. The clock began striking.

"Put out the candle," Didymus said.

Titus closed his palm slowly around the flame, unflinching, snuffing it. The odor of burning string. Titus pinched the wick deliberately. He waited a moment, the clock falling silent, and said, "Father Rector expects you will say a Mass for the Dead at five o'clock."

"Yes, I know." He yawned deliciously. "I told him *that.*" He bit his lips at the memory of the disgusting yawn. Titus had found him asleep. Shame overwhelmed him, and he searched his mind for justification. He found none.

"It is five now," Titus said.

It was maddening. "I don't see anyone else if it's five," he snapped. Immediately he was aware of a light burning in the sacristy. He blushed and grew pale. Had someone besides Titus seen him sleeping? But, listening, he heard nothing. No one else was up yet. He was no longer pale and was only blushing now. He saw it all hopefully. He was saved. Titus had gone to the sacristy to prepare for Mass. He must have come out to light the candles on the main altar. Then he had seen the bereaved keeping vigil on all fours, asleep, snoring even. What did Titus think of that? It withered him to remember, but he was comforted some that the only witness had been Titus. Had the sleeping apostles in Gethsemane been glad it was Christ?

Wrong! Hopelessly wrong! For there had come a noise after all. Someone else was in the sacristy. He stiffened and walked palely toward it. He must go there and get ready to say his Mass. A few steps he took only, his back buckling out, humping, his knees sinking to the floor, his hands last. The floor, with fingers smelling of dust and genesis, reached up and held him. The fingers were really spikes and they were dusty from holding him this way all his life. For a radiant instant, which had something of eternity about it, he saw the justice of his position. Then there was nothing.

A little snow had fallen in the night, enough to powder the dead grass and soften the impression the leafless trees etched in the sky. Grayly the sky promised more snow, but now, at the end of the day following his collapse in the chapel, it was melting. Didymus, bundled around by blankets, sat in a wheel chair at the window, unsleepy. Only the landscape wearied him. Dead and unmoving though it must be—of that he was sure—it conspired to make him see everything in it as living, moving, something to be watched, each visible tuft of grass, each cluster of snow. The influence of the snow perhaps? For the ground, ordinarily uniform in texture and drabness, had split up into individual patches. They appeared to be involved in a struggle of some kind, possibly to overlap each other, constantly shifting. But whether it was equally one against one, or one against all, he could not make out. He reminded himself he did not believe it was actually happening. It was confusing and he closed his eyes. After a time this confused and tired him in the same way. The background of darkness became a field of varicolored factions, warring, and, worse than the landscape, things like worms and comets wriggled and exploded before his closed eyes. Finally, as though to orchestrate their motions, they carried with them a bewildering noise or music which grew louder and cacophonous. The effect was cumulative, inevitably unbearable, and Didymus would have to open his eyes again. The intervals of peace became gradually rarer on the landscape. Likewise when he shut his eyes to it the restful darkness dissolved sooner than before into riot.

The door of his room opened, mercifully dispelling his illusions, and that, because there had been no knock, could only be Titus. Unable to move in his chair, Didymus listened to Titus moving about the room at his back. The tinkle of a glass once, the squeak of the bookcase indicating a book taken out or replaced—they were sounds Didymus could recognize. But that first tap-tap and the consequent click of metal on metal, irregular and scarcely audible, was disconcertingly unfamiliar. His curiosity, centering on it, raised it to a delicious mystery. He kept down the urge to shout at Titus. But he attempted to fish from memory the precise character of the corner from which the sound came with harrowing repetition. The sound stopped then, as though to thwart him on the brink of revelation. Titus's footsteps scraped across the room. The door opened and closed. For a few steps, Didymus heard Titus going down the corridor. He asked himself not to be moved by idle curiosity, a thing of the senses. He would not be tempted now.

A moment later the keystone of his good intention crumbled, and the whole edifice of his detachment with it. More shakily than quickly, Didymus moved his hands to the wheels of the chair. He would roll over to the corner and investigate the sound. . . . He would? His hands lay limply on the wheels, ready to propel him to his mind's destination, but, weak, white, powerless to grip the wheels or anything. He regarded them with contempt. He had known they would fail him; he had been foolish to give them another chance. Disdainful of his hands, he looked out the window. He could still do that, couldn't he? It was raining some now. The landscape started to move, rearing and reeling crazily, as though drunken with the rain. In horror, Didymus damned his eyes. He realized this trouble was probably going to be chronic. He turned his gaze in despair to the trees, to the branches level with his eyes and nearer than the insane ground. Hesitating warily, fearful the gentle boughs under scrutiny would turn into hideous waving tentacles, he looked. With a thrill, he knew he was seeing clearly.

Gauzily rain descended in a fine spray, hanging in fat berries from the wet black branches where leaves had been and buds would be, cold crystal drops. They fell now and then ripely of their own weight, or shaken by the intermittent wind they spilled before their time. Promptly they appeared again, pendulous.

Watching the raindrops prove gravity, he was grateful for nature's, rather than his, return to reason. Still, though he professed faith in his faculties, he would not look away from the trees and down at the ground, nor close his eyes. Gratefully he savored the cosmic truth in the falling drops and the mildly trembling branches. There was order, he thought, which in justice and science ought to include the treacherous landscape. Risking all, he ventured a glance at the ground. All was still there. He smiled. He was going to close his eyes (to make it universal and conclusive), when the door opened again.

Didymus strained to catch the meaning of Titus's movements. Would the clicking sound begin? Titus did go to that corner of the room again. Then it came, louder than before, but only once this time.

Titus came behind his chair, turned it, and wheeled him over to the corner.

On a hook which Titus had screwed into the wall hung a bird cage covered with black cloth.

"What's all this?" Didymus asked.

Titus tapped the covered cage expectantly.

A bird chirped once.

"The bird," Titus explained in excitement, "is inside."

Didymus almost laughed. He sensed in time, however, the necessity of seeming befuddled and severe. Titus expected it.

"I don't believe it," Didymus snapped.

Titus smiled wisely and tapped the cage again.

"There!" he exclaimed when the bird chirped.

Didymus shook his head in mock anger. "You made that beastly noise, Titus, you mountebank!"

Titus, profoundly amused by such skepticism, removed the black cover.

The bird, a canary, flicked its head sidewise in interest, looking them up and down. Then it turned its darting attention to the room. It chirped once in curt acceptance of the new surroundings. Didymus and Titus came under its black dot of an eye once more, this time for closer analysis. The canary chirped twice, perhaps that they were welcome, even pleasing, and stood on one leg to show them what a gay bird it was. It then returned to the business of pecking a piece of apple.

"I see you've given him something to eat," Didymus said, and felt that Titus, though he seemed content to watch the canary, waited for him to say something more. "I am very happy, Titus, to have this canary," he went on. "I suppose he will come in handy now that I must spend my days in this infernal chair."

Titus did not look at him while he said, "He is a good bird, Father. He is one of the Saint's own good birds."

Through the window Didymus watched the days and nights come and go. For the first time, though his life as a friar had been copiously annotated with significant references, he got a good idea of eternity. Monotony, of course, was one word for it, but like all the others, as well as the allegories worked up by imaginative retreat masters, it was empty beside the experience itself, untranslatable. He would doze and wonder if by some quirk he had been cast out of the world into eternity, but since it was neither heaven nor exactly purgatory or hell, as he understood them, he concluded it must be an uncharted isle subscribing to the mother forms only in the matter of time. And having thought this, he was faintly annoyed at his ponderous whimsy. Titus, like certain of the hours, came periodically. He would read or simply sit with him in silence. The canary was there always, but except as it showed signs of sleepiness at twilight and spirit at dawn, Didymus regarded it as a subtle device, like the days and nights and bells, to give the lie to the vulgar error that time flies. The cage was small and the canary would not sing. Time, hanging in the room like a jealous fog, possessed him and voided everything except it. It seemed impossible each time Titus came that he should be able to escape the room.

" 'After him,' " Titus read from Bishop Bale one day, " 'came Fabius, a Roman born, who (as Eusebius witnesseth) as he was returning home out of the field, and with his countrymen present to elect a new bishop, there was a pigeon seen standing on his head and suddenly he was created pastor of the Church, which he looked not for.' "

They smiled at having the same thought and both looked up at the canary. Since Didymus sat by the window most of the day now, he had asked Titus to put a hook there for the cage. He had to admit to himself he did this to let Titus know he appreciated the canary. Also, as a secondary motive, he reasoned, it enabled the canary to look out the window. What a little yellow bird could see to interest it in the frozen scene was a mystery, but that, Didymus sighed, was a two-edged sword. And he took to watching the canary more.

So far as he was able to detect the moods of the canary he participated in them. In the morning the canary, bright and clownish, flitted back and forth between the two perches in the cage, hanging from the sides and cocking its little tufted head at Didymus querulously. During these acrobatics Didymus would twitch his hands in quick imitation of the canary's stunts. He asked Titus to construct a tiny swing, such as he had seen, which the canary might learn to use, since it appeared to be an intelligent and daring sort. Titus got the swing, the canary did master it, but there seemed to be nothing Didymus could do with his hands that was like swinging. In fact, after he had been watching awhile, it was as though the canary were fixed to a pendulum, inanimate, a piece of machinery, a yellow blur—ticking, for the swing made a little sound, and Didymus went to sleep, and often when he woke the canary was still going, like a clock. Didymus had no idea how long he slept at these times, maybe a minute, maybe hours. Gradually the canary got bored with the swing and used it less and less. In the same way, Didymus suspected, he himself had wearied of looking out the window. The first meager satisfaction had worn off. The dead trees, the sleeping snow, like the swing for the canary, were sources of diversion which soon grew stale. They were captives, he and the canary, and the only thing they craved was escape. Didymus slowly considered the problem. There was nothing, obviously, for him to do. He could pray, which he did, but he was not sure the only thing wrong with him was the fact he could not walk and that to devote his prayer to that end was justifiable. Inevitably it occurred to him his plight might well be an act of God. Why this punishment, though, he asked himself, and immediately supplied the answer. He had, for one thing, gloried too much in having it in him to turn down Seraphin's request to come to St. Louis. The intention—that was all important, and he, he feared, had done the right thing for the wrong reason. He had noticed something of the faker in himself before. But it was not clear if he had erred. There was a certain consolation, at bottom dismal, in this doubt. It was true there appeared to be a nice justice in being stricken a cripple if he had been wrong in refusing to travel to see Seraphin, if human love was all he was fitted for, if he was incapable of renunciation for the right reason, if the mystic counsels were too strong for him, if he was still too pedestrian after all these years of prayer and contemplation, if . . .

The canary was swinging, the first time in several days.

The reality of his position was insupportable. There were two ways of regarding it and he could not make up his mind. Humbly he wished to get well and to be able to walk. But if this was a punishment, was not prayer to lift it declining to see the divine point? He did wish to get well; that would settle it. Otherwise his predicament could only be resolved through means more serious than he dared cope with. It would be like refusing to see Seraphin all over again. By some mistake, he protested, he had at last been placed in a position vital with meaning and precedents inescapably Christian. But was he the man for it? Unsure of himself, he was afraid to go on trial. It would be no minor trial, so construed, but one in which the greatest values were involved—a human soul and the means of its salvation or damnation. Not watered down suburban precautions and routine pious exercises, but Faith such as saints and martyrs had, and Despair such as only they had been tempted by. No, he was not the man for it. He was unworthy. He simply desired to walk and in a few years to die a normal, uninspired death. He did not wish to see (what was apparent) the greatest significance in his affliction. He preferred to think in terms of physical betterment. He was so sure he was not a saint that he did not consider this easier road beneath him, though attracted by the higher one. That was the rub. Humbly, then, he wanted to be able to walk, but he wondered if there was not presumption in such humility.

Thus he decided to pray for health and count the divine hand not there. Decided. A clean decision—not distinction—no mean feat in the light of all the moral theology he had swallowed. The canary, all its rocking come to naught once more, slept motionless in the swing. Despite the manifest prudence of the course he had settled upon, Didymus dozed off ill at ease in his wheel chair by the window. Distastefully, the last thing he remembered was that "prudence" is a virtue more celebrated in the modern Church.

At his request in the days following a doctor visited him. The Rector came along, too. When Didymus tried to find out the nature of his illness, the doctor looked solemn and pronounced it to be one of those things. Didymus received this with a look of mystification. So the doctor went on to say there was no telling about it. Time alone would tell. Didymus asked the doctor to recommend some books dealing with cases like his. They might have one of them in the monastery library. Titus could read to him in the meantime. For, though he disliked being troublesome, "one of those things" as a diagnosis meant very little to an unscientific beggar like him. The phrase had a philosophic ring to it, but to his knowledge neither the Early Fathers nor the Scholastics seemed to have dealt with it. The Rector smiled. The doctor, annoyed, replied drily:

"Is that a fact?"

Impatiently Didymus said, "I know how old I am, if that's it."

Nothing was lost of the communion he kept with the canary. He still watched its antics and his fingers in his lap followed them clumsily. He did not forget about himself, that he must pray for health, that it was best that way—"prudence" dictated it—but he did think more of the canary's share of their captivity. A canary in a cage, he reasoned, is like a bud which never blooms.

He asked Titus to get a book on canaries, but nothing came of it and he did not mention it again.

Some days later Titus read:

" 'Twenty-ninth pope, Marcellus, a Roman, was pastor of the Church, feeding it with wisdom and doctrine. And (as I may say with the Prophet) a man according to God's heart and full of Christian works. This man admonished Maximianus the Emperor and endeavored to remove him from persecuting the saints——' "

"Stop a moment, Titus," Didymus interrupted.

Steadily, since Titus began to read, the canary had been jumping from the swing to the bottom of the cage and back again. Now it was quietly standing on one foot in the swing. Suddenly it flew at the side of the cage nearest them and hung there, its ugly little claws, like bent wire, hooked to the slender bars. It observed them intently, first Titus and then Didymus, at whom it continued to stare. Didymus's hands were tense in his lap.

"Go ahead, read," Didymus said, relaxing his hands.

" 'But the Emperor being more hardened, commanded Marcellus to be beaten with cudgels and to be driven out of the city, wherefore he entered into the house of one Lucina, a widow, and there kept the congregation secretly, which the tyrant hearing, made a stable for cattle of the same house and committed the keeping of it to the bishop Marcellus. After that he governed the Church by writing Epistles, without any other kind of teaching, being condemned to such a vile service. And being thus daily tormented with strife and noisomeness, at length gave up the ghost. Anno 308.' "

"Very good, Titus. I wonder how we missed that one before."

The canary, still hanging on the side of the cage, had not moved, its head turned sidewise, its eye as before fixed on Didymus.

"Would you bring me a glass of water, Titus?"

Titus got up and looked in the cage. The canary hung there, as though waiting, not a feather stirring.

"The bird has water here," Titus said, pointing to the small cup fastened to the cage.

"For me, Titus, the water's for me. Don't you think I know you look after the canary? You don't forget us, though I don't see why you don't."

Titus left the room with a glass.

Didymus's hands were tense again. Eyes on the canary's eye, he got up from his wheel chair, his face strained and white with the impossible effort, and, his fingers somehow managing it, he opened the cage. The canary darted out and circled the room chirping. Before it lit, though it seemed about to make its perch triumphantly on the top of the cage, Didymus fell over on his face and lay prone on the floor.

In bed that night, unsuffering and barely alive, he saw at will everything revealed in his past. Events long forgotten happened again before his eyes. Clearly, sensitively, he saw Seraphin and himself, just as they had always been—himself, never quite sure. He heard all that he had ever said, and that anyone had said to him. He had talked too much, too. The past mingled with the present. In the same moment and scene he made his first Communion, was ordained, and confessed his sins for the last time.

The canary perched in the dark atop the cage, head warm under wing, already, it seemed to Didymus, without memory of its captivity, dreaming of a former freedom, an ancestral summer day with flowers and trees. Outside it was snowing.

The Rector, followed by others, came into the room and administered the last sacrament. Didymus heard them all gathered prayerfully around his bed thinking (they thought) secretly: this sacrament often strengthens the dying, tip-of-the-tongue wisdom indigenous to the priesthood, Henry the Eighth had six wives. He saw the same hackneyed smile, designed to cheer, pass bravely among them, and marveled at the cruelty of it. They went away then, all except Titus, their individual footsteps sounding (for him) the character of each friar. He might have been Francis himself for what he knew then of the little brothers and the cure of souls. He heard them thinking their expectation to be called from bed before daybreak to return to his room and say the office of the dead over his body, become the body, and whispering hopefully to the contrary. Death was now an unwelcome guest in the cloister.

He wanted nothing in the world for himself at last. This may have been the first time he found his will amenable to the Divine. He had never been less himself and more the saint. Yet now, so close to sublimity, or perhaps only tempted to believe so (the Devil is most wily at the deathbed), he was beset by the grossest distractions. They were to be expected, he knew, as indelible in the order of things: the bingo game going on under the Cross for the seamless garment of the Son of Man: everywhere the sign of the contradiction, and always. When would he cease to be surprised by it? Incidents repeated themselves, twined, parted, faded away, came back clear, and would not be prayed out of mind. He watched himself mounting the pulpit of a metropolitan church, heralded by the pastor as the renowned Franciscan father sent by God in His goodness to preach this novena—like to say a little prayer to test the microphone, Father?—and later reading through the petitions to Our Blessed Mother, cynically tabulating the pleas for a Catholic boy friend, drunkenness banished, the sale of real estate and coming furiously upon one: "that I'm not pregnant." And at the same church on Good Friday carrying the crucifix along the communion rail for the people to kiss, giving them the indulgence, and afterwards in the sacristy wiping the lipstick of the faithful from the image of Christ crucified.

"Take down a book, any book, Titus, and read. Begin anywhere."

Roused by his voice, the canary fluttered, looked sharply about and buried its head once more in the warmth of its wing.

"'By the lions,'" Titus read, "'are understood the acrimonies and impetuosities of the irascible faculty, which faculty is as bold and daring in its acts as are the lions. By the harts and the leaping does is understood the other faculty of the soul, which is the concupiscible—that is——.'"

"Skip the exegesis," Didymus broke in weakly. "I can do without that now. Read the verse."

Titus read: "'Birds of swift wing, lions, harts, leaping does, mountains, valleys, banks, waters, breezes, heats and terrors that keep watch by night, by the pleasant lyres and by the siren's song, I conjure you, cease your wrath and touch not the wall . . .'"

"Turn off the light, Titus."

Titus went over to the switch. There was a brief period of darkness during which Didymus's eyes became accustomed to a different shade, a glow rather, which possessed the room slowly. Then he saw the full moon had let down a ladder of light through the window. He could see the snow, strangely blue, falling outside. So sensitive was his mind and eye (because his body, now faint, no longer blurred his vision?) he could count the snowflakes, all of them separately, before they drifted, winding, below the sill.

With the same wonderful clarity, he saw what he had made of his life. He saw himself tied down, caged, stunted in his apostolate, seeking the crumbs, the little pleasure, neglecting the source, always knowing death changes nothing, only immortalizes . . . and still ever lukewarm. In trivial attachments, in love of things, was death, no matter the appearance of life. In the highest attachment only, no matter the appearance of death, was life. He had always known this truth, but now he was feeling it. Unable to move his hand, only his lips, and hardly breathing, was it too late to act?

"Open the window, Titus," he whispered.

And suddenly he could pray. *Hail Mary . . . Holy Mary, Mother of God, pray for us sinners now and at the hour of our death . . .* finally the time to say, *pray for* me *now—the hour of my death, amen.* Lest he deceive himself at the very end that this was the answer to a lifetime of praying for a happy death, happy because painless, he tried to turn his thoughts from himself, to join them to God, thinking how at last he did—didn't he *now?*— prefer God above all else. But ashamedly not sure he did, perhaps only fearing hell, with an uneasy sense of justice he put himself foremost among the wise in their own generation, the perennials seeking after God when doctor, lawyer, and bank fails. If he wronged himself, he did so out of humility—a holy error. He ended, to make certain he had not fallen under the same old presumption disguised as the face of humility, by flooding his mind with maledictions. He suffered the piercing white voice of the Apocalypse to echo in his soul: *But because thou art lukewarm, and neither cold, nor hot, I will begin to vomit thee out of my mouth.* And St. Bernard, fiery-eyed in a white habit, thundered at him from the twelfth century: "Hell is paved with the bald pates of priests!"

There was a soft flutter, the canary flew to the window sill, paused, and tilted into the snow. Titus stepped too late to the window and stood gazing dumbly after it. He raised a trembling old hand, fingers bent in awe and sorrow, to his forehead, and turned stealthily to Didymus.

Didymus closed his eyes. He let a long moment pass before he opened them. Titus, seeing him awake then, fussed with the window latch and held a hand down to feel the draught, nodding anxiously as though it were the only evil abroad in the world, all the time straining his old eyes for a glimpse of the canary somewhere in the trees.

Didymus said nothing, letting Titus keep his secret. With his whole will he tried to lose himself in the sight of God, and failed. He was not in the least transported. Even now he could find no divine sign within himself. He knew he still had to look outside, to Titus. God still chose to manifest Himself most in sanctity.

Titus, nervous under his stare, and to account for staying at the window so long, felt for the draught again, frowned, and kept his eye hunting among the trees.

The thought of being the cause of such elaborate dissimulation in so simple a soul made Didymus want to smile—or cry, he did not know which . . . and could do neither. Titus persisted. How long would it be, Didymus wondered faintly, before Titus ungrievingly gave the canary up for lost in the snowy arms of God? The snowflakes whirled at the window, for a moment for all their bright blue beauty as though struck still by lightning, and Didymus closed his eyes, only to find them there also, but darkly falling.

Peter Taylor

SKY LINE

"IS IT God knocking?"

"No, no. That isn't God. That isn't God."

"Then it's the hanging baskets. The wind is blowing the vine-baskets against the house."

"After the wind has died, you may go out on the porch and look at the wall of the house, at the places where the wire baskets have chipped more paint off the boarding."

"They are Grandmother's baskets."

Then his little humpbacked grandmother is found dead in her bed one morning, and he must play in his room upstairs for two days. Out his window he watches automobiles coming from far off. They turn on streets which wind for no reason through a field, wide streets with sidewalks but with few houses and no trees along their borders. Down his street there is only the house on the corner and the speckled stucco next door where the little girl comes and leans against one of the porch pillars.

Everywhere in the fields are white signs with blue and red lettering that hurts the eye.

During the second day the Negro cook Cleo comes up and plays par-cheesi with him while downstairs the music and the preaching go on. From his window he watches the hearse drive away with the long line of cars following it. On the winding street through the fields the long line moves like a black snake. Cleo says, "She wuz lyin' 'ere in bed when we find 'er—just like she be asleep."

Cleo leads him down the stairs by his hand, and they watch the Negro men loading stacks of folding chairs on a truck.

After the funeral some big wicker baskets are left sitting about in the front hall and on the porch. Just at twilight one day everything outside the living room window looks yellowish. Then the rain comes like a burst of tears; and the wind blows the wicker baskets over, and the tin cans from inside them roll about the porch floor. The tin cans and the wicker stands and the swinging baskets make a clatter like a jazz band. Even his mother goes to the window and looks out. And he says to her, "The wood will look pinkish in the spots where the paint is gone."

All the wicker baskets are at last stacked behind the garage and burned like old boxes. The tin cans serve in turn, as one after another rusts, for watering troughs to the white pointer which runs on a wire in the back yard. And the swinging baskets ("your poor grandmother's last efforts at gardening") are missing from the porch. After dinner on Sunday Cleo wraps them in newspaper and goes off toward the trolley with one under each arm.

The painters arrive that spring with ladders and spotted canvas, and paint his house a fresh white. Ever after he can see only sunken places on the white clapboard where the baskets knocked for years.

His father and the father of the little girl next door like to play "catch." They play on Sunday afternoons through every spring. Then his father wears a black sweater with yellow stripes that go around him like tiger stripes; and her father, whose hair is gray, wears a sweater that buttons down the front. Each of the men has a big five-fingered glove, and they sit on the porch the first spring-like Sunday and oil their gloves. Sometimes Joseph, the Negro who works next door, plays with them, and then the three men will yell such things as "Out on first!"

Once the little girl's mother calls Joseph into the house, and Joseph throws his glove to the boy as he runs toward the kitchen. His father whistles through his fingers and shouts, "Replacement on third!" Joseph's glove smells sweatier than his father's. It has more stuffing and no fingers outside; and it's wet inside. But the boy soon forgets, for he has caught the first baseball ever thrown to him.

In a few weeks he is thinking, "I can catch about as well as either of them." And after his own yellow mitt comes and a ball and a bat with black taping, he plays catch with other boys during school recess. There he sometimes recalls Joseph and his smelly mitt and wonders what ever has become of the two, for the little girl's mother now has a Negro who doesn't like to play catch.

After two years of baseball he is certain that he can catch as well as the men, though he can't throw as hard as they might. He plays with them often.

A ball comes so straight and hard from the little girl's father that the boy throws off his glove and rubs his palm on his pants leg.

His father, without a word, speeds toward him and picks up the ball.

The boy did not have to take off his glove. He just feels disgraced because he cannot throw one back as hard.

His father hurls the ball at the neighbor who sees it barely in time to shield his glasses with his forearm. But the ball strikes the man's elbow and falls to the ground. As he straightens his arm, he winces. But he makes a sudden lurch and sweeps the ball from the ground with his right hand. His upper lip shortens under his nose, showing his purplish gums. He squints and sends the ball back to the younger man.

The boy watches the ball as it flies. With a quick wave of his hand his father motions him to go. He feels his way backward toward his house, his eyes on the two men who have never before thrown much harder than he.

The ball bounces from his father's glove, but he catches it in the air and shoots it back.

The older man is smiling. His face is red and moist.

The ball goes straight back and forth.

They stand about sixty feet apart with the big round bed of zinnias and petunias between them.

Again the ball bounces from the younger man's glove. It falls on the grass. He stoops slowly to pick it up, his gaze on his neighbor. The sod is a fresh green and his body makes no shadow on it, for dark clouds have been gathering in the sky of the March afternoon. The father takes a slow, deliberate wind-up which seems so professional to the boy that his mouth falls open.

But the neighbor laughs aloud and sends a ball back that jolts the boy's father. The boy blushes.

The speed of the ball is slow for a few throws, then gathers speed, then slows, and suddenly speeds again.

The boy's back is to the white clapboard of his house. He is breathing heavily, his little chest rising and falling. Across the lawns he sees the little girl leaning against a pillar on her own porch. She is bouncing a red rubber ball, and he thinks, "Why, the dumb thing doesn't see it at all." He is sweating as hard as the men when the rain begins to fall; but he feels only an occasional drop, for he is under the eaves of the house. As the rain comes harder and the two men pay no heed, he sees the little girl give closer attention to the game of catch. He smiles in his scorn for her as she steps to the edge of the porch and stands in the afternoon light which is yellow now.

The rain streams now like a waterfall.

It pours off the eaves of the house as from a pitcher and runs about his feet.

Either man can hardly hold the ball. It will slip from his fingers, and he will pick it up and hurl it toward the other. The striped sweater and the buttoned sweater both are heavy and are dripping water.

The older man takes off his fogged glasses and puts them in the pocket of his sweater, and then he throws the ball straight again.

The boy's father shoots it back quickly, with an oath.

His neighbor stops the ball high above his head and laughs. He dries the ball on the underside of his sweater before he throws it this time.

Now the little girl has begun to cry. She lets her red rubber ball go, and it rolls off the porch and into the rain.

The boy's father slips and falls on the grass when he stops the baseball in his wet glove, but he jumps up, dries his hand and the ball, and throws the ball again. It smacks the wet leather of the older man's glove, and he stands shaking a stinging hand, and he has begun to cough now. As he draws back his arm to throw, the little girl begins bouncing herself up and down on the porch and calling to him. And the baseball crashes through his neighbor's garage window.

The two men stand in the rain, each with his gaze fixed on the blurred figure of the other. Then the boy's father turns his back and starts slowly through the rain toward his own house. The little girl runs to meet her father, but he pushes her and looks back once more toward the little boy and his father.

The boy and the little girl walk on opposite sides of the street from that time, but, anyway, he is now too old for girls. There are little boys who live in new houses which are now scattered along the winding streets and along his own block, and he is learning to fight with his fists. One day he tears the scab off a sore on his deskmate's wrist. After school they fight behind a white and red and blue For Sale sign in the lot where the Catholic church is going to be built. During his bath after the fight he finds that the deskmate has given him a bruise on his thigh, and the bruise is still there the next Friday when the deskmate's sore has gotten a new scab; so he, all of a sudden, tears off the second scab with his fingernail. This time the deskmate goes to the teacher and shows her his sore. The teacher changes their seats. And the last he remembers of the matter is his former deskmate's writing on the blackboard with a white bandage on his wrist.

The new Catholic church is hardly finished in August when the new school building is started in the next block. The church is of yellow brick with a great round window above the main doorway. And for the new school the workmen are digging in the ground all through August. The lot they work in has always been covered with waist-high yellow grass, and every day the boy looks at the grass which the workmen have trampled down until it lies flat like the hair on a boy's head. He has never played in that lot with its high grass as he once used to do in the church lot, and has felt that it looked like "the central plains of Africa." But the workmen dig deep, and now the heaps of red dirt look like the "forbidding Caucasian mountains."

By Christmas the workmen have only laid the concrete in the long, narrow basement and put up a few concrete shafts, and the thing stands like that until spring. Finally he gets used to the lot looking that way.

Some of the children, especially the new children, like to climb down into the long basement, and they build a snow man there during the last snow in March. But a feeling that the lot isn't completely changed and yet isn't as it has been keeps the boy away. Things have changed in the suburb; repeatedly he has told the new children how things once were, he is that conscious of it; but something forever keeps him from trying to observe too closely just how the new buildings go up.

One day the little girl's father is dead. The boy's own mother and father talk for a long while in their bedroom with the door closed. Afterward his father goes next door, and still later the Negro man comes and asks his mother to come. The boy sits at the window of his little room upstairs all afternoon and watches the other neighbors come and go across the lawns.

Two young neighbor women stand on a lawn across the street and talk, gesticulating; and one keeps shrugging her shoulders. The little girl appears outside the back door of her house with a pair of scissors which glisten in the sunlight. Her dress is white and it's so plain and long that her legs look short and her body very long. She goes to the round zinnia bed and looks ponderously at the flowers.

The window is up, and the boy sits on the sill, his head leaning against the screen. The girl bobs up and down among dull-colored flowers, very soon holding an armful of zinnias.

The boy begins to whistle a doleful cowboy tune.

She looks up from the center of the zinnia bed. He stops short. She scans the windows of the house, but she cannot make out his figure through the black wire screen. She stoops again, and he whistles one high note. She peers suddenly up at his window, opens her mouth and, sobbing, scampers on her short legs into her house.

And he stays at the window, looking out over the tile and shingled rooftops of the new houses and at the yellow tower of the new Catholic church.

Soon after school starts that fall the house next door is sold, and the little girl and her mother are moved into his own mother's guest room, the room which was once his grandmother's.

"I'll miss having a guest room," his mother says, "but it's not permanent."

One afternoon people come in automobiles and on foot from the neighborhood, and the furniture is moved out of the stucco house into the yard and sold. The boy sits on the edge of the porch and thinks, This is a sight I won't forget—beds and tables and easy chairs on the lawn, especially with men and women dropping down into the chairs and then getting up and looking at them with their heads cocked to one side.

What didn't sell is brought into his house, and the sitting room seems a different place with the new green chair and footstool which doesn't match the set.

The little girl is a grade ahead of him and so goes to the new school which is called "Junior High." She has to go to school earlier than he, and he is grateful for this. For she is now an inch taller than himself, and it makes him uncomfortable to walk with her.

One Saturday at noon, as he comes in from baseball, she meets him at the front door.

"Something's happened," she says.

He is putting his mitt and ball into the closet under the stairs. He looks at her and feels that she is somehow too tall to be wearing the plaid knee socks.

"Your daddy's lost his job," she says.

The boy answers resentfully that his father will get another as quickly as he has lost this one, and he goes upstairs. But as he passes his father's room he sees him stretched across the bed and sees the two women seated in rocking chairs, looking at one another. He tiptoes back downstairs and goes into the sitting room where the little girl is reading a magazine. He sits down and looks at her—lounging in the green chair with her round, bare knees over the green stool. She puts the magazine aside.

"Mama's going to work," she says. "And I guess I will, some way."

The changes that will come flood his imagination. The past seems absolutely static in the light of what he feels is to come.

"So will I," he says.

Soon he is able to get a paper route, and now his mother rouses him at three every morning and gives him coffee before he goes out. Through the winter he wears a pair of his father's hunting boots with several pairs of socks to make them fit. One morning his mother runs barefooted through the snow on the lawn, shining the flashlight that he has forgotten. She calls to him:

"Your light! Your light! You forgot your light!"

The sight of her there in the dark and cold, barefooted and in her kimono, is so literally dreadful to him that he turns and runs from the sight. And he can hear her calling, "Your light! Your light! Your light!" until he is almost to the trolley line where he picks up his papers.

The boy's imagination is soon conjuring pictures of the two families on the fourth floor of a downtown tenement house. Several families on his block have had to move from their houses during the fall, and other houses on his route have been found empty on collection day. But his mother will say to him over his cup of coffee, "The house is mine. I'll work my fingers to the bone to keep it." She finally has to give up Cleo, the cook; and they only feed the Negro man who has worked for the little girl's mother, until he can pick up another job.

The little girl's mother has started to business school. She and his father leave in the automobile each morning. He can see them pass from the schoolhouse window and realizes that the automobile is getting to be an old number. When he comes home in the afternoons, his mother will sometimes be washing or ironing the clothes in the kitchen. It's when he comes in one day and sees her on her knees waxing the dining room floor that he first observes how narrow her hips have got; and he turns from her and goes up the stair, two steps at a time, to his room. He looks at the school pennants about the walls, and his tears blur the scene. He looks out his window over the rooftops of the suburb and hears the boys yelling down behind the new school. And he takes off his leather jacket and slips his black football jersey on over his head.

But it seems that even his father's loss of his job hasn't been as simple and as quick as he had supposed. His father's whole company is going out of business, and there are articles about it in the newspaper every few days, his father's testimony in the courtroom being quoted once. During the weeks that his father is at home, before he has found the new job "on commission," he will sometimes walk up and down the front porch with his hat and coat on; and the boy's mother will look out the window at him and say to her son or to the little girl, "Through the whole litigation his innocence, honesty, and integrity were not once questioned."

By spring the little girl's mother has an office job at the same place his father sells from. They have not renewed the automobile license this year, and every morning the two breadwinners walk three blocks, by the little hedges and young Lombardy poplars, to the trolley.

One Saturday morning the boy comes back from his paper route late and passes the pair on the sidewalk. The little girl's mother says something to his father who calls out to him, "Hold yourself up straight!" and calls him, "Longlegs." So he throws his shoulders back and begins to run. He hears them laughing until he turns the corner, and then he feels shaken up inside and hot about the forehead.

His mother is at her sewing machine by her bedroom window. He comes and stands beside her and with a half smile on his face says, "I'm catching lockjaw, I guess. I feel stiff in my jaw, under here, and everybody says that's the first symptom." His mother slips two fingers down his shirt collar, feeling the nape of his neck.

"Why, you're cooked with fever," she says. And she hasn't got him into bed in his little room before he begins to cough from his chest. It had poured rain through the first half of his route that morning; and she had tried to persuade him to wear his "rain things." "You've caught your death of cold in that rain," she says.

By the next afternoon he is considered "a very sick boy." His temperature is $103\frac{1}{2}$. The doctor comes and says that it may turn into pneumonia.

"Now, if this does take a turn for the worst, it will be best to have him in a hospital."

"No, I want him at home."

"They can take better care of him."

"I think not, Doctor."

"You'll need a nurse."

"I must take care of him, Doctor."

The voices sound like echoes, and the human figures seem far away. Later he can hear the murmur of voices in his mother's room. His father and the little girl's mother are arguing with her, and they sound as though they may be away in some valley.

The next day, Monday, his mother tiptoes about his room, and the doctor comes twice. He can hear the doctor's voice more distinctly in the front hall downstairs than when he is by his bed talking to him.

Sometimes the little girl will sit in the room with him and read her magazine. He lies there during the afternoon with flannel and plasters about him, content to look at the walls and think of the other wallpapers that he remembers there. One can hardly see the wallpaper, for it is decorated with pennants and calendars.

In the middle of the night he wakes and sees that the light is wrapped in a piece of blue tissue paper. His mother says, "You've been out of your head for five hours."

"How sick am I, Mother?"

"You haven't pneumonia."

The doctor comes in a while and tells him he'll begin to get better now.

His father comes too and pats him on the back of his warm, limp hand, but says nothing. And when he leaves the room, the boy remembers the dreams of his delirium: His father and the mother of the little girl lay dead on the street car tracks. Cleo, the cook, was back in the kitchen, and his mother was telling her, "You can't really call the accident a tragedy." And he and his mother broke into gales of laughter.

The next fall the boy himself goes to Junior High. But the little girl dresses and acts so much older than he does now that he doesn't mind walking with her. She has gotten very fat, and he teases her about that and about the boys that talk to her at recess. Occasionally she will lend him money, but it is only to keep him from teasing her about the boys during dinner at night. She is so fat and so polite in public now that she seems a different person from "the little girl," as different as his mother is from her former self, as different as the corner on the trolley line is with the new drug store on it.

He works in the drug store after school. He serves sodas to the high-schoolers in automobiles and wears a white apron and a white fatigue cap on the side of his head. One afternoon he sees, through the drug store window, a tall, thin woman approaching the store. It is a familiar figure, yet he can't identify it as his mother for several seconds. She rarely leaves their street now that the automobile is shut up in the garage without any license, and she has lost even more weight in the past months. He thinks, I have a right to resent her coming to the store if it is not on business. He steps away from the window and waits.

When she doesn't come through the door, he looks out again; and it is just in time to see her step up into the trolley car that rumbles off toward town.

And yet it is not many days after this that he hears her tell his father over the telephone that she won't meet him in town for dinner because she dislikes to ride the trolley.

The little girl's mother and his father stay in town to work two, sometimes three, nights a week, and they never come out on Saturday afternoons now. They usually call and try to get his mother to meet them somewhere. When they come to dinner on Saturday nights his father invariably smells of whisky, and the boy sometimes feels certain that a part of the odor comes from the little girl's mother. His father will say at the dinner table, "I'll tell you this selling game is different. Sociability counts for everything."

Again and again he sees his mother take the trolley for town in the afternoons. He suspects her of going in the mornings some days, for twice he has found her making the beds when he comes by home to leave his books after school. He wonders, sitting in the glare of the many-windowed schoolroom, if his mother is this very minute on one of her mysterious missions and if his father and the little girl's mother are drinking with someone over a sale downtown. If so, his house, a few blocks away, is empty. Not even the white pointer runs in the yard, for his father never hunts any more and has said that he's not mean enough to keep a dog and not hunt him. It pleases the boy to think of the house totally empty and to reflect that under the paint the marks that the vine-baskets made are actually still there.

At home he listens. He pretends to sleep on the couch after dinner at night. Spring comes, and he sits on the porch—under the window. He never closes the door to his room. He listens, and at last he hears.

He stands in the upstairs hall one night, poised, ready to move to the bathroom if the parents' door opens. His mother has made some sort of confession, and his father is saying, "Why didn't you tell me?" Those are the only audible words. But in a few days his father tells him that his mother is going to the hospital. She is going to have a mighty serious operation.

And she packs a little Gladstone bag at bedtime one night. He watches her from the hall, putting in the pink silk nightgowns, the quilted bathrobe, and her hair brush. In the morning his father and the little girl's mother and his mother go into town on the trolley together.

He is called to the principal's office from his geometry class. The principal, Miss Cartright, is an unpredictable, white-haired woman behind a pair of horn-rimmed glasses. The expression on her face is an absolutely new one this time.

"My child . . ."

"Yes, ma'am, Miss Cartright."

"You are a young man now. Do you understand?"

"Yes'm."

"I feel that you are unprepared for what I have to tell you, but you must accept it bravely."

"Yes'm."

"You are aware that your mother has not been well?"

"She's in the hospital. She's not dead, is she?"

"She died this morning . . . under the knife."

"May I get my books?"

"Yes, but wait a moment, child."

"Hadn't I better hurry home?"

"Wait, child. We must be sure that you know what this means."

"I know."

"You'll not see your mother alive again. You'll not have her careful, guiding hand to help you."

"Yes'm, I know, Miss Cartright."

"There will be hours of loneliness. And your father's not your mother. He can't take her place, however hard he try. . . . There, there. None of this in a big boy like you. Come to me. I want to be some comfort to you, not just a teacher."

The funeral is held in the undertaker's parlor, and the boy looks in the coffin at his mother's powdered face. At the cemetery, when they are arranging the flowers over the grave, he recalls how the wicker baskets blew about the porch after his grandmother's funeral and how his mother went to the window and looked out.

For several weeks he waits to hear of his father's plans to sell the house. The other two argued with his mother over that the night before she went to the hospital, and he heard his father say after the funeral that it would have added ten years to her life if she had sold the house. "This house," he said, "was the biggest tumor she had." But nothing was said of a sale after that.

All that summer the boy keeps the yard as though his mother were alive and nagging him about it. The girl does the housekeeping with the help of a Negro woman named Jessie. Their parents take them to a downtown picture show at least one night a week now. Coming back one night on the trolley he says to the little girl's mother, "Why doesn't Daddy sell the place and move to town?" But she changes to another topic for conversation as though she had not heard him.

When he and the girl are at the top of the stairs that night, she whispers, "Don't you know, Foolish, that you own the house and can't sell it till you're twenty-one?"

This year the girl has begun at the high school; so she has to take the trolley into town with her mother and his father. She wears silk stockings all of the time and she fixes her black hair in a knot on the back of her fat, white neck. She has a friend named Susie who uses quantities of lipstick and cheek rouge and who comes home with her many afternoons. The boy pays little attention to them until one night Susie stays for dinner, a night when the grown people don't come home. During dinner the girls tell long stories with elements in them which he thinks are very funny but which he thinks they don't understand, being girls. After this he likes to talk with them and to try to find out how much they do understand. He will sit sometimes and just watch them file their fingernails. But when Susie offers him her picture once, he says he doesn't want it.

Then his father calls him into the living room one Sunday and tells him that the girl is a young lady now; and tells him that he must let her have his room and that he must move his belongings into his father's room. The boy hangs his head in protest. Finally he looks up and says, "I don't want to, Daddy."

The girl's mother is sitting across the room, and she looks at him soberly and says nothing. He sees, as if for the first time, that she wears as much lipstick and cheek rouge as Susie, and that her hair, gray on top, is bobbed and combed close to her head like a man's. His father stands up; he goes and sits on the arm of her chair. "You'll move your things after dinner tonight," he says. As the boy leaves the room, the father calls, "I'll help you, old man." And the girl's mother says something in too hushed a tone for him to hear her words.

But he likes rooming with his father. He is allowed to put his pennants on the walls of the big room and is told that he can arrange the furniture any way he likes. Often the two will go to bed at the same time and will lie in the dark talking of baseball. He sees the whole household with a different perspective. And now it is his father who is a different person.

There are times when he hears his father come into the room long after he has been in bed. And when the heavy body slips under the cover beside him, he can smell the alcohol and feel and hear the heavy breathing. Then he dreams of a day, certainly not more than a year or two hence, when he will be able to ask his father for a cigarette.

One night the boy and his father are in bed in their dark room when the clock thumps past ten.

"Are you awake still, son?"

"Wide awake."

"Tell me how much you are saving of what you earn."

"All right, s'r. Half of it."

"You must learn just how much it means to save money. If you don't save, then you will have to work when you are tired."

"When I'm old?"

"You may get tired before you get old. And if you're tired and know you'll never be able to rest, you'll get desperate."

"Oh, I suppose that *would* make you turn crooked."

"It might, if you could let yourself. If you can't let yourself turn crooked, despair will make things bad in a hundred other ways, anyhow."

"How much money do you make, Daddy?"

"In a good month?"

"Yes, that'll do."

"Enough to pay back what I borrow in a bad month."

"You aren't mentioning figures, I guess?"

"I didn't press *you,* did I?—for how much you save."

"I'll tell you."

"No. No, don't."

"It's a good deal."

"Yes. I'm afraid of how much it might sound like to me."

One night the boy is awakened by the sound of heavy rain. "I must put down the window," he thinks. But presently someone, barefooted, tiptoes through the bedroom door, across the room, toward the window. It is his father; and he removes the prop and lowers the window noiselessly but for the squeak of the sash, and he leaves the room again. Then quite distinctly his voice comes from the hallway: "Both of them." And presently the door to Grandmother's former bedroom scrapes the floor as it closes, and the boy tries to visualize the dark scene on his mother's guest room bed.

It is a day when the wind rustles the treetops, even the tops of slender poplars; and yet the wind is so soft, nearer to the earth, that it barely stirs the flaps of the boy's shirt collar. The sky is turquoise, and the hurried clouds look pink in their centers. The boy stands in the middle of the circular flower bed, surveying his work. His shirt is khaki and his trousers are faded blue jeans. His height measures somewhat over five feet, and atop his head his straight, brown hair stirs gently with the flaps of his shirt collar. His shirt sleeves are rolled above the elbows of his long, thin, white arms. In his right hand he holds a rusty trowel.

One third done, he says. From his feet, in the center of the flower bed, a section of broken earth, cleared of all the green spring shoots but the little zinnia and petunia plants, stretches out to the rock border. One hundred and twenty degrees, he says; and he turns to the other two thirds of the bed, which are green with clover and grass and dandelion. His long shadow falls across those two thirds to the border and divides them evenly. He points with the trowel to the section on his left and pronounces: "Four-thirty." Then he points to that at his right hand and says: "Five o'clock." He stoops, drives the trowel around the roots of a dandelion plant, and shaking the dirt from the root throws the weed beyond the stone border of the bed.

Inside the house the telephone is ringing. It rings for so long a time that he stands up and looks over his shoulder toward the house. The ringing ceases, and he stoops again and digs. It is not long before the girl is walking along the wall of the white clapboard house. The boy is on his knees working carefully between two tiny zinnia shoots. He watches her approach from the corner of his eye. She wears high-heeled brown and white shoes and no stockings on her legs which are fat and at the same time muscular. Her skirt, a plaid material with a predominance of green and orange, is stretched around her big hips. And her tan sweater fits too closely under the arms and is drawn across her matronly breasts too tight to be less than obscene.

She stands close to him with her shaven legs far apart. He looks up at her; she is standing with her hands on her hips, and he thinks that her clothes fit her as the shrunken summer covers do the big living room chairs. Her brown, bobbed hair blows in the wind, and one strand plays over her unpowdered face.

"Jim, darling," she says, "they're married."

"Who's married?" he says as though to deny the possibility.

"Mother and . . . Mommy and your father."

"And you're glad?" he asks.

She weighs the question for a moment. "I don't think I care a snap, Jim."

He looks at his trowel and then inquires with indifference in his voice: "Did you know they would?"

"Only by conjecture. But Mommy just called on the phone, and I talked to both of them."

With some deliberation he digs his trowel into the ground and pulls up a clod of dirt with grass on it; but she remains before him. Then he asks, "Will they be out to dinner tonight?"

"No," she says, brushing the strand of hair from her face with her pink hand, "they've gone to Chicago for the week end. I think they'll stay even longer. It's a long way up to Chicago."

The girl has turned and is walking toward the house. She walks over the grass on the balls of her feet. And he gazes after her heavy figure.

He is digging in the last green third. Of a sudden his breath seems to catch in his chest and his temples grow hot. He is squatted, resting his haunches on his heels. He raises his head in surprise at his own sensation, and he speaks out loud to himself: "I'm not sorry about *them.*" But he cannot say what it is.

The light of the afternoon has a yellow tint in it. He looks at the sky. The whole western sky is a black mass, one that is advancing rapidly to meet the puffy gray clouds which clutter the eastern horizon and the sky overhead. He digs his trowel into the earth, uproots, tears, and digs again.

The shrill whistles in the distance have blown for five o'clock, and he is working assiduously at the blades of grass that grow from between the rocks of the border. He has finished the last third of the bed, but he works on. He does not raise his head; his eyes follow his fingers plucking grass from between the rocks. Something has filled him with a dread of quitting. It isn't, he tells himself, the thought that he must realize the marriage of his father to the mother of the girl, that he must go into the house with only that to occupy his mind. And yet he can't assure himself that it is only a dread of the memories that the yellow light will bring when he looks up into it. He feels the first drop of water on the back of his neck at exactly the moment that he hears the voice of the girl:

"Jim, darling, do come in out of the rain."

He stares up at the white clapboard house through the bilious light and discerns the figure of the girl at the window of her bedroom, the room which once was his own.

He drops his trowel on the grass and walks, with his heart beating under his tongue. The electric light burns in the girl's room, and he can see her in the window through the black screen. He walks with his arms hanging straight at his sides as though he carries two heavy pails of water in his hands. In that strange light his eyes meet the girl's eyes through the fine mesh of the screen. Her eyes are darker than her hair.

A clap of thunder jerks the eyes of both toward the sky, and the rain bursts upon him. He runs three steps and leaps over the shrubbery onto the end of the porch. There he turns his face toward the yard and stands rigid, and his pulse throbs in his wrists. He senses that the girl is still at the window.

His hand turns the cold brass knob of the front door, and he flings open the door. The furniture of the hall is a group of strange objects to him. How weird are the roosters in the design of the floor rug, the crack on the table top mended with yellow plastic wood, and the crazy angle of the mirror. He is unbuttoning his wet shirt as he runs up the stairs and he tears it off as he shoves open the door of the room in which he once used to sleep.

The bed is between him and the girl, who is wearing a crepe de Chine negligee. She sits down on the other side of the bed, puts one hand softly on the pillow, and says, "What do you want, Jimmy?" He crosses the room. She twists her body and throws herself face downward on the bed. The boy stands over her, his wet shirt in his hand, looking at the back of her head. The girl rolls over on her back and smiles up at him.

He looks into her brown eyes under her heavy low brow and sees, he feels, the innocence of someone years younger than himself, the innocence of a very little girl. Her head is sunk in the fat, white pillow. She crooks her elbow behind her head and smiles up at him. She shifts the position of her body and rubs her bare feet together. Her eyes, he thinks, are like the brown eyes of a young dog. His temples are ablaze and presently he knows that his whole face and perhaps his whole bare chest is the color of the girl's rouged cheeks. He quickly turns his back to her and finds himself looking out the window through falling rain at the rooftops of the suburb. While his eyes are fixed on the yellow tower of the Catholic church and he stands braced by his hands on the window sill, the sudden, loud laughter of the girl on the bed slaps his ears.

He doesn't know how long the laughter lasts. The rain falls outside the open window, and now and again a raindrop splashes through the screen onto his face. At last it is almost night when the rain stops, and if there is any unnatural hue in the light, it is green. His heart has stopped pounding now, and all the heat has gone from his face. He has heard the hanging baskets beat against the house and felt the silence after their removal. He has heard the baseball smacking in the wet gloves of the men and seen the furniture auctioned on the lawn. The end of his grandmother, the defeat of his mother, the despair of his father, and the resignation of his new step-mother are all in his mind. The remarkable thing in the changed view from the window which had once been his lies in the tall apartment houses which punctuate the horizon and in the boxlike, flat-roofed ones in his own neighborhood. Through this window the girl too, he knows, must have beheld changes. He takes his hand from the sill and massages his taut face on which the rain-drops have dried.

When he faces her again, he says that they must prepare some sort of welcome, that they must get busy.

Appendices

APPENDIX A

The Arts of Fiction

I. AUTHORITY IN FICTION

On whose authority is the story told? This looks like a simple question, and in the great stories, in which the question is answered successfully, the answer also looks simple; but the simplicity is often deceptive. It is the focus of the point of view from which the story is told that looks simple, for often the material itself is extremely complex and would reveal at a glance its complexity, even to the point of confusion, if the chosen point of view were not the right one for the complete ordering of the subject.

In some large and obvious sense the author must always be the supreme authority, since it is only through him that we penetrate into the world that he has chosen to set before us. But general statements about authority in fiction are without value to either reader or writer. The author's legitimate authority lies not in his *telling* us that the scene is such, that these people did certain things, that what they did meant this or that; it lies rather in convincing us that the scene, the characters, the meaning, all move together in a dynamic pattern that we can believe in apart from the author's personality. The author's problem is so to conduct himself that, as guide, he does not stand between us and the object or person that he wishes us to see. This problem remains the same even when the "author" puts himself dramatically into the story as first-person narrator or even as omniscient commentator; behind the "author" so presented is the author at his desk, whose job is to render as completely as the chair or the picture in the scene the other "author" whom he projects into the action. In order to accomplish this dynamic objectivity he is at liberty to place himself anywhere within the magic circle of his subject; but no two subjects are alike, and no two techniques are alike. For momentary convenience we have "schematized" the infinite possibilities of point of view in four diagrams. We are here considering "authority" in terms of "point of view." We may ask again our original question: On whose authority is the story told? as follows: What "eye" or what "mind," placed in a certain position, or so established as to make it possible for it to be shifted from one position to another, is best suited to the task of revealing the totality of the subject? The four schemes follow:

1. Omniscient Narrator: Panoramic Technique
2. Effaced Narrator: Scenic Technique
3. First Person Narrator: Panoramic-Scenic Technique
4. Roving Narrator (Omniscient Narrator Concealed): The Technique of the Central Intelligence.

These four methods may be crudely represented in the following diagrams:

3. First Person Narrator
Panoramic-Scenic Technique
Authority Direct but Limited and Suspect

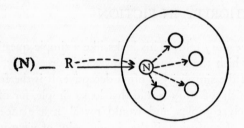

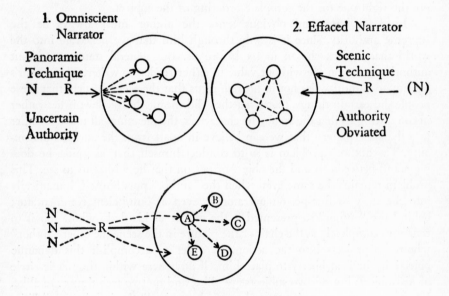

4. Roving Narrator
(Omniscient Narrator Concealed)
Technique of the Central Intelligence
Perfect Authority Possible

It will be understood that no one of these four "methods" or "techniques" is ever found as it is represented here. No two stories or novels, in which the First Person Narrator or any of the three other narrators is employed, are ever alike. For example, two very different stories, James's *The Turn of the Screw* and Ring Lardner's "Haircut," are First Person narratives. The use of such an abstract pattern as that given above is simply to clarify the reader's or the student's mind as to theoretical possibilities in the art of fiction, and to make him *technically aware of how* the story is made as well as of *what* he is receiving from the story. To ask the question: How is the story reaching us? is to ask: By what *means* is the author making the material credible? And this is another way of asking: What relation to the material has the author established that will give him *authority* in presenting it?

This authoritative relation is never wholly a technical matter. A given technique is the result of a moral and philosophical attitude, a bias towards experience on the part of the author; and as the author begins to understand what it is in life that interests him most, he also becomes aware of the techniques which will enable him to create in language his fullest sense of that interest. Material and technique become in the end the same thing, the one discovering the other. With this principle in mind we may proceed to detailed comment on the four theoretical schemes of authority.

1. *THE OMNISCIENT NARRATOR*

This method is the oldest form of story-telling and properly used it is a method that will never be outmoded. It is the method of Homer and of Tolstoy. But it seems to require the greatest genius to be wholly successful, for otherwise it results in formlessness and lack of focus. Its great virtue is the "wide sweep"; it gives us the sense of the vast scope of human life, the panorama as opposed to the minute scene. In both the *Iliad* and *War and Peace* there is the constant change of focus from the large over-all picture to the close-up scene; but there is always also the constant control, the conscious manipulation of the Long View and the Short View (see Appendix A, p. 627) towards a coherent structure.

In *Vanity Fair,* for example, Thackeray is able to keep two distinct groups of characters moving because he has not identified his point of view with that of any one person or with either group of persons; his range is thus not confined, but large and loose. The method permits him to get into his novel a great deal of life, but we wonder at the end how deeply he has explored it. Percy Lubbock makes much of Thackeray's failure to do justice to the close-up scene; Thackeray rather backs away from it, and contents himself with a *report* of how the scene came out. The discovery by Rawdon Crawley of his wife Becky and Lord Steyne at supper could have been intensely dramatic. At the moment of discovery Thackeray rings down the curtain.

This is always the temptation of the Omniscient Narrator. Since he knows everything, he is tempted (if he has an engaging style) to tell the reader what happened and to leave the actual happening vague. He depends upon the sweep, the panorama, the large summary; and he often leaves one group of characters in the air while he loftily turns his gaze to another group miles away, with a transitional statement like this: "Meanwhile at So-and-So . . ."

The fiction writer, in undertaking this method, must decide whether he can manage the broad sweep without collapsing into vagueness and formlessness. His difficulty here is to establish a sufficient authority in relation to the action. Without placing somewhere near the center of the action a Central Intelligence, can he convince us that he *knows* what is happening, and thus transform his report, which as report is usually no better than make-believe, into a reality which we must acknowledge as true within the frame of the action?

2. THE EFFACED NARRATOR

This method is the direct opposite of the Omniscient; its solution of the problem of authority is at once the simplest and most limited available to the writer of fiction. It is simple because the writer attempts to approximate as closely as possible the authority of the dramatist, who has the immense advantage of presenting to the eye and ear what is happening: we see the characters and hear their voices. In this method the narrator effaces himself and shows you the characters in action and conversation, with the minimum of exposition; and this minimum is often as terse as the dramatist's stage directions. One of the finest examples is Hemingway's "The Killers," in which everything that is not dialogue is the briefest sort of behavioristic description. The point to bear in mind about this technique is that the author never *tells* you what the characters feel and think, though he can *show* you, and show you what they say and do. He is never inside their minds: he puts the reader inside. The limitations of the method are obvious. It is difficult for the author to indicate the passage of time because he cannot intervene and tell you that certain things happened between two scenes. *He is confined always to the immediate scene.* It is a method that serves well the purpose of the short story, but it is usually a *tour de force* when it is extended to the full-length novel. For example, in Virginia Woolf's *To the Lighthouse* the situation is presented in two large "scenic blocks" separated in time by ten years. The method in Part I and Part III is strictly scenic in that there is no intercession by the author, although Mrs. Woolf extends the method by putting us inside her characters, one after another. But in order to account for the break in time Mrs. Woolf, in Part II, resorts to the report and the summary. It is done so skillfully that unless the reader is an experienced technical observer he will not be aware of the change of method. Henry James, the greatest of all technicians, tried the scenic method in *The Awkward Age.* It is probably the least read of James's novels; the strain on the reader's attention becomes too great in a work of its length.

3. THE FIRST PERSON NARRATOR

Because Homer interjects himself just once into the *Iliad,* we may say that it is a first person narrative: we are at that instant made aware of a person telling the story. Thus the Omniscient Method may be combined with the First Person, though the combination has been seldom used since the time of primitive saga. The more conscious the writer, the more skeptically will he deal with the critical question: How could one person, this man telling the story, get around the earth and the Olympian heaven fast enough to see all that happens in the *Iliad*? The *authority* of the First Person Narrator is limited: he may tell you only what he sees, or if he exceed his own observation, he may do so only through surmise and inference about other events which he has not actually witnessed; but he cannot convincingly present those distant events *scenically,* as if he had seen them.

If his authority is limited, it is nevertheless immediate and compelling as far as it goes. I know what I am talking about—he seems to say—because I saw it happen to these people. His authority is that of the eye-witness. Because he is the eye-witness, he can give you the close-up, the scenic effect of the Short View, when it is necessary, without committing you to the strain of attention which a consistent use of the scenic method creates. He can, in other words, back off from the immediate scene and meditate upon its significance, for he is always telling a story that happened in the past: he is not telling it at the moment of occurrence. He thus has some of the advantages of the Omniscient Narrator, since he can summarize less important events, develop the more important, and reflect upon the fortunes of his characters.

It would seem, then, that the First Person Narrative ought to be the best all-round method, in that it solves the problem of authority automatically by making the narrator a part of the action which he is depicting. But it is not without justice that Henry James calls it the most "barbarous" of all techniques, even though one of his great masterpieces, *The Turn of the Screw,* is a First Person Narrative. The authority of the First Person Narrator is immediate, as we have said, but it is severely qualified; that is to say, if his own part in the situation is deeply enough involved to make it credible, so that he is an actor as well as an observer, we cannot expect to get from him an unbiased report on the other characters: he will be putting himself in a favorable light. He must necessarily do this or lose our sympathy, for if he is an ignoble person he will be an improper narrator of a serious action. If he remains outside the action, though present at its different stages, we shall question the reasons for his presence; unless he is present as a human being, and personally involved, we shall not believe that he has any reason for being there.

As we shall see when we come to the fourth technique, that of the Central Intelligence, the problem of the artist in fiction is to decide which method has the fewest limitations in view of the nature of his subject; for no method is perfect. In other words, the great artist will contrive to use the disadvantages of his chosen technique in a positive manner. In the case of the First Person Narrator, he must manage to use for positive effect the biased report. This is what James does in *The Turn of the Screw*: we see only what the hypersensitive and dominating Governess sees, but the essence of the story consists in having our view restricted to hers. What she fails to take account of becomes a positive element of drama; it creates the irony of the situation and eventually produces the tragic outcome. Likewise in Ring Lardner's "Haircut," the barber-narrator sees the action at a low level, and in the discrepancy between the way he sees it and the reader's sense of what it must actually have been lies the central dramatic interest. In long works like *Moll Flanders* the method is hard to sustain. Defoe asks us to take a little too seriously the point of view of a female rake and adventuress. We tend to judge the First Person Narrator as we judge his characters. We may agree that he is telling us what happened, but knowing him as we inevitably do, we may question the range and depth of his understanding.

4. *THE ROVING NARRATOR*

This fourth technique provides a method which gains most of the immediacy of the First Person Narrative, yet conceals the narrator in such a fashion that he evades our natural impulse to judge his capacities. In fact, this method combines the advantages of the three others and involves the artist in fewer of their disadvantages than any other known technique. But it requires the greatest possible maturity of judgment, the greatest mastery of life, and the highest technical skill to control it.

We call it the Technique of the Central Intelligence after Henry James, who insisted that all the action of a novel should be evaluated by a single superior mind placed in the center of the main dramatic situation. But having established this single evaluating mind, the artist may range over the whole cast of characters and give you their views upon the action. Thus the placing of the Central Intelligence gives the immediacy of the eye-witness account without committing us to the consistently narrow and biased view of the First Person Narrator. We look at the situation by and large through the eyes of the central character or intelligence, but we stand a little above and to one side, so to speak, and actually use the eyes of the artist himself. We thus enjoy his privilege of omniscience without the dubious authority of the conventional Omniscient Narrator; for here the artist makes his surmises, summaries, and explanations in terms of what the central character sees and feels, and thus these usually inert masses of material are dramatized and given *authority*. The Long and the Short Views are equally possible without sacrificing the dynamic value of the Central Intelligence. Through the Central Intelligence the author may permit us to meditate upon the state of affairs as a whole at a certain stage, and thus give us the panoramic sweep; or he may involve us in the Central Intelligence's immediate concerns, and thus put before us a close-up scene.

Let us briefly apply these observations to two great stories. In James's "The Beast in the Jungle" the Central Intelligence is that of John Marcher: we *see* with his physical eyes, and we see at that level nothing that he does not see. If James had chosen the First Person Narrator technique, we should have been limited merely to what Marcher can see physically. But the problem, for James, was to keep the dramatic immediacy of Marcher's physical *sight* and at the same time to exceed his moral *insight*; otherwise we should not have got this particular story at all. We should not have got May Bartram's side of the story, which is the immense sacrifice of her life to a completely selfish man who has no *insight* into his selfishness. If you will look at the scene (p. 216) in which May Bartram rises from her chair and virtually offers herself to Marcher, you will observe that we see her through Marcher's physical eyes but we understand her situation through the subtly shifted focus that the author brings to bear upon her. In Joyce's "The Dead" we have an even more complex and thorough use of the Central Intelligence presided over by the far-reaching insight of the author. We see nothing that Gabriel Conroy does not see, but in the very language in which his limited view is presented we get an extension of moral insight of which he is incapable; and yet this superior insight is so cunningly adjusted to Conroy's immediate problem that we are scarcely aware at a given moment that we are receiving it.

The technique of the Central Intelligence is employed in one way or another in the greatest nineteenth-century novels, from *The Idiot* and *Madame Bovary* to *The Ambassadors*.

II. THE LONG AND THE SHORT VIEW

In the preceding section, under the heading of Authority, we discussed the problem of Point of View in terms of four extreme technical solutions. We must emphasize again the impossibility of learning to write fiction through the mere critical understanding of these four techniques, as they are described by us, or as they may be presented in other terms by others. Whichever of these leading approaches to the material, or whatever combinations of them, the author may decide to use, the special tact required for the manipulation of the Long View and the Short View constitutes a separate problem. It is a problem that cannot be solved theoretically. Regardless of the over-all technique that the writer may be using, he must learn how to adjust the reader's attention moment by moment, if he is to dramatize his material.

To dramatize the material, in the sense that we have in mind, is to render active *everything* in the story, from the close-up scene to the large summary. The complexity of the problem may be indicated by brief reference to some of the various ways in which writers have understood it in the recent past. For example, by "dramatic structure" Edwin Muir, in *The Structure of the Novel,* means a structure of action, or plot, which may be distinguished from "extensive structure," or the reliance upon scene, background, and character for the main over-all effect. Lubbock, who in *The Craft of Fiction* follows James, would distinguish these two methods quite differently. The latter, "extensive" method Lubbock would call (after

James) the Pictorial, since the main interest is less in *what* happens than in that it happens to a certain character, whose "portrait" is thus created. Lubbock and James are scarcely interested at all in Muir's "dramatic structure"; that is to say, they are not concerned with plot, or the structure of action, as such. By drama they mean roughly what we mean here by the close-up scene, through which the reader seems to be put in immediate relation to what is happening. Thus they oppose Picture and Drama, not to exclude the one from the other, but to permit us to see two polar aspects of fiction. Let us allude to a novel which is primarily Pictorial; for example, *Madame Bovary*. This novel is a portrait of a foolish, pathetic woman, in which "plot" figures very little; yet in order to create the portrait, the real center of interest, Flaubert had to contrive a series of incidents leading to Emma's death; and the incidents are Drama, in the Jamesian sense. They are close-ups. To account for the passage of time, to space the incidents effectively, to give verisimilitude to the representation of many years in the compass of a few hundred pages, Flaubert resorted to a cunning use of Picture. That is to say, he *summarizes, narrates,* and *comments,* not in his own person as Omniscient Narrator, but as Concealed Narrator. Thus, page by page, the novel has all the look of immediate Drama; but its total effect is that of Picture.

Another set of terms, closely connected with Picture and Drama, are Panorama and Scene: these are Lubbock's own terms. We have thus, under Authority, opposed the Panoramic to the Scenic, the Omniscient Narrator to the Effaced Narrator. The Pure Omniscient Narrator (if he exists) never cuts his characters, his scene, his action loose from himself; ideally the Effaced Narrator always does.

To simplify these difficulties of terminology, but by no means with the pretense that we have solved them, we offer for practical purposes the terms which seem to us to be least clouded by theoretical temptations: the Long View and the Short View. Every fiction is made up of both views. If a novel or a story were made up exclusively of Long Views (Pictures, Panoramas, Summaries), no character could ever be shown doing or saying anything; likewise if it were all Short Views (Drama, Incident, Scene) we should never know where the action is taking place, or even *what* the characters are doing, for it would approach the condition of dialogue, and end up by crying to be put into the theatre.

Any piece of fiction consists, then, in an alternation of Views of varying distance from the scene or the action. If it is not effective technique to muddle the Point of View, it is equally ineffective to put the reader into a strait-jacket and ask him to look undeviatingly at the subject. There is a great deal of confusion, even among gifted writers, about this question. It is supposed that the technical acceptance of Point of View as the primary secret of the art of fiction is nothing less than the strait-jacket itself; so, to gain comprehensiveness and flexibility, the writer muddles his Long and Short Views. The only way to gain flexibility of treatment is to master first of all the secrets of the point of view; for without this mastery the flexibility will be mere incoherence.

There is perhaps an ideal distance at which the View, in terms of the work as a whole and of its parts, must be established. It is sometimes called "psychic" or "aesthetic" distance; but these terms refer to the *effect* upon the reader, not to the problems of the writer. Every writer must perceive the distances which are right for his subject: they cannot be taught; and this is why nobody in the long run can be taught to write masterpieces. Let us look at this problem in terms of a simile. The writer is in the position of a photographer who wants to record a public event. (The reader will observe at once the inadequacy of a photographic analogy.) He is photographing a procession. He may post himself at a window of a tall building in order to get a bird's-eye view of the procession as it winds through the streets. But if he wants us to feel that we have *seen* the procession he will descend from the window and focus his lens upon the faces of individuals or small groups which can be taken in at a glance. He will alternate the Long and the Short Views as his main purpose directs.

At one point in the analogy to photography appears an accuracy which we wish to emphasize. The author is the photographer, and although he directs the shots he does not himself appear. He would in this case be the Roving Narrator, or the Omniscient Narrator Concealed. *His direction towards unity of design and effect we would call the Central Intelligence.* His Post of Observation (another phrase of James's) for the exercise of the Central Intelligence may be taken up inside the consciousness of a single character, or in the relations of a group, or it may shift from person to person. It is the exercise of this Central Intelligence which imparts to the work what we have called *activity* or *drama*; that is, everything in the story is seen by somebody *in* the story, and not merely reported by the author, who is outside it.

The amateur frequently expends all his energy on his Short Views, reserving the Long Views to convey information that is indispensable to the proper understanding of the story. The Long View naturally lends itself to this purpose better than the Short, because the Scenic effect requires the author to comment sparingly or to efface himself altogether. The problem is to make the Long or Panoramic View as dramatic as possible, to appear, that is, to present it from the inside, and not simply to lay it on externally. Bunin's "The Gentleman from San Francisco" is a cunning use of the Short or Scenic View so modulated as to contain a general judgment not only upon the hero but upon the civilization that he represents. It would be difficult to put one's finger exactly upon those moments in the story in which the Short View is subtly stretched into summary and panorama; but this double effect is there, and it contributes overwhelmingly to the power of the story. The problem in its general aspects may be summed up as follows: Having taken up a certain post of observation, the writer must manage to stretch his position or contract it, as necessary, without confusing the reader, and without breaking the reader's sense of the organic relation of part to whole.

III. COMPLICATION AND RESOLUTION

Every work of fiction embodies an inner conflict, or a conflict between persons, or between men and nature. If the work is to have form the conflict must be resolved in the victory of one of the forces, or in partial victory, or in victory and defeat viewed ambiguously. Sometimes the significance of the victorious person or force is qualified or given another dimension when, for example, the defeated hero achieves a moral insight which means a kind of victory in defeat, as in the case of Gabriel Conroy at the end of "The Dead"; or this insight may reveal the depth of the hero's defeat, as in the ease of John Marcher in "The Beast in the Jungle."

From the point of view of structure, then, the two parts of a work of fiction are Complication and Resolution. In a well-constructed work they interlock so closely that the casual reader is not conscious of them separately; the Resolution seems to have started at the beginning, as indeed it is implicit in the Complication. It usually appears as an unforeseen incident, but perhaps a higher level of interest is achieved if it is less the incident itself than what it reveals about the plight of the hero, which constitutes the Resolution. In Faulkner's "Spotted Horses" the Complication is the arrival in the community of the crazed horses; but the horses only effect the release of the madness which is already in the hearts of the men. The action moves towards Resolution when the men desert reality and, moon-struck themselves, pursue the moon-eyed horses; it reaches its climax when the Judge, representing reason and justice, holds up his hands and appeals to Heaven, thus acknowledging his impotence against the forces of evil, represented by Flem Snopes. (See pp. 531–534 for a detailed discussion of this scene.)

In Chekhov's "On the Road" the Complication is introduced when Mlle. Ilovaisky enters the room where Liharev is sitting. His conversation with her makes him realize that he has lived his entire life by Faith, a succession of faiths, and as the conversation progresses he discovers his new faith: Woman. But all the time they are talking the snow-storm outside, representing the blindness and lack of direction in human life, is roaring at the windows and even rushing in gusts down the chimney. Liharev is so blind and so self-centered that he does not perceive that this rich, attractive woman is offering him the realization of his dreams. They go out of the inn into a snow-storm so blinding that as they part they can scarcely see each other for the flakes that are settling upon their lashes. On the naturalistic level the snow physically parts and conceals them from each other, and this is the dramatic Resolution; symbolically it points up the Resolution on the spiritual level, at which Liharev is the victim of his own inner blindness. (For a detailed discussion of this story see pp. 175–178.)

IV. ENVELOPING ACTION

The Enveloping Action is usually referred to by historians and sociologists as the "social background" and by some critics as the *milieu* in which the action of the story takes place. These terms are useful for general understanding but they are not practical for the purposes of technical insight. In a broad way we might describe the Enveloping Action as the life that would conceivably continue beyond the frame of the story, just as it preceded it, and out of which the particular drama develops. The classic example of Enveloping Action is the plot of the *Antigone* of Sophocles, in which Creon, representing the continuity of order in the Theban state, forbids Antigone to perform the rites of burial for her dead brothers. The State is the *milieu* that envelops Antigone, frustrating her "higher morality."

For a detailed account of how the Enveloping Action is interfused with the specific action, see the analysis of "The Rocking-Horse Winner" by D. H. Lawrence (pp. 348–351). In the past generation sociological fiction has shown us the Individual opposed to Society, or the reverse, i.e., a "class" or the "people" frustrated by powerful individuals of another class or people. This school tends to personify the Enveloping Action as if it were a single mind. This kind of fiction has been one of the consequences of the naturalistic school as represented originally by Zola, and later in the United States by Dreiser, Lewis, and Dos Passos. The technique of the school has been on the whole photographic and documentary. The other branch of naturalism, which we emphasize in this book, comes down from Flaubert through Chekhov, James, and Joyce—four great masters who perfected the art of dramatizing the Enveloping Action without offering it to the reader in large chunks: the art of making the inert detail move. The "social background" remains inert unless it can be brought into the story through the immediate situations of the leading characters. The Enveloping Action of Gretta Conroy's situation in "The Dead" is her early life, but this is given us solely in terms of her boy lover, Michael Furey, who stands for that part of her early life which is dramatically significant in her marriage to Gabriel. A writer of ordinary ability might have introduced Gretta's "background" somewhat as follows:

> Gretta Conroy was brought up in a peasant village in Western Ireland, where her family were average examples of the small gentry of the region. Her circumstances were narrow. When she was a young girl a boy named Michael Furey fell in love with her, but before anything could come of this affair he died. Gretta romantically felt that he had died for her, and a consciousness of guilt conditioned her emotions so thoroughly that she could not completely give herself to her husband, Gabriel Conroy.

Compare this dead lump of information with the actual presentation by Joyce (pp. 275–277); and see the commentary on the scene on pages 281–282.

V. TONAL UNITY

In the simplest terms Tonal Unity means a consistency of attitude towards the material of the story; and this consistency of attitude in turn means a consistent use of language out of a certain core of meaning appropriate to the scene and the characters. The Tone will be almost entirely controlled by the Point of View from which the story is told. If the First Person Narrator is used, the style throughout should be "in character"; if the narrator is telling a story of the sea, he must be able to command with ease a natural familiarity with the setting. Under First Person Narrator we have referred (p. 624) to the narrator of Ring Lardner's "Haircut," a story in which the control of tone is masterly; but here the author chooses as his narrator the one man perhaps least qualified by knowledge and insight to tell it, in order to underline the pathos of the tragedy through the insensitivity of the narrator.

Shifts of tone are possible in a short story but very difficult because there is not enough time to prepare them properly. In a novel changing emphases of tone can intensify the dramatic structure; the great example of this is the alternating shifts of tone in *War and Peace,* corresponding to the scenes of war and of domestic life. There is perhaps no finer example in the entire range of the short story than the conclusion of Crane's "The Open Boat." Up to the last minute the presentation has been soberly naturalistic, without commentary or interpretation; then at the end we get this sentence: "When it came night, the white waves paced to and fro in the moonlight, and the wind brought the sound of the great sea's voice to the men on the shore, and they felt that they could then be interpreters." Here the *elevation* of the tone is not only unpredictable and in itself dramatic; it also effects the Resolution of the tensions in the story.

An extreme, special use of Tonal Unity is that of "The Fall of the House of Usher." Here the Tone is the personal tone of the narrator-visitor to the House, and it relies for its consistency of effect upon *sound*. The defect of this sort of Tonal Unity is perhaps its failure to "render" the subject; it is outside the subject to a high degree; and we are affected by the sound of the language rather than by the dramatic realization of the action. Sound as the basis of Tonal Unity cannot be sustained in a work of considerable length, and it is more appropriate in lyric poetry.

The exploration of the arts of tone which has accompanied the rise of the naturalistic-symbolic tradition of fiction emphasized in this book has developed from the increasing self-consciousness of the fiction writer concerning the dramatic center of his work. Even in the use of Omniscient Narrator Tonal Unity can be achieved with great consistency. Bunin's "The Gentleman from San Francisco" provides a fine example of this: the Tone is not that of the author but very subtly that of the hero and his plight. Even when, as in the Effaced Narrator, the author excludes himself, the

Tone of the work tends to be that of the character who provides the Central Intelligence in the action.

VI. SYMBOLISM

To discuss this subject properly one would have to go far beyond the range of the short story or even the larger arts of fiction and drama. It is the last and crowning problem in all critical discussion, for imaginative literature that endures must in some sense be symbolic: it must stand for something which is not special to the time in which it was written and which permits us to acknowledge what Edmund Wilson has called the "shock of recognition." If we can still see in the character of Moll Flanders or of Humphrey Clinker some human quality or cluster of qualities which we recognize as permanent in human nature, then Moll and Humphrey are at least in a rudimentary sense symbols. They stand for something beyond their own particular selves.

Symbolism means in the simplest sense a throwing together of qualities or of elements. There are natural symbols like the sea and the sky; there are social, religious, and historical symbols, the commonest of which are words like Home, the Cross, the Hearth, the Flag; there are created symbols which are the result of individual imaginative power on the literary level; there is above all "insight symbolism," of which the fissure in the façade of the House of Usher is an example; and there are symbols which combine all these in infinite permutations.

Since the end of the eighteenth century the social and historical symbol has more and more been cut off from an even deeper source of symbolic insight: the religious source. Little by little, through the development of narrative fiction, symbolism has tended to become merely social and merely historical; and with the decline of historical insight in the modern world the social symbol has come to predominate in literature, poetry as well as fiction. We get a man or a group of men who "stand" for a group or class, and if the older types of symbolism appear in modern literature they are not expected by the author or the reader to operate upon the mind with anything like a fixed meaning. They must in every case be re-imagined; that is to say, they must reach the reader's consciousness through the *experience* of the fictional character; we should understand a modern use of the symbol, for example, of the Crucifixion, not by means of common agreement, but through what it means to a character in the story. The simplest example in modern fiction of this reversal of symbolic understanding is Hemingway's "Today is Friday" (see p. 287); it is typical of even more complex uses of traditional symbolism today. To make the symbol of the Cross dramatically *real* Hemingway felt that he had to reduce its vast scale and power to the scope of awareness of a group of drunken Roman soldiers, who talk like, and are, modern *l'homme moyen et sensuel*. But to the extent that Hemingway can use the symbol at all he uses it *actively,* in terms of the dramatic structure of the situation.

This symbolic procedure of the imaginative writer no doubt represents a loss in depth and range, but at the same time it accounts for some of the most powerful effects in modern fiction. Elsewhere, principally in our discussion of Joyce's "The Dead," we have shown how the natural object and the mere incident can achieve through repetition and juxtaposition the significance of symbolism (pp. 279–282). The snow in "The Dead" and the snow in Chekhov's "On the Road" are the same natural snow, but symbolically they stand for widely opposite meanings. In "The Dead" the snow is a palpable image which develops from the flakes on Gabriel Conroy's rubbers into the snow-filled sky, where it represents Gabriel's escape from his Narcissism. In "On the Road" it represents, because it blinds, Liharev's return to his inner self. If either Conroy or Liharev could be imagined as characters in a great religious drama resulting in ritual, liturgy, and theology, then snow could become a religious symbol and its meaning "fixed" either in the direction of Conroy's situation or in the direction of Liharev's.

APPENDIX B

Faults of the Amateur

1. THE UNWRITTEN STORY

An amateur writer usually puts only half of his story on paper, and this half, made up often of lame sentences and thin incidents, does not make the same impression on him as it makes on other people. The half of the story which remains in his mind unwritten, being ideal and therefore not subject to the vicissitudes of actuality, sheds a glow over the thin written half. In this transfiguring effulgence the two halves unite. He reads the story over and sees, not the story he has written but the story he had hoped to write and had partially conceived. To distinguish between the actual story and the imagined story one must, as it were, follow the painter's practice of stepping back from the easel to survey the work with narrowed, coldly critical, and self-excluding eyes. The writer who has developed this moral discipline is well on the way to achieving technical discipline, and has passed an important milestone in his progress.

2. LACK OF PROPORTION

A second weakness of amateur writing grows out of the inability to distinguish between the ideal and the real: a failure to achieve proportion. An author who engages to offer us an imitation of life is in the position, say, of the man who attempts to make a manikin. The figure's arms and legs will not be as long and as wide as the arms and legs of a real man, but they must bear the same relation to his torso as a real man's arms and legs do, or we will not accept the representation as lifelike. The amateur may profitably think of his story under the metaphor of a human body. The scene he has just written may be a convincing leg, but it is not the leg that goes with the juxtaposed chest and arm. He has violated the proper pace and timing. In a well-constructed story there is an ideal proportion for every paragraph, every sentence, every word, even, in fact, every comma that indicates a pause of breath. The amateur writer, convinced that the work is already done because half of it glows so vividly in his vanity, is inclined not to give his incidents enough "body" in the right proportions; or if he has the discipline and patience to build up a scene properly, he may then hurry over its climax so fast that the reader will not have time to take in what has happened. The structure of his narrative collapses for lack of proper proportion in its parts, however "good" each part may be in isolation.

3. *NEGLECT OF THE READER*

Allied to the fault of disproportion is the failure to take into consideration the "psychology" of the reader. When we are reading for pleasure, our critical faculties, powers of analysis and synthesis, are not consciously functioning. We listen, and are supposed to listen, like a three-year's—or at the most like a thirteen-year's—child. We do not question what the author tells us, but we must have time to take it in. An expert narrator, like Coleridge's Ancient Mariner, "hath his will" with us but to work his will he employs certain devices which seem to us quite natural. One of the most effective "devices" is what James called "under-cutting." If James's key incidents stand out like mountain peaks, they stand out because, *like* mountain peaks, they are furnished with slopes, either steep or gentle: a succession of minor incidents so cunningly arranged that they throw into sharp relief the peak which they support. Yeats has put the matter another way when, in speaking of poetry, he says that a tense line ought to be preceded and followed by a "numb line." A mountain peak cannot exist without a valley on each side of it. Another way to make sure that the reader has time to take in what he is being told is to use a Scheherazade-like technique of delay. We keep the reader tarrying at a particular spot by entertaining him so well that he does not notice that time is passing. We offer him not one diversion but two. The author is in reality saying the same thing twice in order to make sure that the reader "gets" it. But he says it differently each time; he embodies it in different incidents. Stephen Crane uses this device frequently and brilliantly. Katherine Anne Porter uses it powerfully in "Old Mortality": Amy, Gabriel's first wife, is a gentlewoman; the second wife, Miss Honey, is not; but the young girl Miranda, who is forming her image of life from her uncle's marriages, gets exactly the same "lesson" from both. She is convinced of the inadequacy of her traditional background for life in a new age.

4. *DEAD DIALOGUE*

In amateur fiction conversation is seldom life-like. The beginning writer will do well to remember that in life one rarely succeed in emitting more than three sentences at a time. At a party the man who is determined to do most of the talking often signalizes his decision by taking his stand on the hearth-rug. In a story, the character who is elected to deliver monologues had better be placed by the author in that position; that is, the fact that he is making a speech ought to be *dramatized*. If it is not, the speech, though it may seem in itself "all right," will be like the leg that does not go with the arm. But the short speech is not necessarily, in itself, dramatic. One of the leading amateur faults, of which most popular novelists are guilty, is to convey to the reader through dialogue features of the scene or mere expository information. Imagine a scene in which a little boy enters the room where his grandmother is sitting. "There's the window over there beyond the bed, son," says Grandma, "go and shut it." The little boy would already know where the window is, and the author who does this sort of thing is merely telling the reader where it is, because he has been too clumsy to tell him otherwise. The fault can be subtly committed, but in principle it is never better than our example. This is merely one way in which the author gets between us and his characters and his scene. It is well to remember that in life conversation is not logical or systematically informative, but allusive, proceeding through a series of antiphonal explosions. Each sentence that we utter is like a bullet moulded in the heat of our desire to communicate, and fired at our interlocutor, who in turn fires back at us his rapidly moulded bullets. At any rate conversation today is very much like that.

APPENDIX C

Bibliography

This list of readings is not exhaustive but suggestive, and is intended equally for the curious general reader and the student of fiction. The books and articles are of varying merit, but we have not included titles that seemed to us without interest.

BOOKS

BATES, H. E. *The Modern Short Story: A Survey*. London, 1942.

BLACKMUR, R. P. *The Expense of Greatness*. New York, 1940. "Notes on the Novel," pp. 176–198.

BEACH, JOSEPH WARREN. *The Method of Henry James*. New Haven, 1918.

DAICHES, DAVID. *The Novel and the Modern World*. Chicago, 1940.

DUPEE, F. W., ed. *The Question of Henry James*. New York, 1945. Essays by Blackmur, Eliot, Troy, Wilson, Ford, and Zabel particularly valuable.

FORSTER, E. M. *Aspects of the Novel*. New York, 1927.

JAMES, HENRY. *The Art of the Novel*. With an Introduction by R. P. Blackmur. New York, 1941. James's invaluable Prefaces to the New York edition of his works.

JAMES, HENRY. *The Notebooks of Henry James*. Edited with an Introduction by F. O. Matthiessen and Kenneth Murdoch. New York, 1947.

JAMES, HENRY. *The Art of Fiction and Other Essays*. Edited by Morris Roberts. New York, 1948. James's essays on his contemporaries and immediate predecessors. The title essay is of great historical importance.

JAMES, HENRY. *The Letters of Henry James*. Edited by Percy Lubbock. 2 vols. New York, 1920.

LEVIN, HARRY. *James Joyce: A Critical Introduction*. New York, 1941. The best brief account of the development of Joyce.

LUBBOCK, PERCY. *The Craft of Fiction*. New York, 1921. Based upon James, this book is a landmark in the criticism of fiction.

MATTHIESSEN, F. O. *Henry James: The Major Phase*. New York, 1945.

MUIR, EDWIN. *The Structure of the Novel*. London, 1928, 1947. With Lubbock's *The Craft of Fiction,* one of the two most important general works.

MULLER, HERBERT J. *Modern Fiction*. New York, 1937.

O'CONNOR, WILLIAM VAN, ed. *Forms of Modern Fiction*. Minneapolis, 1948. An anthology of recent essays on fiction.

READ, HERBERT. *Collected Essays*. London, 1938. "Henry James," pp. 354–366.

ROBERTS, MORRIS. *Henry James' Criticism*. Cambridge, 1929.

STEEGMULLER, FRANCIS. *Flaubert and Madame Bovary*. New York, 1938.

TATE, ALLEN. *On the Limits of Poetry*. New York, 1948. "Techniques of Fiction," pp. 129–145.

THIBAUDET, ALBERT. *Gustave Flaubert, 1821–1880*. Paris, 1922.

WARREN, AUSTIN. *Rage for Order*. Chicago, 1948. Chapters on Hawthorne and James.

WARREN, A., and WELLEK, R. *Theory of Literature*. New York, 1949. Especially Ch. XVI, "The Nature and Modes of Narrative Fiction," pp. 219–234.

WILSON, EDMUND. *Axel's Castle*. New York, 1931. Chapter on Joyce.

WILSON, EDMUND. *The Triple Thinkers*. New York, 1938. "Flaubert's Politics," pp. 100–121.

WOOLF, VIRGINIA. *Mr. Bennett and Mrs. Brown*. London, 1927.

ESSAYS

BAKER, HOWARD. "An Essay on Fiction with Examples," *Southern Review,* Vol 3 (Autumn, 1941), pp. 385–406.

BAUDELAIRE, CHARLES. "Madame Bovary," *Partisan Review,* Vol. 13 (Nov., 1946), pp. 586–597.

BLACKMUR, R. P. "The Sacred Fount," *Kenyon Review,* Vol. 4 (Autumn, 1942), pp. 328–352. "In the Country of the Blue," *Kenyon Review,* Vol. 5 (Autumn, 1943), pp. 595–617.

FERGUSSON, FRANCIS. "James' Idea of Dramatic Form," *Kenyon Review,* Vol. 5 (Autumn 1943), pp. 495–507.

FLINT, F. CUDWORTH. "Remarks on the Novel," *Symposium,* Vol. 1 (Jan., 1930), pp. 84–96.

FORD, FORD MADOX. "Techniques," *Southern Review,* Vol. 1 (July, 1935), pp. 20–35.

FRANK, JOSEPH. "Spatial Form in Modern Literature," *Sewanee Review,* Vol. 53 (Spring, 1945), pp. 221–240. (Parts II and III in following issues.)

KNIGHT, L. C. "Henry James and the Trapped Spectator," *Southern Review,* Vol. 3 (Winter, 1937), pp. 600–617.

ROBERTS, MORRIS. "Henry James and the Art of Foreshortening," *Review of English Studies,* Vol. 22 (July, 1946), pp. 207–215.

ZABEL, M. D. "Henry James' Place," *Nation,* Vol. 156 (April 24, 1943), pp. 597–599.

For critical readers as well as for the student of the techniques of fiction, two valuable symposia on Henry James are available in libraries:

Hound and Horn, Vol. 7 (April–May, 1934). Contains essays by Marianne Moore, Francis Fergusson, H. R. Hays, R. P. Blackmur, Edna Kenton, Glenway Wescott, Newton Arvin, Robert Cantwell, Edmund Wilson, and Stephen Spender.

The Kenyon Review, Vol. 5 (Autumn, 1943). Contains essays by Katherine Anne Porter, Francis Fergusson, Jacques Barzun, John L. Sweeney, F. O. Matthiessen, Austin Warren, David Daiches, Eliseo Vivas, and R. P. Blackmur.

BIOGRAPHICAL NOTES

ELIZABETH BOWEN

Elizabeth Dorothea Cole Bowen is the only child of Henry Cole Bowen, of Bowen's Court, County Cork, Ireland, and of Isabel Conroy Colley. In 1923 she married Alan Charles Cameron. Miss Bowen was educated at Downe House, Downe, Kent. Her collections of short stories are: *Encounters* (1923), *Ann Lee's* (1926), *Joining Charles* (1929), *Look at All Those Roses* (1941), and *The Demon Lover* (1945). Miss Bowen is the author of several novels and the editor of *The Faber Book of Modern Short Stories.*

ANTON CHEKHOV

Anton Pavlovich Chekhov was born in Taganrog, on the Sea of Azov, on January 17, 1860, the son of a tradesman whose father had been a serf. He was educated at the gymnasium of his native town; in 1879 he began his medical studies at the University of Moscow, where he took his degree in 1884. As a medical student he supported himself by writing comic sketches under the pseudonym, A. Tchekhonte. By 1889 he had reached the summit of his powers as a writer, and one masterpiece followed another until his death from tuberculosis in 1904. In addition to his plays he wrote many volumes of short stories (but no novels). Some books available in English translation are: *The Black Monk and Other Stories* (1915), *The Bet and Other Stories* (1915), *Russian Silhouettes* (1915), *The Duel and Other Stories* (1916), *The Wife and Other Stories* (1918), *The Schoolmistress and Other Stories* (1921), *The Cook's Wedding and Other Stories* (1922), *The Bishop and Other Stories* (1930), *The Portable Chekhov* (1947.)

COLETTE

Sidonie Gabrielle Claudine Colette was born on January 28, 1873, at Saint-Saveur-en-Puisaye, in Burgundy. In a country where factions dominate literature she has remained aloof, and has produced a body of fiction which has won the admiration of all parties. The books available in English translation are: *The Vagrant* (1910), *Backs and Purrs* (1913), *The Gentle Libertine* (1931), *Young Lady of Paris* (1931), and *The Indulgent Husband* (1935).

STEPHEN CRANE

Crane was born on November 1, 1871, in Newark, New Jersey, the fourteenth and last child of the Rev. Jonathan Townley Crane, a Methodist minister, and his wife Helen Peck Crane. When Crane was nine his father died; the widow supported her children by acting as correspondent for religious newspapers. Crane spent a year each at Lafayette College and Syracuse University, paying his way by writing articles for the New York *Tribune*. He went to New York and became a free lance for the *Tribune* and the *Herald*. No publisher would print the first American realistic novel, *Maggie, a Girl of the Streets*. Crane borrowed $700 from his brother and had it printed himself: one hundred copies were sold. But it was admired by Garland and Howells, and his next novel, *The Red Badge of Courage* (1895), made him famous. He became a war correspondent; on a voyage to Cuba the ship was wrecked, and he drifted four days in an open boat. The exposure ruined his health, but it gave him the material for his greatest and most famous story, "The Open Boat." He was married in 1898 and went to England; but he was recalled by the New York *World* to cover the Spanish-American war in Cuba. He then returned to England, his health greatly impaired. On June 5, 1900, he died at Badenweiler in the Black Forest, where he had gone to regain his health. In the eight years from 1892 to his death he published twelve books.

WILLIAM FAULKNER

William Faulkner was born in New Albany, Mississippi, on September 25, 1897. His early education was desultory. In the First World War he enlisted in the Canadian Air Force because he was unwilling to fight with Yankees. After the war he was admitted as a veteran to the University of Mississippi, where he took a few courses. His first published work was a poem in the New Orleans magazine, *The Double Dealer,* in 1922. He lives on a farm near Oxford, Mississippi, but spends a part of each year in Hollywood as a "writer." His books are: *The Marble Faun,* poems (1924), *Soldiers' Pay* (1926), *Mosquitoes* (1927), *Sartoris* (1929), *The Sound and the Fury* (1929), *As I Lay Dying* (1930), *Sanctuary* (1931), *These Thirteen* (1931), *Idyll in the Desert* (1931), *Light in August* (1932), *A Green Bough,* poems (1933), *Pylon* (1933), *Absolom, Absolom!* (1936), *The Unvanquished* (1938), *The Wild Palms* (1939), *The Hamlet* (1940), *Go Down Moses and Other Stories* (1942), *Intruder in the Dust* (1948).

GUSTAVE FLAUBERT

Flaubert was born in Rouen, the son of a leading physician, on December 12, 1821, and died at his villa at Croisset, a village near Rouen, on May 8, 1880. Except for a trip to Egypt and his intermittent affair with Madame Colet, his life was uneventful. *Madame Bovary* appeared in 1859; it created a scandal but brought him immediate fame. This was followed in 1862 by the archaeological romance of Carthage, *Salammbô*; in 1869, by *L'Education Sentimentale,* and by *La Tentation de Saint Antoine* in 1874. *Bouvard et Pecuchet* he left unfinished at his death. "Un Coeur Simple" is one of the stories in *Trois Contes*.

NIKOLAY GOGOL

Gogol was born on March 31, 1809, at Sorochintsky, in the province of Poltava, of a family of Ukrainian Cossack gentry. He died at the age of forty-two, ten years after the publication of *Dead Souls*. His famous comedy "The Government Inspector," produced in 1836, was received enthusiastically by the intelligentsia, but with horror by officialdom. He left Russia immediately and lived for twelve years in Europe, chiefly in Rome, where he wrote *Dead Souls*. His great story "The Coat" (variously translated as "The Great Coat" and "The Overcoat") was the first story in Russian literature to express compassion for the masses. Tolstoy said, "We all come out of 'The Overcoat.'" Gogol is the father of Russian realism.

NATHANIEL HAWTHORNE

The life of Hawthorne (July 4, 1804–May 19, 1864) is one of the American literary heritages, and it is not necessary to summarize it here. The definitive biography is *Nathaniel Hawthorne: A Biography,* by Randall Stewart (New Haven, 1948); the most thorough critical study is that of Mark Van Doren, *Nathaniel Hawthorne* (New York, 1949). The most useful bibliography for the general reader is *Nathaniel Hawthorne: Representative Selections,* by Austin Warren (New York, 1934).

ERNEST HEMINGWAY

Ernest Hemingway was born in Oak Park, Illinois, on July 21, 1898, the son of Dr. Clarence Edmonds and Grace Hall Hemingway. He was graduated from the Oak Park High School, but instead of going to college he went abroad as a newspaper correspondent. He joined the Italian Army in the First World War, and was wounded in the retreat from Caporetto. He is an original and powerful writer who won critical acclaim with his first book and a popular following with the publication of *A Farewell to Arms* in 1929. His books are: *In Our Time* (1924), *The Sun Also Rises* (1926), *Men Without Women* (1927), *A Farewell to Arms* (1929), *Winner Take Nothing* (1933), *To Have and Have Not* (1937), *The Fifth Column and the First Forty-Nine* (1938), *For Whom the Bell Tolls* (1940).

HENRY JAMES

This great novelist was born in New York City on April 15, 1843, and died in England on February 28, 1916. Like Hawthorne and Poe, he is at the center of the American literary heritage; no summary of his career is necessary or even possible in a brief note. The definitive biography of Henry James remains to be written. The essential critical works about James are given in Appendix C.

JAMES JOYCE

James Joyce (February 2, 1882–January 13, 1941) is the climax of the great naturalist-symbolist school of fiction founded by Flaubert. For the essential facts of his life the reader may consult *James Joyce,* by Herbert Gorman (New York, 1940); the best brief critical survey is Harry Levin's *James Joyce* (New York, 1941).

FRANZ KAFKA

Franz Kafka was born of a wealthy family of Czech Jews in Prague on July 3, 1883; he died on June 3, 1924. On finishing the Volksschule he enrolled in the Gymnasium in the Alstader Ring, and later entered the law school, though his chief interest was already literature. In the year 1906, when he received his doctorate in jurisprudence, he began his career as a writer. In 1908 he obtained a coveted job in a workers' accident insurance office. In 1912, at Max Brod's suggestion, he put together his first writings under the title "Observations." When the war began in 1914 he insisted upon going to the front, where his chronically bad health broke down; he spent the rest of his life moving from one sanitarium to another. The writing career of this great fictionist was only ten years; only a few of his stories appeared in his lifetime. He destroyed much of his work, and asked Max Brod to destroy all of it after his death. Fortunately Brod preserved it. Kafka's works are available in English in six volumes: *The Castle* (1930), *The Great Wall of China* (1933), *The Metamorphosis* (1937), *The Trial* (1937), *Amerika* (1938), *A Franz Kafka Miscellany* (1940).

RUDYARD KIPLING

Kipling was born on December 30, 1865, at Bombay, of an Anglo-Indian family; he died on January 18, 1936. He was sent to England for his education at the United Services College, Westward Ho, in North Devon. Returning to India at seventeen, he became sub-editor of *The Lahore Civil and Military Gazette*. In 1886, when he was twenty-one, he published his first book, *Departmental Ditties.* In 1887 he published *Plain Tales from the Hills*; this was followed in the next two years by six volumes of stories (*Soldiers Three, the Phantom Rickshaw,* etc.) which revealed a new master of prose fiction; these stories were all written before he was twenty-four. In 1907 he was awarded the Nobel Prize.

RING LARDNER

Ringgold Wilmer Lardner was born at Niles, Michigan, on March 6, 1885; and died on September 25, 1933. After he was graduated from the Niles High School he wanted to go to the University of Michigan "to take football and dentistry," but went instead to the Armour Institute in Chicago for mechanical engineering. He was by turns freight agent, bookkeeper, and handy man in a gas office. His first newspaper job was with the South Bend *Times*; he went to Chicago as a reporter on the *Inter-Ocean,* and from there to the Chicago *Examiner,* where he became a sports writer. His books are: *You Know Me, Al* (1916), *Gullible's Travels* (1917), *Treat 'Em Rough* (1918), *How to Write Short Stories* (1924), *The Love Nest and Other Stories* (1926).

D. H. LAWRENCE

D. H. Lawrence was born in the coal village of Eastwood, Nottingham-shire, on September 11, 1885; he died in Vence, France, on March 2, 1930. His father, John Arthur Lawrence, was a coal-miner; his mother, Lydia Beardsall Lawrence, a school-teacher. At the age of fifteen he won his own teacher's certificate, and was appointed to the Davidson Road Elementary School at Croydon. As a writer he was discovered by Ford Madox Ford, who first printed him in *The English Review,* and called his work to the attention of Edward Garnett, who saw to it that his first novel, *The White Peacock,* was published, in 1911. His principal books are as follows: *The Trespasser* (1912), *Sons and Lovers* (1913), *The Rainbow* (1915), *The Lost Girl* (1920), *Women in Love* (1920), *Aaron's Rod* (1922), *The Plumed Serpent* (1926), *Lady Chatterley's Lover* (1928).

ANDREW LYTLE

Andrew Lytle was born in Murfreesboro, Tennessee, on December 26, 1903; he was educated at Vanderbilt and Yale. He has been Professor of History at the University of the South and Editor of *The Sewanee Review* (1942–43), and has taught at the University of Iowa and the University of Florida. His short stories have not been collected. He is the author of four books: *Bedford Forest,* biography (1931), *The Long Night,* novel (1936), *At the Moon's Inn,* novel (1941), *A Name for Evil,* novel (1947).

THOMAS MANN

Thomas Mann, born on June 6, 1875, is a native of the ancient Hanseatic town of Lübeck. His father was a prosperous merchant and leading citizen, having served as senator and twice as mayor of Lübeck. It was expected that Thomas Mann would succeed to his father's business, but his literary talent showed early, and his first publication, *Gefällen,* brought him moderate suc-cess. His first novel, *Buddenbrooks,* appearing in 1901, won him international fame, which eventually led to the Nobel Prize. Mr. Mann and his family have lived in the United States since before the Second World War. His works available in English translation are, in part, in addition to those named:

The Magic Mountain (1927), *Joseph and His Brothers* (1924), *Death in Venice,* a nouvelle (1925), *Disorder and Early Sorrow,* stories (1930), *Young Joseph* (1934), *Joseph in Egypt* (1938), *The Beloved Returns* (1940), *Doctor Faustus* (1948).

W. SOMERSET MAUGHAM

W. Somerset Maugham was born in Paris, January 25, 1874, the son of English parents. His father was solicitor to the British Embassy. Left an orphan at ten, he was brought up by a paternal uncle, a clergyman in White-stable, Kent, who insisted that he study medicine. He finished the course but never practiced beyond his internship. Out of his hospital experience he wrote his first novel, *Liza of Lambeth,* and has devoted himself to writing ever since. Among his works are: *The Making of a Saint* (1898), *Mrs. Craddock* (1902), *Of Human Bondage* (1915), *The Moon and Sixpence* (1919), *The Trembling of a Leaf,* short stories (1922), *The Painted Veil* (1925), *The Constant Wife* (1927), *The Summing Up,* autobiography (1938).

GUY DE MAUPASSANT

Henri René Albert Guy de Maupassant was born at the Chateau de Miromesnil (Seine-Inferieure) on August 5, 1850; he died in 1893. In a brief writing career he produced a powerful and impressive body of work. After his education at the Rouen Lycée, he entered the Ministry of Marine and was soon promoted to the Cabinet de l'Instruction Publique. He attended literary gatherings which included Flaubert, Turgenev, Daudet, Heredia, and Zola. He became the disciple of Flaubert, who undertook to teach him the principles of naturalism. His leading works are: *La Maison Tellier* (1881), *Boule de Suif* (1880), *Mademoiselle Fifi* (1883), *Une Vie* (1883), *Pierre et Jean* (1888), *Fort Comme La Mort* (1889), *Notre Coeur* (1890).

HERMAN MELVILLE

Herman Melville was born in New York City on August 1, 1819, the son of Allan Melville, a merchant of Scots descent, and of Maria Gansvoort Melville, daughter of a Dutch patroon family. His father died bankrupt in 1832; Melville lived with relatives until he was seventeen. In 1837 he shipped as cabin boy on a freighter bound for Liverpool, and never afterwards lived a settled life. Like James, Melville has yet to receive his definitive biography; but the revival of Melville in the past twenty years has produced interesting critical studies; and a new scholarly edition of his works is in progress. His principal works are: *Typee* (1846), *Omoo* (1847), *Mardi* (1849), *Redburn* (1849), *White Jacket* (1850), *Moby Dick* (1851), *Pierre* (1852), *Israel Potter* (1855), *Piazza Tales* (1856), *The Confidence Man* (1857), *Battle Pieces and Aspects of the War* (1866). *Billy Budd* was not published until

1924. Melville died on September 28, 1891, after a silence of a quarter of a century.

SEAN O'FAOLAIN

Sean O'Faolain was born in Dublin on February 22, 1900. He was educated at the National University in Dublin and at Harvard. He lectured on English literature at Boston College in 1929. He is a charter member of the Irish Royal Academy of Letters. His first writing was in Gaelic. He is the author of the following books: *Midsummer Madness* (1932), *A Nest of Simple Folk* (1933), *There's a Birdie in the Birdcage* (1935), *A Born Genius* (1936), *Bird Alone* (1936), *A Purse of Coppers* (1937), *Come Back to Erin* (1940), *The Great O'Neill* (1942).

FRANK O'CONNOR

Frank O'Connor (pseudonym of Michael O'Donovan) was born in 1903. He was educated by the Christian Brothers in Cork. He is a librarian by profession. He was a director of the Abbey Theatre until 1939, when he resigned in protest against the views of his fellow directors on censorship. His books are: *The Guests of the Nation* (1931), *The Wild Bird's Nest* (1932), and *Bones of Contention* (1936).

EDGAR ALLAN POE

Edgar Allan Poe was born in Boston, Massachusetts, on January 19, 1809, and died in Baltimore, Maryland, on October 7, 1849. As in the cases of Hawthorne and James, no brief biographical note can do justice to the deep ramifications of Poe's importance and influence. Among the countless biographical studies two are to be recommended: Hervey Allen's *Israfel: The Life and Times of Edgar Allan Poe* (New York, 1926), the fullest and most readable of the biographies; and Arthur Hobson Quinn's *Edgar Allan Poe: A Critical Biography,* the definitive scholarly work on the biographical side, but naive critically. The most reliable edition of Poe is *The Complete Works of Edgar Allan Poe* (The Virginia Edition), edited by James A. Harrison (17 vols., New York, 1902). A convenient edition of the poetry and the prose works, exclusive of the criticism, is the one-volume *The Complete Tales and Poems of Edgar Allan Poe,* edited by Hervey Allen (New York, 1938).

KATHERINE ANNE PORTER

Katherine Anne Porter was born in Indian Creek, Texas, on May 15, 1894. She was brought up in Louisiana and Texas, and educated at various convents. Her first stories were published in *The Century Magazine,* under the editorship of Carl Van Doren. Miss Porter now lives in California, where she teaches at Stanford University. Her books are: *Flowering Judas* (1930), *Hacienda* (1934), *Noon Wine* (1937), *Pale Horse, Pale Rider* (1939), *The Leaning Tower* (1942).

J. F. POWERS

J. F. Powers was born in Jacksonville, Illinois, on July 8, 1917. He was educated at public and parochial schools, and attended the Chicago branch of Northwestern University without taking a degree. He worked editorially on the Historical Records Survey. His first published story appeared in *Accent*. His work has appeared in *Best American Short Stories, O. Henry Prize Stories,* and *Accent Anthology*. His one book so far is *The Prince of Darkness and Other Stories* (New York, 1947).

PETER TAYLOR

Peter Hillsman Taylor was born in Trenton, Tennessee, on January 8, 1917. His father wanted him to be a lawyer, but when he did badly in mathematics he was permitted to study literature. He attended Southwestern, Vanderbilt, and Kenyon (B. A. 1940), and did graduate work at Louisiana State. Since the war he has taught at The Woman's College of the University of North Carolina and at Indiana University. His first story appeared in *The Southern Review*. He is the author of *A Long Fourth and Other Stories* (1948).

LEO TOLSTOY

Count Leov Nikolayevich Tolstoy was born on August 28, 1828, of an old Russian noble family on his parents' estate, Yasnaya Polyana, in the province of Tula. Orphaned at nine, he was brought up by relatives who sent him to the University of Kazan where he lived a gay social life and learned little. In 1851 he joined an artillery regiment in the Caucasas and took part in the Crimean campaign. He resigned from the army and went abroad; he became disgusted with the artificiality and materialism of the West; returning home, to the family estate, he conducted a school for peasant children. After the publication of *Anna Karenina* in 1877 he began to question his mode of life, and decided to return to primitive Christianity. A cult of Tolstoy appeared in Russia and abroad. His prestige was so great that the government refrained from interference, though he was excommunicated by the Holy Synod in 1901. His religious beliefs and practices created a breach between him and his wife. In 1910 he left home with his daughter Alexandra, the only child who took his side, and died on November 21st in the railroad station at Astapovo. Countless translations and editions of his works are available in English.

IVAN TURGENEV

Ivan Turgenev (1818–1883) was born at Orel, Russia, of a family of provincial gentry. He was educated at home and at the Universities of Moscow and St. Petersburg, and later at Berlin, where he came in contact with the young Russian intellectuals and became a Westernizer. *A Sportsman's Sketches* (1852) was received as a protest against serfdom, and because of his laudatory obituary of Gogol he was exiled to his estate. He lived most of his life in France where he was on intimate terms with the great French writers of the naturalistic generation. His complete works are available in English translation in sixteen volumes: *The Novels and Tales of Ivan Turgenieff* (Translated from the Russian by Isabel F. Hapgood. With an Introduction by Henry James. New York, 1903–1904). Miscellaneous collections of his stories are available in many editions.

ROBERT PENN WARREN

Robert Penn Warren was born in Guthrie, Kentucky, on April 24, 1905. He was educated at Vanderbilt University, Yale University, and New College, Oxford. He was, with Cleanth Brooks, editor of *The Southern Review* (1935–1942). At present he is Professor of English at the University of Minnesota. In 1945 he won the Pulitzer Prize for his novel *All the King's Men.* His books are: *John Brown: The Making of a Martyr,* biography (1929), *XXXVI Poems* (1935), *Understanding Poetry* (with Cleanth Brooks, 1938), *Night Rider,* novel (1938), *Eleven Poems on the Same Theme* (1942), *At Heaven's Gate,* novel (1941), *Selected Poems* (1942), *All the King's Men,* novel (1945), *The Circus in the Attic,* stories (1948).

EUDORA WELTY

Eudora Welty was born in Jackson, Mississippi, and was educated at the Mississippi State College for Women. Her first published story appeared in *The Southern Review.* She is the author of four books: *A Curtain of Green,* stories (1941), *The Robber Bridegroom,* novel (1942), *The Wide Net,* stories (1943), *Delta Wedding,* novel (1946).